THE CRIME OF GALILEO

THE CRIME OF
GALILEO

by Giorgio de Santillana

 TIME Reading Program Special Edition
Time-Life Books Inc., Alexandria, Virginia

Time-Life Books Inc.
is a wholly owned subsidiary of
TIME INCORPORATED

TIME Reading Program: *Editor*, Max Gissen

Copyright 1955 by The University of Chicago.
Reprinted 1981.
Editors' Preface, TIME Reading Program Introduction
and cover design (paperback edition) © 1962 Time-Life Books Inc.
All rights reserved.
Printed in the United States of America.
TIME-LIFE is a trademark of Time Incorporated U.S.A.

Library of Congress CIP data following page 371.

For information about any Time-Life book, please write:
Reader Information, Time-Life Books,
541 North Fairbanks Court, Chicago, Illinois 60611

Contents

Illustrations

Editors' Preface

In these capricious times history seems to have a special attraction—perhaps the same interest that the lighthouse, the fixed point, holds for the uncertain sailor. We measure our directions and speeds by references to great events of the past. Most such calculations flatter us because the past is full of examples of what we know to be ignorance. Error after error that our age could not possibly make leaps to our eyes from the pages of history. The general conclusion is comforting: we have been traveling very fast in the right direction.

But what if certain great beacons are imprecisely placed on the historical charts? Then we have traded uncertainty for misplaced confidence—which, navigationally speaking, is more dangerous.

The ordeal of Galileo Galilei in 17th Century Rome is frequently referred to as one of the great landmarks of history. A quick mention of it conjures up a familiar story—the brilliant astronomer, mathematician and physicist who, because he insisted that the earth revolves around the sun, was disgraced, imprisoned and repressed by Church obscurantists. In this reading, Galileo symbolizes the bright new age suffering at the hands of the ignorant past. He is science standing forth against religion; he is the rebel confronting authority and tradition.

In *The Crime of Galileo,* Giorgio de Santillana provides a new chart. His purpose is not to debunk Galileo or to provide excuses for those who sought to suppress his work. On the contrary, Galileo appears in De Santillana's pages not only as an important contributor to scientific discovery, but in the even more honorable role of a great humanist who set for himself the task of integrating into the Western cultural tradition the great astronomical discoveries of Copernicus—discoveries which had been published, without ecclesiastical condemnation, almost 70 years before the action in the Galileo story began.

Taking up his task, Galileo deliberately removed himself from the jurisdiction of the Republic of Venice, where Church authority was ignored and where he had met a fierce resistance that was not at all theological from "vested academic interests." He moved to Florence and immediately began to circulate in the upper reaches of ecclesiastical and intellectual society. The change was appropriate to his goal. He did not intend to leave Copernicus' work and his own to languish in undisturbed isolation from the main body of knowledge. He wanted the new truths to be recognized, and he never doubted that recognition entailed incorporation into the philosophical and educational system which was identified with the Church.

De Santillana suggests that if Galileo's effort had been made a few centuries earlier he would have found churchmen far more receptive. But by the beginning of the 17th Century the essential unity of Europe was cracking under various pressures. Organizational techniques, on the other hand, were improving. Rome, especially, had developed many administrative devices for replacing unity with unification. And it was in a tangle of bureaucratic fact-finding and administrative law that Galileo's case twice was tried and twice lost. De Santillana's viewpoint is disclosed in this judgment: ". . . within the specific frame of Western Christendom the actual conflict reveals Galileo, like all free men, seeking a support in established custom, credit and tradition, while [Pope] Urban VIII, like all organizers of power, becomes the unwitting tool of the streamlined, the 'efficient,' and the new."

This, of course, is the corrective significance of De Santillana's "chart" for 20th Century readers, who know quite well that the earth goes around the sun but whose appreciation of the unity of truth and whose grasp of the relation of power to knowledge may be inferior to that of either Galileo or Pope Urban.

Before Galileo's ordeal can be made to yield its true meaning for the 20th Century, it has to be understood in the context of its own time. Here is the heart of De Santillana's extraordinary achievement. He understands thoroughly the scientific side of the story—what proofs Galileo had, what he lacked and how his evidence impressed his contemporaries, steeped as they were in Aristotle's physics. But the scientific history is not the most difficult part of the material. De Santillana is also able to make comprehensible the procedures of the ecclesiastical bureaucracy and the general cultural environment in which Galileo's ordeal occurred.

By the standards of that time, certain aspects of the case against Galileo were handled in a way that was sloppy at best; De Santillana believes that deliberate chicanery was involved. But many readers will be surprised to see how well the standards of the time compare with proceedings that have occurred within living memory. After all, Galileo's first judge (or rather the administrator in charge of security clearance) was Robert Bellarmine, a man of great learning and common sense, a gentleman and a saint. What modern bureaucracy possesses his equal? Urban VIII, who in the end turned against Galileo, had been for many years the scientist's friend and admirer. It was Urban, indeed, who urged Galileo to write the book on the basis of which Galileo was finally prosecuted. The Pope had made a suggestion for getting around Galileo's earlier troubles with ecclesiastical authority. Consciously or not, Galileo in writing *The Dialogue on the Great World Systems* did not follow the Pope's suggestion. Explaining Urban's subsequent severity, De Santillana remarks wryly that "there is no fury like a philosopher scorned." But De Santillana does not leave it there; more than editorial spite was involved in this rupture of old allies who had thought they were pursuing similar ends.

The situation which the Galileo drama epitomizes has not disappeared from the modern world. What, in a world that can be upset by science, are the rights and responsibilities of the scientist? What are the rights and responsibilities of the artist? (De Santillana considers Galileo the greatest Italian prose stylist of his time.) True, in the free world today power does not explicitly ban the work of scientist or artist. But has power unwittingly found subtler and more effective means of diverting their thought? And if power is not to perform the task of integration, where are the scientists and artists who accept responsibility for relating one kind of truth to another? Certainly, the job that Galileo set himself is unfinished; possibly it has not advanced in 250 years. Galileo's contemporaries were as eagerly receptive as any moderns to the practical advantages—including the military advantages—to be derived from science. And most moderns, in their way, are as unable as Galileo's contemporaries to come to grips with the problem of enveloping the spirit of scientific discovery within the larger values of the Western tradition.

At this level De Santillana's book is profoundly disquieting—as befits a story about a man of good will who created a most disquieting "scandal." At another level De Santillana has constructed a marvelously satisfying narrative, an intellectual whodunit with suspense and surprise in every chapter. At the end of the story we may be less smugly overconfident about where our own age stands in relation to Galileo's, but we may be more solidly familiar with "the crime of Galileo."

De Santillana, who was born in Rome, had a special interest in the science of the Renaissance. A modern historian of science working backward toward this crossroads can, of course, isolate the purely scientific aspects of any Renaissance scientist's work. But this operation runs dangerous risks of distortion because in that period the sciences were just beginning to develop independent disciplines. De Santillana, steeped in general Renaissance culture, was able to tell his scientific story against the philosophical and cultural background of the time.

—THE EDITORS

LUDOVICO AND ANNA

DIAZ DE SANTILLANA

✤

XXVIII DEC. MCMLIII

Q. B. F. S.

Author's Preface

This work is not the result of a plan aforethought. As I tried to clear up the astonishingly complex background of Galileo's *Dialogue on the Great World Systems*,[1] I was drawn to the drama which played a decisive part in that fateful event of modern history, the secularization of thought. It seemed strange to me that, after so much research and controversy, the story of events as I found it should make so little sense. As I worked, it became clear that a large area of the puzzle had remained oddly disassembled to the present day, by what looks like an inexplicable tacit agreement between the warring factions.

Galileo did not come to grief as "the scientist" facing a religious credo. He was far from standing in the role of a technician of science; had he done so, he would have escaped all trouble. Everyone knows that his discoveries went unchallenged. Those of Descartes did too. And so did Descartes himself. But then, as he admitted, he "went forth under a mask," whereas Galileo is the man without a mask. Both his friends and his enemies saw in him a unique type of creative personality, whose essential achievement might very well be conceived to stand or fall with him. He was a classic type of humanist, trying to

---

1. Galileo Galilei, *Dialogue on the Great World Systems*. The Salusbury translation. Revised, annotated, and with an Introduction by Giorgio de Santillana. Chicago: University of Chicago Press, 1953.

bring his culture to the awareness of the new scientific ideas, and among the forces that he found aligned against him religious fundamentalism was by no means the strongest.

It is difficult to see the actual shape of the conflict in these matters so long as we remain under the spell of a misunderstanding tacitly accepted by both sides: the idea of the scientist as a bold "free-thinker" and "progressive" facing the static resistance of conservatism. This may well be the aspect on the level of personalities, for it is usually the scientist who shows the freer and more speculative mind in contrast with prejudiced opponents. But the core of the thing is different: there the scientist appears more often than not as the conservative overtaken by fast-moving social forces. He usually has the Law and the Prophets on his side.

This ought to become immediately clear if we think of contemporary events. The tragedy of the geneticists in Russia, with its lamentable apologies and recantations, is a faithful rehearsal of the Galileo story; yet we could not accuse the Soviet government of clinging to ancient superstitions or of underestimating the pressing need for science and technology. And lest our straining for beams make us overlook our own domestic gnats, we may perceive in the Oppenheimer case a parallel which is a shade too close for comfort. In such vastly different climates of time and thought, whenever the conflict comes up, we find a similarity of symptoms and behavior which points to a fundamental relation.

True, the Oppenheimer case is very different from Galileo's as to context. Today there is a tendency not to suppress physics but rather to exploit it; a tendency to act not on deep philosophic differences but on mere issues of expediency. Yet, as the story unfolds before the public, the exact analogy in structure, in symptoms and behaviors, shows us that we are dealing with the same disease. Through the little that we are allowed to know, we can discern the scientific mind as it has ever been—with its free-roaming curiosity, its unconventional interests, its detachment, its ancient and somewhat esoteric set of values (it is the scientist, we may remember, who is reproached with having brought the concept of "sin" into modern contexts)—surprised by policy decisions dictated by "Reasons of State" or what are judged to be such.

It might be a mere game of tally, but it is tempting to establish a one-to-one correspondence between the actors of the two dramas three centuries apart and to follow them through parallel convolutions. One might say, for instance: for "Holy Office" read "AEC Board," for "Caccini" read "Crouch," for "Lorini" read "Borden," for "S.J." (*Societas Jesu*) read "SAC" (Strategic Air Command), for "Report of the Preliminary Commission" read "Gray-Morgan Majority Report," for "Grienberger" read "Teller," for "certain German mathematicians" read "a certain Dr. Malraux," and so on. As for the hooded figure of Michelangelo Segizi de Lauda, the craftsman of iniquity, the number of high-placed contestants in public life and in the Communications Empire would make it invidious to choose.

The two chief figures of authority, too, are remarkably similar in their complex motivations. But the chairman of the Atomic Energy Commission wrote out his own résumé of the case, which turned out to be also the decision, whereas it will appear reasonably proved in this work that Urban VIII's decision was based on a deliberately arranged résumé which was submitted to him in order to lead him astray.

There is no doubt that the ecclesiastical figures of the seventeenth century come out ahead of their modern counterparts. After all, the question revolved at that time around metaphysical and cosmological questions of such majestic import that even the gravest moral errors committed in defense of the traditional view may appear today as concern for the ultimate salvation of mankind. The findings of our contemporary authorities, in their absent-mindedness, are much closer to the prosecutor's conclusion against Lavoisier: "La République n'a pas besoin de savants." And, as then, science has to keep silence.

But parallels are at best an invitation to thought, and this one should not be pushed too far. What I think can be brought out in all these cases is that—at least when the question reaches the higher echelons—it is not so much a matter of "science" versus "prejudice" as of the classic question coming up again: "What *is* the scientist?" It is usually the scientist who is taken by surprise by a redefinition of his activities coming from outside. And the result is always one more turn racked up on the old screw. By subjecting the scientist as a cultural being to the administrative suspicion that usually attaches to questionable adventurers in international traffics, we have simply brought one step further the process of secularization of thought.

So much is sure, that in the seventeenth-century episode the seeming paradox comes out with full force: within the specific frame of Western Christendom the actual conflict reveals Galileo, like all free men, seeking a support in established custom, credit, and tradition, while Urban VIII, like all organizers of power, becomes the unwitting tool of the streamlined, the "efficient," and the new.

This may not be conformable, I readily admit, to the perspective set up by current historiography, largely built up as it is on hindsight. But this is how it was experienced, more or less consciously, by the actors of the drama; and that ought to be a not wholly negligible aspect of historical reality.

Galileo may be excused for wondering why his discoveries were dubbed alarming "novelties," since science was only supposed to discover things that must have been eternally so. What appeared to him much more of a "novelty" was the way in which authorities had taken to handing down administrative decisions in a field in which they were not supposed to have any competence. It was to him a startling interpretation of that other new thing which might be called the Tridentine Amendment to the immemorial constitutions of Christendom.

In thinking of Galileo's universe, an image that comes to mind is the bare, strong interior of the Pazzi Chapel in Florence, that meeting point of Christ and geometry. If we try to populate it in our fancy, it will have to be a singular mixture of characters from Ghirlandaio and Mantegna, with some disdainful personages of Titian or Bronzino to represent the intellectual ruling class. After all, Galileo had been born way back in 1564; the world of his conceptions is still that of the sixteenth century. He has at best, of the seventeenth, the "Edwardian" or Jacobean coloring of its beginnings.

Far from that is Pope Urban's world—the splendor of the "sumptuous palaces" of the Barberinis in the renovated Capital, the magnificent declaratory flights of Borromini's façades, the colossal grip of Bernini's colonnades, the noisy massiveness and ornamental flourish of St. Peter's. It is space-embracing organization against delicate permanence. The contrast would not be more marked between Grand Central Terminal and a New England town common.

In his concern with enduring things, in his confessional simplicity, Galileo spans the centuries. Through him, what we call science is speaking out unequivocally for the first time; yet there lives in him a spirit more ancient and ample than that of the ecclesiastical statesman in Rome. It is the spirit of ecumenic and conciliar Christianity which warns and exhorts with the dignity of a Father of the early centuries. The contrast between the theological style of his epistles and that of the official apologetic literature is enough to tell the story. The elaborate baroque formulas of submissiveness do not prevent the reader from feeling that here is someone like Ambrose, Augustine, or Bonaventure, reprehending sleepy shepherds and degenerate epigones. He speaks in the name of the community of the faithful which joins the ancient dead to the yet unborn. He is not simply the consulting astronomer; he is the adviser in matters of natural philosophy and metaphysics who requests to be heard, and, if, as he intimates, it is holiness of intention and gravity of counsel that makes authority, he deserves heeding no less than Aquinas himself.

He was not wrong either, as a matter of record. The content of his spurned and incriminated theological letters has become official Church doctrine since 1893. Had there been in Rome, at the time of the first crisis of 1616, a youthful Aquinas to take up his lead, instead of an aged Bellarmine—but there was no Aquinas, and there was no time.

The whole drama turns out to be in the nature of a surprise encounter for both sides. Both the authorities and the scientist had the mutual impression of being ambushed, and in neither case was it true. The ambush, in so far as there was one, had been carefully laid by third parties, who carefully exploited the critical situation of the times. But Galileo never felt himself in the figure of an innovator and a rebel. As the central figure of accepted science, as the acknowledged leader of his culture in thought and expression, not last as a perfectly orthodox representative of metaphysical Christianity, he could not but stand his ground, in growing bewilderment, until administrative violence established a quietus, leaving everybody, including the authorities themselves, in a state of utter confusion.

The confusion goes on unremittingly even today, for the Galileo affair is far from dead, and every decade brings a new "line" and new suggestions meant to explain it away, just as it brings a repetition of the ancient rationalist war whoops. The side that stands for the authorities neither is, nor by any means has been, all Catholic. One of the most irresponsible and widely used accounts came from a Protestant publicist of the eighteenth century, Mallet du Pan, and a popular prejudiced version from the pen of another Protestant, Sir David Brewster. Some of the silliest accusations against Galileo have been accredited by the antireligious French Encyclopedists. On the other hand, some of the more honest efforts to restore the facts are due to professedly Catholic historians like L'Epinois and Reusch.

Since names have been mentioned, I should add, to honor them, those of scholars who, belonging to neither camp, labored to attain an impartial view of the situation: mainly Emil Wohlwill, Th. H. Martin, Karl von Gebler, and Antonio Favaro. Most of the literature through which one has to wade deserves no mention at all. It ranges from average casual incompetence to prevarication and plain filth. Let it go back to whence it came. There is no common measure between the policy problems of long ago—the motives, the hesitation, the eventual refusal, of men who felt intrusted with the fate of millions of people who pray—and the gratuitous distortions that later and self-appointed apologists scattered abroad in their name. The long-drawn-out polemic is not strictly, I hope to have made it clear, one between the confessional and the anti-confessional faction. It has been made to look like that; in reality it is a confused free-for-all in which prejudice, inveterate rancor, and all sorts of special and corporate interests have been the prime movers. Those who dragged and keep dragging the Church into it are no candid souls. As L'Epinois says rightly, the Church has all to gain and nothing to lose from the truth.

As far as I can make out, the unsolved state of the puzzle is due to this: that the "freethinkers" are only too glad to put the Roman Church as a whole under accusation in the affair, while inside the ecclesiastic hierarchy powerful corporate interests are ready to accept the terrain chosen by the attackers rather than have some of their long-deceased members stand under the spotlight of history. Thus, they are willing to involve the Church in this quarrel, with the inevitable consequences that they have to resort to laborious smoke screens, devious implications, and all sorts of unfair tactics.

Did, indeed, the conflict have to take place at all under this form? It has been known for a long time that a major part of the Church intellectuals were on the side of Galileo, while the clearest opposition to him came from secular ideas. It can be proved further (or at least I hope I have done so) that the tragedy was the result of a plot of which the hierarchies themselves turned out to be the victims no less than Galileo—an intrigue engineered by a group of obcure and disparate characters in strange collusion who planted false documents in the file, who later misinformed the Pope and then presented to him a misleading account of the trial for decision.

The real story affords a fascinating insight into the way in which such decisions actually take place and in which the ponderous state machinery is set into motion by what seem to be Reasons of State and perhaps later become so, but originate really as a constellation of accidents and personal motives. An objective account ought to be more relevant to a decent understanding than all the innuendoes, diversions, and stage sets invented around it on both sides. By pinpointing the culpability of a few individuals, it tends to absolve a far greater number who had stood hitherto under the darkest suspicions, and among them the Commissary-General of the Inquisition himself, who conducted the trial. Once recognized, the facts should lead us forward to the problems of present reality and disperse this perennial battle with windmills.

I want to express my gratitude to Father Robert Lord, S.J., Father Joseph Clark, S.J., and Professor Edward Rosen for their criticism and their helpful suggestions; to Miss Elizabeth Cameron and Mrs. Nancy Chivers for their invaluable assistance in preparing the manuscript.

GIORGIO DE SANTILLANA
Massachusetts Institute of Technology
November 30, 1954

Introduction

*Our fight is against some devilry that lies
in the very process of things.*

H. BUTTERFIELD

Scientific endeavor and social authority, in one form or another, are characteristics of man's life on this planet that are expected to endure for as long as we can see ahead. In this essay, which aims at analyzing their complex relations, we intend to go at length into the episode which provides, as it were, a grand overture to their conflict in the modern age, namely, the trial of Galileo and the circumstances that brought it about. But, as we work out the general conditions attendant on such a conflict, we shall not pass in silence what similarities and dissimilarities occur with the further phase of conflict which is being played out in our time.

In fact, if one is still fascinated by the details of an episode which is three centuries old, it is mainly because the trial provides a demonstration piece such as could hardly be found elsewhere. We are going to offer no apology for dwelling on the past. Sometime, when other now well-guarded archives are open, and the historical point of view is sufficiently remote, historians may be able to anatomize the events of the present day with something resembling objectivity. Even so, we may be prepared to find it dull reading, for the modern state produces its own kind of dreary setting and ever worsening prose, while the events surrounding Galileo's trial remain a Baroque production as articulate and spectacular as a painting by Veronese, peopled with amply gesturing characters who continually and irresistibly "compose" in the eloquent seventeenth-century style.

It has become a set piece in history to present Pope Urban VIII and his counselors as the bigoted oppressors of science. It would be possibly more accurate to say that they were the first bewildered victims of the scientific age. They had come into collision with a force of which they had not the faintest notion. In that sense, they are almost the polar opposite of the "progressive" rulers of the twentieth century, who are, one and all, bigoted believers in "scientism" while dealing with science in a no less highhanded manner. Still, the dramatic shape remains the same.

"Our fight," Professor Butterfield lately wrote, "is against some devilry that lies in the very process of things, against something that we might even call demonic forces existing in the air. The forces get men into their grip, so that the men themselves are victims in a sense, even if it is by some fault of their own nature—they are victims of a sort of possession."

These words are not written by a poet or a Doctor of Divinity but by one of the ranking historians of our time. We feel encouraged by them to face the problem in a somewhat similar spirit, if it be understood that his words are to apply to all participants without exception.

Galileo Galilei was born in Pisa in 1564, the year in which Michelangelo died and Shakespeare came into the world. He sprang of an old Florentine family whose main stem had borne the name of Buonaiuti. His rather singular Christian name comes of an old Tuscan custom of duplicating the surname in the firstborn, as, for example, in Braccio Bracci or Pazzino de' Pazzi. His father Vincenzio Galilei was a musician and composer.

The boy had a happy childhood and received his first education from the friars of Vallombrosa; in 1581 he entered the University of Pisa as a student of medicine and philosophy. His natural bent, however, as well as a disinclination toward the natural philosophy then taught in the schools, drew him to geometry and mechanics. At nineteen, he is said to have discovered the isochronism of the pendulum; at twenty-two, he invented his hydrostatic balance. Archimedes, who had but recently become known in the full Latin translation, became his scientific model. He decided to create a mathematical science which should do for the motion of bodies what Archimedes had achieved for statics. The Greek endeavor had broken down on the theory of motion, and Galileo had to struggle for many years with the suasive theories he had been taught out of Aristotle as well as with his own preconceptions. It was only after twenty years of searching and false starts that he was able to give, in 1604, the correct law of the motion of falling bodies.

A first lectureship in his own University of Pisa had not been a happy experience, as he had aroused antagonism in the faculty. He left after three years, in 1592, to take up a vacancy in the ancient University of Padua under the jurisdiction of the Venetian Republic. The salary was 180 florins a year, later increased to 520. Cremonini, the "great philosopher" of the university and a straightforward pedant, earned 2,000. This goes to show what academic authorities thought of the importance of mathematics; the chair of "mathematics" then covered the teaching of geometry, astronomy, military engineering, and fortification.

Galileo's success as a lecturer and humanist with students from all parts of Europe brought him international renown. He published in that period treatises on mechanics, spherical geometry, and fortifications. But a new and fascinating subject had meanwhile begun to hold his attention: the Copernican theory. Nicolaus Copernicus had published in Germany many years previously, in 1543, a treatise on the *Revolutions of the Celestial Orbs,* dedicated to Pope Paul III, which went counter to the established theories. The natural philosophy of Aristotle, as well as the astronomy of Ptolemy adopted both by the universities and by the Church, taught that the Earth was at the center of things and that the heavens revolved around it in twenty-four hours, together with the Sun, Moon, and planets. Copernicus, taking up some hints of half-forgotten theories of the Greeks, had suggested that this might come of an optical illusion and that the whole geometrical device worked out by Ptolemy made more rational sense if the Sun were placed in the center of the universe, and the Earth among the planets, covering its orbit in one year, as the Sun had been supposed to do, as well as turning on itself in twenty-four hours.

The great treatise of Copernicus had been known for a half-century, but in all this time it had aroused mostly skepticism. A few romantic and daring spirits had been captured by the new idea, but they could not master the difficult details of the system. Official astronomy, represented by the great Tycho Brahe, had declared against it, and Tycho had advanced instead a compromise system of his own in which the Earth remained at the center of things. The philosophers of the schools dismissed Copernicus because his theory could not be reconciled with their physics. The Protestants were against him because they felt he cast doubt upon the literal truth of Scripture. As for the Catholic hierarchies, they held Copernicus in respect as a church man and scholar, but they considered his system as one more of those ingenious mathematical devices which could lay no claim to physical reality. Mathematics was rated at the time as a thing for technicians and *virtuosi*, as they were called, with no claim to philosophical relevance; and the mystical and metaphysical speculations of some adventurous minds who searched for the "divine secret" in proportion and number were not such as to compel the assent of responsible scholars. Added to this, the Churchmen derived some good reasons for their reserve from the book of Copernicus himself, which had come to them provided with a spurious preface written really by Osiander, a Protestant clergyman, which disclaimed any pretension of physical validity for the theory.

Galileo, who had been maturing in those years since 1585 a completely new natural philosophy based on mathematics, saw the book in a very different light. To him it made excellent physical sense and showed the way to a truer cosmology. He admitted as much to his friends in 1597. But, knowing that one would have "to mold anew the brains of men" before bringing them over to his point of view, he decided to bide his time. He knew he had no proof as yet which would look convincing to the unprepared mind. The proof came to him by a stroke of luck, with the discovery of the telescope in 1610, which also established his name in the mind of the public at large as that of the leading scientist of his time. And this is where our story begins.

G. DE S.

I

The Days of Discovery

These novelties of ancient truths, of new worlds, new systems, new nations, are the beginning of a new era. Let God not make delay, and let us for our small part do all we can.

CAMPANELLA

I

In March, 1610, Galileo announced to the world, in his *Message from the Stars,* the discovery of the telescope. "That universe," as he was to say later, "that I enlarged a hundred and a thousand times from what the wise men of all past ages had thought" was not only bringing in its message new and unimagined things in heaven. It was also bringing new ideas to the mind of its discoverer.

Others might think that here was "a new America in the skies" and more magnificence of stars. To the explorer himself, the *Nuncius sidereus*[1] brought a very clear decision: Copernicus had been right in making the Earth a planet and not the center of the universe. Galileo had divined as much long ago, while engaged in his less-known work in mechanics. No one could have guessed then his ultimate aim, but, as he sought the laws of missiles and falling bodies, he told himself he would not show his hand in cosmology until he could come forward as an entirely new type of Copernican—not the mere astronomer but "the astronomer philosophical," the physicist of the skies. The sudden discovery of the telescope had decided the matter for him, since it

---

1. This was the title of the pamphlet in its original Latin.

brought unexpected observational confirmation to his theory while it catapulted him into fame and fortune. He was now forty-five years of age. The work of his life lay ahead of him.

On May 7, 1610, two months after the publication of his *Message,* he wrote a long letter to his faithful friend Belisario Vinta, the Florentine secretary of state. He spoke of all the great plans he would be able to carry through, once relieved of the obligation of teaching in Padua, and of his desire to serve the Grand Duke:

"I have many and most admirable plans and devices; but they could only be put to work by princes, because it is they who are able to carry on war, build and defend fortresses, and for their regal sport make most splendid expenditure, and not I or any private gentleman. The works that I intend to bring to a conclusion are principally two books on the *System* or *Constitution of the World,* an immense design, full of philosophy, astronomy, and geometry. Then there are three books *On Motion,* a science entirely new. . . ." [2]

This is the first explicit mention of the project to which he had previously only alluded: a work of natural philosophy establishing the Copernican systems in the light of the new discoveries in astronomy and physics after two decades of thought given to the problem. What he needed now was a "perfect state of quiet of mind."

For twenty years he had struggled along in an underpaid position, harassed with the financial needs of his relatives, compelled to eke out his salary by tutoring and boarding students and giving extra hours to what people really expected of a man of his profession: the theory of fortifications, "saps, mines, gabions, palisadoes, ravelins, half-moons, and such trumpery." Apart from that, universities did not have much to offer to a mathematician. The learned profession, in this decline of the Renaissance, had come upon dull times. The outlook was shrinking under the impact of the religious tension; it was as though learning

---

2. This letter, as well as all further texts whose source is not otherwise specified, is to be found in the National Edition of Galileo's *Works,* by Antonio Favaro, in twenty volumes. The correspondence is arranged in strict chronological order, so that the date constitutes a sufficient reference.

had lost its point. Had it not been for the presence of Fabricius of Acquapendente, the great anatomist, and a few jurists, consultors of the Venetian Republic and worthy successors of the learned Bellario, Galileo would have found it difficult to put up with the self-importance of his Paduan colleagues; and too rare were the escapes he could allow himself into the cosmopolitan atmosphere of Venice twenty miles away, where he and Fabricius were always welcomed by the small senatorial circle gathering for free conversation in the famous counting-house of Ca' Morosini.

True, fame had come now with his discoveries, and his salary had been raised to one thousand florins. But Galileo had made up his mind long since. It was not so much, as has been suggested at times, that he wanted his little revenge on the scholars of Tuscany who had refused him a post in his early days; he had enough weighty reasons without that and had stated some of those in his letter to Vinta. In the secretary of state he had the right kind of friend who could understand him.[3] Under Vinta's stewardship the little Tuscan principality, less than a million in population but still not forgetful of the glories of the past centuries, had embarked on a bold economic policy aimed at fighting the prevalent economic depression of the times. Canals had been dug, vast stretches of land had been reclaimed in the provinces of Siena, Arezzo, and Grosseto, and the new port of Leghorn, with its shipyards and arsenal, had been built up out of nothing. Vinta had even underwritten a venture in Brazilian colonization to be directed by two Englishmen, Dudley and Thornton. It was through Vinta that Galileo had prevailed on the Grand Duke to accept the dedication of the still controversial satellites of Jupiter in the name of the House of Medici, a master-stroke of scientific diplomacy.

Galileo had good reason, then, to feel that this was the place for him. He wanted to be back in his own native country, amid people

3. The closeness between the two men shows throughout their correspondence, even conducted as it is in the formal official tone. At one point Vinta is quoted back in direct speech: "Galileo, nelle cose tue tratta con me e non con altri"—a significant phrase both in the meaning and in the form of address.

of his own speech and friends of his own choosing.

There were risks, he was willing to admit. It was not completely safe to exchange the rigid contractual obligations of such a state as the Republic of Venice for the personal favor of a monarch. As his faithful Sagredo (who was later to become a character in his *Dialogue on the Great World Systems*) wrote with the wisdom of a Venetian aristocrat: "Where will you find the same liberty as here in Venetian territory, where a contract makes you the master of those who command? . . . If not ruined, you may be harried by the surging billows of court life and by the raging winds of envy. . . . Also, your being in a place where the authority of the friends of Berlinzone,[4] from what I am told, stands high gives me cause for worry."

But the die had been cast. In June, 1610, Galileo resigned his position in Padua, and by September he was in Florence, where he took up his new post.

Truly, he was not overmuch concerned with the dangers of Jesuit power, spanning the continents over his head in vast political machinations; for he himself had never been interested in the jurisdiction of princes, and he did not want to share the quarrel of the Venetian state against the Holy See. On his own account, he knew the Jesuits as modern-minded humanists, friends of science and discovery. Those he feared were the professors.

The "immense design" was indeed one of the main reasons which urged him to his fateful emigration. What he thought, and could not say for various reasons, was that, if he was to challenge the universities with decisive pronouncements, it was better to do so as "a patrician of Florence, chief philosopher and mathematician to His Most Serene Highness," a friend and protégé of the monarch to whom he had dedi-

4. "Messer Rocco Berlinzone" was a nickname for the Jesuits. The Society had been expelled from Venetian territory for political intrigue in 1606 by decree of the Senate. They had been previously banished from France in 1594 but were allowed to return by Henry IV. They were expelled both from France and from Spain in 1767 and finally suppressed by Pope Clement XIV in 1776. That suppression was revoked only in 1814.

cated the satellites of Jupiter, than as a penurious lecturer harried by a faculty council which might decide that the subject of his teaching must remain unchanged in the program.

The project intimated in the *Starry Message* had been slowly changing shape in his mind. The reaction to the telescope, among the learned and semilearned, had been discouraging. He had felt a solid front building against him, from his alma mater of Pisa to Bologna and Padua. The man who should have helped him most, Magini, the professor of astronomy in Bologna, had cast aside the mask of friendship and agitated against him among the bookish Aristotelians. If help had not come from outside, he would have found himself in serious difficulties, his new planets "extirpated from the sky," as Magini had promised. "My dear Kepler," Galileo wrote to the man who had always upheld the cause, "what would you say of the learned here, who, replete with the pertinacity of the asp, have steadfastly refused to cast a glance through the telescope? What shall we make of all this? Shall we laugh, or shall we cry?"

Even before the Jesuit astronomers and more than they, it was public opinion which had helped him. His own printers in Padua had subscribed for an ode to him; writers celebrated the telescope in tracts and in verse both Latin and vernacular, elegiac, pindaric, playful, epigrammatic; in language courtly, precious, and popular; in odes, blank verse, sonnets, octaves, and terza rima. The new discoveries were argued about at princely dinner tables and by the people on the steps of the cathedral. They were frescoed by Cigoli in the very cupola of Santa Maria Maggiore in Rome. The leading poets of the day, Marino and Chiabrera, brought their contributions. From England came news that the telescope had invaded philosophy and the metaphysical lyric.[5] "And who," wrote a professor of philosophy, La Galla,

---

5. Cf. Leonardo Olschki, *Geschichte d. neusprachlichen wissenschaftlichen Litteratur,* Vol. III: *Galilei und seine Zeit* (1927). On the effect in English circles see M. H. Nicholson, "The Telescope and Imagination," *Modern Philology,* 1935, and *Studies in Philology* (1935); and F. Johnson, *Astronomical Thought in Renaissance England* (1937).

as a prelude to his own underhanded disparagement, "who, even plunged in deepest sleep, would not be awakened by the rumor of this new miracle, which has spread throughout his world?" This was support from new quarters, such as Copernicus had never had. Even from this point of view, the Court was a much better center of operations.

The "Medicean stars" had been cleverly placed under the protection of the Grand Duke, for, once the House of Medici had accepted the dedication, it became mandatory for them to exist; and they were indeed the strategic key point of the operation. Anyone looking at Jupiter through a telescope saw right there, in the visual field, a solar system demonstrated on a small scale.

The face of the Moon seen through the telescope was perhaps more impressive, but one had to follow a train of thought to see what it implied; the valleys, peaks, and ridges like to those of the Earth seen on a celestial body showed that there is no basic difference in physical constitution; and with this the whole official distinction between celestial and terrestrial was obliterated—to anyone who cared to think.

Then, close on each other, the telescope had brought two new decisive discoveries: the phases of Venus and the "companions" of Saturn. Galileo had written to Giuliano de' Medici, the Florentine ambassador in Prague, in 1610: "I am anxiously waiting for what il Sig. Keplero may have to say about the new marvels. . . . He and the rest of the school of Copernicus have good reason for boasting that they have shown themselves excellent philosophers; however much it has been their lot, and may be hereafter, to be regarded by the philosophers of our times who philosophize on paper, with an universal agreement, as men of no intellect and little better than absolute fools."

The ambassador duly forwarded the request to Kepler ("Il Sig. Gleppero," as he called him), and the reaction came back prompt and vivid. "My dear Galileo," wrote Kepler, "I must tell you what occurred the other day. My friend the Baron Wakher von Wachenfels drove up to my door and started shouting excitedly from his carriage: 'Is it true? Is it really true that he has found stars moving around stars?' I told him that it was indeed so, and only then did he step into the house." Kepler left it prudently unsaid that his good friend Wakher was hoping for a proof of Bruno's intimations of infinity and of the plurality of the worlds, for not only were those ideas dangerous but he, Kepler, did not incline to them. But there was enough in the discoveries, notwithstanding his own reserves about the untested new instrument, to call forth his characteristic enthusiasm: "What now, dear reader, shall we make out of our telescope? Shall we make it a Mercury's magic-wand with which to cross the liquid ether, and, like Lucian, lead a colony to the uninhabited evening star? Or shall we make it Cupid's arrow, which, entering by our eyes, has pierced our inmost mind and fired us with a love of Venus?"

But vested learning, unimpressed by the new dicoveries, went on considering the Copernicans as "men of no intellect." In fact, rancor and disdain of the doctors could only be increased by the "unfair" easy successes of their opponents in society. This is what Galileo had foreseen all along. As early as 1597, thirteen years before, he had written to Kepler: "Like you, I accepted the Copernican position several years ago and discovered from thence the causes of many natural effects which are doubtless inexplicible by the current theories. I have written up many reasons and refutations on the subject, but I have not dared until now to bring them into the open, being warned by the fortunes of Copernicus himself, our master, who procured for himself immortal fame among a few but stepped down among the great crowd (for this is how foolish people are numbered), only to be derided and dishonored. I would dare publish my thoughts if there were many like you; but, since there are not, I shall forbear."

The discoveries of the telescope, Galileo had thought for a while in 1610, would change all this by providing irrefutable proof to any man in good faith. Perhaps the time had come. . . . But a few months were enough to undeceive him. Certain doctors, who at least had the courage of their convictions, did actually and steadfastly refuse to look through the telescope, as has been recounted many times. Some did look and professed to see nothing; most of them, however, gave it the silent treatment or said they had never gotten around to looking through it but that they knew already that it would show nothing of philosophical value. One maintained that it was impossible that the ancients should not have had such instruments, since they had excelled in everything, and that their silence on the subject implied an unfavorable judgment of their performance. Another affirmed right away, although he had not yet seen a telescope, that the invention was taken from Aristotle. "Having his works brought, he turned to the place where the philosopher gives the reason why, from the bottom of a very deep well, one may see the stars in heaven at noonday. . . . 'See here,' says he, 'the well, which represents the tube, see here the gross vapours, from whence is taken the invention of the crystals, and see here lastly the sight fortified by the passage of rays through a diaphanous but more dense and obscure medium.' " [6] But surely, said still another, this did not mean that Aristotle approved of such devices, for it could be shown from the text of the philosopher that his conclusions were derived from unaided sight and that therefore instruments could be of no use for the study of heavenly things; but that if, on the other hand, there really happened to be discovered something new in the heavens, it too could be figured out of the text of Aristotle with only the use of a little ingenuity. Galileo's comments rose to heights of scorn:

"O most profound Doctor, this! that can command me; for he will not be led around by Aristotle, but will lead him by the nose and make him speak as he pleases! See how important it is to learn to seize an opportunity. Nor is it seasonable to have to do with Hercules while he is enraged and beside himself but when he is telling merry tales among the Maeonian damosels. Ah, unheard-of sordidness of servile minds! to make themselves willing slaves, to receive as inviolable decrees, to

6. This and the following quotation are from the *Dialogue on the Great World Systems* (English trans.; Chicago: University of Chicago Press, 1953 [henceforth cited simply as *"Dialogue"*]), pp. 122 and 125; but they belong to sections which were written long before 1630, probably at the time of the polemic with Magini. We know, besides, that such sarcastic remarks were frequently uttered by Galileo from the start of his polemic with the schools.

engage themselves to seem satisfied and convinced by arguments of such efficacy and so manifestly conclusive that they themselves cannot resolve whether they were written to that purpose or serve to prove the assumption in hand! . . . What is this but to make an oracle of a wooden image and to run to that for answers, to fear it, to reverence and adore it?"

Such lamentable intellectual contortions were a proof indeed that his enemies were ready to go to any lengths; and out of that grew clear and present danger, for Galileo soon realized that the learned coalition, embittered by the feats of this slight "optical reed" which threatened to undo whole libraries of ponderous folios, patrimonies of vested intellecual interests—and the very art of academic disputation which brought them their stipends—was ready to hurl Holy Scripture itself at him. This was, in the academic custom of the time, a distinctly unfair means of attack: not only because it brought about the intervention of ecclesiastical authority in philosophical disputes but also because it gave the rowdies among the monks another pretext to inflame the populace against learning. But, like many a politician before and since, these men preferred to aggravate the incoherence of public opinion in order to dissimulate their own.

II

A young religious fanatic, Francesco Sizi, was prompted to fire the opening gun[7]—a popgun at best—with his *Dianoia astronomica* (1610). The argument, apart from some curious explanations about lenses, is not very different from that of Dr. Slop: "Why, Sir, are there

---

7. We say "prompted," because Magini was behind it (see the letter of Sertini, August 7, 1610 [Ed. Naz., X, 411]). Magini had also encouraged Martin Horky's hate-mad pamphlet, which backfired on its author. Since Father Müller (Adolf Müller, S.J., *Galilei und die Katholische Kirche* [1910]) chose to quote its personal remarks, it might be well to give an idea of this kind of polemic, leaving it in Latin as Gibbon does with his most impolite quotes: Galileo, says Horky, was unpopular in Bologna "quia capilli decidunt, tota cutis et cuticula flore Gallico scatet, cranium laesum, in cerebro delirium, optici nervi, quia nimis curiose et pompose scrupula circa Jovem observavit, rupti. . . ."

not seven cardinal virtues?—seven mortal sins?—seven golden candle-sticks in Moses?—seven heavens?—'Tis more than I know, replied my uncle Toby.—Are there not seven wonders of the world?—seven days of the creation?—seven plagues?" And also, added Sizi—and this was taken from Tycho's ideas—seven metals in alchemical theory? There-fore, there can be no more than seven planets in heaven, and the new ones revealed by the lenses of the "perspicil" [8] are an optical illusion. Sizi's pamphlet is clearly inspired by the cabalistic theories of Pico della Mirandola and is much more excusable in its mystical passion than Lodovico delle Colombe's *Contro il moto della terra,* circulated soon after; for Colombe's academic arrogance is manifest in his Aristo-telian arguments, which he combines with a lot of pretentious geo-metrical nonsense; and yet he, who claims to be speaking in the name of natural reason, does not refrain from quoting a whole lot of scrip-tural passages which put the Copernicans in a difficult position for arguing back. Father Benedetto Castelli, a monk of Montecassino, Galileo's favorite disciple, had written that, if Venus could be shown to have phases, it would convince everybody. Now the phases had been discovered, and this was the result. "In order to convince those obdurate men," Galileo wrote back to Castelli, "who are out for the vain approval of the stupid vulgar, it would not be enough even if the stars came down on earth to bring witness about themelves. Let us be concerned only with gaining knowledge for ourselves, and let us find therein our consolation."

But such beautiful ivory-tower attitudes could hardly last longer than a melancholy afternoon. It was not in Galileo's nature to retreat into solitude. Now that certainty had been reached, the motives for silence that he had explained to Kepler no longer were valid. In fact, Kepler's impassioned reply, those many years back, must have been strongly present to his mind:

8. The telescope had been called *occhiale* by Galileo, and in Latin it became *perspicil-lum, arundo optica,* etc. The Greek name of *telescope* was suggested later by Demisiano, a member of the Lyncean Academy (cf. Rosen, "The Naming of the Telescope," *Isis,* 1947).

I could only have wished that you, who have so profound an insight, would choose another way. You advise us, by your personal example, and in discreetly veiled fashion, to retreat before the general ignorance and not to expose ourselves or heedlessly to oppose the violent attacks of the mob of scholars (and in this you follow Plato and Pythagoras, our true preceptors). But after a tremendous task has been begun in our time, first by Copernicus and then by many very learned mathematicians, and when the assertion that the Earth moves can no longer be considered something new, would it not be much better to pull the wagon to its goal by our joint efforts, now that we have got it under way, and gradually, with powerful voices, to shout down the common herd, which really does not weigh the arguments very carefully? Thus perhaps by cleverness we may bring it to a knowledge of the truth. With your arguments you would at the same time help your comrades who endure so many unjust judgments, for they would obtain either comfort from your agreement or protection from your influential position. It is not only your Italians who cannot believe that they move if they do not feel it, but we in Germany also do not by any means endear ourselves with this idea. Yet there are ways by which we protect ourselves against these difficulties. . . .

Be of good cheer, Galileo, and come out publicly. If I judge correctly, there are only a few of the distinguished mathematicians of Europe who would part company with us, so great is the power of truth. If Italy seems less a favorable place for your publication, and if you look for difficulties there, perhaps Germany will allow us this freedom.

This, Galileo decided, was exactly what he was going to do—and from Florence. The time had come when he could build up a tidal wave of opinion and sweep the new ideas into acceptance. But, for that, he must by-pass the universities and address himself in the vernacular to the intelligent public at large. This involved no doubt a sacrifice of the international value of Latin, but Galileo did not care to mark himself as an exclusive member of the light-shy and scattered republic of scholars; he had written enough satirical rhymes in his time against the nervous blinking doctor, lost in the public thoroughfare, entangled in his robe, who makes for the safety of his study like a frightened cat for a hole.[9] He felt right at ease in the street, in the square, and at the dining table, and he knew he could handle Italian better than most.

He states his reasons straightforwardly in a letter to Paolo Gualdo of May, 1612:

I notice that young men go to the universities in order to become doctors or philosophers or anything so long as it is a title and that many go in for those professions who are utterly unfit for them, while others who would be very competent are prevented by business or their daily cares which keep them away from letters. Now these people, while provided with a good intelligence, yet, because they cannot understand what is written in *baos* [a word coined by the comic playwright Ruzzante to indicate the learned language], retain through life the idea that those big folios contain matters beyond their capacity which will forever remain closed to them; whereas I want them to realize that nature, as she has given them eyes to see her works, has given them a brain apt to grasp and understand them.

We are reminded of Copernicus in his dedication. There are many, he had told the Pope seventy years before, who despise science unless it pays; there are others who, although they have taken up the study

9. Galileo's poetry, like Maxwell's and Minkowski's, is almost nowhere to be found in print, although the rhymes of the latter two are part of the physicists' secret lore. We think we ought to reproduce here, for those who can read Italian, this portrayal of the doctor in the Bernesque manner:

Tu non lo vedi andar se non pe' chiassi
  Per la vergogna, o ver lungo le mura,
  E in simili altri luoghi da papassi.
E par ch' ei fugga la mala ventura;
  Volgesi or da man manca or da man destra
  Come un che del bargello abbia paura.
Pare una gatta in una via maestra
  Che sbalordita fugga le persone
  Quando è caduta giù dalla finestra,
Che se ne corre via carpon carpone

Tanto che la s'imbuchi e e si difenda,
  Perchè le spiace la conversazione....

Perchè la toga non ti lascia andare,
  Ti s'attraversa t'impaccia t'intrica,
  Ch' è uno stento a poter camminare:
E però non par ch' ella si disdica
  A quei che fanno le lor cose adagio
  E non han troppo a grado la fatica.
Anzi han per voto lo star sempre in agio,
  Come a dir frati o qualche prete grasso,
  Nemici capital d'ogni disagio.

of philosophy, are worse than useless in it because of their stupidity and behave like drones among the bees. There is still another kind of chatterers, he adds, but to these he will give no thought whatever; it is those who would maliciously and rashly use passages of Scripture to contradict him. This kind of opposition he considers negligible. Did not Lactantius, "a great ecclesiastial writer but a poor mathematician, say childish things about the shape of the Earth, deriding those who had discovered it to be a sphere?"

Like Galileo, Copernicus had forseen resistance not at all from the Church authorities but from vested academic interests. Their common judgment corresponds to the decline of the traditional universities in that era of transition. But from here on the two men diverge. The delicate and retiring soul of Copernicus wanted his subject to be kept among scientific initiates, and he wished that the Pythagorean privacy of research could be restored. "Mathematics are for mathematicians," he reminded gravely, and no one should apply himself to these studies who has not purified his soul. But, then, his theory did appeal only to the abstract intellect. As Galileo says admiringly: "Not being able to solve a number of grave difficulties, yet notwithstanding by other significant occurrences he was induced to confide so much in what reason dictated to him as to affirm confidently that the structure of the universe could have no other figure than that which he designed himself." But, he goes on, "since it has pleased God in our age to vouchsafe to human ingenuity the admirable invention of perfecting our sight by multiplying it as much as forty times," any good mind now can grasp the new truth without the need for Copernicus' daring genius.

Was this Galileo's appeal to the common people, as has been so often said? Hardly. He no more believed that the masses as such were capable of independent judgment than Voltaire was to do, or Samuel Johnson, for that matter. This ought to be made clear, since it has been more than once misrepresented. He had himself explained to Kepler how unwise it had been for Copernicus to be persuaded to step down among the multitude, "for so indeed are foolish people numbered," only to be derided and dishonored. He naturally believed, like

Machiavelli, that nostalgic republican, that few are those who can think and that the rest are sheep. Such, too, had been the judgment of their common forebears who had run the free cities of Tuscany; and, like them, he believed that the "vulgar" are much more easily swayed by superstition and violent emotions than by reasonable argument. He knew only too well that the real manipulators of those passions were the rabble-rousing preachers and demagogues, who could turn magic words of fright or authority "into clubs wherewith to crush the endeavors of science." But he also believed, quite classically, that in all walks of life, from the highest to the lowest, there arise men who can think by themselves and who are the natural elite. The last centuries had proved how freely and powerfully such men could shape civilization; it was to them that he was making his appeal, as the "open ruling class," and it was bound to antagonize the interlocking caste interest of the custodians of wisdom.

Whether he realized it or not, he had there on its way a movement bound to cause violent reaction in the measure in which it shook the old edifice to its foundations. It is still maintained in our day[10] that Galileo's fatal mistake lay in his rash indiscretion, his insistence on throwing open to the common people, by writing in the vernacular, a question which was far from being settled and could only, in that form, give scandal to the pious, whereas the proper approach would have been to write elaborate tomes in Latin and then patiently wait for the appraisal of the scholars and theologians. This disingenuous argument has long ago been pinned down in a little popular rhyme: "Cet animal est très méchant, quand on l'attaque, il se défend." The learned apologists seem to forget that their late learned colleagues of the universities had quickly appraised the new theories and decided to make short work of them. Not only that, but, fearing their own power might not be enough, they enlisted, as we shall see, the aid of a few ecclesiastics hardly deserving of the title of theologians in order to create the de-

10. See, e.g., Müller, op. cit., and the Catholic Encyclopedia (New York: Appleton, 1910), art. "Galileo."

cisive scandal which would result in a ban. Those particular gentlemen were perfectly willing to deliver their sermons in Italian, or, rather, let us say, in a vernacular as close to Italian as the language of the Hearst press is to English.

Thus, it was not at all a question of the tranquillity of the masses. It was well understood on all sides that Galileo was not writing for the masses. He was writing in literary style upon philosophical subjects for the open ruling class, which included prelates, princes, gentlemen, and men of business; and this could not but threaten the caste privileges of the average literati. Hence he was made out to be, like Socrates, a "poisoner of the people." Terms were coined rapidly to designate his kind: "free mind," "proud curiosity," *"esprit fort,"* "lovers of novelities," "those Florentine minds which are too subtle and curious," in order to cast suspicion on such activities as could not lawfully be impeached. The strange paradox of the drama is that those frightened clerics were dealing at last with what they had tried in vain to shape through the late Middle Ages, the orthodox natural philosopher. In him the junction *had* been effected between science and humanism. In Galileo's thinking there is nowhere to be detected the cold sneer of Valla, or the impenetrable and disdainful aloofness of Leonardo, or the dodge of the "double truth" so freely used by Pomponazzi and the Averroists, or the perilous fantasies of Pico or Campanella. He wants to act as a consultant of the theologians in natural philosophy and help them understand correctly the new discoveries. The simple fact is that these were much too upsetting for unprepared minds, even for such minds as John Donne's.

III

It must be admitted that Galileo the man corresponded as little to the clichés of his epoch concerning the Philosopher as he would to those of our time concerning the Scientist.

"He who gazes highest," he will say without false modesty, "is of highest quality; and the turning to the great volume of Nature, which is the proper object of philosophy, is the way to make one look high;

in which book, although whatsoever we read, as being the work of Almighty God, is most proportionate: yet notwithstanding, that is more absolute and noble wherein most greatly is revealed his art and skill. The constitution of the universe, among all things of Nature that fall within human comprehension, may, in my opinion, be set in first place; for as in regard of universal extent it excels all others, it ought as the rule and standard of the rest to go before them in nobility." These are lofty words, worthy of a Cambridge Platonist. But the marking of "the great volume of Nature" as the proper object of all philosophy will tell us that here is no contemplative temperament, although in his work the rigor and detachment of thought remain undeviating, free of the facile enthusiasms and the turgid fancies of his contemporaries.

At a time when force of style was held to be in conceits, the Galilean style strikes an independent note which goes back to the Machiavellis and Albertis and the master-craftsmen of his own Florentine past. His thought has the same unconcerned, secure, and apparently effortless *démarche* of the ordering mind amid unfolding realities. In the perpetual dialogue that is his life, his need is for equals, and he is willing to admit that company is all: "It is a great sweetness," he says, "to go wandering and discoursing together amid truths."

The "togetherness" implied in these words is a deeply social realization, away from caste and rank—and also from the prestige of the wizard in technique—even such a one as Socrates had been twenty centuries earlier; it is the free togetherness of thinking men going through unreckoned time toward an ultimate clarification. "Man's intellect," Bovillus had said, "achieves itself in time; it goes from change to change until it has become all things." This was the Platonic hint, understandable to all. Here it is firmly turned from romantic identification to the development of a clear operating abstraction.

For if it could be abstract, Galileo's thought never became otherworldly. He followed with the same keen interest the elegant turning of verse, the knowledgeable tending of a vineyard, or the experienced handling of mechanical problems in the Venice arsenal. "Among those," he wrote, "who have trained themselves over the years to solve the most difficult problems of their craft, there are bound to be some of comprehensive knowledge and very strong intelligence." It was among such men, both high and low, that he would find congenial company; a joyous convivial temperament with all the passions of the amateur and the gourmet, he would plunge with equal zest into a literary argument, a difficult legal case, a well-appointed dinner party, a new "natural effect," or a good wench. Both in work and in pleasure, he drove his vigorous frame to the limits of endurance.

There was still too much Renaissance in the air to have people condemn him for his lack of Puritanism. What the learned class reproached him with were rather his virtues: his unconstrained and direct approach to intellectual problems, his discarding the erudite polysyllabic vestment of thought that was so conveniently used by others to cloak their lack of originality. Typically enough, he never thought up the present Greek names for his instruments. The telescope he named *occhiale*, "eyeglass"; the microscope, *occhialino;* the hydrostatic balance, *bilancetta,* "little balance." In his very indulgences he stood for the uncomplicated and genuine as much as he did in his scientific syle. His own gentle and candid Benedetto Castelli, who led throughout uncomplainingly the penurious existence of a miserably underpaid and underfed monk, knew well how to share with his master the simple but epicurean delights of good wine, good cheese, and good figs; their scientific correspondence is interlaced with fanciful excursions and glad exclamations about the very special barrels and parcels that they send in gift to each other.

It becomes rather easy to understand why Galileo should have found his warmest partisans among writers, artists, and enlightened amateurs, while he had most of the professional scholars aligned against him. The latter he could only drive to obloquy by his bantering tone and the light irony of his polemic, whereas the former found in him a protector of the open mind and the "wise ignorance." Typical of them was Ludovico Cigoli, the painter, who had become his unofficial representative in Rome, a man who dearly loved a good fight. Thus, he wrote in 1611 that Kepler's *Dioptrics* had reached the city and was proving a valuable ally: "This is going to discomfit further all the satraps and stuffed robes of learning. . . . I love to see them stuck, silent with popping eyes, that if I had to portray the figure of ignorance I would not draw it otherwise. . . . Kepler should be in all the bookshops, and I wish you would come to his help with your works, so *they* may burst, and that your writings should be around to hound them even in the stalls of the marketplace [*su per le pancaccie*]." Another time, after the *Letters on the Solar Spots,* he writes: "Try to let the booksellers have it freely; it would make the Pigeon League[11] die with rage if they could not look at a stall without finding them. . . . By the way, I have an idea for an emblem those pedants could put on their shingle: A fireplace with a stuffed flue, and the smoke curling back to fill the house in which are assembled people to whom dark comes before evening." [12]

Cigoli's scorn might be thought to be that of the unlettered man toward scholarship, but, as a successful and respected painter, Cigoli did not have to contend with any feelings of inferiority; and his judgment is as independently founded as that of a true Renaissance artist. As he watches with attention and concern the attitude of Father Clavius, the Jesuit astronomical authority, he reports to Galileo that Clavius cannot reconcile himself to the idea that there can be real mountains in the Moon and is trying to explain what is observed by certain differences of density inside the polished and pellucid body of the satellite: "He really seems to believe this kind of explanation, and I find no excuse for him except that a mathematician, however great, without the help of a good drawing, is not only half a mathematician, but also a man without eyes." [13]

---

11. The "Pigeon League" was the Peripatetic coalition headed by Lodovico delle Colombe, of which more later. Since *colombe* means "doves," Galileo's friends often called Colombe "the pigeon."

12. A line which had become a familiar proverb: "Gente a cui si fa notte innanzi sera."

13. Letter to Galileo, August 11, 1611. The theory went on being propounded for many years, and Galileo still had to cope with it in his *Dialogue,* pp. 96 ff.

Leonardo might have spoken thus concerning the knowledge of nature. The man who knows how to see is also the man who can understand the use of the new instruments. It is the Renaissance mind with its irrepressible vitality which is carrying on the fight against Scholasticism; it is only such temperaments (and they are found in the Church as well as among the laity) who could feel cheerfully at ease in the shimmering world of new facts, new hints, "intelligence" brought from afar.

It was not left for Galileo to choose. From 1611 on, his literary activity takes the form of tracts, pamphlets, letters, dialogues, and comments. From the systematic treatise it veers off into *littérature d'occasion,* stylistic elegance, rhetorical ingenuity, and indefatigable oral persuasion. Against the unnatural coalition of his opponents, whom he considered a grubby lot, he turned, as Copernicus had done, to the leaders of the social and spiritual order.[14]

The first thing, of course, was to secure an indorsement of his discoveries from the Jesuit astronomers in Rome, who were the experts of the Vatican in such matters. This would put an end to the sly attempts of his academic enemies to drag the controversy onto the ground of religious taboos. He did not expect, surely, the Roman astronomers to come over bag and baggage to the new theories. That was not their way. But he trusted them, once they had the facts, to draw the consequences on their own and to clear the ground quietly for any coming changes.

Hence he did not tarry in Florence. He had barely settled down when, with the end of the winter season of 1611, he was again on his way to Rome.

Things went as well as he had anticipated. Soon he was writing to Filippo Salviati, the friend who was later to become the chief character

14. Copernicus' work had been announced before its publication, in 1533, by Johannes Widmanstetter to Pope Clement VII, who had approved of the ideas. It had been sponsored by Cardinal Schönberg, then president of the Commission on the Calendar; and Tiedemann Giese, the bishop of Kulm, assisted its publication.

in his *Dialogue:* "I have been received and feted by many illustrious cardinals, prelates, and princes of this city, who wanted to see the things I have observed and were much pleased, as I was too on my part in viewing the marvels of their statuary, paintings, frescoed rooms, palaces, gardens, etc." Monsignor Piero Dini writes to Cosimo Sassetti: "He is converting unbelievers one after another; for there are still a few capons who, that they may not know about the satellites of Jupiter, refuse even to look; and if I meet any of them, I want to hear what he has to say. The Lord Cardinal Bellarmine asked the Jesuits for an opinion on Galileo, and the learned Fathers sent the most favorable letter you could think of, and they are great friends of his; in this Order there are very great men, and the most outstanding are here." The Pope himself had given audience to the astronomer and showed him benevolence. On the part of a Pontiff like Paul V, "so circumspect and reserved," writes a contemporary, "that he is held for somber," this was a signal recognition indeed.

The Jesuit astronomers, or at least Clavius and Grienberger, had been shaken in their strict Ptolemaic faith. It had been a difficult decision for old Father Clavius, the author of the Gregorian calendar reform and the undisputed leader of Jesuit astronomy, to yield to the new things in the skies. In the beginning he had laughed at them and said that this new-fangled instrument would have first to put them there in order to see them; but, after looking through Galileo's best telescope, he had surrendered with good grace. This alone was worth the trip to Rome. But there was another important gain: Galileo was made a member of the new Accademia dei Lincei (the "Lynceans," or "lynx-eyed") [15] and established a firm friendship with its founder, Prince Federico Cesi.

The Roman environment was not the most favorable to natural science. But the frail and earnest young nobleman, averse by temperament from the pursuits usual to men of his station, had used his

15. The mythological reference is to Lynceus the Argonaut, noted in that earliest company of pioneers for his keenness of sight.

wealth and influence to gather around him some friends interested in the new fields of learning. His own taste went toward botany, and his life's work was to be dedicated to the Central American flora; but what united these men of very disparate interests, and as yet without a productive method of work, was the same urge which caused the rise of such groups all over Europe: the sterility of the universities, the inadequacy of their curriculum, and the resistance of official scholarship to the new ideas. The common endeavor of the Lynceans was, as Cesi put it, "to fight Aristotelianism all the way," which of course implied looking somewhere else for a philosophical inspiration; and, of the respected systems, it could only be Plato's. Just while the "scientific-minded" Jesuits, their friends, were battening down the hatches and tying up their theory to the most guaranteed commonplaces of Peripatetic doctrine, some Lynceans revived a strain of romantic Renaissance Platonism which opened their imagination to intellectual adventure.

Thus we see rehearsed again the paradox of naturalists refusing to acknowledge the greatest naturalist of antiquity and turning for guidance to the prophet who had taught the flight from nature. But, then, we have seen the reasons for it already. Aristotle had been degraded by his epigones into a master of quibbles, and his system had been adopted by educators not so much for its capacity to organize information as for its capacity to dispose of it.

Notwithstanding his youth, Federico Cesi was and remained the natural leader of the Lyncean group. The Roman world respected him not only for his title but for his quiet and mature judgment. He became the spokesman of Galileo and was to be his adviser and support in the difficult period ahead.

Galileo was then absorbed in the "Atlas-like" undertaking of determining the periods of the satellites of Jupiter, which the Jesuits had tried in vain to work out, and hundreds of observations date from that year. But his main task he considered to be that of educating opinion, mainly through letters addressed to men in positions of influence. Therefore, he proceeded gradually, leaving the Copernican conception aside and touching only on those conclusions for which direct evidence was overwhelming, like the mountains of the Moon. Through this approach (which is also that used later in the First Day of the *Dialogue*), he could hope to dismantle the Aristotelian position without arguing about its main tenets; he could show that all the conventional talk about perfect globes and jewel-like celestial substances was a literary commonplace rather than a considered philosophical conclusion.[16]

Still, he had few illusions about the receptiveness of people even to these simple ideas. He was only hoping they would sink in very gradually. The very same ones who hailed his discoveries balked at considering their consequences; and, whenever he felt too confident in his logic, his friends were there to remind him. Thus Paolo Gualdo, whom he trusted, wrote him in May, 1612:

As to this matter of the Earth turning round, I have found hitherto no philosopher or astrologer who is willing to subscribe to the opinion of Your Honor, and much less a theologian; be pleased therefore to consider carefully before you publish this opinion assertively, for many things can be uttered by way of disputation which it is not wise to affirm.

But, when he received this warning, Galileo had already made a new discovery which he felt ought to give pause even to the most obdurate. On observing the spots on the Sun, which had only recently been found, he showed that they belonged to the solar globe itself and were not dark bodies moving around it, as suggested by Father Scheiner. With this, the Sun's rotation was established—and also its deviation from the established canons of perfection and immutability. "This novelty," he wrote to a friend, "may well be the funeral, or rather the last judgment, of pseudo-philosophy."

The *Letters on the Solar Spots,* published in 1613, after Galileo's return to Florence, and under the sponsorship of the Accademia dei Lincei, is Copernican throughout. It is the first open admission that

16. Letter to Gallanzoni, June 16; to Cigoli, October 1, 1611. Gallanzoni was the secretary of Cardinal Joyeuse, and the fourteen-page letter is obviously meant for the Cardinal himself and also for Bellarmine.

the new theory is the only one for which the telescopic discoveries make sense.

Fortified by official recognition, he sees the road open ahead for the great change. In this meridian hour of his life he concludes triumphantly his third and final Solar Letter: "Saturn and Venus bring in marvelous manner their contribution to the harmony of the great Copernican system, whose complete discovery favorable winds assist, with such shining escort showing the way, that we need fear darkness and adverse storms no longer."

This was written on December 1, 1613. Three weeks earlier the clergy had launched its first open attack.

II

"Domini Canes"

A throwen Evangelist indeed, full of throward Divinitie:
Surely, if there were no more than his unmannerly manner,
it is enough to disgrace the whole matter thereof.

KING JAMES I, "APOLOGIE"

I

Father Lorini of the Dominicans, professor of ecclesiastical history in Florence, was the man who took the initiative. Preaching on All Souls' Day, 1613, he inveighed against the new theories in unbecoming terms. Hauled up for this breach of custom, he wrote a fumbling letter of apology: he had never mentioned science in his sermon, he asserted. "It was only later, in a discussion, and in order not to stand there like a log, that I said a couple of words to the effect that the doctrine of that Ipernicus, or whatever his name is, was against Holy Scripture."

So the monks were on the warpath after all; Cigoli had been right in warning, a year before, about their goings-on in Rome. But that was to be expected. Monks always agitated about something: incomes, privileges, books, jurisdiction, personal quarrels, or the resistance of some official to their everlasting claims. Galileo had taken the precaution of "checking signals" in the Vatican. Cardinal Conti, beseeched for guidance, had written him in July, 1612, that "the statements of Holy Scripture were against rather than for the Aristotelian principle of the unalterability of the heavens, but that the case was different with the Pythagorean doctrine of the Earth's revolution." Some kind

25

of "progressive" motion was admissible, on the word of a learned doctor who had spoken of *imperceptibilis motus,* but a rotation did not seem to agree with Scripture unless it was assumed that it merely adopted the customary mode of expression. But, Conti added, that was a method of interpretation to be employed only in case of the greatest necessity; Didacus à Stunica's pro-Copernican suggestions had not been generally accepted.[1]

This meant, in sum, that the authorities were open to persuasion if someone produced an adequate "necessity." It was exactly what Galileo felt he could do in the next few years. He could ignore the monks as well as a certain hostile activity that he knew to be centered in the archbishopric of Florence. So long as he had the favor of the Roman Curia, the road was still open ahead.

There was one thing, however, that Galileo did not know. Cardinal Bellarmine himself, the chief theologian of the Church, was keeping an eye on him. He had heard much about the scientist in Rome; he had even looked through the telescope. All this had brought the Copernican issue to his attention. What the discoveries could mean was not clear to him, and he was not a man to form hasty judgments. But Bellarmine was no friend of "novelties" or of sensations that were not edifying. There was confusion enough in the world already. Sixteen years earlier it had been his grievous task to frame the decision which led Giordano Bruno to his death at the stake. Admittedly, there was little else that he could have done, for Bruno remained throughout, and to his last moment, an impenitent apostate from the Church. But this, he concluded, was what the "Pythagorean" exaltation could lead men into; and here now was the same Pythagorean astronomy cropping up again, albeit in more respectful garb. It was sure that Galileo had been making a sensation in Rome.

1. Didacus à Stunica (Diego de Zuñiga), a Spanish monk, had written a commentary on Job's passage: "He that hath suspended the Earth above the void." Galileo had also thought of this passage, as appears from his marginal comments to Colombe. The "learned doctor" of the Cardinal's letter is obviously Nicholas of Cusa.

One can see from the dates what took place in Bellarmine's mind. On April 24, 1611, he asked Father Clavius whether the discoveries were serious, and was answered that they were. A few days later he gave audience to Galileo and tried, during the exchange of the usual civilities and protestations, to form an opinion of the man. On May 17, as we know now from the secret archives, at a meeting of the Congregation of the Holy Office,[2] he introduced a small item on the agenda: "Let it be seen [*videatur*] whether in the proceedings against Doctor Cesare Cremonini there is a mention of Galileo, professor of philosophy and mathematics." That is all, and it led nowhere; Cremonini himself was never brought to trial. But in its very irrelevance the item is revealing. Cremonini had nothing to do with Galileo except that he quarreled with him. He was a hidebound Aristotelian, one of the few who had really refused to look through the telescope.[3] But Cremonini

2. The Congregations functioned as the equivalent of our Cabinet and Senate committees, but each of them also headed a department. When the Pope was not in the chair, they met at the residence of one or another member. The Congregation of the Holy Office was the most important, as it corresponded more or less to our National Security Council. Its members at the time were the Cardinals Bellarmine, Veralli, Centino detto d'Ascoli, Taberna (di S. Eusebio), Mellini, Gallamino (d'Aracoeli), Bonsi (di S. Clemente), and Sfondrati (di S. Cecilia), "by the mercy of God, cardinals of the Holy Roman Church, Inquisitors-General throughout the Christian Commonwealth against heretical pravity."

3. Cremonini stands in history books as the abstract figure of the pedant, but he was a vivid and colorful personality in his time. The successor of Francesco Zabarella, he had become the leading light of Paduan philosophy as a powerful and systematic teacher of the true Peripatetic doctrine, which, of course, involved a disbelief in the immortality of the individual soul. He had strongly defended the privileges of the university against the attempts of the Jesuits at gaining a foothold in teaching and was twice challenged by the Inquisition, which he disregarded from his position of immunity guaranteed by the Venetian state. Hence it was thought more politic not to press the case against him. His salary of two thousand florins was higher than anyone else's and twice what Galileo had been granted in recognition of his discoveries. He lived in state, with "many servants, two coaches and six horses." As to his personal attitude toward Galileo, it is best expressed in a letter of Paolo Gualdo: "Having met him on the street, I told him: 'Mr. Galileo is exceedingly sorry that you wrote a whole great book about heaven while refusing to see his stars.' He replied: 'I don't believe that anyone

was a nuisance, and Galileo looked as though he might become another. This is known, in the language of the modern state, as spotting by Objective Characteristics. A few months later the Cardinal said confidentially to the Tuscan ambassador: "Whatever the respect we owe to the Grand Duke, if Galileo had stayed longer, it could not but have come to his being called to account." [4]

This, in his mind, had nothing to do with the scientific issue, toward which he always preserved what he felt to be an open attitude. But his position was so far from what we still fondly call our modern one that only the subsequent developments can make it clear. To Galileo himself, it was difficult to gauge and remained so to the last.

II

Galileo's friends were giving conflicting advice. Some were telling him to go on with his discoveries and renounce the cosmological controversy; others, that this was the time to come forward with convincing demonstrations and get the Jesuit experts on his side. True enough, old Father Clavius was wavering, in those last months of his life, in his Ptolemaic position;[5] and the others, Grienberger, van Maelcote, Lembo, ought not to have been hard to persuade. Father Campanella, the generous and ever bellicose confusionist, wrote to him from his dungeon in Naples (those were happy times when one could keep up a philosophical correspondence from the prisons of the secret police):

but he saw them, and besides, that looking through glasses would make me dizzy. Enough, I don't want to hear any more about it. But what a pity that Mr. Galileo has gotten involved in these entertainment tricks, and has forsaken our company, and his safe haven of Padua. He may yet come to regret it.' "

4. "A qualche giustificatione de' casi suoi." This came out only four years later, in a letter by Guicciardini dated December 5, 1615. Galileo's letter to Gallanzoni, which had been shown to Bellarmine, had obviously made no impression at all.

5. It was Kepler who pointed out later that there was evidence of hesitation in Clavius' comments on Sacrobosco, written shortly before his death in 1612. This is confirmed by Father Kircher's admissions (see n. 7, p. 315). But the Jesuits had other lines of retreat, as will be shown on p. 35.

"All the philosophers of the world receive the law from your pen, for in truth it is impossible to philosophize without an assured system of the world as we expect it from you. . . . Arm yourself with perfect mathematics, leave for heaven's sake all other business, and think only of this one; for you do not know if you will be dead tomorrow."

This was what Galileo would have liked to do, but, as far as we can penetrate through his pretexts, he did not feel ready for a "showdown." The astronomical proofs were brilliant, but he knew better than anybody else that the Copernican hypothesis would remain what it had been for its inceptor—a formal diagram to be accepted on purely optical and kinematic grounds, without a natural philosophy in which to frame it. What Galileo needed was a Newton, and he did not have him; he had only Copernicus, an unconventional, imaginative, mystical mathematician. He had also Kepler, to be sure, "Caesar's astronomer" and a brave fighter, but a dangerous fantast and, as misfortune would have it, a Protestant as well. Against the physical principles of conventional cosmology, which were always brought out against him, he needed an equally solid set of principles—indeed, more solid—because he did not appeal to ordinary experience and common sense as his opponents did. He did not want to stand in the eyes of his enemies as one of "these mathematicians who come forward with claims to new natural theories while themselves devoid of all philosophy." That was why he had always insisted that he had spent more years in the study of philosophy than months in the study of mathematics.

It must be admitted that his opponents had a strong point: the theories of the astronomers had never made any sense physically, and this still applied to both camps. The ancient astronomers had had the good sense to present only abstract mathematical models (Figs. 1 and 2). This man Copernicus, they were being told now, took his ideas as physical truth. But, then, how did he account for the epicycles which still crowded his diagram, a full thirty-four of them? [6] He must have been thinking that, through some special grace, abstract circles move

6. For an explanation of the problem see chap. iii.

FIG. I. The Ptolemaic System

These drawings have been designed to point out how similar in complexity were the Ptolemaic and Copernican systems. Even a cursory glance convinces one that neither system is essentially simpler geometrically than its competitor. Drawings cannot be made accurate in radial dimensions, but special care has been taken properly to orient the centers of the planetary orbits relative to the zodiac. Thus, if one traces in the Ptolemaic diagram the radial line from the Sun to the point under "A" in "EARTH," the point which is the center of the Sun's orbit, it is seen to be between the centers of rotation of Venus and Mars, precisely as Ptolemy's geocentric theory requires. The relative senses of rotation of the epicycles on their deferent circles and the planets on the epicycles are indicated by the arrows. The planetary distances remain arbitrary, which is not so in Copernicus.

FIG. 2.   The New System as Conceived by Copernicus

In the Copernican system the Sun appears in the center of the stage, but the actual momentary centers of rotation of the planets cluster around the momentary center *C* of the Earth's orbit. In this system Mercury was handled in a unique fashion, librating on the center of an epicycle instead of traveling on the epicycle. The planetary symbols are as follows:

☉	Sun	⊕	Earth
☿	Mercury	♂	Mars
♀	Venus	♃	Jupiter
☽	Moon	♄	Saturn

Drawings are by the courtesy of Dr. W. D. Stahlman (see also p. 71).

by themselves. In fact, he did. He had no better explanation than that. With the insouciance of genius, he had left it to his successors to fill in the gaps in his theory.

The Aristotelians—at least some intelligent ones, who disregarded their master's halfhearted attempt at a mechanism of spheres—could well claim that here was shown the soundness of Aristotle's general policy which eschewed such constructions. Always intent on tidying up the world, it was enough for them to demonstrate the immutable nature of heavenly substance and then assign to it figure and local motion; whereas in terrestrial substance, always in process, much more complex forms of motion and becoming occurred. They might have said of heaven as Pascal was to say later of physics: "One should say: 'It is done by figure and movement; but to say which, and to construct the mechanism, is pointless, for it is difficult and uncertain and laborious.'" The Aristotelians might have added: "and impossible." For the heavens are not to be reached, and what we can know of them is strictly limited. The philosopher should legislate about general principles and attributions in the universe and leave the astronomer to present a variety of abstract models (had not Tycho come out with a new one?) adequate for "saving the phenomena" without involving the philosopher in his impossible suppositions; in the same way as local motion on earth should be classified into a few types, such as natural and violent, and further details left "to the mechanician or other inferior artist." The heavens remain inaccessible, even with the telescope, and we know already far too much about tricky optical effects. Should we now subvert the vast and documented discourse of the schools, which allows us to account in orderly manner for nature and life and the soul itself—and fits in so handsomely with revealed Truth—to launch ourselves in a sea of paradoxes and unnatural conclusions, simply because a man has come forward with two lenses in a length of pipe?

The argument, as we have suggested, is not so empty as it looks. We may understand such a predicament better by referring to modern problems. Cosmology is, and is expected to remain, a conjectural science, for it ought to be safe to say that we shall never know anything final about the universe as a whole and that, in fact, as Galileo thought, the range of acknowledged ignorance will grow with the advance of science. Comte wanted to forbid such speculations no longer than a century ago. Supposing now that the ruling section of public opinion decided that such speculations are in some essential way dangerous for social stability, it is easy to see what would follow. In an unmetaphysical society like ours the universe is a matter of small concern, and economic orthodoxy has replaced the religious, but the response to an alert in that field is just as prompt or even more so.

To the above-mentioned reasons of high policy, Galileo knew that he could not yet oppose any adequate ones of his own. He did have a natural philosophy, too, which would provide most of the answers, but it was contained in his dynamics and was not yet sufficiently organized. (It was to be concluded later—too late to be of any help—in the *Discorsi* of 1638.) He knew he could eventually prove that motion in the heavens obeys the same laws as motion on earth, that those laws are mathematical, for the book of Nature is written in the form of equations and not in the pattern of a discourse made up of predicative sentences, where nouns represent substances and adjectives qualities. That book with seven seals, once deciphered, brought startling conclusions: there is no difference between heaven and earth; we are in heaven, and heaven is on earth. The pleasing "architectonic" disposition of substances makes way for the grandiose and mysterious unity of mathematical law, which starts from first principles unknown to us and leads toward conclusions unforeseeable; but we must follow it wherever it leads us, trusting that God and Nature know better than we do what is best.

Before Galileo could come forward in the open field with such a disturbing philosophy, he felt he needed an organized physics to support his contentions. The "immense project" became more and more immense. Perhaps it ought to be preceded, rather than followed, by the books *On Motion*. This is what we can infer of his thoughts, as he gave dilatory answers to his friends who urged him to come out with his *System of the World*.

III

For the present, he felt he had better go on with his semijournalistic activity, shaking his opponents' system at the weakest points, converting men of influence, creating a favorable climate of opinion. In friendly discussion he knew he could be invincibly persuasive. He could skirt delicate points by choosing his terrain; he could surprise and carry away by bold admission. Thus to Prince Cesi, who had said that he would gladly favor the Copernican system if only it removed the excentrics and the epicycles, he replies: "We should not desire that Nature should adjust to that which seems to us best arranged and ordered, but we ought rather to adjust our intellect to her works, since they are certainly most perfect and admirable, and all other constructions would reveal themselves eventually as devoid of elegance, incongruous, and puerile. . . . If anyone wants to deny the epicycles, he must deny the paths of the satellites of Jupiter. . . . Excentrics exist, for what else is the path of Mars according to the best observations?" [7]

Thus he was trying to overcome his friend's doubts, hoping that he would not notice that the official epicycles were something entirely different, not, as with Jupiter, the paths of real satellites moving around a real planet, but mere geometric devices moving around imaginary centers—but, then, there were so many things of which he was certain without being able yet to prove them that a little illusionism appeared excusable.[8] As he put it, one does not pull down a perfectly good house just because the fireplace happens to smoke.

7. Letter to Cesi, June 30, 1612.
8. The Aristotelians were undoubtedly right on this point. The epicycles would not fit in with any system of natural philosophy, and it is one of the strangest mysteries of that history why Galileo should have refused the proffered help of Kepler with his theory of elliptical orbits. The excentricity of Mars is present in his thought, the ideas of Kepler are being discussed among his friends, but nothing happens (see p. 178 and n. 10 to same).

It should be added, too, that he had to confront some more dangerous illusionisms on the other side. The Jesuits, always polite, had
shown a certain tendency to retreat out of reach; and it was unfortunately Tycho Brahe himself who had provided the easiest way out.
They had their own reasons. We are apt to forget that anti-Aris-
totelianism had been for long a very confused movement indeed.
Ramus, the opponent of the schools, had called in 1569 for an astronomy without theories based *ab initio* on observation. Tycho, then in
his early twenties, could well reply that theories were necessary to give
direction to observation. He eventually suggested a theory which
saved most phenomena by having the planets revolve around the Sun,
and the Sun in its turn around an unmoved Earth. It was another
purely geometrical scheme which left untouched the foundation of
official philosophy and the sayings of Scripture. This made Galileo's
task all the more difficult, and it explains the bitterness that he later
manifests against Tycho in the *Dialogue*. He refused to consider even
for a moment the Tychonic variant as a "third system." To him it was
a miserable red herring brought in at the last moment. But he could
not prevent the Jesuits from thinking—or at least saying—that, if
this geometrical device solved one half of the difficulties, a further
device might possibly solve the remaining half. This was not a real
excuse, but it could be very helpful to minds that did not know which
way to turn. In his letter to Clavius of March 12, 1610, Galileo had
carefully spelled out the reasons which made the Tychonic system
hopelessly obsolete.[9] That system could be proved to withstand the
telescope as little as did the Ptolemaic. But there is no persuading

9. Tycho's main astronomical reason (apart from his frivolous physical ones [see
   pp. 9 and 61]) had been that he had not been able to detect a stellar parallax of
   even a half-minute, which removed the stars to a distance of at least eight million
   semidiameters of the Earth; whereas the last circle of Saturn did not go beyond
   twelve thousand. This, in turn, given the *apparent* stellar diameters, would have
   made the stars each greater than the solar system. Moreover, Tycho had insisted
   that the planets shone by their own light, which made them different from the
   Earth. Now the telescope showed the apparent stellar diameters to have been due
   to irradiation, and it showed Venus to be dark where the Sun did not strike it.

someone who chooses not to be persuaded.

Another welcome occasion to strike at an undefended flank soon offered itself. One hot day in August, 1612, Galileo was sitting at the Grand Duke's table with other learned gentlemen, and the talk came around, as it would, to the virtues of ice. A doctor explained that ice is heavier than water, being water condensed, and that it floats only due to its peculiar shape, just as needles or metal foils will at times be supported on the water's surface. Galileo interposed some pointed remarks, and the controversy was on. It developed into a long polemic in which Aristotelian professors plunged with fury and at one meeting almost came to blows with some opponents. Cardinal Maffeo Barberini himself, on a visit, participated with delight and came out openly on Galileo's side. Out of the polemic, at the Grand Duke's urging, was born the *Discourse on Floating Bodies,* in which Galileo brought his fundamental contribution to hydrostatics on the Archimedean model. Acting as usual in the thick of events, he had not lost sight of his goal. The professors had been shown up as dimwits and retreated in a rage to write learned commentaries. Meanwhile, Galileo had dug the foundation for his physics a little deeper.

The "Galileisti" were growing in number too. He noticed that since his *Discourse* many gentlemen of Florence had taken up the study of mathematics, "for without it the mind lacks the wings to raise itself to the contemplation of Nature." [10] It was indeed difficult to resist the lure of the new discoveries. "O much-knowing perspicil," Kepler exclaimed, "more precious than any scepter! He who holds thee in his right hand is a true king, a world ruler. . . ."

There were some—there are even now—inclined to feel that the empire had been won by a freak of chance. It was not quite so. First of all, the construction of a working telescope involved advanced physical thinking. The mere discovery that two lenses brought things nearer had really been a freak of chance for an optician's boy. But the crude lenses that were used for eyeglasses could have showed nothing

10. Ed. Naz., IV, 445.

at all in the sky, and it was Galileo who had come upon the idea of a method whereby they could be ground correctly by checking them upon a star—and then had focused his instrument on Jupiter. Let us imagine the telescope in the hands of a Giambattista della Porta or some such known contemporary, and we shall understand how much its importance was a matter of the intellectual personality of its author. As Olschki rightly remarks:

"The domination that Galileo's thought exercised over all the branches of knowledge and application was not so much the result of his many-sidedness, as of his great capacity for the 'common touch,' and of his personal influence on the intellectual formation of generations which saw in him an incarnation of wisdom, a leader and master figure. They did so because in his achievements and thoughts they could recognize a concern of the whole of mankind, and not only the fruit of the learned efforts of a specialist. The reproaches of vainglory, self-importance and impatience, which are still raised against him today for leaving his study for the public scene, fall by the wayside if we consider him in his own world, and show themselves as petty judgments or hypocrisy." [11] We may add—as the results of an enmity that will not abate.

Galileo ought indeed to be considered, as we have tried to show, as the last great leader of the Renaissance; his appeal to the people continues Leonardo's struggle against the preconceptions of the learned and the "Halls of Vain Disputation." It was still the world of the Renaissance which was around him, with its curiosity and excitement, its vivid controversies, its violent involvement in high quarrels, its popular juries on art, and its interest in technology; it was the social surge of the new times that was providing him with its power.[12]

The whole system of the schools was in danger. This explains the sudden jelling of the opposition into a kind of mutual defense league,

---

11. Leonardo Olschki, *Geschichte d. neusprachlichen wissenschaftlichen Litteratur*, Vol. III: *Galilei und seine Zeit* (1927).

12. "The learned are plagued by those eager for knowledge, just as the rich are by the poor who press at their door" (letter of Nozzolini, Ed. Naz., VI, 598).

ready for anything. They realized that there was no time to lose in compromising their dangerous enemy by a *fait accompli*. The first step, they decided, was to hurt him at Court, where his strength lay, by arousing against him the strict piety of the Grand Duchess Dowager, Madama Cristina of Lorraine. In March, 1613, with a confessor and a Peripatetic professor, Boscaglia, working together in strange collusion, the occasion was brought about at a Court dinner in Pisa, at which Father Castelli was challenged by the Grand Duchess on the orthodoxy of the Copernican theory. Castelli, candid soul, rose to the bait and answered spiritedly, using his authority as a theologian. The Grand Duchess was appeased. But, as he discussed the incident with his master, Galileo realized that he owed it to his disciple, and to the Grand Duchess, to step forward and take the responsibility of a seriously considered statement which should protect their good names against these organized provocations. In the upright Benedictine soul of Castelli there was also the will, shared by Galileo, not to let a gang of blackmailers compromise the Church for their own convenience.

The "conspiracy" of which Galileo so often speaks is not imagined. It called itself a "League." There were several men in the outfield, engaged in more or less concerted action, like Boscaglia, Coresio, and D'Elci in Pisa, the astronomer Magini in Bologna, Grazia and the Archbishop in Florence, and a number of nameless Dominicans in Rome. But the aggressive leadership belonged to the Lorini-Caccini-Colombe triumvirate, of which more later. Of the tie-up between Colombe and Father Caccini we have positive proof in letters addressed by Matteo Caccini to his brother: "It was a silly thing [for Tommaso] to get himself embroiled in this business by these pigeons [*colombi*]." [13]

IV

Galileo, on the other hand, was too shrewd not to understand that his enemies were trying to draw him onto controversial ground. His

13. See pp. 109–10 and 114–15.

reply in the form of a *Letter to Castelli* (December 13, 1613), to be circulated among their friends, was a model of restraint and dialectical skill.[14]

Galileo reminds his readers first that Scripture, although absolute and inviolable truth itself, has always been understood to speak figuratively at many points, as when it mentions the hand of God or the tent of heaven, and that it is our duty to understand it so that the two truths, that of God's Nature and that of God's Writ, never appear to be in conflict. Why, then, should Holy Writ be used to support the opinions of certain fallible philosophers against others, to the jeopardy of its authority? "For who would set a limit to the mind of man? Who would dare assert that we know all there is to be known? Therefore, it would be well not to burden the articles concerning salvation and the establishment of the Faith—against which there is no danger that valid contradiction ever may arise—with official interpretations beyond need; all the more so, when the request comes from people of whom it is permitted to doubt that they speak under heavenly inspiration, whereas we see most clearly that they are wholly devoid of that understanding which would be necessary, I will not say to refute, but first of all to grasp the demonstrations offered by science."

Scripture, he goes on, deals with natural matters in such a cursory and allusive way that it looks as though it wanted to remind us that its business is not about them but about the soul and that, as concerns Nature, it is willing to adjust its language to the simple minds of the people. And, indeed, adds Galileo with a brilliant dialectical turn, it is obvious that the word about Joshua stopping the Sun in Gibeon cannot have been meant literally if we take the official geocentric interpretation; for it is admitted, with Ptolemy, that the diurnal motion of the

14. It reached Francis Bacon by way of Toby Matthews, who wrote from Brussels: "I presume to send you the copy of a letter, which Galileo, of whom I am sure you have heard, wrote to a monk of my acquaintance. . . . To an Attorney-General in the midst of a town, and such a one, as is employed in the weightiest affairs of the kingdom, it might seem unseasonable for me to interrupt you with matter of this nature. But I know well enough, etc."

Sun as well as of the stars and planets depends on the *primum mobile.* Therefore, if the whole of the heavenly movements was not to be deranged, it must be understood that Joshua stopped the *primum mobile.* On the other hand, by adopting the Copernican theory, we might even understand the words literally; for, if we admit that their revolution is impressed on the planets by the Sun, which is in the center, we might conceive that, by stopping the Sun, Joshua stopped the whole solar system for three hours without disarranging the respective positions.

Needless to say, this is quick fencing rather than sound science. Faced with people who thought only dialectically, Galileo has to be something of a sophist, too, in order to gain attention. He attacks first by showing that the official Greek theory does not really fit the Bible story as believed; then he suggests that a more modern theory might possibly fit better. Since there is really none that does, he has to invent something. But the rather Keplerian idea adopted here of a magnetic rotational force emanating from the Sun denied his own theory of planetary motion as inertial, and, also, it did not in the least explain the daily rotation of the Earth. With all that, the suggestion is not at all on the dead level of casuistic bad faith current among his opponents. It is a brilliant intuition of unknown forces from which it was hoped that some day an explanation of the Holy Text would come, since an explanation there had to be, which to Galileo was axiomatic. It was not science, but neither was it bad fiction. It was faith in conciliation and hope in science.

V

Unfortunately, he provided exactly the opportunity that his enemies had been waiting for. They proclaimed everywhere that he had assailed the authority of Scripture and that he had tried to meddle in theological matters. Few had seen the letter; many came to think they knew what it said. The Bishop of Fiesole wanted to have Copernicus jailed and had to be informed that the good man had been dead for quite some time. Father Tommaso Caccini, a Dominican monk with several acquaintances in the "League," who had already been disciplined by the Archbishop of Bologna as a scandal-maker, saw an excellent occasion for fresh scandal. On December 20, 1614, he preached a sermon in Santa Maria Novella on the text, "Ye men of Galilee [*viri Galilaei*], why stand ye gazing up into heaven?" announcing that mathematics was of the Devil, that mathematicians should be banished from Christian states, and that these ideas about a moving Earth were very close to heresy, as Serrarius himself averred and many another learned text.

Educated opinion has made merry ever since over the antics of Father Thomas. There are one or two things, however, which seem to have escaped attention in his rather artless performance. One is that, although it was not infrequent to have preachers in their zeal upbraid academic learning and the pride of universities,[15] it was not done to start shouting heresy and damnation from the pulpit until and unless the correct position has been defined by Rome; and it was well known instead that the authorities were keeping an open mind about the new discoveries. Another is that Caccini, although a man of no intellectual interests, was not an illiterate for all that. He had just then entered his candidacy for the title of Bachelor of Arts. He knew what stood under the heading of mathematics in the order of studies. Now mathematics, were it only because of its limited attributions, had always been theologically white as wool. Whatever trouble there was came from philosophy, which comprised physics and which might come up with all sorts of godless deviations like Averroism, atomism, pantheism, and even Pythagoreanism. But that was not "mathematics."

In order to make it understood that he was concerned with the system of the world, Galileo had had to explain that he was really

---

15. These motifs were stressed in Counter-Reformation preaching up to our days as a countermeasure to the growth of secular thought:

> "Diceva bene ar Caravita er prete:
> Li libri so' invenzione der demonio,
> Dunque, fijoli mii, no' li leggete."
>
> G. G. Belli

("The priest said it well at the Caravita oratory: books are an invention of the Devil; therefore, my children, don't read them.")

a philosopher; and he had moved Vinta to state as much explicitly in his official title at Court, which made him out to be "chief philosopher and mathematician to His Most Serene Highness." If Caccini's object had really been the heliocentric theory, his language habits would have caused him to speak of "the new philosophy which puts all in doubt." He said instead that mathematics and mathematicians were all of them of the Devil, and he said it because he knew that "mathematicians" stood mostly for astrologers in the popular mind. The loose usage of the word went back to late antiquity, and princes had kept "court mathematicians" ever since for no other real purpose than the casting of horoscopes. Kepler knew it only too well; although he sincerely believed in astrology, it annoyed him to be paid only for that. Now, since the Order of Preachers had appointed themselves "watchdogs of the Faith," it was only natural that they should go after magicmongering and vain curiosity in the spirit of the Apostolic instruction: *Increpa illos dure*. Caccini had cast himself in that most natural role, the better to promote the confusion between the new ideas, which were even then applying for orthodox and approved standing, and all sorts of subversive and discredited stuff. Seventeen years later, when the campaign started again against Galileo, certain anonymous but well-trained gentlemen in Rome were to resort to the same opening move: They spread the rumor that Galileo had astrologically predicted the Pope's death.

There was no chance that any of these charges could be made to stick in court, but that mattered little. The master-plan, conceived apparently by Lodovico delle Colombe in the interests of the academic group, was simple but effective: Have the friars create a scandal and uproar centered around the person of Galileo and thus compel the Roman authorities, always very sensitive on the subject of "scandal," to take for reasons of public order the measures that they seemed reluctant to take on grounds of theory. The name of "provocateur" had not been invented yet, but the dodge was as old as the world.

The sermon worked according to plan. Florentine opinion had been accustomed for centuries to the ways of the friars; it regarded them with a variety of feelings not all friendly, and it talked of them mainly as ubiquitous, innumerable, and largely self-invited dinner guests. For one Savonarola or San Bernardino, it had decided, there were lots of fakes; and it had coined a number of easygoing disrespectful proverbs to cover the situation.[16] What shocked public opinion now and caused it to take notice was that, in his eagerness to "get into the act," Father Thomas had tackled not the usual small fry but a popular member of the ruling class, a personal friend of the Grand Duke, and a renowned scholar whose discoveries had been applauded by the Pope and the cardinals. In the carefully graded society of the time this was clearly a major social solecism unless—as gossip promptly suggested—Caccini could count on some powerful backers who kept in the shadows. But who could they be? Speculation and rumor went buzzing through Florence. The effect had been obtained.

Father Maraffi, Preacher-General of the Dominicans, wrote a letter of apology to Galileo. "Unfortunately," he added, "I have to answer for all the idiocies [bestialità] that thirty or forty thousand brothers may and do actually commit." But Galileo was this time alarmed. Some Dominicans might be on his side, but their headquarters in Rome was definitely not. They had been working against him since his visit to Rome, and he knew how close Dominicans were to the Inquisition personnel.

He thought seriously of writing and asking for redress. But Prince Cesi and his older friend, Piero Dini, archbishop of Fermo, urgently advised him to let the matter drop. Cardinal Bellarmine was not too favorably inclined. They might take occasion of his request in Rome, he warned, to consult whether or not the further spread of this opinion should be permitted or condemned. In that case, it would probably

16. Galileo's own youthful burlesque poetry that we have given on p. 12 quotes one of those in the last verse. The doctors, he says, have undertaken to live at ease, "no less than if they were friars or fat priests, capital enemies of all and any discomfort."

43

be condemned, as the Peripatetic school was in the majority there; besides, it was very easy to prohibit or suspend by simple administrative procedure.

Galileo understood that this was exactly what the compeers of the "League" had been working toward, so he held his peace. But the operation against him went into its second phase according to plan. The opening moves had been to draw him into a theological controversy and then to counterattack by creating a scandal. In the meantime Lorini, the character who had first entered the list against "Ipernicus," had not been inactive. Having secured a copy of the *Letter to Castelli,* he dispatched it on February 7, 1615, to the Inquisition by way of Cardinal Sfondrati, who was on its board. He added the following comments on the "Galileists," never mentioning Galileo by name:

All our Fathers of this devout convent of St. Mark are of opinion that the letter contains many propositions which appear to be suspicious or presumptuous, as when it asserts that the language of Holy Scripture does not mean what it seems to mean; that in discussions about natural phenomena the last and lowest place ought to be given to the authority of the sacred text; that its commentators have very often erred in their interpretation; that the Holy Scriptures should not be mixed up with anything except matters of religion . . . ; that in Nature philosophical and astronomical evidence is of more value than holy and divine (which passages your Lordship will find underlined by me in the said letter, of which I send an exact copy); and finally that, when Joshua commanded the Sun to stand still, we must understand that the command was addressed only to the *primum mobile,* as this itself is the Sun. . . . Ever mindful of our vow to be the "black and white hounds" of the Holy Office . . . when I saw that they expounded the Holy Scriptures according to their private lights and in a manner different from that of the common interpretation of the Fathers of the Church; that they strove to defend an opinion which appeared to be quite contrary to the sacred text; that they spoke in slighting terms of the ancient Fathers and of St. Thomas Aquinas; that they were treading underfoot the entire philosophy of Aristotle which has been of such service to Scholastic theology; and, in fine, that to show their cleverness they were airing and scattering broadcast in our steadfastly Catholic city a thousand saucy and irreverent surmises; when, I say, I became aware of all this, I made up my mind to acquaint your Lordship with the state of affairs, that you in your holy zeal for the Faith may, in conjunction with your most illustrious colleagues, provide such remedies as will appear advisable. . . . I, who hold that those who call themselves Galileists are orderly men and good Christians all, but a little overwise and conceited in their opinions, declare that I am actuated by nothing in this business but zeal for the sacred cause.

Lorini had displayed suitable priestly charity by describing the errant characters as "good Christians all, but a little overwise and conceited in their opinions" (*un poco saccenti e duretti nelle loro opinioni*). In his heart, however, he felt otherwise; they were black souls who did not deserve justice, let alone mercy, and nothing should be left undone for their destruction. His indomitable zeal thought nothing of boldly forging a couple of heresies in his "exact" copy of the letter at the most opportune spots. Galileo had written: "There are in Scripture words which, taken in the strict literal meaning, look as if they differed from the truth." Lorini wrote instead: "which are false in the literal meaning." Galileo had written: "Scripture does not refrain from overshadowing [*adombrare*] [17] its most essential dogmas by attributing to God qualities very far from and contrary to His essence." Lorini changed "overshadowing" into "perverting" (*pervertire*). The startled Inquisitor was bound to comment: "Such words as 'false' and 'perverting' sound very bad" (fol. 341^r).[18] They were about the only points where he found fault with the text, which otherwise seemed orthodox enough. Even so, he added, they might be construed innocently within the general context. Lorini's attempt had misfired.

The report set the machinery in motion nonetheless. The Holy

17. The word *adombrare* is used here in the old sense, as in Dante, *Purg.*, XXXI, 144, and not in the more current sense, which is also to be found in the English "to adumbrate."

18. The documents of the Inquisition file are to be found in Vol. XIX of Favaro's National Edition of Galileo's *Works*. But, as they have also been reproduced by L'Epinois and Berti in their earlier publications of the dossier, we refer to them by the number of the actual folio, which is to be found in all three works.

Office, ever careful, wrote on the twenty-sixth of February, 1615, to the Archbishop of Pisa and the Inquisitor there, instructing them to secure a signed copy of the *Letter to Castelli,* "in a skilful manner," without arousing attention. The Archbishop accordingly showed a sudden interest in the doctrinal problem and asked to see the letter, which pleased Castelli greatly. But Galileo's reflexes of prudence unfortunately stood in the way. To Castelli's repeated requests for authorization, he first replied with silence; he then sent him an unsigned copy with strict orders not to let it out of his hands.[19] The Archbishop had it read to him and diplomatically professed himself satisfied.

This first reconnaissance had yielded almost nothing; it is closed by a routine annotation dated March 13. But the third phase of the combined operation came in with perfect timing to give the Inquisitors a new and more promising start. Caccini had arrived in Rome and had promptly approached the Holy Office by way of the Cardinal of Aracoeli, who was on its board. At the next weekly sitting of the Congregation, which took place on March 19, his request was granted: "Sanctissimus gave orders for the examination of Father Thomas Caccini, who, the Cardinal of Aracoeli says, is informed concerning the errors of Galileo and begs to testify on them for the exoneration of his conscience."

Caccini was called in the next day, March 20, and unburdened his soul. What came out would hardly deserve the honor of history; but, as it provided the principal evidence in the whole affair, it should stand on record. The city of Florence, Caccini revealed, was full of "Galileists" publicly holding impious discourses inspired by their master: such things as that God is not a self-existent being but an accident; that God is a sentient being who can laugh and weep; that

19. This was prudence with respect to the Archbishop and the use he might make of his words, not with respect to the Vatican, for Galileo had already forwarded the true text of the letter by way of Dini, on February 16, 1615; but it was disregarded. Some modern historians like Monsignor Marini, who were apparently acquainted with Galileo's writings only from police reports, found in the term "perverting" further proof of Galileo's arrogance.

the miracles performed by the saints are not real miracles. Caccini managed to suggest that such abominations were only natural coming from a man who had written *Letters on the Solar Spots,* which was full of damnable matter, who belonged to "a certain Academy of the Lincei," who was a friend of the infamous Sarpi,[20] and who corresponded with German mathematicians.—How did he know all this?— He had been told by Lorini and by a certain Jesuit, who also told him that Galileo had barely escaped arrest by the Inquisition when he was in Rome in 1611. He was speaking out of pious zeal, he averred, and would not like to have it known. But Father Lorini was the man who could tell them more. He even could show a copy of a certain letter that Galileo had written to Father Castelli.—Under cross-examination, Caccini began to hedge. About Galileo's Copernican opinions, the Bishop of Cortona would confirm. As to the godless propositions quoted, he stated he had learned them from his friend, Father

20. Sarpi is Milton's "Padre Paolo, the great unmasker of the Trentine Council," who "observed that the primitive councils and bishops were wont only to declare what books were not commendable, passing no further but leaving it to each one's conscience to read or lay by" (*Areopagitica*). Paolo Sarpi (1552–1618) had been a friend of Sixtus V and Bellarmine, but the controversy of the Venetian interdict had driven them apart. The Curia excommunicated him, and its agents tried to kidnap him and even to assassinate him in 1607. He remained to the end the consultant of the Venetian Republic and the leader in the fight of the state against the claims of the Vatican, as he defended the ancient and republican *libertas Ecclesiae* against the Jesuits and papal absolutism. "The new name of blind obedience invented by Loyola," he wrote, "was ever unknown to the Church and to all good theologians; it removes the essential feature of virtue which is operating by certain knowledge and choice, it exposes to the risk of offending God, and it does not excuse him who has been deceived by the spiritual ruler."

Needless to say, Galileo's friendship with Sarpi implied no connection whatever with the latter's religious and political activities. Sarpi was one of the great scholarly minds of his time; he had been keenly interested in Galileo's physical theories and had even collaborated in his experiments. He was sure that Copernicanism would be accepted eventually as true and stated as much in a written opinion to the Venetian Senate after the prohibition of 1616. All of this did not concern Caccini. The mere mention of Sarpi was an effective smear, and he knew it would stick in Rome.

Ximenes,[21] who said he had heard it from some of "them," several times.—And specifically from whom?—Well, he could only remember the name of one. It was something like Attivanti—youngish, dark beard, thin face. He had heard him disputing with Father Ximenes. He could not produce proof, but he was sure the man was a Galileist, for he had also upheld Galileo's theories. Father Ximenes would know. This, in any case, he could say for sure, that Galileo taught these two propositions: that the Earth moves and that the Sun does not.—Did he know Galileo?—No, he had never met him.—Did he have anything against this other man Attivanti?—Nothing at all. There was nothing in his heart but love for everybody. He spoke out of Christian zeal.— Witness dismissed.

It took quite some time to locate Father Ximenes, a Spaniard, for he was traveling; but, when he was called in (November 13), he picked up the ball with great deftness. Yes, he said, quite true, there was this lamentable scandal caused by the Galileists.—Who were they?—He did not know very well. There was this one man, Giannozzo Attavanti, a parish priest he knew, who had said terrible things. He was sure he had not really meant them; he was no heretic, surely, not informed enough to have a serious opinion. He must have picked them up from Galileo or from some Galileist.—What did he say?—He said that God is an accident and that there is no substance of things or continuous quality but that everything is a discrete quantity composed of vacua (sic); that God is sensitive, that He laughs and weeps. "But I do not know whether they speak from their opinion or someone else's."—Did they say that the miracles ascribed to saints were not

21. The technique must be again admired. Caccini states that Lorini gave him the *Letter to Castelli* to read; therefore, he knows that Galileo's position is exactly the contrary. "The literal understanding of Scripture," it is said there, "would lead to grave heresies and even to blasphemies, such that God has hands and feet and eyes, that He is subject to bodily affections such as anger, repentance, hatred, and even forgetfulness and ignorance." But, by calling in Ximenes as an independent source, who can be supposed not to know about Galileo's text, he gives himself full latitude. The whole deposition is such an interminable mass of twists and innuendoes and double talk that a summary does no justice to it.

real miracles?—No, he had never heard that.—Where and when had he heard these opinions?—From this young man, Attavanti, several times, both upstairs and downstairs in the Monastery of Santa Maria Novella. He had begged him not to speak thus, had represented to him the enormity of his sayings, but still he thought the man was not giving his own opinion but Galileo's.—Witness dismissed.

Attavanti was called in on the next day and questioned about the damnable propositions. He answered with assurance. Father Ximenes, he said, can tell you how it happened. We were practicing disputation for our theses, he and I, and I held the contrary part, *addiscendi gratia*. We had taken the section on absolutes, of Aquinas' *Contra Gentes*, where these questions occur.[22] Ximenes will tell you that it was so. This other man must have eavesdropped and imagined something, because another time, as I was telling Ximenes about the motion of the Earth, he came in from the next room, screaming that this was heretical and that he was going to deliver a sermon about it, as he subsequently did. That is all there is to it.—Did he know Galileo?—Yes, I have met him a few times. We talked about philosophical matters, like the motion of the Earth and the Sun standing still in Gibeon.—What did he know of his theological opinions?—I hold him to be a very good Catholic, otherwise the Grand Duke would not have him around.—Did he have anything against Caccini?—I never talked with him before or after. I did not even know him by name.—Witness dismissed.

The evidence was forwarded to Rome. The official who read it in the last days of November must have used his own judgment about this *roba fratina,* as it was currently called even inside the administration. The still unsuspecting Attavanti had obviously been used as a

22. The investigator dropped of his own initiative the proposition about things being made up "of vacua," whatever that may mean. Caccini had not mentioned it, and he seems to have concluded that Ximenes invented it for good measure. The other proposition about the miracles had been given by Caccini and not by Ximenes, so only two propositions were left: those concerning the substance and the attributes of God, which do actually occur in Aquinas. The compeers had gotten their signals slightly mixed over that unfortunate interval of eight months that had elapsed since Caccini's deposition in March.

dupe in a confidence game by the two associates. Nothing much there.[23] But the first part was relevant. He marked in the margin with vertical strokes of his pen several points: *Letters on the Solar Spots, Lincei, German mathematicians, Sarpi, Galileists, propositions.* He went on farther down and underlined Attavanti's words: *very good Catholic, otherwise the Grand Duke would not have him around.*

Then there comes a note in the file, dated November 25, 1615, which transcribes the decision of the Congregation taken on that day: "See the *Letters on the Solar Spots* by the said Galilei." On the next sheet, but dated three months later, comes the convocation of the Qualifiers on February 23.

At this point we should like to show here by an example how shots are called, and how history happens to be written, on this difficult subject. We shall take no less a historian than Father J. Brodrick, S.J., who stands out among his confreres for charm of style, cultivated taste, and discriminating scholarship, as well as for the genuine Christian warmth which pervades his work. Now Father Brodrick gives the following considered judgment on Caccini's deposition which he discusses briefly but omits to analyze: "All the signs point to Caccini having been a very good and honest, if somewhat hot-headed man. As we are asked to accept so much on the evidence of Galileo's friends, why should we not be allowed to believe one of his foes for a change?" [24] This is a somewhat vain question. Anyone will accept this or that detail of the deposition.[25] It is we rather who should ask: Why

23. The marks made by the examiner are clear in the manuscript. They have been noted, at least most of them, in L'Epinois's edition of the documents of the trial.
24. J. Brodrick, *The Life and Work of Blessed Robert Francis, Cardinal Bellarmine, S.J.* (1928), II, 353.
25. The single point brought out from the deposition is that the Galileists tried to persuade a Jesuit favorably inclined to Copernicanism to preach a counter-sermon to Caccini and did not succeed. Father Brodrick seems to find this move very wicked. In any case, he might have found it duly acknowledged in Wohl-will's account among others, including a small detail that Caccini had omitted, viz., that the unnamed Jesuit had been willing but was apparently prevented from speaking by Archbishop Marzi Medici. In very much the same vein, Father

does Father Brodrick ask the reader to believe on his word as a historian that Caccini was a good and honest man? No one doubts the author's Christian motives, but he need not ask why historians who want to get at the facts have taken to relying rather more on the estimate of the situation provided by Galileo and his friends. In this particular case, Galileo never got to know Caccini's deposition; he never even was told that Caccini had denounced him to the Holy Office. But, when Caccini came to pay him a "courtesy" visit in Rome a few months later, he wrote back to Florence: "That person was with me for over four hours, with many demonstrations of humility, and tried to persuade me that he had not been the original mover of the other activity here. . . . but from all his discourses I discovered a very great ignorance, no less than a mind full of venom and devoid of charity." From all we know now out of the secret archives and so many other sources, Galileo had guessed exactly right.

VI

The goings-on we have described took place in deepest secrecy, but Galileo was man of the world enough to know that somewhere things had been set in motion. Cesi had advised him to lie low and wait for the clouds to disperse, but he knew what was at stake and decided to take a calculated risk. He sought out intercessors. He wrote in February, 1615, and then again on March 23, to his friend, Monsignor Dini, asking him to have his letters reach the Jesuit mathematicians, also Cardinal Bellarmine, and, if possible, the Pope himself. This time, he inclosed an authentic copy of the *Letter to Castelli* in order to have all his cards on the table.

Brodrick asks us to understand (p. 355) that Lorini's letter is "not an official denunciation of Galileo, Lorini himself writes Cardinal Sfondrati that he did not wish it be considered as such, but merely as a private piece of information for the guidance of the authorities." The *distinguo* is quite interesting, but it may leave a few people puzzled. One runs up against this kind of thing all the time; we have gone into this one particular case only so that we may be excused from further discussing and polemicizing.

In these later missives there is no longer the quiet irony of the early one. They are urgently pleading to have any decision suspended; and, since the *Letter to Castelli*, he says, was written in haste, he is asking for more time to give a considered philosophical statement. Meanwhile, he shows himself very much concerned with what Dini had told him—that heliocentrism might be ruled to be acceptable as a simple mathematical hypothesis. This might appease the mathematicians, he says, but is absolutely contrary to what Copernicus had meant and tried to show. He had held his system to be physically true, evidence had since accumulated in his favor, and it would be disastrous if the Church froze the situation by decreeing that physics and mathematics must be kept in separate compartments and controlled by the literal sense of Scripture.

But since Bellarmine, in a conversation with Dini, had quoted the Psalmist as proving beyond doubt that the Sun moves and had said that he would like to know what Galileo thought of it, Galileo finds himself compelled to move again into theological territory to confront him—not for discussion among the public, he protests humbly, but only as a brief submitted to the authorities. A ray of light from heaven may come even to the ignorant if the intention is pure. He is offering his thoughts to his mother, the Church; let them be destroyed if such is her infallible decision. He will gladly submit.

After this premise Galileo suggests that it might be consonant with Scripture to conceive of the great forces of Nature, light and heat, as finding their proper focus in the Sun, located in the middle. There must have been, he says, some primeval force spread over the universe in the beginning, for Scripture speaks of the Spirit moving upon the face of the waters, even before the firmament was made, and it says of God: "Thou hast made the Light and the Sun," speaking as of two distinct entities. From the most ancient sages to Dionysius the Areopagite, there seems to be a consensus about light as the original power, closest in nature and analogy to God.

Now the Cardinal had referred to Psalm 19; Galileo does not try to by-pass the famous text but faces it resolutely to seek therein, even as his opponents had done, a confirmation of his own views:

The heavens declare the glory of God; and the firmament sheweth his handiwork.

Day unto day uttereth speech, and night unto night sheweth knowledge. There is no speech nor language where their voice is not heard.

Their line is gone out through all the earth, and their words to the end of the world. In them hath he set a tabernacle for the sun.

Which is as a bridegroom coming out of his chamber, and rejoiceth as a strong man to run a race.

His going forth is from the end of heaven, and his circuit unto the ends of it: and there is nothing hid from the heat thereof.

The law of the Lord is perfect, converting the soul: the testimony of the Lord is sure, making wise the simple.

This is, however, the King James Version. The Vulgate says: "in Sole posuit tabernaculum suum," which is more amenable. If the Sun is the tabernacle *for* the power of God, then, suggests Galileo, that power is clearly represented here by the light and the heat which circulate in the universe, fecundating it throughout. It is they, rather than the Sun, who can be aptly called the "bridegroom" and the "strong man running his course." This he supports with sundry subtle reasons, such as that the bridegroom "cometh out of his chamber," a simile which does not fit very well the doings of a tabernacle whose only function is to sit still. Similar ideas about that text (but Galileo did not know it) had come to Copernicus, too; he had erased them from the first draft of his text, fearing that they might look too markedly "Pythagorean." This kind of speculation stemmed from the great epoch of medieval Christianity, which had found a theme in the "Metaphysics of Light" brought over from Neo-Platonism into mystical theology. If Galileo had found St. Bonaventure instead of St. Robert Bellarmine[26] still in the seat of theological authority, he might

26. Bellarmine was beatified by Pius XI on May 13, 1923, and canonized in 1930.

have become a pillar of the Church. But those times were over. Bellarmine was in authority, a masterful Scholastic mind charged with keeping the Church in line with the decisions of the Council of Trent, and as a Jesuit regretfully resolved never again to disregard the *sinistra cura*.[27]

27. Cf. Dante, *Parad.*, XII, 125:

> "Io son la vita di Bonaventura
> da Bagnorègio, che nei grandi uffici
> sempre posposi la sinistra cura."

III

Philosophical Intermezzo

And, oh, it can no more be questionèd
That Beautie's self, Proportion, is dead.

JOHN DONNE

The controversy had thus reached the higher echelons. It would be only fair at this point not to let the mind dwell on the futile or ridiculous aspects of the conflict and to consider the issue of old versus new in its full dimensions. Galileo's vocal opponents were third-rate Scholastics, but their arguments rested upon a most important doctrine, and it was the groundwork of that which was put in question.

The philosophical synthesis taught in the schools was essentially worked out by many generations from Aristotle, in which the Church and the larger part of the lay scholars agreed.[1] All things and all activities found their natural place in that system. God and Nature are

---

1. The dissenters, Averroists and Aristotelians of the stricter observance, among whom was Cremonini, did disagree only in points which had nothing to do with the present issue, like the eternity of the world and the immortality of the soul. There was a "scientific" school trying out its own way, in which Pomponazzi and Zabarella had distinguished themselves; but in the alignment of ideas that we are considering their influence was against Galileo. They still belonged to the Aristotelian circle of thought, with Stoic influxes, and they were at one with the other "independents" on the anti-mathematical issue, as well as against the consensus of humanists. The fact that they were considered "scientific" in their own way did nothing to help the term, since Pomponazzi's books were publicly burned for impiety. Thus, they could only add to the confusion in the public mind about the meaning of science.

ample enough and opulent enough to afford a niche for all the endless diversity that makes up finite existence. Above the single sciences is philosophy itself, a rational discipline which seeks to formulate the universal principles of all the sciences. It leads to the knowledge of the First Cause. Above that is theology depending on revelation, the end point of the whole system: faith is the fulfilment of reason.

Physics, the "science of Nature," found its place in the structure without difficulty. The universe forms a hierarchy reaching from God down to the lowest being. Every being acts under the internal urge of its own nature, seeking the "good" natural to its kind; and that good is one form of perfection which finds its place in the scale according to its degree. No matter how lowly it may be, no being is wholly lacking in value, for it has its station, its duties, and its rights, through which it contributes to the perfection of the whole. The essence of the scheme is subordination to an end. But, within that hierarchy, the "nature of things" is a tolerant and liberal constitution. All beings of a kind have an essence in common, but they do not cease to be individual "substances." Of all men, all nettles, all cats, there are no two exacty alike, yet they remain true to their essence.

It was, indeed, all one science, as it should be. What else is the science of Nature, a man of that time would have said, if not to know how the natural substances go toward their appointed ends in an ordered way?

The idea of an *order* is paramount. Not the order of the abstract formula but that of a multitude of varied beings whose behaviors co-exist and mesh in a vast symphony, the order of the seed that becomes a tree according to the rhythm of the seasons, and then again earth and then life again, with a dim perception of its own purpose.

> Birds sigh for the air
> Soul for it knows not where—

And what, then, could the ambition of science be, except to describe that order and its goals, in a vast discourse, as natural history does even today, but revealing the eternal scale of values underlying it?

In that order a very clear distinction seems to impose itself upon all who are not blind—that which severs the things of heaven from those here below. The stars last forever, whereas on earth all is change and passing-away; the skies turn around us everlastingly, while on earth anything let free will fall to the ground and stop. Thus, there must be an essential difference of nature between the two realms, and practically all philosophers had been agreed that nothing under the Moon can be similar to celestial things.

What things are in heaven, or why they are that way, cannot be guessed, except by raising the soul to contemplate those other entities beyond time that are of its own nature, such as the Beautiful and the Good, which seem to be, as it were, reflected in the perfections of heaven. To explain the order of things on this earth, we may appeal to our close experience of them. But the heavenly order seems to be the mirror of a pure metaphysical or aesthetic thought; it will be, in Plato's words, a moving image of eternity. The very matter of heaven will in deliberate fancy be conceived as such an image, whether it be ethereal crystal or subtle fire; the absolute geometric regularity of its orbs will scan the over-all rhythm that is followed by the life of perishable nature here below.

> . . . the rest
> From Man or Angel the great Architect
> Did wisely to conceal, and not divulge
> His secrets, to be scanned by them who ought
> Rather admire. Or, if they list to try
> Conjecture, he his fabric of the Heavens
> Hath left to their disputes—perhaps to move
> His laughter at their quaint opinions wide
> Hereafter, when they come to model heaven,
> And calculate the stars; how they will wield
> The mighty frame; how build, unbuild, contrive
> To save appearances; how gird the sphere
> With centric and eccentric scribbled o'er,
> Cycle and epicycle, orb in orb.

How wise God had been in setting right at this point the Pillars of Hercules of discovery was very clear to Milton: so clear that he did not feel he had to explain or to hedge on the spectacularly unauthorized commitment—even a generation after Galileo. The fact is that the placement of the Earth at the separate center of things is not for Aristotle, or for Milton, a purely astronomical solution or a mere complement of the system. It is the actual foundation of Aristotle's cosmology, which he has chosen after having carefully discussed and rejected the opinions of those "ancients," as he calls them, who made out the Earth to be a planet. It is on this foundation that he has built the elaborate and closely knit structure of his physics. To undermine it at any point, his followers will contend, would "tend to the subversion of all natural philosophy and to the disorder and upsetting of heaven and earth and the whole universe."

It is thus, at least, that Doctor Simplicio will exclaim against the new ideas in Galileo's *Dialogue*. But Simplicio, although invented to serve the author's convenience, is hardly a caricature; he is merely a composite portrait. Galileo makes fun of him in so far as he identifies the welfare of the universe with that of his own school, but the premise underlying the protest he is not far from conceding himself; it is, in fact, explicitly stated in the very opening sentences of the *Dialogue* as a point of general agreement: The universe cannot but be perfect, a thing of beauty and proportion, a totally ordered whole, otherwise Creation would make no sense, and there would be no point to philosophy.

The principle seemed to Galileo himself so obvious, in a way, that it prevented him from following his discoveries to their logical end. He who had discovered the principle of inertia always refused to think of a straight inertial path, because it would have been "disorderly." Natural motion, according to him, cannot be other than circular, since it is intended to keep things in their proper order. Thus, Aristotle, too, had been on common-sense ground when he stated the principle that all things tend toward their proper position in the order. It is this way of being in time and space—which will be no more than free fall in the stone, but growth in the plant, intelligent action in man—that Aristotle calls "motion." The way in which these individual searches for each thing's "proper good" combine and co-operate can be constructed into a system which reveals the order whereby all things tend toward the Supreme Good.

Motion could be defined, hence, as the instrument for this eternal process. But it is even more than that; it is the process itself: the simple word has a rich and multiple content, equivalent to what we would call in modern words "universal becoming."

The technical definition of motion in the Aristotelian language might possibly not convey as much to the modern mind: "Motion is the passage of what is in potency to what is in act, in so far as it is in potency." This definition was to be held up to ridicule by Descartes, who maintained that it made no sense in any language. And so indeed it does not for the type of scientific mind that Descartes represents; but, then, for that scientific mind, motion is understood already as something simpler and clearer, the change of position undergone by a body with respect to other bodies. It is not an activity; it is a state. With it goes the whole Cartesian mechanical universe, a universe of simple location where matter is described only by size, relative place, and movement, where nothing "happens," but everything goes on shifting around blindly according to inertial law. Even animals become, in that world, pure automats; all the world is dead except for the immortal soul of man.

Old-fashioned indeed with respect to that is the conception of Aristotle and its phrasing; yet in essence it says nothing stranger about reality than the word of the poet to man: Become what thou art. The ancient universe is, as it were, a vast republic of gods, men, animals, plants, and things realizing their respective natures and coming to rest in their appointed places, as the eternal forms embody themselves perpetually in new matter according to the heart-beat of life and death.

A limited universe, it is inevitably bounded on all sides as an organism should be; and the space inside it a qualitative field, so to speak, where each being has a proper place and where the place corresponds to the full realization of that being, neither more nor less as each organ has a place in the body. In that universe there are several ways to move and act, of which the shifting of place is only one; there is also growth, shrinking, and change of quality and aspect. All these are "motions." But such a universe is also one where things really "come to be," where the word "realization" has a meaning, whereas in a purely mechanical universe it has none; for it is axiomatic in the Cartesian conception that inert matter only, barely, manages to subsist, identical to itself, by God's decree. Such a harsh simplification as that of Descartes was necessary, it would appear, for clearing the way to the vaster and subtler constructions of science. But one can understand the puzzlement of Goethe, and Keats, and so many of their time, of how anyone could ever accept such an image of reality stripped of its color, variety, and life.

As far as mechanics went, however, Galileo was right in seeing there the weakest point of the Aristotelian system—so weak that it dragged down the rest along with it. In a system patterned on life, centered on the Earth, the motion that is simply a shifting of place becomes the most flat and uninteresting aspect of the general process; it serves only to take things where they should be and function. The stone can express its nature only in one way—by getting to its proper place. Hence the only thing that it knows how to do is to fall. It is the ultimate poverty of being, far below what can be achieved by the poorest fungus. It can change in no way by itself, except in position. We ought to see, then, why the Aristotelian found it absurd to look just in that most blind and uncouth of events, the fall of matter, for a mathematical clarity that he knew he could not find in the so much more important process of the growth of a living being. "Please consider," he would have said, "that mathematics cannot apply to change in any form, for it concerns only what is static or abstract. You may hope to find it perchance in the accomplished form, where Platonists are always searching for it, in the mysteries of divine proportion; but how could you expect to discover it at the most confused and shapeless point of being, in the nascent act, in the urge of pure possibility toward realization, whether it be the sprouting of the seed or the fall of the stone? If you ever find geometry in nature, it will not be there; it will be at the opposite farthest removed from it, in the immobile and accomplished crystal. And this alone ought to show you how right we are. But even the crystal that you find in Nature will express geometry only imperfectly, because Nature, being life, has no use for rigid abstract perfection. See how even the hardest metal sphere will never touch a marble plane on one point only, as geometry would have it."

To this, Galileo, mindful of Archimedes, replied, as we have his words in the *Dialogue:* "Do you admit that any piece of rock has the shape, the weight, the size it happens to have to the greatest degree of precision imaginable? Yes, surely. Why then you ought to see that number and precision appear in nature at levels that you refuse to consider." But his opponents went on refusing to consider, for it would have only upset them uselessly. To be inside the frame of thought of Aristotle meant to have banished number, weight, and measure from philosophical significance. "Mathematics," said the schools, "cannot concern motion, for motion is always toward a given good; and there is no mention of the good in mathematics."

This was, needless to say, only the metaphysical justification. But the strength of the schools did not lie in such arguments; it lay in the earthy obviousness of the principles from which they started. It was the mathematicians who had been, through history, dreamers of wonderful dreams and searchers for mystical hidden harmonies. Reality was surely much closer to what we all know and "understand," to the familiar simplicity of life and organism. It is on this level of life that the Aristotelian position becomes common sense itself. In all things that count, function seems to be clearly marked; we live in a world of distinctive purposes. At a time when all that man dealt with was provided, so to speak, ready-made by Nature, from food to timber and simple tools, when the very word "force," outside of magic, could mean only laborers, horses, or oxen, it cannot be denied that a vitalist explanation found itself at the center of gravity of thought.

"To ignore movement is to ignore Nature." The principle seemed sound enough. And where did one see on earth a motion that went on by itself forever? Even the flowing of streams needed the sun and the rain; one was led from one cause to a larger cause up to the First Cause; one always found an action caused by another action. Man knew only too well from himself that movement is the result of an effort against a resistance; the strength must come from somewhere, and, as it is spent, it leaves behind real change, namely, fatigue and wear.

We see again thought focused on the idea of a process. Something new is always coming in; something is being lost. The familiar images are those of a man carrying a burden, of a cart being pulled along on a rutted road. It would look, then, as though all were clear to the mind so long as it does not move out of the patient works and days. But what of the stone that is hurled from the hand? Common sense here suggests a kind of energy that it picks up and then loses quickly until it falls to the ground.

At this point, unfortunately, the Aristotelian is no longer free to adopt immediate common sense, for he is a prisoner of the mesh of concepts that he has built up already in order to have a proper theory. He will say, then, that spontaneous motion, being an attribute of substance, cannot be transferred. It is axiomatic that attributes are nontransferable. A man who happens to be blond and blue-eyed has no way of transferring these attributes to a man who is not. He can only beget another man who is. And spontaneous motion is no more transferable than blondness or blue eyes.

Yet, there were the facts. Any small boy could prove to Aristotle conclusively that a rock could be thrown to good purpose. Hence Aristotle was compelled to suppose that the rock was urged on its way by something still in contact with it, and it had to be the circumambient air. His disciples admitted discreetly that this was not the strongest point in the master's theory; but, so long as nothing better showed up, they had to accept it bravely as the only way to save the intangible principles.

Galileo had learned this theory at the time when he was a student in Pisa, and he saw at once that there was no way to save it. Casting overboard the intangible principles, he went back, as Hipparchus the astronomer and a number of Parisian doctors had done before him, to the more natural idea of an *impetus* received by the missile. But this idea, too, stemmed from a vitalistic imagination. The missile was supposed to have been "fed" a certain amount of force that it dispersed on its way. To work out the idea meant to find one's self up against the old difficulties. As late as 1587, in his early graduate years, Galileo was still trying out analogies with the heat of an iron bar or the sound of a bell, which dissipate into space. His ingenious efforts in theory and experiment (for it was at this time that he dropped bodies from the Leaning Tower of Pisa with completely deceptive results) came to nothing. The whole idea of impetus was a dead end.

It was about at this time, as far as we can make out, that Galileo became interested in the new Copernican ideas. But as he already had a problem on his mind, a flash of creative imagination brought things together. Here was a case very similar to that of the flywheel which his master Benedetti had already shown to be the most intractable by the old theories. A flywheel whirling on the spot suggests the idea that, barring resistances, it might go on forever, and even better in a void. The mind is led to conceive of a sphere suspended in the void, turning without friction—and why should that not be the Earth? What emerged out of it in its pure state, so to speak, was the new idea of *inertia*—an idea prodigiously abstract and even unnatural for minds working with the ordinary material of experience, and one that Galileo himself had not been able to extract previously.

Now suddenly everything had become clear. If the Earth could be such a sphere, why could not the orbs of the planets obey some such inertial law? What had looked absurd in the Copernican doctrine became now a hint in its favor; for Copernicus, while "making of the Earth a star," had attributed to it motions which seemed incompatible with its nature so "eminently heavy and terrestrial," as the doctors said. If now it appeared that celestial bodies might move owing to just such a nature, the system of the world could cease to be a dreamy geometrical diagram and become a physical reality. A "natural philosophy" began to outline itself which encompassed both heaven and the Earth, with the planets subject to the same physical laws that we can study here below—in fact, with no above or below, since we ourselves are a planet among many.

A wide and wild guess it was, no doubt, in those years around 1590: a perilous leap of the imagination into uncharted regions. No one but Galileo, and at the other end of Europe, Kepler, could see how it could make sense ultimately. But, as soon as their minds had grasped the idea, it became clear that this was a rebirth of Pythagorean intuition of the unity of Nature and that it solved many of the unnoticed absurdities of the traditional conception.

That traditional conception, to be sure, made persuasive and comfortable sense as far as the Earth was concerned; but, as for the things of heaven, it had to consider them some sort of decorative adjunct to the earthly setting. It had never developed any real physics for them. It insisted, in fact, on heaven being "different." The thought of Aristotle, always absorbed in the concrete, had dwelt on describing separate behaviors. For him, it was proper of the stone to strive downward as of fire to strive upward, and each living being in turn had a different kind of motion; as to the motion of the stars in heaven, it could not but be infinitely different in quality from anything here on earth. So the astronomers and mathematical specialists had been left, with barely disguised condescension, to devise diagrams which might "save the appearances" but were understood to explain nothing. The assignment was to devise as many circular and uniform motions as, combined, could be said to describe the apparent path of the planets on the vault of heaven. The astronomers, and chief among them Ptolemy, had proceeded in this modest spirit to devise a dodge which was called the "theory of epicycles." If one circle was not enough to describe the motion of a planet, another smaller circle was added, fastened onto its circumference like a roller bearing, and, going around on that the planet, it could perform all the curlicues that its apparent path in

Galileus Galileus   Florentinus

Superior   licentia
16   24

Eques Octavius Leoni   Roman° pictor fecit

Galileo, Aged Sixty

This portrait, by Ottavio Leoni, was made in 1624 and probably during the stay in
Rome in which Galileo obtained permission from the Pope to write the *Dialogue*.

Paul V Borghese in 1614

D:BENEDĪ:CASTELLI

Benedetto Castelli, Galileo's Disciple and Correspondent

Roberto Bellarmino in 1604, Aged Fifty-Two

The view is from his palace near Santa Maria in Via; in the background, the Antonine Column.

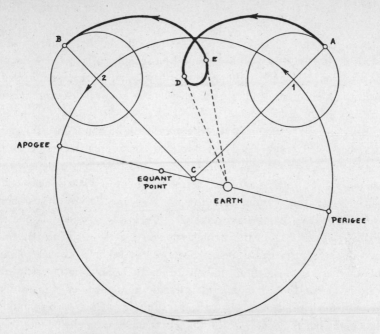

FIG. 3. Function of an Epicycle

Since the planets travel around the Sun at different speeds, their motions relative
to an observer on the moving Earth are complex. One phenomenon in particular
was puzzling to those who thought the Earth motionless in the center of the universe. This was known as "retrogradation" and is easily explained in the heliocentric Copernican system. In the case of the outer planets, since the Earth travels
faster than they, it periodically overtakes them and "laps the field," so to speak.
When this happens, an observer on Earth sees the phenomenon in question. The
planet being overtaken appears to slow down in its normal easterly course, stop,
reverse directions and travel west for some weeks, then stop and reverse directions once more and continue on in its regular orbit. This strange appearance is
neatly handled in the Ptolemaic system by one of the several uses of epicycles.
(The other use, that of accounting for the actual ellipticity of the orbit, is dealt
with by use of extra epicycles, which are those that Galileo thought he had to retain.) In Figure 3 imagine the planet to be located at point A of the *epicycle*
with center at *1*. The epicycle in turn is on the *deferent* circle whose center is C.
The stationary Earth is located within the deferent. Now (1) the planet at A
begins traveling around its epicycle in a counterclockwise direction and (2) the
epicycle itself is carried around the deferent from *1* to *2*. The combination of
these two motions is the supposed motion of the planet and is represented by the
heavy line between A and B. In the loop the motion appears retrograde.

69

heaven suggested (Fig. 3). By adjusting speeds and dimensions in this kind of diagram, the positions could be predicted with a fair amount of precision, including conjunctions, eclipses, and all that was needed. But it was well understood that this was not a *physical* description and was not meant to be.

Still, there it was, and it was the only one available. Since the philosophers, who had retained legislative authority in physics, had nothing of their own to offer as a mechanism, the irresistible tendency was to materialize the device of the astronomers into crystal spheres and hope no one would inquire as to how it made sense. The result, through the Middle Ages, had been a visualized Chinese-box system of spheres within spheres, each of them thick enough to carry its own little epicyclic sphere, just as a ball bearing carries its steel balls. Such a system bore a merely coincidental analogy to anything physical or mechanical; but again there it was, and it looked miraculous enough to discourage people from asking further. With it went a corresponding fancy of what the bodies of the planets themselves might be like: obviously hard matter, more dense and luminous than the crystal sphere bearing them, since we can see it, but at least as durable—certainly at least as good as diamond and more exalted. It was all a coherent chain of images (Fig. 4). The official prerogative of heaven being its eternity and immutability, any attempt at forming a physical idea, however honorific, e.g., of the Moon, made it out as an exquisitely polished sphere of some jewel-like substance. This was felt on all sides as the proper thing for the Moon to be. But there are certain minds which have a different sense of values. A revealing passage of Frank Lloyd Wright's autobiography shows a mind of this singular type:

> Grandfather preached as Isaiah preached: "The flower fadeth, the grass withereth, but the word of the Lord thy God endureth forever." The boy, his grandson, grew to distrust Isaiah. Was the flower any less desirable because it seemed to have been condemned to die that it might live more abundantly? As they all went to work in the fields, the grass seemed always necessary to life in the valley, most of all when it withered and was hay to keep the stock alive in winter so the preacher himself might live.

FIG. 4. Reconstruction of a Fifteenth-Century Cosmological Scheme Utilizing Solid Spheres

The notion of the planets—the "wandering stars"—being attached to spheres and spheres within spheres which carry them around the stationary Earth has a long history, developing with the Arabs into something that looks like modern ball bearings. By the fifteenth century this idea was being seriously questioned, and by Copernicus' time it had completely lost favor. The drawing is by courtesy of Dr. W. D. Stahlman.

Galileo would never have thought of challenging the eternity of the Word of God, but it appeared to him very clearly that these other worldly symbols of eternity, understood by the pious to represent the virtues of heaven, were by way of becoming very shabby literary clichés, out of place in any philosophy mindful of the majesty of the Cosmos:

I cannot without great wonder, nay more, disbelief, hear it being attributed to natural bodies as a great honour and perfection that they are impassible, immuatable, inalterable, etc.: as, conversely, I hear it esteemed a great imperfection to be alterable, generable, and mutable. It is my opinion that the Earth is very noble and admirable by reason of the many and different alterations, mutations, and generations which incessantly occur in it. And if, without being subject to any alteration, it had been all one vast heap of sand, or a mass of jade, or if, since the time of the deluge, the waters freezing which covered it, it had continued an immense globe of crystal, wherein nothing had ever grown, altered, or changed, I should have esteemed it a wretched lump of no benefit to the Universe, a mass of idleness, and in a word superfluous, exactly as if it had never been in Nature. The difference for me would be the same as between a living and a dead creature. I say the same concerning the Moon, Jupiter, and all the other globes of the Universe. The more I delve into the consideration of the vanity of popular discourses, the more empty and simple I find them. What greater folly can be imagined than to call gems, silver, and gold noble, and earth and dirt base? For do not these persons consider that, if there were as great a scarcity of earth as there is of jewels and precious metals, there would be no king who would not gladly give a heap of diamonds and rubies and many ingots of gold to purchase only so much earth as would suffice to plant a jessamine in a little pot or to set a tangerine in it, that he might see it sprout, grow up, and bring forth such goodly leaves, fragrant flowers, and delicate fruit?

It is scarcity and plenty that makes things esteemed and despised by the vulgar, who will say that here is a most beautiful diamond, for it resembles a clear water, and yet would not part with it for ten tons of water. These men who so extol incorruptibility, inalterability, and so on, speak thus, I believe, out of the great desire they have to live long and for fear of death, not considering that, if men had been immortal, they would not have had to come into the world. These people deserve to meet with a Medusa's head that would transform them into statues of diamond and jade, that so they might become more perfect than they are.[2]

Here we see a profoundly new idea of the universe taking shape, ancient and powerful in its roots, incalculable in its expansion, and as different from the Aristotelian caricature taught in the schools as it is from the scant and angular mechanistic dogmatism that Descartes was to introduce a few years later and Newton was reluctantly to adopt as a basis for his theories. Not quite biological, for Galileo is essentially a physicist; not mechanical, surely, for the underlying reality is imagined to be a flow of transforming and vivifying energy which is in essence, as will be revealed eventually, light itself. It is what Galileo does not shy from calling by its proper name, the "Pythagorean philosophy."

The later mystical and contemplative overtones which had been transmitted as part of that philosophy are originally reinterpreted in a way not very different from what ancient Philolaus himself would have meant,[3] and we see Galileo finding expressive symbols of the unifying power of reason in the creative force of life: "It seems to me that, if the celestial bodies concur to the generation and alteration of the Earth, they themselves are also of necessity alterable; for otherwise I cannot understand how the application of the Sun and Moon to the Earth to effect production should be any other than to lay a marble statue in the chamber of the bride and from that conjunction to expect children."

In such words Galileo shows himself truly as a figure of that Renaissance which had been struggling to transfer the full dimensions of the

2. *Dialogue,* pp. 68–69.

3. Philolaus was a Pythagorean of the "second generation" (fifth century B.C.) who suggested for the first time that the Earth may be a planet revolving around the center of the universe, which he imagined to be a Central Fire. He also taught the plurality of inhabited worlds. Modern critics have doubted the authenticity of the few fragments that have been transmitted of his writings, but their reasons are not convincing (cf. G. de Santillana and W. Pitts, "Philolaus in Limbo," *Isis,* Vol. XLII, n. 128 [June, 1951]).

ancient and medieval heritage into a new world. Born in the same year as Shakespeare, he had worked his way through the echoing wilderness of the sixteenth century, full of hints, vast possibilities, half-understood realizations, great words from the past, panic emotions, and limitless outlooks. He had proceeded amid a multitude of problems and answers, which his responsive and experimental mind had "weighed" (the so-oft-repeated word) and sifted in every direction, turning down answers that were merely verbal and searching for the real "clues." A couple of ideas in dioptrics, and the vision of analytical geometry, were enough for Descartes in his Dutch hermitage to project a complete explanation of the universe; whereas the powerful auxiliary of the telescope was used by Galileo to show some new physical characters of the planets, but from those could be deduced conclusions more valid and far-reaching than Descartes's cosmology. Another "clue," that of accelerated motion, had extended Galileo's thinking. Then, others had come—hydrostatics, the novae, virtual velocities, magnetism, tidal motion. Always in the midst of arguments, events, and "effects," Galileo conceived of science as an endeavor without end, reaching down toward the principles even as it reached out forever to an impossible completion.

More fortunate than Leonardo, Bruno, Campanella, and a great many predecessors, he had formed the opinion that the real clues were to be found in the "demonstrations of mathematical science," which, whenever they could be applied to Nature, provided reasons not merely plausible but necessary and, as such, indistinguishable from truth itself. But all his life he had had to wage a long uphill fight to establish it against the obtaining system of values. It was next to impossible to prove to a well-conditioned scholar that mathematics was not merely a sport for the curious mind or an auxiliary to the menial and mechanical arts but an integral part of philosophy and, indeed, the proper language of science which ought to replace the disputation about purposes and attributes. As he said once, physical science told him nothing about a *why* that anyone could dig up to please his sense of fitnesses, but it gave him at times a *how* that was certainly true.

As he found that these truths tied up into a system of natural philosophy extending in all directions, he fortified himself in the conclusion that here was a glimpse of the groundwork, or at least of *a* groundwork, of Nature. But it was not before his sixtieth year that he dared to write that "the book of Nature is written in mathematical characters." Thirty-five years of search stood in back of that, which showed, not only on earth, but throughout the universe, the "Pythagorean supposition" to be no supposition at all but corresponding to a state of fact. It was his work in dynamics which had provided the chief clue. In creating "a very new science on a very ancient subject," he had given as early as 1604 the correct law for the path of missiles and had shown that it was composed of an inertial horizontal trajectory and a vertical uniformly accelerated one. The horizontal path he imagined as being really a vast circle described around the Earth, as he was, after all, entitled to do at that stage of the game; and this in turn had become a hint of how planets keep to their circular orbits, "the path that neither rises nor descends" with respect to the Sun. A fragile supposition, but it was like the rope bridge that the climber throws across a crevasse. After all, was there any mechanism, real or conceivable, in his opponents' image of the heavenly spheres? Surely not, and yet it had found acceptance. Why should he not venture ahead, then, at least in his own thoughts? For, as he wrote to Kepler, he did not dare come forward yet with such ideas. But then, suddenly, the telescope had come to turn what had been for him an intellectual wager into a shining certainty. "Oh, Nicolaus Copernicus," he must have thought as he makes Sagredo say in the *Dialogue*, "what would have been thy joy in seeing thy system confirmed by such manifest experiences!" The Great Project seemed at last possible, where mathematics, physics, and astronomy would converge into a wholly new theory of the world system.

That it would ultimately prove acceptable he never doubted, for he could not imagine that it could be contrary to revealed truth. Like Newton, he felt he had been gathering some new and beautiful shells on the shore of the vast unknown, whose nature remained inaccessible

THE CRIME OF GALILEO

to man except through faith. He merely intended to suggest that official philosophy bring up to date its "argument from design." The new design, as he gained a first glimpse of it, he could not but find infinitely more worthy of God's majesty and hence, in all senses from the metaphysical to the common, more intrinsically *true:*

I think we arrogate too much to ourselves when we take it for granted that only the care of us is the adequate reason and limit, beyond which Divine Wisdom and Power does or disposes nothing. I will not consent that we should so much shorten its hand, but desire that we may content ourselves with an assurance that God and Nature are so employed in the governing of human affairs that they could not apply themselves more thereto if they truly had no other care than only that of mankind. And this, I think, I am able to make out by a most pertinent and most noble example, taken from the operation of the Sun's light, which, while it attracts these vapours, or heats that plant, attracts and heats them as if it had no more to do; yea, in ripening that bunch of grapes, nay, that one single grape, it does apply itself so that it could not be more intense, if the sum of all its business had been the maturation of that one grape. Now if this grape receives all that it is possible for it to receive from the Sun, not suffering the least injury by the Sun's production of a thousand other effects at the same time, well might we accuse that grape of envy or folly if it should think or wish that the Sun would appropriate all of its rays to its advantage. I am confident that nothing is omitted by the Divine Providence of what concerns the government of human affairs; but that there may not be other things in the Universe that depend upon the same infinite wisdom, I cannot, of myself, by what my reason holds forth to me, bring myself to believe. Surely, I should not forbear to believe any reasons to the contrary laid before me by some higher intellect. But, as I stand, if one should tell me that an immense space interposed between the orbs of the planets and the starry sphere, deprived of stars and idle, would be vain and useless, as likewise that so great an immensity for receipt of the fixed stars as exceeds our utmost comprehension would be superfluous, I would reply that it is rashness to go about to make our shallow reason judge of the works of God, and to call vain and superfluous whatever thing in the Universe is not of use to us.[4]

4. *Dialogue,* pp. 378-79.

This was beautifully said. But it was subversive of traditional cosmology and of all its motives, from the higher eschatological ones to the less avowable. Resistance against it did not even have to be rationalized in order to be immediate and clamorous. It came from the depths. The course of his thought could not but remain impenetrable to the doctors and divines of his time, had they even taken pains to understand it, which they did not. To them, notwithstanding his discoveries, and even while they flatteringly called him to his face "a second Archimedes," he remained a presumptuous and froward technician who was trying to go beyond the limits of his art and to draw the attention of the curious by means of some novel subtilities and paradoxical conclusions.

IV *Saint Robert Bellarmine*

Most Holy Father, you say that the question [de auxiliis] *appertains to the faith, but if that be so it is everybody's concern, according to the dictum of Pope Nicholas. Therefore it should be discussed in the full light of day, and not secretly, with a mere handful of advisers.*

BELLARMINE TO CLEMENT VIII, 1601

I

With his theological letters of 1615, Galileo had appealed to the hierarchies of the Church against the troublemakers of the lower echelons. Throughout this crisis it is Cardinal Bellarmine much more than Pope Paul V who is in command. The nature of the man therefore becomes important.

Roberto Bellarmino was by then in his seventy-fourth year. His (rather inadequate) portraits reveal an Etruscan prow-nosed face, heavy in the lower part, eyes slightly too close together, suggesting ready peasant wit, but brooding and tense in expression, the face of a dedicated man. His had never been a speculative metaphysical temperament; he was a Jesuit, a soldier of the Church, and a specialist in applied theology. The Catholic catechism in its present form is his. He had fought the Venetian Senate, the Neapolitan Primatists, the Gallicans, the Lutherans, the Anglicans, the Calvinists, the physical premotionists, and all other deviationists and "innovators" in the name of orthodoxy and papal supremacy. His enemies paid him the

79

compliment of stealing his arguments whenever they could,[1] for he had brought to the fight all that consummate apologetic skill and vast patristic scholarship could produce in the way of weapons. His leading activity, in fact, had been mostly as "Master of Controversial Questions" in the Collegio Romano, where he supplied armament for the Jesuits on all fronts.

His name is now almost forgotten in our countries, but it was once a name to conjure with. Madison and Jefferson are known to have consulted his texts. As the chief advocate of the papal position, he had become to the loyal English of his time a byword and a bugaboo; they did not refrain from calling him responsible for the Gunpowder Plot. Doctors organized refutation colleges against him; preachers belabored him with epithets: a "petulant railer," "the head of the popish kennel of Monks and Mendicants," "a furious and devilish Jebusite." Doggerels pursued him:

> First to breakfast, then to dine,
> Is to conquer Bellarmine.

The common people had found their own way of copious refutation, if not of liquidation, by giving the name of "bellarmines" to certain paunchy jugs used for liquor, whose neck was in the grotesque effigy of a bearded man.

As to the reasons for this animosity, we may take them from Dr. Johnson's own summary of Bellarmine's contention, which minces no words: "That the Pope is invested with all the authority on heaven and earth. That all princes are his vassals, and that he may annul their laws at his pleasure. That he may depose kings if the good of the Church requires it. . . . That the Pope is God upon earth . . . and that to call his power in question is to call in question the power of God: maxims equally shocking, weak, pernicious and absurd; which

---

1. "But of our priests and doctors how many have been corrupted by studying the comments of Jesuits and Sorbonists, and how fast they could transfuse that corruption into the people, our experience is both late and sad" (Milton, *Areopagitica*).

did not require the abilities and learning of Father Paul [Sarpi] to demonstrate their falsehoods and destructive tendencies." We have deleted certain clauses in his text to keep it within the bounds of fairness, for Dr. Johnson was apt to resort to the "scurrility of expression" with which he taxes his late learned opponent. But, then, Johnson as a loyal subject of the king felt good reason to be exercised, for Bellarmine had been a not imaginary threat to the English state.

The Oath of Allegiance of 1605, with the following Act against the Recusants, had been itself England's answer to the Jesuit challenge contained in Bellarmine's theory of the Pope's indirect power, and it marks a turning point in the history of modern politics.[2]

Englishmen were ordered to "abhorre, detest and abjure as impious and hereticall, this damnable doctrine and position that Princes which be excommunicated or deprived by the Pope may be deposed by their subjects," and this was the essential point of the oath, which had been drafted long before the Gunpowder Plot. Small wonder, then, that the controversialist who pursued the Cardinal in choicest language, and with prodigious expenditure of learned labor, should have been no less than King James I himself, "Professor, Maintainer and Defender of the True, Christian, Catholic and Apostolique Faith." Bellarmine had reminded him coldly that this very title had been bestowed by the Pope upon Henry VIII only "for his fight against Luther and the other innovators" and had gone on taking Queen Elizabeth herself to task:

Indeed Our Lord might very aptly have addressed her as he once addressed the woman of Samaria: "Thou hast well said, I have no husband, for thou hast five husbands, and he whom thou now hast is no husband." However, though Her Majesty's life was not chaste, it was cautious . . . and she showed her great prudence too, by skilfully fostering wars and seditions in her neighbors' kingdoms, that she might enjoy peace in her own . . . and yet further evidence of the same virtue was provided by her treatment of your Majesty's mother. . . . But she freely followed her fancies in

2. This is C. H. McIlwain's own summing-up in his Introduction to *The Political Works of James I* (Cambridge, Mass., 1928), pp. xlix and lvi.

everything, and proclaimed herself the first *Sacerdos magna* or rather *Pontifex maxima* since the world began, although not only human and divine law but even grammar itself protested.

There was bitter point enough here to cause James to forget the treatment of Mary Stuart. "Christ is no more contrary to Belial," he thundered, "light to darkness, and heaven to hell, than Bellarmine's estimation of Kings is to God's." But he was launched, and there was nothing to do but go on: *Apologia, Responsio, Premonitio,* went back and forth in wearisome succession, with the contestants heaving tonloads of quotations at each other. "I was never the man, I confesse," remarks the King haughtily, "that could think a Cardinall a meete match for a King; especially having many hundred thousands of my subjects of as good birth as he." But he is not going to leave that task to his doctors, however impatient they may be to serve him:

No desire of vaine glory by matching wits with so learned a man, maketh mee to undertake this taske; but onely the care and conscience I have, that such smooth Circes charm and guilded pilles, as full of exterior eloquence as of inward untrueths, may not have that publique passage through the world without an answere.

Soon, however, James I perceives that he has an incalculable bear by the tail, and his tone grows peevish:

My booke being first written in English and translated into Latine, it commeth home unto me now answered in both the languages. And, I thinke, if it had been set forth in all the tongues that were at the confusion of Babel, it would have returned answered in them all again. Thus may a man see how busie a Bishop the Devil is. . . .

A modern Alexander *in partibus,* the King was moved to bring out a book entitled *Triplici nodo triplex cuneus,* or "A Threefold Wedge for a Triple Knot." The most serviceable wedge, of course, still was the Gunpowder Plot itself, that early version of the Reichstag fire. A pioneer in the techniques of the cold war and a man of uncommon intelligence, James used it in order to prove that the Catholic religion was really not a religion but a conspiracy. But, for all his understandable grievances against "caitiffe monsters, traitours and pestilent papists," it was not easy for him to extricate himself from the knot of his own actions. The Cardinal could retort with stringent logic:

Even though it were true, which it is not, that no one suffered death for conscience' sake in England who had not first openly transgressed the law, yet since the law forbids anyone to receive a priest into his house under grievous penalties, to be reconciled to the Church, and to hear Mass, one who dies for transgressing such a law may rightly be said to have died for his religion. It is an old pagan device to make a law and then murder men, not intolerantly for religion's sake, of course, but with wise statesmanship, because they offended against the majesty of the constitution.[3] . . . As for the gracious proclamation whereby all priests who are not actually in chains might go out of the country by such a day, what wonderful kindness it was to allow men to go into exile whom His Majesty could not catch, try he ever so hard! And if exile seems a mercy to the royal author, one may wonder what sweet names he has for the rack and rope.

Truly, as the King said, "if the Devil had studied a thousand yeeres," he could not have made more mischief than those men in Rome:

For some of such Priests and Jesuits who were the greatest Traitours and fomenters of the greatest conspiracies against the late Queene, gave up Bellarmine for one of their greatest authorities and oracles. And therefore I doe not envie the great honour he can win by his vaunt of his inward familiaritie with another Princes' traitours and fugitives; whom if he teach no better manners than hitherto he hath done, I think his fellowship are little beholding unto him.

Of the two contestants, the King was clearly the more painful casuist, if by far the greater writer. But his case was resting on a couple of very solid realities, namely, that the British were disinclined to be

3. When the trial of Father Ogilvie began, in 1613, the books of Bellarmine and Suárez were on his judge's table. He was asked whether he believed the doctrines taught in them, and, answering that indeed he did, he was condemned to death. This is one of the many instances in which James I did act undeniably as a Roman emperor.

ruled by the Pope, even symbolically, and that they did not want their Parliament to be blown up; hence he had won out even before starting.[4] In his later years the King seems to have felt secure enough to relent, for "he constantly carried about his person" a copy of Bellarmine's little devotional book, *The Lament of the Dove,* and spoke of it as a wondrous aid to spiritual comfort. It is hard to imagine today the President of the United States carrying about his person a copy of Lenin's *What Is To Be Done?* for spiritual consolation, or Mr. Malenkov taking an occasional look at the homiletics of Dale Carnegie.

We have dwelt at some length with the Anglican controversy for reasons of familiarity and also for the amusement that could be afforded by the prancing periods of the King. But it represents a too simple issue and should not distract the attention from the vast and complex crisis in which Bellarmine was playing the leading role. His fight was no less against the Venetian Senate and the parliamentary faction in France, all of them solid Catholics, than against the avowed schismatics of England. The bitterest words are from orthodox Catholic politicians. Take a passage from the anonymous *Tocsin to the King,* printed in Paris in 1610, when young Louis XIII was under the regency of Marie de Medici:

This precious Cardinal, this sophistical dunderhead, this blood-sucker of princes, this reptile with hooked teeth, would cram his pontiffs with ambition to possess the whole world and reduce every nation to their sway. The pages of his book are as dangerous as the drooling slime of a mad dog. O drowsy France, open thy eyes. . . .

4. The battle of the books went on for a long time, with learned doctors on both sides plunging into the fray. Mountains labored to bring forth more mountains; it was *Bellarminus Destructus, B. Enervatus, B. Defensus, B. Vindicatus.* Divines told each other violently and vainly to shut up in several languages; it went from the *Confutation of Certaine Absurdities, Falsities and Follies, etc., etc., by F. T.,* to *Collins' Epphata to F. T.,* then to *The Obmutesce of F. T. to the Epphata of Dr. Collins,* and so on. We need not dwell upon the "revelations" of Dr. Titus Oates. They had their effect, which was more tragically serious. Two centuries later old men were still declaiming against "Rum, Romanism, and Rebellion."

This is no more than a pamphleteer's violence, coming a few months after the assassination of Henry IV. But the Catholic polemic was carried on also on a level of strong juridical argument by such men as Barclay and Widdrington. The names are enough to show how the quarrel cut across frontiers, for here are Scottish and English Catholics defending the sovereign rights not only of France, which was harboring them, but of England, which had sent them into banishment, and even writing an apology for the Oath of Allegiance.

Bellarmine personally had never hidden his partiality for monarchy against all other forms of government, but to the French *politiques* he was the worst of monarchomachs, because he pitted his authority against the absolute monarchic principle. The "divine right of kings" was a term which hid the most modern development of the times, namely, the birth of the present national and secular state. Against that, Bellarmine and Suárez at the head of the Jesuit legions were not simply reaffirming, as they believed they were, the proud age-old doctrine of Boniface's *Unam Sanctam*. For they, too, who wanted only to maintain eternal verities, were men of their own time. In them and around them were those new things, Jesuit spirit and Jesuit discipline; against the theorists of the national state, they were, in a way they would never have dreamed of, the early theorists of the modern superstate.

II

As such Bellarmine stands today, enshrined forever in sainthood by his Church, his figure so completely identified with his function that the name has become as much of a cipher as Caesar's Tenth Legion. Yet, if we probe beneath the layers of conventional panegyric and vituperation, we find a very interesting personality indeed.

A nobleman from Montepulciano in Tuscany, and a distant nephew of Machiavelli on the distaff side, he had of his own the vivid and powerful nature which might have made him, three centuries earlier, into a great political leader in the turbulent affairs of the free communes, a figure not unworthy of Dante's Farinata or Provenzano

Salvani. One can still discern from scattered bits of testimonial the original man, immensely ambitious, direct, prompt to flashing anger, as passionate for Virgil since his childhood as his own fellow-townsman Poliziano; musical and artistic, conceited about his intellectual and rhetorical gifts, as he reveals candidly in his scant autobiographical notes. That original man is in more than one way a fitting counterpart to Galileo. He was quite sure, on the other hand—while modestly discounting it—that he had the gift of prophecy; and one wonders whither this would have led him in a Protestant environment.

But, once the man has been plowed up and remolded by the discipline of Loyola, all these qualities are transmuted into dedication, as Galileo's were tempered by the discipline of science. We have the Bellarmine of history, an indefatigable self-denying laborer consumed in prayer and penance, ascetic in his vows of poverty, patient, humble in obedience, prone to copious tears. The original man flowers then unexpectedly in the other side of his Tuscan nature, easygoing, light, and unassuming, with nothing in it of the *romana grandezza* so much in evidence in the Vatican of those times. He comes, then, to resemble in more than one way his older fellow-townsman, St. Philip Neri. The profound security and trust of his inner life allowed Bellarmine to preserve to the end a childlike quality that was noted by all who came in contact with him, and which was nowhere more in evidence than in his streaks of subdued but undeniably impish merriment and in his addiction to lighthearted punning. It was at times his escape. His heart must have been set against Paul V's policy of pompous monumental display, which he felt deprived the Church of the money she owed to the poor; for, on hearing the Pope criticized for it, he winked slyly and said: "At least you cannot deny that he is a man of great edification." It was as much irony as he could allow himself toward the master who was for him God on earth. Had he found himself face to face with the grimness of New England divines, he would have remarked that it was clearly the mark of the Evil One that these people had no gaiety in them.

We are trying here to liberate something that was present and authentic in him from the testimonial of his own expressions, for the effusions of humility, tenderness, and holy joy have become such a cloying cliché of Counter-Reformation writing that the reader who delved through the actual Jesuit prose might be tempted to find them as unconvincing as his famous syllogisms. The man's whole life was the living of an impenetrable convention, yet the seal of his nature is on it, a Tuscan simplicity as genuine as Loyola's Spanish fire.

The reports of realistic ambassadors are a very revealing source, as we shall also see presently in the case of Galileo. The Count of Olivares was writing to the King of Spain after the death of Pope Sixtus: "Bellarmine is beloved for his great goodness, but he is a scholar who lives only among books and not of much practical ability [*de poca sustancia in agibilibus*]. . . . He would not do for a Pope, for he is mindful only of the interests of the Church and is unresponsive to the reasons of princes. . . . He would scruple to accept gifts. . . . I suggest that we exert no action in his favor." The King annotated curtly: "To be left to run his chance."

There remains the intellectual side of the man to be considered. If Galileo was laying considerable hope in his benevolence, he had reasons which were obvious to any person of his time. In his anomalous position as a Jesuit in the Curia, Bellarmine was sure not to have his judgment swayed by any excessive sympathy for the Brothers of St. Dominic. The controversy *de auxiliis* was not far behind him, with its fantastic battle of the books which had plunged Rome in a cloud of theological dust; and from that battle the Jesuits had not come out well. Bellarmine himself, in his role of papal theologian, had tried to reconcile the contestants, while not letting down his brethren of the Company, and had gotten himself diplomatically exiled for his pains to the archbishopric of Capua.

What had happened was this. Certain Dominicans of Spain, succumbing to one of those recurrent attacks of the Puritan genie which comes out of the pages of St. Augustine to take hold of the indiscreet logician, had developed a theory of divine grace which ran perilously close to Calvinism. The Jesuit Luis Molina had tried to resist with a closely reasoned argument and had been subjected to an implacable barrage of refutation on the part of the Dominicans, led by Domingo Bañes, who were reasserting the position of theological paramountcy held by their Order. The Jesuits had come to the help of their brother, and it had become a pitched battle. The gradually multiplying subtilities of the Jesuit position have been pitilessly exposed and preserved by Pascal for literature two generations later; but, if it is sure that the controversy brought forth some of the strangest specimens of quibbling that the world has ever seen, this still should not cause us to forget that the issue was as clear and fundamental as could be: Do all men stand a chance of saving their souls with the help of divine grace, or is their fate irresistibly predetermined? [5]

5. Once Augustine had firmly established the need of God's grace for salvation, any theory of ethical decision developed on the basis of God's omniscience and omnipotence was bound to get itself into a maelstrom of logical difficulties: One way to keep out of it was to do as Calvin had done and to follow the logical line inflexibly to the conclusion of predestination irrespective of faith and of merit—and also of infant damnation. A Scots Dominie might find it all very simple, but a truly Evangelic soul would have balked at following the logic to its bitter end, or, maybe, we should say, starting from the gloomy assumption of mankind's utter indigence and vileness, as expressed in Jonathan Edwards' famous simile of the "loathsome spider." Even the Dominicans of Bañes had avoided doing so; they had discovered an entity called "physical premotion" which was not quite predestination. But the formal terrain remained very slippery, as Molina had pointed out.

The technical point (all too briefly) is this. God is the First Cause, and no secondary cause can act efficaciously unless predetermined by Him. Moreover, since secondary causes cannot act until moved by the First Cause, God's concurrence with His creatures must be conceived as antecedent and not merely simultaneous. It is not a motion but a "premotion," and, since He is an omnipotent being whose decrees are irresistible, this premotion is a "force of Nature" in this sense; it is a "physical premotion." Now God has determined men's wills freely to determine themselves. This is a case of physical premotion. But corresponding to it in the supernatural sphere is efficacious (not merely sufficient) grace, and corresponding to both in the mind of God is the predetermination whereby from all eternity He decreed to influence His creatures in such and such ways, using premotions and efficacious graces of infinite variety, but all infallibly certain of their effect. God foresees everything that men will do in the decrees of His divine will, because it is only in virtue of these decrees that men can act at

In this quarrel Bellarmine interposed himself with a good sense that was to gain him later the unexpected sympathy of Bayle.[6] The efficacy of divine grace had to be defended against Pelagians old and new,[7] and the freedom of the will had to be defended against Lutherans, Calvinists, and Catholic deviationists. The Cardinal works back to the strict orthodoxy of the Thomist line, even if it involves being accused of the "abomination of semi-Pelagianism." As the Dominicans, indeed, have recourse to Caccini-like practices, he recalls them brusquely to correct behavior:

As the matter is still *sub judice*, the authors of the *Memorial* show a great deal of impudence by talking as if it had been decided, and as if the Fathers of the Society, whom they invariably style innovators, had already been condemned.

No doubt, in order to restore a difficult philosophical balance, the Cardinal is compelled at times to use many an *"argumentum stramineum* framed upon strawes,"* as King James would call it; but there is no mistaking the firm line of the whole, as also the humanistic spirit in which he undertakes to defend the essential freedom of man.

Throughout the *Controversies* there is such evidence of an ample,

all. Against this, Molina (and Bellarmine) had created for God's foreknowledge of the conditioned future the term *scientia media*, or "middle knowledge," because it embraces all objects that are found neither in the realm of pure possibility nor, strictly speaking, in the realm of actuality. They are actual in the sense that they would exist, were certain conditions granted. In the light of this knowledge God foresees from all eternity what attitude the will of man would adopt under any conceivable combination of circumstances, and then only, though the relation is not temporal but ontological, does He decree to share out His graces according to His pleasure. Sufficient grace in this scheme does not differ really from efficacious, or irresistible. It is perfectly adequate in itself for the purposes of salvation, but God foresees that such and such ones to whom it is offered will infallibly refuse it.

6. See Pierre Bayle, *Dictionnaire historique et critique* (1697), art. "Bellarmin."

7. Pelagius, a monk of the third century A.D. (his original name was Morgan), had practically denied the effect of original sin by maintaining that man is naturally good and does not need the help of divine grace to attain salvation. His doctrine was condemned by the Council of Ephesus in 431.

organic, and orderly mind, with an immense storage capacity for texts of the Fathers, and a unifying vision that supports its effort unerringly, even to the disregard of any conflict among the actual authorities so carefully quoted. Bellarmine does not stand out as a rigorous logician; he does not have the steel-trap mind of a Suárez. But, then, his pre-occupation is to keep away from any "original" development, and he takes infinite pains to show that he is rediscovering or reaffirming only the "common sentence" of the Fathers and doctors. His mind is a smoothly running organization aimed at restoring the intellectual status quo.

In his capacity to incorporate new facts and new techniques in the structure, Bellarmine the Jesuit is a modern personality; and, as such, he could arouse hopes in Galileo. But his modern thought, as we have said, really tends to the creation of the frame of a theological super-state, which means that, as far as his time went, he was working in a kind of historic vacuum. It is only on the formal plane that his work takes on the solidity of a Baroque monument. Like the architecture of the time, it is based upon unerring craftsmanship which can hold to-gether incredible voids and apparently conflicting elements in a strong and subtle design.

In this over-all design the scientific component is far from negli-gible. But, if we try to take it by itself, it will show no consistency of its own.

As sometimes occurs with men immersed in the affairs of state, Bellarmine liked to play with the ideas of astronomy. It stimulated his sense of wonderment. We might think, for instance, that his appeal to the words of the Psalm, "He rejoiceth like a giant in running his course," is nothing but reference to a normative text; but it is not. He liked to dwell upon the grandeur of the thing, even to do a bit of reckoning on it, as we can see from some thoughts he was writing for a devotional treatise, in those very same months in which Galileo was hoping he would give some thoughts to his problems:

I myself being once desirous to know in what space of time the Sun set at sea, at the beginning thereof I began to recite the Psalm *Miserere*, and scarce had read it twice over before the Sun was wholly set. It must needs be, therefore, that the Sun in that short time did run much more than the space of 7,000 miles. Who would believe this unless certain reason did demonstrate it? [8]

He finds it natural here to rely on "certain reason." At other times he is apt to get a little impatient with it, if it wants to legislate too much. Thus, in a sermon preached in 1571 on the text "There shall be signs in the Sun and in the Moon and in the stars," he speculates as follows:

It is a matter of the very greatest difficulty to decide what ought to be understood by the expression, the "falling of the stars." Should we wish to interpret the word "stars" as meaning those igneous appearances which are commonly called falling stars . . . we ought to be careful lest we find ourselves in contradiction with the Gospel, for if the Gospel speaks of the real Sun and the real Moon, does it not follow that it also means real stars? On the other hand, if, swayed by the authority of the Gospel, we dare to affirm that the stars will really fall from heaven at the Last Day, we are immediately confronted by a mighty mob of mathematicians, out of whose hands there is no means of escape. They will vociferate and clamor in our ears, just as if they themselves had measured the size of the stars, that it is impossible for the stars to fall upon the Earth, for even the least of the fixed stars is so much bigger than the Earth, that the Earth could not possibly receive it if it were to fall.

To these asseverations of the mathematicians we might oppose the opinion of St. Basil the Great, St. John Chrysostom, St. Ambrose, the most learned St. Augustine, and very many others, who hold that, with the single exception of the Sun, the Moon is bigger than any of the stars, from which it follows that the Earth must be much bigger than any of them, for even the mathematicians admit that the Moon is much smaller than the Earth.

Still, such an argument would not keep the mathematicians quiet, and, as we have no wish to be drawn into a dispute with them, we give as our opinion . . . that the problem cannot be solved until the signs actually appear. In this way the confession of our ignorance would be our answer to the difficulty. All that Our Lord said about the judgment to come, the end of

8. *De ascensione mentis in Deum.*

the world, and the signs that would precede it, was said in prophecy, and it is a characteristic of the sayings of the Prophets that, until what they have foretold comes to pass, their speech remains almost completely enigmatic to us. . . .

This is rather revealing. Bellarmine was not going to deny the claims of mathematicians, but he thought of them as we in our time tend to think of statisticians and pollsters: wizards in their own way, but simple-minded and heavy-fingered gents who are apt to go wrong with great assurance.

Yet he did not lack a knowledge of the subject. He had even taught it in his young years, out of a romantic interest which had sprung from an early study of Macrobius' solemn and mystical speculations on the *Somnium Scipionis*. In 1564 he had lectured in Florence cn "the doctrine of the spheres and the fixed stars." However much he may have dwelt on such subjects as "the number and places of the elements, whether each of the stars is a separate species, and the ultimate boundaries of the world," [9] it did not go without a minimum of geometry. This was actually at about the same time as Galileo was being born. . . .

The following year, lecturing at the College of Mondovi in Piedmont, he had taught again about the theory of the heavens, "philosophically and astrologically." We remarked already how astrologically minded scholars were inclined to be cold to Copernicus, whom they considered to have deluded their expectations. This may be one reason why Bellarmine never examined the Copernican ideas. Much more solid reasons, no doubt, were that the stability of the Earth was for him a truism, Aristotle's the only sensible way of dealing with physics, and astronomers a curious kind of people who wasted a lot of time making up unrealistic suppositions. We have a record of his opinions from his encounter with Vimercati, an elderly pedagogue of the Duke of Savoy:

9. J. Fuligatti, *Vita del Cardinale Bellarmino* (Rome, 1624), p. 32.

Many years ago I had a discussion with Vimercati, the celebrated philosopher, about the number of the celestial spheres. Personally I was convinced that there were eight of them and no more, but I found it impossible to win over any of these astronomers to my opinions, because they all persisted in clinging to the observations of Hipparchus and Ptolemy, as if they were articles of faith.

These few lines are a dead giveaway. His own simple and uncorrected observations on the speed of the Sun he is willing to take for reason itself, but the precision of the astronomers is irritating. It spoils the physical system of the philosophers. In this Bellarmine is more Thomist than Thomas himself, for the Angelic Doctor had never gone so far in his distrust of mathematics. In his commentary on the books *On Heaven* Thomas had made it clear that the Ptolemaic hypotheses had to be taken as the best description of appearances, although "we must not say that they are thereby proved to be facts, because perhaps it would be possible to explain the apparent movements of the stars by some other method which men have not yet thought out." In other words, as a serious thinker would, Aquinas held that this split between mathematics and physics was only a temporary makeshift and that with time a way would be found to incorporate both into a cogent system. But Galileo would never have dared quote this as a hint in his favor, for it was clear that Aquinas was expecting it would be done out of Aristotle as the only acceptable physics: he was looking one way in time while Galileo was working the other way.

With all this, however, Aquinas was adequately comprehensive.[10] He was waiting for a third solution. But Bellarmine is quite satisfied with the Aristotelian idea of reality *en gros,* an attitude which goes on par with his belief in astrological forces and which is out of sympathy

10. Aquinas did hope for a real mathematical system which should be closer to the homocentric diagram of Eudoxus than to the unnatural epicycles of Hipparchus; on the other hand, he did not believe much in the crystal spheres that Aristotle had tried to construct out of Eudoxus. But he thought, rightly, that any physical system ought to be homocentric.

with precisionism and the "paradoxical conclusions sought after by curious minds." No doubt, too, he shared a feeling common to many thinkers interested mainly in human affairs, which has been expressed for them by Montesquieu: "I have come to be deeply suspicious of the tyranny of geometry." Bellarmine's very humanism is typically that of a Jesuit, in that it tends to stress the practical side:

The soul of man is endowed with another kind of science, whose object is more practical than speculative. Out of it were born so many books of philosphers about vices and virtues, so many laws of princes, so many opinions of jurists, so many institutions and treatises which teach the art of right living.[11]

In a more homely vein this attitude reappears in his sermons: "Men are so like frogs. They go open-mouthed for the lure of things which do not concern them, and that wily angler the Devil knows how to capture multitudes of them."

Such, then, was the personal thought of the Cardinal on the delicate subject. It is to his wisdom that Galileo is now commending his cause as he writes his desperate letters to Monsignor Dini[12] (dispatched posthaste as soon as he heard that the sinister Caccini was on his way to Rome), which are really meant for Bellarmine. He realizes what is the Cardinal's main concern, as he protests humbly, in the words of Scripture: "I would tear out my own eye, rather than have it give scandal." What he offers is meant not as an argument but as a submissive request, to be further developed if given a hint of encouragement. Prudently, he concludes his last letter to Dini thus:

"What you have here is but a poor and rough offspring, which would need to be patiently and lovingly licked into shape; I hope to bring it some time to better symmetry; meanwhile, I beg of you that you let it not come into the hands of any who, using on it, in lieu of the softness of the motherly tongue, the cutting sharpness of the novercal tooth, might rend and tear instead of shaping it. With this I respectfully kiss

11. *De ascensione mentis in Deum* viii. 4.
12. See p. 51.

your hand, together with Messrs. Buonarroti,[13] Guiducci, Soldani, and Giraldi, who are present at the closing of this letter."

III

The "stepmotherly tooth" was so vigorously at work already that Dini delayed showing the letter to the Cardinal. A few weeks later he writes: "You see how right I was. The inclosed document will show you the humor of these Lords." (The document was Bellarmine's answer to Father Foscarini, of which more later.) To Dini's personal entreaties, however, the Cardinal had answered that "he did not think the work of Copernicus would be prohibited, at most some saving addition [*postilla*] might be made to the effect that it was only meant to explain appearances, or some such phrase, and with this reservation Signor Galileo would be able to discuss the subject without further impediment."

Bellarmine may have added "with a countenance not very grave" (so a biographer describes him): What if Copernicus *did* get suspended pending correction? Such things happened all the time. He need not remind Dini that he himself, Bellarmine, had had his great text of *Controversies* put on the Index "pending correction" in 1590 by the irascible Sixtus V for not going far enough in his championship of papal absolutism and that, had Sixtus not died, he might have stayed on the Index for a good long time. As a matter of fact, the Jesuit general Acquaviva had written to him, twenty-five years earlier, in exactly the same vein: "The most that could be asked of you would be the change of a few words in a new edition, as, for instance, where you speak of *errors,* that you should say instead *errors or opinions of certain writers*." [14]

13. This is the younger Buonarroti, a distinguished poet, the nephew of Michelangelo. He was to prove a constant friend in adversity. Mario Guiducci was the secretary of the Florentine Academy and was later to write, together with Galileo, the *Discourse on the Comets.*

14. It had been the hope of a moment. Sixtus was bent on prohibiting. Wrote the Spanish ambassador, Olivares: "The cardinals of the Congregation of the Index

Cardinals Barberini and del Monte sent similarly soothing reports through Dini and Ciàmpoli.[15] The latter added on his own (March 21, 1615): "Of these roaring waters of which allusion has been made to you, one does not hear anything here, and yet I am not deaf, and I go around in many places where I ought to detect the noise." Father Maraffi, the friendly Preacher-General,[16] had tried to sound out influential members of his Order, but the Dominicans had heard nothing; they knew nothing. Caccini, it was said, had come to Rome for a certain baccalaureate of his.

Ciàmpoli's suggestions, however, end up in the same note of uncertainty as Cesi's and Dini's. Yes, it would be a good idea if Galileo came to Rome. He hears that there are Jesuits who are holding back but who are secretly of the Copernican persuasion. On the other hand, it is essential to give no chance for provocation, to go on working, let the fuss die down; then the road will be clear again. In these men's minds there is no conflict. Like Galileo, they are good Christians unafraid. Whoever heard of the Church opposing true science, since she is the guardian of all truth? But it is hard going "in these matters in which the monks are not wont to concede defeat." High quarters have let it

did not dare tell His Holiness that the teaching of the book is drawn from the works of the saints for fear he might give them a bit of his brusque temper and perhaps put the saints themselves on the Index." Even beyond the time of Sixtus, the "consecrated whirlwind," the feeling seems to have been current in Rome that the Index was a kind of administrative misadventure that occurred sooner or later to anyone writing on serious subjects and that it was a matter of waiting until the official line changed again. Of the three theologians of the Inquisition who were the experts at Galileo's trial, two subsequently incurred prohibition— and one of them a cardinal, Oregius.

15. Monsignor Giovanni Ciàmpoli (the accent is on the *a*) was a recent recruit to the circle of Galileists. A brilliant young Latinist, he was marked for a great career. "It seems impossible to me," he had written to Galileo, "that one should frequent you and not love you. There is no greater magic than the beauty of virtue and the power of eloquence; to hear you is to be convinced by your truth, and whatever I can do will always be at your service." He kept faith only too well, as we shall see.

16. See p. 43.

be understood that it is well to soft-pedal the issue for a while, and they have their good reasons. Avoid new occasions for scandal-makers. Do not ruffle high quarters while they are pondering high policy. Send us your briefs. "We shall get them into the hands of honest people when the occasion arises; for, as to the others, we had rather leave them out of it." You have more friends than you would think; etc.

To see duplicity, on the other hand, in the evasive statements of the prelates of the Tuscan clan,[17] as so many historians have done, is unfair. They themselves are in the dark. Their advice, on the whole, is sound: The less noise the better. As to Bellarmine, himself, who is the only one to know, he does not try to deceive. His forecast corresponds to the decision he has already taken. He is not thinking or pondering much. He is waiting for the Commissary of the Inquisition to tell him when the thing will be ready to go on the docket. (Caccini's denunciation had come in on March 21, 1615, but the interrogatories lasted, as we have seen, until the end of November.) There is occasional consultation with the friendly cardinals—even Grienberger is called in—but it all amounts to periodic *tours d'horizon,* as they are called in the trade. The scientific issue itself obviously is not touched upon; no one gives it a thought. Even Grienberger has obediently made up his mind that it is irrelevant.

It is difficult to generalize on this occasion. Church education did not prevent the rise of first-rate mathematical talent, as in Castelli and Cavalieri. Churchmen like Dini, Ciàmpoli, Foscarini, Stunica, Piccolomini, Maraffi, and, not least, Sarpi were among the most fervid promoters of the Copernican cause; but they were at most in the position of executive assistants. Where responsibility began, perception ceased; and the top echelons, as we can see now, seem to have thought of intellectual issues purely as a matter of administration. The trouble with these leaders' minds, so subtly logical on points of law, was that they stopped functioning as soon as they dealt with a diagram or with

17. The Cardinals Bellarmine, Bonsi, Barberini, and del Monte were Tuscans and under the allegiance of the Grand Duke, and so were Dini and Ciàmpoli.

this kind of "new stuff, paradox to the philosophical vulgar," as Ciàmpoli called it.[18]

They had a high regard for all sciences, but as lawyers they would always come back with the question: Is there not another way to present this case? Could you reverse a finding on that? It was not a good sign that Cardinal Joyeuse found Colombe's *Discorso* (which is a mass of errant nonsense) quite plausible and said that he would like to have Galileo's opinion on it.[19]

Brought up to mental compromise, the clerical mind shied away even from what it had learned in its own schools. Nothing is more revealing than a little speech of Cardinal Federigo Borromeo, as good a scholar as any and the founder of the great Ambrosian Library, to the Jesuits embarking for the South Seas. While exhorting them to contribute to the knowledge of Nature in those far places, he added the hope that, since they were going to the antipodes, they would find out about "the foundations of the deep." Now he might have known from Aquinas, over whom he had labored for so many years, that there was no such thing, since the Earth was no longer in official doctrine a pillar "founded on the deep," as the Old Testament suggests, but a sphere symmetrically suspended at the center of the universe. But even the orthodox diagram had not registered on his mind.

Such men could not react favorably to Galileo's attempt at showing inherent deficiencies in the official interpretation of Scripture. Granted, Joshua's story was not so easy to account for in Ptolemaic theory. Granted, even Aristotle and Ptolemy did not get along any too well together. But, once the layers, so laboriously joined, of Greek, Hellenistic, and Hebrew tradition were pried apart, a swarm of most indis-

18. Ingoli, a much-esteemed lawyer and polymath in the employ of Propaganda Fide, submitted a counterbrief which was considered excellent by the authorities (cf. Ed. Naz., VI, 510). His level of geometrical reasoning can be inferred from this one remark: "The point in the center will have a greater distance from the surface of the sphere than any other inside the sphere, and a parallax correspondingly greater; but the Moon has a greater parallax than the Sun; therefore the Sun cannot be in the center."

19. Letter of Gallanzoni, June 26, 1611 (Ed. Naz., XI, 131).

creet doubts would assail the mind. We know from Ciàmpoli's gossip the kind of alarmed questions that were raised among a certain public about the new ideas: Did it mean that there were men in the Moon? What then of Adam and of Noah's Ark? What of the Devil that is supposed to be at the center of the world? Where is the angel that moves the Earth? For it is clear from Aquinas that planets do not move by themselves.[20]

20. Aquinas states that the heavens are said to move naturally because they have no repugnance to circular motion but still have no inclination to it (i.e., have no active potency toward motion but only passive), and they are moved supernaturally because the motor, which is an angel, is a voluntary motor.

As to the previous point, viz., the location of hell, it also remains a serious difficulty today if we consider "grave opinion." The present stand of the question may be gathered from the learned pen of Father J. Hontheim, in the *Catholic Encyclopedia* (New York: Appleton. 1910). We can see better from it how the mind of the Qualifiers of the Holy Office was bound to work: "Holy Writ seems to indicate that hell is within the earth, for it describes hell as an abyss to which the wicked descend. We even read of the earth opening and of the wicked sinking down into hell (Num., xvi, 31 sqq./ Ps., liv, 16; Is., v, 14; Ez., xxvi, 20; Phil., ii, 10, etc.). Is this merely a metaphor to illustrate the state of separation from God? Although God is omnipresent, He is said to dwell in heaven, because the light and grandeur of the stars and the firmament are the brightest manifestations of His infinite splendour. But the damned are utterly estranged from God; hence their abode is said to be as remote as possible from His dwelling, far from heaven above and its light, and consequently hidden away in the dark abysses of the earth. However, no cogent reason has been advanced for accepting a metaphorical interpretation in preference to the most natural meaning of the words of Scripture. Hence theologians generally accept the opinion that hell is really within the earth."

The author then sets forth tentatively his own personal opinion, which is that we know that there is a hell but that we do not know exactly where it is. Then he goes on: "Beyond the possibility of doubt, the Church expressly teaches the eternity of the pains of hell as a truth of faith which no one can deny or call in question without manifest heresy. But what is the attitude of mere reason towards this doctrine? Just as God must appoint some fixed term for the time of trial, after which the just will enter into the secure possession of a happiness that can never again be lost in all eternity, so it is likewise appropriate that after the expiration of that term the wicked will be cut off from all hope of conversion and happiness. For the malice of men cannot compel God to prolong the appointed time of probation and to grant them again and again, without end, the

Ciàmpoli and Dini went on, like loyal servants of a great administration, thinking of inscrutable long-range designs; they would have been astonished to know how great a place those same "simple-minded" alarms that they had derided took in Bellarmine's mind. He knew how much had been conceded through the centuries; still, he knew best what an incredibly disparate assemblage of notions, principles, beliefs, and sentiments he had kept together in a lifetime of heroic struggle. As a Jesuit, too, he seems to have been concerned with hints from Germany that certain of his confreres favored secretly the Copernican idea but dared not discuss it with their superiors. Now that he thought of it, had not Grienberger himself looked a little lost? There was a beginning of confusion in the ranks. Once he allowed ideas to start moving, he could feel no longer responsible for the outcome. *Sint ut sunt, aut non sint.*[21]

power of deciding their lot for eternity. Any obligation to act in this manner would be unworthy of God, because it would make Him dependent on the caprice of human malice, would rob His threats in great part of their efficacy, and would offer the amplest scope and the strongest incentives to human presumption. . . . According to the greater number of theologians the term *fire* denotes a material fire, and so a real fire. We hold to this teaching as absolutely true and correct. However, we must not forget two things: from Catharinus (d. 1553) to our times there have never been wanting theologians who interpret the Scriptural term *fire* metaphorically, as denoting an incorporeal fire; and secondly, thus far the Church has not censured their opinion. Some few of the Fathers also thought of a metaphorical explanation. Nevertheless, Scripture and tradition speak again and again of the fire of hell, and there is no sufficient reason for taking the term as a mere metaphor. It is urged: How can a material fire torment demons, or human souls before the resurrection of the body? But, if our soul is so joined to the body as to be keenly sensitive to the pain of fire, why should the omnipotent God be unable to bind even pure spirits to some material substance in such a manner that they may suffer a torment more or less similar to the pain of fire which the soul can feel on earth? This reply indicates, as far as possible, how we may form an idea of the pain of fire which the demons suffer. Theologians have elaborated various theories on this subject, which, however we do not wish to detail here (cf. the very minute study by Franz Schmid, 'Quaestiones selectae ex theol. dogm.,' Paderborn, 1891, q. iii; also Gutberlet, 'Die poena sensus' in 'Katholik,' II, 1901, 305 sqq., 385 sqq.)."

21. Among the arguments against Galileo that are quoted by Campanella in his *De-*

The modern reader may feel that we are more intelligent about these things, but it is largely an optical illusion. Our statesmen are legal minds, too, if not so well trained as Bellarmine's, and they too would be somewhat baffled, even today, by Galileo's proofs. If it had not been indoctrinated into them that the irresistible black magic that stems from those ancient proofs has been able to deliver the conveniences of modern life and one-hundred-billion-dollar budgets, they would not stand in awe whenever the word "science" is spoken. In those times even such a sensitive and adventurous mind as John Donne, in *Ignatius His Conclave,* had wanted Copernicus haled before the Judge of Hell, with Machiavelli and Paracelsus, as one of those "innovators" who had upset the world. Church statesmen like Bellarmine, to whom science was still an ornament of the mind, may be excused for wondering whether these novelties about the heavens would be all to the good of the spiritual order that it was their duty to uphold.

IV

Galileo himself was not at all reassured. In the confident letters from Rome he could see only the tragic gap that separated him from his best friends there; for they insisted that all would be well, as Bellarmine had said, and that Copernicanism would at most be restricted to the geometrical field. They themselves saw nothing very serious in this; they were not physicists or, even less, independent metaphysicians, although in some of them there was a romantic overtone of Platonism. They were "open minds," disliking the crabbed Aristotelian pedantry, and they wanted their friend to have a free hand in his "new and marvelous demonstrations." Most of all, they wanted to have him

---

fense of Galileo (1622), there is this: "Holy Scripture counsels us to seek 'nothing higher, nor attempt to know,' that we 'leap not over the bounds which the Fathers set'; and that 'the diligent searcher of majesty is overcome by vainglory.' Galileo disregards this counsel, subjects the heavens to his invention, and constructs the whole fabric of the world according to his pleasure."

vindicated as a good Christian against the monks.[22]

Galileo instead was in deadly earnest. He saw the irrevocable taking place before he had time to convince anybody. On the repeated urging of Monsignor Dini, he set out to complete his great apologetic letter to Madama Cristina, the Grand Duchess Dowager.[23] So long as the guillotine of mandatory interpretation had not fallen, there was still hope.

The *Letter to the Grand Duchess* is a powerful solemn plea, worthy to stand beside Milton's *Areopagitica,* though less secular in tone and less polemical. There is only expressed, in the beginning, a measured grievance against those who insist on distorting his thought and against such as slandered it from the pulpit "with hardly charitable and still less considerate indictment of all of mathematics and of mathematicians also." It is prefaced by a grave reminder from St. Augustine: "We should not hold rashly an opinion in a scientific matter, so that we may not come to hate later whatever truth may reveal to us, out of love for our own error." After vindicating the memory of Copernicus, Galileo claims to be the one who has the interests of religion at heart, "insomuch as I am proposing not that this book be not condemned, but *that it be not condemned, as they would, without understanding it, without hearing it, without even having seen it.*" Scripture often speaks figuratively, as is well recognized, whereas Nature is inexorable and immutable and never goes beyond the terms of the laws imposed on her, does not care whether her recondite reasons and ways of working are accessible to the capacity of men; but it is hardly reverent toward the Spirit of God to suppose that it may have laid pitfalls for man by establishing contradictory truths.

Galileo then quotes again from St. Augustine (being apparently

22. They did not dare pronounce themselves in the delicate matter of metaphysics; but they would have nothing to do with compromisers. When the cowardly Luca Valerio, who was the only mathematician among them, tried to dissociate himself from their defense of Galileo after the decree, they expelled him from the Lincei for unworthiness.

23. See above, p. 38.

unaware, like the Jansenists a few years later, that Augustine had become a "controversial" authority to be quoted at one's own risk): "The inspired writers knew what the truth was about the heavens, but the Spirit of God that spoke through them did not choose to teach it to men, as it was of no use for salvation." God expressly has left His works to our disputations, and it has been found good that the wise men of antiquity should have speculated profoundly about them. Are we then to leave the vulgar, whom any rabble-rouser can inflame with base passions and prejudices, to grab any passage of Scripture they please and swing it as a club to crush the endeavor of science?

There are, on the other hand, he goes on, theologians (very saintly no doubt) who claim supreme authority in all matters simply because theology is supreme. "It is as if an absolute ruler should demand, without being either a physician or an architect, that people should treat themselves, or erect buildings, according to his directions, to the great jeopardy of the poor patients and the manifest ruination of edifices."

As far as new discoveries are concerned, the Church could have suppressed astronomy altogether, or suppressed Copernicus' book as it came out. But to permit the book and condemn the doctrine, while so much evidence is publicly accumulating in its favor, *would be the most pernicious possible way for the souls of men, as it would allow them the opportunity of convincing themselves of the truth of an opinion which it was a sin to believe.* "Do not hope to find among the Fathers, or in the wisdom of Him who cannot err, those hasty conclusions to which you might be led by some passion or particular interest; beware of moving the Church to flash her sword in your cause; for in all these propositions which are not directly *de fide,* the Supreme Pontiff no doubt retains absolute power to admit or condemn; but it is in the power of no creature whatever to make them true or false, otherwise than they are *de facto.*"

The views concerning the interpretation of Scripture contained in Galileo's theological letters have become the official doctrine of the Church since Leo XIII's encyclical *Providentissimus Deus* of 1893. But in 1615, when the *Letter to the Grand Duchess* was forwarded to

Rome, it sank out of sight as softly as a penny in a snowbank. Dini did not dare any longer discuss it with his superiors. Father Foscarini's tract, which had recently come out, had been raising fresh and most unfortunate trouble.

V

Paolo Antonio Foscarini was a Carmelite monk from Naples, of excellent reputation, a Provincial of his Order, and the work he had published showed real understanding of the Copernican system. It was in the form of a letter addressed to his General. After mentioning Galileo's pioneer work, he suggested that it was time heliocentrism be considered as a physical reality and embarked with theological zeal on a reconciliation of the system with the relevant passages of Scripture. As he wanted to be an obedient monk above all, Foscarini had submitted his text to Cardinal Bellarmine for criticism.

Bellarmine's answer was courteous and earnest, and it gives us the full measure of his thought on the subject:

My Very Reverend Father,

It has been a pleasure to me to read the Italian letter and the Latin paper you sent me. I thank you for both the one and the other, and I may tell you that I found them replete with skill and learning. As you ask for my opinion, I will give it as briefly as possible because, at the moment, you have very little time for reading and I have very little time for writing.

1. It seems to me that your Reverence and Signor Galileo act prudently when you content yourselves with speaking hypothetically and not absolutely, as I have always understood that Copernicus spoke. To say that on the supposition of the Earth's movement and the Sun's quiescence all the celestial appearances are explained better than by the theory of eccentrics and epicycles is to speak with excellent good sense and to run no risk whatever. Such a manner of speaking is enough for a mathematician. But to want to affirm that the Sun, in very truth, is at the center of the universe and only rotates on its axis without going from east to west, is a very dangerous attitude and one calculated not only to arouse all Scholastic philosophers and theologians but also to injure our holy faith by contradicting the Scriptures. Your Reverence has clearly shown that there are several ways of interpreting

the Word of God, but you have not applied these methods to any particular passage; and, had you wished to expound by the method of your choice all the texts which you have cited, I feel certain that you would have met with the very greatest difficulties.

2. As you are aware, the Council of Trent forbids the interpretation of the Scriptures in a way contrary to the common opinion of the holy Fathers. Now if your Reverence will read, not merely the Fathers, but modern commentators on Genesis, the Psalms, Ecclesiastes, and Joshua, you will discover that all agree in interpreting them literally as teaching that the Sun is in the heavens and revolves round the Earth with immense speed and that the Earth is very distant from the heavens, at the center of the universe, and motionless. Consider, then, in your prudence, whether the Church can tolerate that the Scriptures should be interpreted in a manner contrary to that of the holy Fathers and of all modern commentators, both Latin and Greek. It will not do to say that this is not a matter of faith, because though it may not be a matter of faith *ex parte objecti* or as regards the subject treated, yet it is a matter of faith *ex parte dicentis,* or as regards him who enounces it. Thus he who should deny that Abraham had two sons and Jacob twelve would be just as much a heretic as a man who should deny the Virgin Birth of Christ, because it is the Holy Spirit who makes known both truths by the mouth of the Prophets and Apostles.

3. If there were a real proof that the Sun is in the center of the universe, that the Earth is in the third heaven, and that the Sun does not go round the Earth but the Earth round the Sun, then we should have to proceed with great circumspection in explaining passages of Scripture which appear to teach the contrary, and rather admit that we did not understand them than declare an opinion to be false which is proved to be true. But, as for myself, I shall not believe that there are such proofs until they are shown to me. Nor is it a proof that, if the Sun be supposed at the center of the universe and the Earth in the third heaven, everything works out the same as if it were the other way around. In case of doubt we ought not to abandon the interpretation of the sacred text as given by the holy Fathers.

I may add that the man who wrote: *The Earth abideth for ever; the Sun also riseth, and the Sun goeth down, and hasteth to his place whence he arose,* was Solomon, who not only spoke by divine inspiration but was wise and learned, above all others, in human sciences and in the knowledge of created things. As he had all this wisdom from God Himself, it is not likely that he would have made a statement contrary to a truth, either proven or capable of proof. If you tell me that Solomon speaks according to appearances, inasmuch as though the Sun seems to us to revolve, it is really the Earth that does so, just as when the poet says: "The shore is now receding from us," I answer that, though it may appear to a voyager as if the shore were receding from the vessel on which he stands rather than the vessel from the shore, yet he knows this to be an illusion and is able to correct it because he understands clearly that it is the ship that is in movement. But as to the Sun and the Earth, a wise man has no need to correct his judgment, for his experience tells him plainly that the Earth is standing still and that his eyes are not deceived when they report that the Sun, Moon, and stars are in motion.

With this I salute your Paternity affectionately and pray God to grant you all happiness.

From my house, 12 April 1615.

Your very Reverend Paternity's brother,

R. CAR. BELLARMINO[24]

The modern reader may well be bewildered by the type of reasoning evinced in this letter. It must be admitted that Bellarmine's dismissal of Copernicus is not bred of any notable familiarity with his work. But then very few people had read Copernicus, or even Rheticus' summary, and what they had come across would have been much more a repetitive amount of windy refutation. It is all the more deserving on the part of the Cardinal not to dismiss Copernicus summarily as "that fool" in the way Martin Luther had done; on the other hand— and this is a point often forgotten—what Bellarmine *had* read, or at least heard of, was a very distinctive part of Copernicus' book as it stood, namely, the famous Introduction. In that introduction it is expressly stated that the theory is purely a mathematical supposition, which has no bearing on the reality of the heavens, whatever it may be. Thus, Bellarmine was entitled to think that Copernicus himself was philosophically on his side. This impression would have promptly been dispelled by a perusal of the book itself, but that was beyond

24. Ed. Naz., XII, 159–60.

anyone but a specialist; and no one knew then that the unsigned Introduction was not the work of Copernicus at all but had been added by Osiander, a Lutheran pastor who was trying in this way to make it acceptable to fundamentalist prejudice. It was, as Kepler said, "written by a jackass for the use of other jackasses," but the difference could not be detected by the casual observer; and Bellarmine was only too glad to have there a confirmation of his views.

Had he looked a little further, in the dedication to Paul III, he might have found Copernicus' very own remarks about the danger of mixing Scripture with science: "Did not Lactantius say childish things about the shape of the Earth?" He might have heeded Copernicus' grave warning: *"Illos nihil moror. . . ."* But it would have been too much to ask of a man who had never re-examined anything in a spirit of doubt, who instead had trained himself to re-establishing, reasserting, and reconfirming an acknowledged truth throughout his life. Thus, Bellarmine did not go back to studying Copernicus before he wrote his letter, nor did he spend the midnight oil in perpending the profound modern ratiocinations that later apologists have construed into his text.[25] He had, as he stated candidly, very little time; he was an old man, plagued with ill-health, harassed with work, who found escape from it only in prayer and in sighing for the consolations of the other world. At this very same time he was using the watches of the night not at all on natural philosophy but in composing a little treatise to be called *The Lament of the Dove, or Of the Value of Tears.* It was a comment on the text: "Who will give me wings like a dove, and I will fly and be at rest." In it he showed the necessity of penance, compunction, and holy tears from passages in Scripture and in the Fathers and then went on to describe twelve sources of sorrow for the Christian heart in as many chapters, namely, the consideration of sin, of hell, of

25. "It is a curious and paradoxical circumstance . . . that as a piece of Scriptural exegesis Galileo's theological letters are much superior to Bellarmine's, while as an essay on scientific method Bellarmine's letter is far sounder and more modern in its views that Galileo's" (J. Brodrick, *The Life and Work of Blessed Robert Francis, Cardinal Bellarmine, S.J.* [1928], II, 360).

the Passion of Christ, of the persecutions of the Church, of laxity among priests, of the decline of fervor in religious Orders, of the careless lives of worldlings, of the miseries of mankind, of Purgatory, of the love of God, of the uncertainty of salvation, and of the temptations of the Devil.[26]

This was indeed what Bellarmine cared about. Even his great controversialist work was now far behind him, as he meditated his *nunc dimittis*. It was only an iron sense of duty which led him to answer at length on the wearisome question to a good friar who was asking for advice.

On the other side, Galileo, when he got to read the letter to Foscarini, felt the noose tightening. He had been trying to say, as clearly and as dangerously as he could, what the point was; and all that he was getting back was the considerate reply: "I trust I have not heard you."

Surely, he wrote back to Dini, it had never been his desire to enter the scriptural field, "that no astronomer, or natural philosopher, has ever had to deal with, who stayed within his limits." He had never wanted to do anything but insure freedom for a physical theory. There would be the sure and direct way—he adds with despair—to show that it is not against Scripture, without going out of his province, "and it would be to show by a thousand proofs that it is true, and the contrary one can in no way subsist. But how am I to do this, and how is all effort not going to be in vain, if my mouth is locked, if these Peripatetics,

26. The book came out in 1617, was reprinted times without number, and was translated into many languages. St. Francis of Sales praised it beyond measure. It became, as we said earlier, the favorite devotional reading of Bellarmine's archenemy, James I of England. But it did also arouse anger among certain religious who had found their order criticized, though ever so mildly. In 1625 a Dominican named Gravina published—in Naples of all places—a book called *Vox turturis, or The Voice of the Turtle-Dove, a Declaration concerning the Flourishing Condition Up to Our Times of the Benedictine, Dominican, Franciscan and Other Religious Orders.* He was answered by a French Jesuit with a counterblast: *A Cage for the Turtle-Dove That Crows over Bellarmine's Mourning Dove.* Gravina's counter-counterreply was called *The Doubly Powerful Voice of the Turtle-Dove Reiterating the Flourishing Condition, etc., after the Collapse of a Certain Anonymous Person's Cage.* We do not know what followed next.

who ought to be persuaded, show themselves incapable of understanding even the simplest and most easy reasons?"

This was a veiled indictment of Bellarmine himself, and it was the inescapable truth. (Dini certainly did not allow it at the time to escape his drawer.) As a theologian you tell a man to restrict himself to natural philosophy and not to meddle with Scripture; then you invade his own scientific field with your Peripatetic prejudice without troubling to understand his reasons, and you shut him up with the theological taboo. This is the way that cannot but lead to the "subversion of commonwealths," as Galileo was to write later.

This instinctive confidence shared by his friends, that it was he, Galileo, after all, who stood for the traditions of Christendom, and that it was Bellarmine who was failing, is not what good Catholics are supposed to feel; but, as a matter of fact, they often do, and they consider it no crime.[27] It must have been actually queer to these men to see the leaders of the Roman Church committed to a fundamentalist position which has always belonged to Protestant sects. In a hierarchy which in its long experience had seen the denial of the antipodes come and go, and many more important things besides, this must have seemed moonstruck obstinacy; and it was becoming clear that it was not Bellarmine's religious convictions that stood in the way but simply his Aristotelian conditioning and his fear of "scandal." Copernicus in his quiet dedication to the Pope is more exactly the Catholic than Bellarmine was at this moment.

Such reactions find an interesting echo on the other side of the fence. The brothers of Tommaso Caccini were very far from any intellectual interest. They were of that conformist small gentry which was forever busy wangling pensions or preferments from the favor of the mighty. When Matteo Caccini, who lived in Rome and in the employ of the Vatican, heard of Tommaso's oratorical venture, he

27. As we have said, it is Galileo's views which have become official Church doctrine since the encyclical *Providentissimus Deus* of 1893, and Bellarmine's have been in fact rejected, although their author has since been canonized.

wrote him forthwith, stumbling over his own sentences from rage and haste:

I hear of such greatly extravagant antics on your part that I am amazed and disgusted beyond measure. It may yet come to such a pass that you'll regret ever having learned to read. You could have done nothing more annoying to the high authorities here, up to the very highest. God grant you may not have to learn it the bitter way.

It is no use your draping yourself with the mantle of zeal and religion, because here [in Rome] everybody knows how you friars use such cover currently to indulge your ugly drives, and far from believing you they are able to see you all the better as you are.

Truly it is a great impertinence, in matters that have to be judged by men far above you, and where there are men of such authority and wisdom, and they don't speak, that the impertinence of a friar should come prancing in thus. What idiocy is this of being set abellowing at the prompting of those nasty pigeons or whatever they are [*da piccione, da coglione, o da certi colombi,* referring to Lodovico delle Colombe and his Academic League].

Yet you got into trouble enough in the past, and will you never learn?

Brother Thomas, take it from me, reputation rules the world, and those who make such *coglionerie* as you do lose their good name. Just as we were trying to open up a career for you through high protections. . . . What will the Order and the world think of you? This performance of yours makes no sense in heaven or earth, and no one cares for it, and the proof is that it is very poorly appreciated here, let me tell you, because I know for sure. Now don't let people hoist you on your high horse again for running such a ridiculous race. I ask that you stop preaching, and, if you won't do this for me, I know a way to make you do it. You have been warned.

Try to think where you would like to go, because I don't like it where you are, and here even less; and, if you don't find a way to move out, I shall find one for you. I who am no theologian can tell you what I am telling you, that you have behaved like a dreadful fool. With this you have my good wishes.[28]

Matteo dispatched this letter with orders to show it to Fra Tommaso

---

28. Cf. A. Ricci-Riccardi, *Galileo e Fra Tommaso Caccini: Una corrispondenza inedita* (1902). The letter is dated January 2, 1615.

but not to let him retain it in his hands. One could not be too careful in that vicious political struggle, where everything might change overnight through an upset or the death of the reigning Pontiff, and it explains why no one dared write what he knew. Matteo's words are thus doubly valuable, because they reflect an assurance derived from his master, Cardinal Arrigoni, and from the latter's friends in the Curia with whom Matteo was in daily contact; we see whence came the confidence expressed by Ciàmpoli. It is sound conservatism itself. The perpetual encroachments and aggressiveness of those monks at Santa Maria sopra Minerva raised undisguised annoyance in the Vatican. Top-level decisions were not reserved for them. The Church has always been wiser than her children.

Galileo himself, in fact, did not indulge in his despairing mood. "Go again and knock at the door of the Jesuits," he wrote to Dini. "I still think that, if I came down and explained my reasons in person, I would get some result."

The correspondence from the next few months is lost, probably destroyed by Galileo in order not to compromise his friends who had taken to writing him in more and more covered terms. But it was already clear from what Ciàmpoli had written that there was not much to hope for in the direction of the Collegio Romano.

Galileo did not have too many illusions on that score. He had been told that he was being fenced in, oh, so lightly, for his own good; but he saw the disastrous reactionary attempt in its true nature: a deadly consolidation that was imperceptibly closing in to freeze him like a fly in amber, or, rather, in Dante's image, which corresponded much more to those men's minds, a lost soul imbedded forever in eternal ice. Nineteen centuries of organized thought were piling up to smother him, which had started with the "loss of nerve" of Greek science after Aristarchus. The astronomers, still groping toward a physical system dimly seen, had been told off then by the philosophers, who had what they considered a satisfactory cosmology; they had accepted not without some plaintive protest the subordinate role of "saving phenomena" by means of abstract models and fictions. The minds of men had been molded through ages on the tenets of solid Scholastic logic and experience. The statesmen of thought could not but smile at the pathetic attempt of a few astronomers, repeated over the centuries, to erect a house on sand. The smile was now turning to impatience. A ruling seemed in order, as Colombe suggested, to prevent rash people from building again on the unsafe spots.

To such men Galileo could not explain what only he and Kepler saw: the three forces of mathematics, physics, and astronomy converging rapidly toward a junction which would make them irresistible. He was not bringing any facts that the Jesuits did not know.[29] He was pleading for time, but he was pleading also for much more: for the rights of scientific imagination to build its own world, to follow its quest for the secrets of the universe wherever it led; and this meant inevitably invading the reserved field of metaphysics. "With what right did he expect them," writes a modern apologist, "to believe him on his word?" There is a grim unintended irony in these words. For any aggressive lawyer, indeed, his case would have been less than airtight. What scientific speculation is made of is volatile stuff to a blinkered and sophistic mind.

29. This would have been the time indeed to produce Kepler's laws, at least the two first ones, which had been published. But the ignorance (or ignoring) of those laws pursues Galileo through the years like an irony of fate. He probably had the *Astronomia nova* of 1609 right on his shelf, for there is evidence that Kepler had sent it to him and waited in vain for his comments (Letter, *Opera omnia,* ed. Ch. Frisch [Frankfurt, 1858–71], II, 489). But he invincibly distrusted Kepler's cosmological fantasies, and it would have taken much faith and much labor to find the discoveries about the orbit of Mars, deeply buried as they are in that strange book. Kepler admitted later that he himself had difficulty with it: "My brain gets tired," he says, "when I try to understand what I wrote, and I find it hard to rediscover the connexion between the figures and the text, that I established myself" (III, 146). Galileo seems to have heard from someone (Cesi or Cavalieri) a casual mention of the elliptical orbits, but it must have set in motion a protective mechanism in his own mind, for his theory needed circles as a physical reality.

One can watch this kind of sophistry going on even in our own time. Thus Pierre Duhem, a distinguished French physicist who has also gained a great and deserved renown in history of science, could write in 1908: "Logic was on the side of Osiander and Bellarmine and not on that of Kepler and Galileo; the former had grasped the exact significance of the experimental method, while the latter had been mistaken. . . . Suppose the hypotheses of Copernicus were able to explain all known appearances. What can be concluded is that they may be true, not that they are necessarily true, for in order to legitimate this last conclusion, it would have to be proved that no other system of hypotheses could possibly be imagined which could explain the appearances just as well." [30]

The last statement is of course, as far as it goes, scientifically quite correct. To take it with modern connotation and project it backward into the historical picture of the seventeenth century turns it into worse than a paradox, an intellectual solecism which would be enough to reveal in its author the unscrupulous apologist *ex parte*. If those prelates knew exactly, in advance of everybody, what true scientific method was, it is permissible to ask why they never made use of it.

Duhem was perfectly well in a position to know that Bellarmine's alleged "positivism" was only a position of indifference in a limited area of knowledge (viz., the theory of heaven) completely contained by a physical and metaphysical realism of the Scholastic kind. In no admissible way could it be presented as the permanent starting point (as if there were such a thing) for an organized natural philosophy and an "experimental method." So far from being that, the conventional theory of heaven defined for Bellarmine, as well as for Aquinas himself, an area of ignorance or "soft spot" that ought to be reabsorbed eventually into the surrounding Aristotelian coherency. The idea of that area expanding instead to cover the field of natural knowledge

30. *Essai sur la notion de théorie physique de Platon à Galilée* (1908). Translated in English under the title, *The Theory of Physical Reality* (New York, 1952).

with its empty "hypotheses" would have been received by Bellarmine with a shudder, for it would have looked to him as an intellectual cancer. It would have shocked Galileo no less, who would have refused to accept Duhem's costive dogmatic formalism as the refined version of his procedure and would have asked indignantly whether the greater cosmos that he had started out to discover was bound to turn out again an unendingly pointless paper universe scribbled o'er with intellectual epicycles and excentrics;[31] whereas it is fair to surmise that the actual universe of Maxwell, Einstein, and Heisenberg would have made fascinating if difficult sense to his mind.

Socrates had remarked already that unnatural reasoning has a way of turning against its author. To disperse it artfully over the landscape of history affords only momentary protection, for it will appear even more clearly, in the end, whether a contention does make sense in actual time. Minerva's bird is supposed to fly in the dusk, not in the murk of smoke-pots.

If the good faith of the modern nonscientific reader can still be led astray by such painful quibbling, it is no wonder that three centuries ago it should have been difficult to get minds much more prejudiced to see what Kepler had seen, "the telescope as a ladder to scale the highest walls of the visible world, and from there to look down on our hovels, I mean the planets, comparing the outmost with the inmost, the highest with the lowest"; nor to make them understand that such an intuitive certainty could be legitimate even while there remained problems to be solved.[32] Galileo could only demonstrate past absurdity, flash impressive "natural effects" before the eyes of his judges, make what he had found "make do" for what he had not found yet. He must dissociate himself from the dreaded memory of Bruno, reassure suspicious officials about their metaphysics, and yet make them feel that its physi-

31. "We are concerned with the real universe, not with a paper one," remarks Salviati impatiently in the *Dialogue,* and it turns out an effective jab at Duhem's early dogmatic form of positivism. It goes far to explain why Duhem's great work in thermodynamics has been so rapidly forgotten.

32. Cf. Kepler's *Astronomia nova* (*Opera omnia,* ed. Frisch, VI, 450).

Saint Robert Bellarmine

cal foundations were coming apart. And he must do so in, of all places, Rome.

We do not know under what circumstances the final decision was taken. Young Attavanti, after his hearing on November 14, may have warned him, breaking his oath of silence, that he was accused of more sins than he dreamed of. Armed with strong recommendations from the Grand Duke, Galileo set off for Rome on December 3, 1615. He must save those men in spite of themselves from the disastrous consequences that he could foresee for their obduracy.

V

The Decree

Mi vien serrata la bocca . . . GALILEO

Auf Teufel reimt der Zweifel nur
Da bin ich recht am Platze.
MEPHISTOPHELES

I

The Florentine ambassador in Rome, Piero Guicciardini, had been informed by the secretary of state of Galileo's impending arrival. He felt that pointless trouble was coming his way and wished him somewhere else. "I do not know," he wrote back on December 5, "whether he has changed his theories or his disposition, but this I know, that certain brothers of St. Dominic, who are in the Holy Office, and others are ill disposed toward him, and this is no fit place to argue about the Moon or, especially in these times, to try and bring in new ideas." But his instructions were explicit. Galileo was lodged at the "Gardens of the Embassy," which was the Villa Medici at Trinità de'Monti (today the Academy of France), "with board for himself, a secretary, a valet, and a small mule."

He found himself but a small item of interest in the turmoil of the capital, now that the excitement about the telescope had worn off. Rome was being born anew in those years. The vast architectural transformation undertaken by Sixtus V and carried on by his power-minded successors was tearing down the old medieval city and replacing it with the modern design of monumental squares and thoroughfares, with the harmony of palaces, statues, ever green gardens, and splashing fountains intended to proclaim to the world the restored magnificence of Catholicity, triumphant over the disorganized forces of life and the hapless confusion of history.

As for the role of science in all this, the ambassador's dim-viewed diagnosis was correct. Paul V Borghese was not an open mind, nor much of any kind of mind. He was a strong and somber executive, a canonist by training, by temperament doctrinaire and inflexible. As he once said, he preferred new jobs for workmen to new ideas from scholars.

Galileo for his part, no doubt stung to action by the ambassador's cold skepticism, was not to be discouraged. On January 8, 1616, he wrote to Curzio Picchena, who was Vinta's successor as secretary of state: "From day to day I am discovering what a good inspiration it was for me to come here, for such snares had been laid against me that I could not have hoped to save myself later." From Caccini's denunciation we have an idea of what those "snares" were—part of an organized campaign to make the astronomers look like blasphemous enemies of Christianity in all its most sacred tenets.

The reception that Galileo found in official quarters was flattering. His detractors, who had spread the news that he had fallen into disgrace at Florence, were discomfited to see him arrive with the full favor of his sovereign. But his letters back home describe what he had to cope with:

My business is far more difficult, and takes much longer owing to outward circumstances, than the nature of it would require; because I cannot communicate directly with those persons with whom I have to negotiate, partly to avoid doing injury to any of my friends, partly because they cannot communicate anything to me without running the risk of grave censure. And so I am compelled, with much pains and caution, to seek out third persons, who, without even knowing my object, may serve as mediators with the principals, so that I may have the opportunity of setting forth, incidentally as it were, and at their request, the particulars of my interests. I have also to set down some points in writing, and to cause that they should come privately into the hands of those whom I wish should see them; for I find in many quarters that people are more ready to yield to dead writing than to living speech, for the former permits them to agree or dissent without blushing, and then finally to yield to the arguments used—since in such discussions we have no witnesses but ourselves, whereas people do not so readily change their opinions if it has to be done publicly.

On February 6, 1616, he felt he could write confidently:

I have terminated the business as far as my own person is concerned; but there is a decision which affects all those who in the last eighty years have written about a certain doctrine not unknown to Your Excellency; and I owe it to my conscience to provide what information I can, deriving from the sciences that I profess.[1] I reserve for your ear alone an account of the truly incredible deeds that could be perpetrated by those three most powerful operators, ignorance, malice, and impiety. Be it enough to say that my enemies, once defeated and disgruntled in their enterprise against my person as I have been freely assured by these Lords, have now turned their batteries against the ideas I stand for.

This difficult lobbying (as we would call it now) Galileo implemented with a social activity which would keep him, he hoped, in the limelight of the gossipy Roman world as an orthodox and unchallenged scientist. He loved discussion and seems to have had an inexhaustible faith in man's capacity to understand. Writes a typical man about town, Monsignor Querengo:

We have here Sig. Galileo, who, often, in gatherings of men of curious mind, bemuses many concerning the opinion of Copernicus that he holds for true. . . . He discourses often amid fifteen or twenty guests who make hot assaults upon him, now in one house, now in another. But he is so well

1. We have a few of those memoranda for the authorities (Ed. Naz., V, 351–66). They are first drafts of the arguments that are developed in the Third Day of the *Dialogue*. They are impersonal and dispassionate to the point that we no longer recognize the author behind them. It is as though the emotional tension of those days had resolved itself into a higher objective clarity. We have also the names of "those persons" to whom they were addressed from Galileo's later deposition in 1633. They were the Cardinals Bellarmine, Bonsi, d'Ascoli, S. Eusebio, and Aracoeli. Not one of them did anything.

buttressed that he laughs them off; and although the novelty of his opinion leaves people unpersuaded, yet he convicts of vanity the greater part of the arguments with which his opponents try to overthrow him. Monday in particular, in the house of Federico Ghisilieri, he achieved wonderful feats; and what I liked most was that, before answering the opposing reasons, he amplified them and fortified them himself with new grounds which appeared invincible, so that, in demolishing them subsequently, he made his opponents look all the more ridiculous.

Visitors also came to him, one of whom startled him considerably. It was Tommaso Caccini. "The person who started the trouble," he writes guardedly to Picchena, "was with me for over four hours, trying to draw me out about the controversy; in the first half-hour he tried with many demonstrations of humility to make excuses for what he preached in Florence; then tried to persuade me that he had not been the mover [*motore*] for the other mover here. . . . But in all his discourses I discovered a very great ignorance, no less than a mind full of venom and devoid of charity. What he and some others have done since shows me again how dangerous it is to have to deal with such people and how inevitable to have them arrayed against me."

Of what those people had been actually doing we may be afforded a glimpse through the letters of Matteo Caccini. Matteo was a discreet man of the world; he had grown up to respect Galileo, were it only because his elder brother Alessandro had made his early career in the banking interests controlled by Filippo Salviati, Galileo's close friend and sponsor. He had settled in Rome and found solace from the intrigues of the Court in the pursuit of horticulture (it may interest the modern reader to know that he had an important part in the shaping of the admirable Villa Borghese, which is now the public park of the city).

As a matter of family interest, Matteo Caccini was trying to get lucrative preferments for his Dominican brother, but he was also greatly concerned with getting him away from Florence and from his scandalous involvement with those "nasty pigeons." A gentleman-in-waiting to Cardinal Arrigoni, and friend of several members of the Curia, he was very much *au courant* of Roman affairs. He strove now with might and main, mobilizing all sorts of Court influences, to get Tommaso the title of Resident Bachelor of Arts at the Minerva so as to have him under control in Rome. His early concern is seen from what he writes Alessandro on January 9, 1615: "If F. T. looks like more trouble, let me know. I have ways to have him removed out of Italy if necessary." But F. T. seems willing to calm down, and on February 6 Matteo writes triumphantly that he has been able by moving heaven and earth to secure the post over a dangerous competitor; let Tommaso come to Rome immediately: "But for heaven's sake let him try to keep his trap shut; he might ruin all our plans. His confreres in the Order seem to think well of his capacities, but, as I know him, he is lighter than a leaf and emptier than a pumpkin. I shall not feel comfortable until the deal is closed."

Tommaso, as we know, did come down to Rome on February 20, but without showing much interest in the prospects opened to him by his brother. He had other and greater plans in mind. His arrival had been timed to coincide with that of Lorini's letter. While Ciàmpoli was writing Galileo (February 28) that "the Friars don't seem to talk or think about that business any more," Tommaso Caccini was busily conferring with his fellow-Dominicans, and on March 13 he was introduced to Cardinal Aracoeli, who was to sponsor his secret denunciation.

It was only on April 30 that Matteo realized what had been going on.

"As to F. T.," he writes, "I am so angry that I could not be more, but I don't care to discuss it. He opened up with me in private the other day, and he came out with such dreadful plans that I could control myself only with difficulty. In any case, I wash my hands of him forever and ever."

What Tommaso had revealed, obviously, was that he was out to "get" Galileo by fair means or foul; that he had found powerful associates; and that, if the Holy Office could be moved to action, he had ahead of him a career of honors and preferments far greater than the one his brother had planned for him. He was suggesting now that the latter give up his previous efforts (they had come to nothing anyway) and follow his lead.

Matteo was as good as his word and refused to see the friar again. In November, 1615, he followed his Cardinal to Naples (this was while Galileo was still in Florence), and from then on he could only relay indirect information. But a new note of aloofness has crept into his writing. Obviously, he had been told that the Galileo affair had indeed become an Inquisition matter and that it was wise to have strictly nothing to do with it. On February 19, 1616, he writes: "I understand Sig. Gl. went to the Holy Office." The dealings that Galileo alludes to confidently and even cheerfully in his letter of February 6 to Picchena have become here the object of a frightened whisper. The worldly Matteo has concluded that his brother did make the right bet after all. "He seems to stand high with the Order. Well, let us hope that this will recoup his fortunes." [2]

Galileo knew only too well that the town was alive with informers and *agents provocateurs* in many official and unofficial capacities. That was why he diplomatically understated his real errand and insisted that he had come only to vindicate his good name. His diplomacy found approval. But he went on waiting for an audience that never came.

II

He was moving in a haze of equivocation. Whenever he tried to persuade, he found listeners who were merely amused. Amusement, even

---

2. As it turned out, Tommaso Caccini never attained the reward that he considered adequate to his merits. After taking up and dropping a couple of small preferments he had been granted, he got himself embarrassingly involved in a feud between Duchess Sforza and Cardinal Borghese. A compromising letter of his to the Duchess came into the hands of the all-powerful Cardinal, and he had to leave Rome. Although he tried again and again to attach himself to the powerful, he never rose in the hierarchy, and he was to end his days in 1648 as Prior of S. Marco in Florence.

cruel, was at a premium in that atmosphere of weary conformism. But the originality had to be that of "conceits."

It remained Galileo's fate through life to create an excitement and consensus around him which had little to do with real understanding. His was the tragedy of an excess of gifts; for, while the telescope was his key to success, his real social strength lay in his extraordinary literary capacity, his brilliant repartee, his eloquence and charm, which gave him rank in a culture founded exclusively on belles-lettres and humanistic accomplishments. "You have a way of bewitching people," Ciàmpoli had said. His writing is, indeed, the one achievement of Italian Baroque prose that has survived the centuries. In that, his contemporaries could easily recognize a master; but what remained with them of his "incomparable demonstrations" was as dim as the memory of a symphony to the untrained ear. This Galileo could never bring himself to realize. As he talked reason to his hearers, he believed, he forever wanted to believe, that they were following the course of his thought, and he spent himself unsparingly in explaining and persuading. They applauded; but, when the time came, this success showed again and again as fool's gold in his hands.

The younger men who could understand the full scope of his thought, like Castelli and Cavalieri, were but a handful (of them, Filippo Salviati remains the symbol enshrined in the *Dialogue*). Of men at the age of responsibility and influence, there was almost no one in Rome. His noble friends of the Lyncean Academy were willing souls, but they were romantic Platonists and naturalists who did not really understand his physics. His high-placed sponsors and "protectors" were very much like that United States senator who, when physicists from Los Alamos came to him with pressing pleas about dangers and moral responsibilities, cut them short reassuringly: "Believe me, gentlemen, I have always been a great friend of atomic energy." Galileo thought he was submitting briefs as a consultant and "friend of the court." To the court itself he was simply a patient under observation.

What it must have looked like to a cynical man of the world, we can infer from the letters of the Florentine ambassador, Guicciardini, full of undisguised annoyance:

He is all afire on his opinions, and puts great passion in them, and not enough strength and prudence in controlling it; so that the Roman climate is getting very dangerous for him, and especially in this century; for the present Pope, who abhors the liberal arts and his kind of mind, cannot stand these novelties and subtleties; and everyone here tries to adjust his mind and his nature to that of the ruler. Even those who understand something, and are of curious mind, if they are wise, try to show themselves quite to the contrary, in order not to fall under suspicion and get into trouble themselves. Galileo has monks and others who hate him and persecute him, and, as I said, he is not at all in a good position for a place like this, and he might get himself and others into serious trouble. . . . This gives me grave concern toward the announced coming of the Most Serene Cardinal [de' Medici]. . . . To involve the Grand Ducal House in these embarrassments and risks, without serious motive, is an affair from which there can come no profit but only great damage. I do not see why it should be done, the more so when this happens only to satisfy Galileo. He is passionately involved in this quarrel, as if it were his own business, and he does not see and sense what it would comport; so that he will be snared in it, and will get himself into danger, together with anyone who seconds him. . . . For he is vehement and is all fixed and impassioned in this affair, so that it is impossible, if you have him around, to escape from his hands. And this is a business which is not a joke but may become of great consequence, and this man is here under our protection and responsibility. . . .

Vox clamantis in deserto. We should try to think of the Rome of those times, where much saintly work was being done for the poor and the pilgrims from all parts of the world, where true saints could be found, to be sure, but which otherwise was the most corrupt of administrative capitals, and still and forever such as Du Bellay had found it a century earlier and as Belli was to portray it two centuries later: packed with fanatical and petulant monks, shrewd intriguers, postulants, paid and unpaid observers, diplomats, cynical secretaries, fulsome literati and inane versifiers living off the bounty of some prelate; lazy insolent nobles, curialist lawyers, stony-faced publicans rack-renting for the princes and the convents; spies, informers, go-betweens, men about town, unctuous priests and officials, careful hypocrites, suspicious hard old men, meeching young men on their way to preferments through oily conformism; all the parasitical, torpid, cunning, and malevolent society that vegetated like a pestilent mushroom growth on the fringes of an imperial world bureaucracy and for whom the stability and prestige of that bureaucracy in matters spiritual meant their career and their income. Around it all, the stones and the sky and the people of the Eternal City, expressing its spirit as it endures through time: a rocklike tolerant indifference to ideas, a quick estimate of men's motives, a weary certainty that all has been thought and said already, the eye on what pays. Truly, as Guicciardini said, no place to come and argue about the Moon.

Galileo was writing home in a spirit of unquenched hope. But he knew that he was a marked man and that the door was slowly closing in his face. The audience had never come. Cesi, Ciàmpoli, and Dini found growing reserve against their patient inquiries. The Jesuits, who had given hopes of support, were quietly withdrawing. Father Grienberger had said that it would have been better if he had produced more convincing proofs of his theory before trying to adjust Scripture to it. This was technically correct; but, for a man in Grienberger's position, it was, as Dini admitted, a lamentable out. The worst was that he said it after having been called in by Bellarmine for consultation. He was a broken reed. It was known that the Jesuits had a strict directive, issued to them by their General, to keep away from anything that might weaken the Aristotelian position.[3] Galileo had been hoping against hope from such as he. After three months of pleading, begging, and demonstrating, he realized at last that he stood alone.

3. Letter of Giovanni Bardi, June 14, 1614. Of this we have independent proof. Father Grienberger had written also in 1614 to a friend of Galileo apropos the controversy on floating bodies that, were it not for the deference which by the direction of his superiors he was obliged to show toward Aristotle, he would have spoken his mind clearly on the matter, in which Galileo was perfectly right. This was not the only instance, he added, in which the Stagyrite could be proved to have been wrong.

There was still his Grand Duke in Florence, who had never let him down, although Lorini was known to be working hard in the ducal household. He got himself a pressing letter of commendation, in which Cosimo II made the cause his own personal concern.

It was addressed to Cardinal Alessandro Orsini, a nice youth of twenty-two, who felt flattered by such an important request. To him, as he had previously to Maffeo Barberini, Galileo disclosed the "conclusive physical proof" of the Copernican system, which he had not yet published, and begged him to use his influence with the Pope, so that he might at least suspend judgment. The proof, alas, was the theory of the tides, which is given in the Fourth Day of the *Dialogue* It has turned out not to be valid, but it was impressive enough for anyone who could follow its close reasoning. Galileo could not yet produce Foucault's pendulum, and he must needs make shift with what he had.

III

Here is the ambassador's unsympathetic version of what followed:

Galileo has relied more on his own counsel than on that of his friends. The Lord Cardinal del Monte and myself, and also several cardinals from the Holy Office, had tried to persuade him to be quiet and not to go on irritating this issue. If he wanted to hold this Copernican opinion, he was told, let him hold it quietly and not spend so much effort in trying to have others share it. Everyone fears that his coming here may be very prejudicial and that, instead of justifying himself and succeeding, he may end up with an affront.

As he felt people cold toward his intention, after having pestered and wearied several cardinals, he threw himself on the favor of Cardinal Orsini and extracted to that purpose a warm recommendation from Your Highness. The Cardinal, then, last Wednesday in Consistory, I do not know with what circumspection and prudence, spoke to the Pope on behalf of said Galileo. The Pope told him it would be well if he persuaded him to give up that opinion. Thereupon Orsini replied something, urging the cause, and the Pope cut him short and told him he would refer the business to the Holy Office. As soon as Orsini had left, His Holiness summoned Bellarmine; and, after brief discussion, they decided that the opinion was erroneous and heretical; and day before yesterday, I hear, they had a Congregation on the matter to have it declared such. Copernicus, and the other authors who wrote on this, shall be amended or corrected or prohibited; I believe that Galileo personally is not going to suffer, because he is prudent, and he will feel and desire as Holy Church does. [March 4.]

This report has been discounted as unreliable by historians because of Guicciardini's manifest ill will and because the dates are clearly manipulated in order to accredit his version. The decision was not taken two days before the decree but on the nineteenth of February; therefore, any pressure that Cardinal Orsini may have tried to exert in the Consistory of March 2 (or even February 24) could not have decided the course of events. But it seems to us the account is all the more important because of this misstatement.

Governments have never been averse to feeding the curiosity of ambassadors with timely indiscretions and confidential material colored to suit their purposes. The Vatican knew that Guicciardini was well informed of all that happened in the palace through the Tuscan prelates and officials in every department. Only the doings of the Holy Office were shrouded in secrecy. It was easy for the well-exercised curial skill, after having spread for many weeks dark rumors that Galileo was asking for trouble, to let a couple of known facts (the intervention of Orsini and then the audience of Bellarmine on the second) appear by a calculated "leak" as the decisive events, whereas the decision had already been taken in secret session many days before. In this way, the informers were shielded; things were made to look as though only Galileo's impatience and indiscretion had goaded the long-suffering authorities to action; and, with Guicciardini's co-operation, the best way had been found to discredit Galileo with the Grand Duke. This version has gone on being far from useless to certain modern writers *ex parte.*

What actually happened, as we know now from the archives, was this: On the nineteenth of February of that year 1616 (it may or may not be a coincidence, but Caccini's peculiar visit to Galileo came three days later),[4] the Qualifiers, or experts of the Holy Office, had been summoned by decree to give their opinion. This summons was decided on at a meeting of the General Congregation of the eighteenth, of which all trace is lost. From the general style of the *Decreta* we may infer, however, that this one said no more than strict procedure required: "*Relata causa Galilaei mathematici* by the Most Reverend Commissary-General, Sanctissimus decided to submit for censure two propositions held by defendant."

Historians have always considered the course of events in the Holy Office as hidden behind inquisitional mystery, and yet this one would seem to be a fairly run-of-the-mill affair. For eight months, we should remember, nothing had happened while Father Ximenes was being located. In February less than three months had elapsed since Attavanti's deposition, which concluded the inquiry, and since the last annotation by the Assessor in the file. The case had been allowed to rest while Galileo produced his justifications (we see why his protectors told him it was lucky he had come), for he had been formally denounced, if only by hearsay, for grievous heresy and blasphemy concerning the nature of God. It took him almost two months, as we know from his letter of February 6, to dispel these charges against his person, and it was the way of the Inquisition not to move until some definite opinion had been reached by informal investigation. The suspicion had not been very strong from the start; he had been, as it were, cleared in quarantine of infectious diseases, and he was even told so. But he was still under observation for his scientific opinions, and those were obviously no good; it was time now to act on that part of the imputation, which had been proved.[5] This last decision was a matter of days, and it does not go beyond the ordinary judicial delays. In early

---

4. See above, p. 120.
5. It seems plausible, then, to suppose that Caccini was quietly told to go and apologize to Galileo for the first imputation and to report whether or not the accused stood firm on the second and in what spirit. It is hard to see his visit on the fifth as a coincidence.

February the Commissary reported that the case could be put on the docket for the next Congregation.

The propositions submitted to the censure of the Qualifiers were the following:

I. The Sun is the center of the world and hence immovable of local motion.
II. The Earth is not the center of the world, nor immovable, but moves according to the whole of itself, also with a diurnal motion [*ma si move secondo sè tutta, etiam di moto diurno*].

The theologians met four days later, on February 23, and announced the result of their deliberations on the following day. The first proposition was unanimously declared to be "foolish and absurd [*stultam et absurdam*], philosophically and formally heretical, inasmuch as it expressly contradicts the doctrine of the Holy Scripture in many passages, both in their literal meaning and according to the general interpretation of the Fathers and Doctors." The second proposition was declared unanimously "to receive the same censure in philosophy and, as regards theological truth, to be at least erroneous in faith." [6]

6. The wording of the "propositions" is not of the most felicitous. We shall see later where it came from. But at least it has afforded wonderful material for the casuist. In 1840 Father M. B. Olivieri, Deputy of the Dominicans (see also n. 18, p. 149), set out to prove that Galileo's condemnation had been "according to reason and religion." He is willing to admit (against some other apologists who call this a slander) that Galileo remained a Copernican—an obstinate and "premature" one—while he abjured Copernicanism in 1633. His point is rather that the wording of the condemned propositions must have been inspired by profound wisdom, for it afforded Galileo an opportunity to recant without changing his mind. Galileo could swear in 1633 without perjuring himself that he never believed that (1) "the Sun is the center of the world," because, if "world" means universe, the Sun is not at the center of the universe, and, if it means Earth, the Sun is not at the center of the Earth; that (2) "the Sun is immovable," because he himself had demonstrated its rotation. Further, he could swear with a good conscience that he had never believed that (3) "the Earth is not immovable," because it is immovable with respect to the things moving on it; that (4) "it moves according to the whole of itself, also with a diurnal motion," because the first part of the statement explicitly does not refer to the diurnal motion, and in the case of the yearly revolution the Earth cannot be said with any sense to revolve according to the whole of itself (too true); and therefore it is only motion through the air

The distinction between *heretical* and *erroneous* may sound subtle indeed. It is based on the weight of accredited opinion behind the two statements, quite independently of each other. The reasons may be found in Cardinal Conti's letter.[7]

This censure was submitted to the General Congregation of the Inquisition on February 25 and came back with the executive sanction of the Pope, as we have it in the Inquisition file:

Thursday, 25 February 1616. The Lord Cardinal Mellini notified the Reverend Fathers, the Assessor, and the Commissary of the Holy Office that the censure passed by the theologians upon the propositions of Galileo—to the effect that the Sun is the center of the world and immovable from its place, and that the Earth moves, and also with a diurnal motion—had been reported; and His Holiness has directed the Lord Cardinal Bellarmine to summon before him the said Galileo and admonish him to abandon the said opinion; and, in case of his refusal to obey, that the Commissary is to enjoin on him, before a notary and witnesses, a command to abstain altogether from teaching or defending this opinion and doctrine and even from discussing it; and, if he do not acquiesce therein, that he is to be imprisoned.

On March 3, at the next meeting of the General Congregation, Bellarmine reported that Galileo had submitted (*acquievit*), and the decree of the Congregation of the Index was issued, with the order to publish it immediately:

. . . And whereas it has also come to the knowledge of the said Congregation that the Pythagorean doctrine—which is false and altogether opposed to the Holy Scripture—of the motion of the Earth, and the immobility of the Sun, which is also taught by Nicolaus Copernicus in *De revolutionibus orbium coelestium,* and by Diego de Zuñiga (in his book) on Job, is now being spread abroad and accepted by many—as may be seen from a certain letter of a Carmelite Father, entitled *Letter of the Rev. Father Paolo Antonio Foscarini, Carmelite, on the Opinion of the Pythagoreans and of Copernicus concerning the Motion of the Earth, and the Stability of the Sun, and the*

(?) which is excluded. We are not sure we have done justice to this last point, which takes extensive elaboration in the original.

7. See p. 25.

New Pythagorean System of the World, at Naples, Printed by Lazzaro Scorriggio, 1615: wherein the said Father attempts to show that the aforesaid doctrine of the immobility of the Sun in the center of the world, and of the Earth's motion, is consonant with truth and is not opposed to Holy Scripture. Therefore, in order that this opinion may not insinuate itself any further to the prejudice of Catholic truth, the Holy Congregation has decreed that the said Nicolaus Copernicus, *De revolutionibus orbium,* and Diego de Zuñiga, *On Job,* be suspended until they be corrected; but that the book of the Carmelite Father, Paolo Antonio Foscarini, be altogether prohibited and condemned, and that all other works likewise, in which the same is taught, be prohibited, as by this present decree it prohibits, condemns, and suspends them all respectively. In witness wherof the present decree has been signed and sealed with the hands and with the seal of the most eminent and Reverend Lord Cardinal of St. Cecilia, Bishop of Albano, on the fifth day of March, 1616.[8]

On the fourth, as we have seen, the Tuscan ambassador was informed "confidentially" that the Pope had taken an adverse decision the previous day. On the fifth the decree was published and forwarded to the Inquisitors in all parts of the world with orders to enforce it rigorously. It was read from the pulpits and announced in the universities; books were confiscated in shops and libraries. The Inquisitor

---

8. The decree makes a distinction between scientific hypothesis and theological interpretation, which is not in the findings of the Qualifiers. That distinction is to be seen in the suspension of Copernicus against the suppression of Foscarini. "Paul V was of opinion to declare Copernicus contrary to the faith; but the Cardinals Caetani and Maffeo Barberini withstood the Pope openly and checked him with the good reasons they gave" (from the diary of G. F. Buonamici [Ed. Naz., XV, 111]). This is confirmed by Barberini's own words sixteen years later to Niccolini: "These difficulties of which we relieved Galileo when we were Cardinal." In addition to the above distinction, there is also the fact that the prohibition is issued by the secondary Congregation of the Index and *in forma communi* without higher indorsement. All this was profound strategy born of reflexes of prudence—so profound, indeed, that it remained hidden to most contemporaries, who considered that anything declared in Rome to be false and altogether opposed to Scripture is as good as dogmatically prohibited. But of this later. The official texts are, most of them, from the English edition of Gebler. They have been checked against the originals.

of Naples reported that Foscarini's printer, Scorriggio, had not been able to produce the license and had been cast into jail. The Congregation took time out to confirm that it was "well done."

Roma locuta, causa finita. The affair which had started with Lorini's denunciation was finally settled, and an incipient scandal had been quashed. The Curia could go back to the serious affairs of the Church. Writes the same Querengo who had been so enchanted with Galileo's dialectic:

The disputes of Signor Galileo have dissolved into alchemical smoke, since the Holy Office has declared that to maintain this opinion is to dissent manifestly from the infallible dogmas of the Church. So here we are at last, safely back on a solid Earth, and we do not have to fly with it as so many ants crawling around a balloon. . . .

The Roman world has gone back to "normalcy" with a shrug.

VI
Bellarmine's Audience

MARFORIUS: *Quid agunt dominicani?*
PASQUINUS: *In tympano et choro, in chordis et organo, laetati sunt quia Deus deduxit eos in portum voluntatis eorum.*

I

What had happened actually to Galileo himself? This is what Guicciardini indicates only briefly in his report. He trusts (in other words, he was told in confidence) that he has nothing to fear personally. And, in fact, the *Solar Letters* were not prohibited in the decree, although the "scandal" and the decree itself had been occasioned by Galileo's teaching and writings.

The source for the ambassador's informant is the decree of February 25, 1616, already quoted. We do not have it in the original of the *Decreta* but from the Inquisition file where it was transcribed:

His Holiness has directed the Lord Cardinal Bellarmine to summon before him the said Galileo and admonish him to abandon the said opinion; and, in case of his refusal to obey, that the Commissary of the Holy Office[1] is to

---

1. The Roman Inquisition was not like the Spanish Inquisition, with its "Council of the Supreme" and its Grand Inquisitor. It was really a committee of the Curia and had been devised mainly to keep the bishops in check. Hence there were a number of Cardinal-Inquisitors (usually six) who functioned as a board of directors but could intervene personally. The highest permanent post was that of the Assessor, who seems to have functioned mainly as liaison with the Curia. There was at times, above him, a Cardinal-Secretary. The real executive responsibilities rested on the *Commissarius Generalis,* who had to be a Dominican,

enjoin on him, before a notary and witnesses, a command to abstain altogether from teaching or defending this opinion and doctrine and even from discussing it [Vat. MS, fol. 378ᵛ].

There follows in the same page the procès-verbal which has become the crucial piece in the drama:

Friday, the twenty-sixth. At the palace, the usual residence of the Lord Cardinal Bellarmino, the said Galileo, having been summoned and being present before the said Lord Cardinal, was, in presence of the Most Reverend Michelangelo Segizi of Lodi, of the Order of Preachers, Commissary-General of the Holy Office, by the said Cardinal, warned of the error of the aforesaid opinion and admonished to abandon it; and immediately thereafter, before me and before witnesses, the Lord Cardinal being still present, the said Galileo was by the said Commissary commanded and enjoined, in the name of His Holiness the Pope and the whole Congregation of the Holy Office, to relinquish altogether the said opinion that the Sun is the center of the world and immovable and that the Earth moves; nor further to hold, teach, or defend it in any way whatsoever, verbally or in writing; otherwise proceedings would be taken against him by the Holy Office; which injunction the said Galileo acquiesced in and promised to obey. Done at Rome, in the place aforesaid, in the presence of R. Badino Nores, of Nicosia in the kingdom of Cyprus, and Agostino Mongardo, from a place in the Abbey of Rose in the diocese of Montepulciano, members of the household of said Cardinal, witnesses.

The document is startling even on first inspection, for we have a very different procedure being followed from that prescribed. The instructions had said: "in case of his refusal to obey"; but there is no indication here that Galileo objected or demurred. What we have instead is: "immediately thereafter" (*successive ac incontinenti*) the Commissary-General read to him the formal injunction to cease and desist "in any way whatsoever."

Now this makes no sense as to substance, for the notification by the Cardinal himself was an act of juridical and social consideration. To

and on his staff (composed of a Vice-Commissary, two associates, and a number of assistants). See also n. 2, p. 27.

have called in Galileo a week before the public release was not only intended to spare him embarrassment; it was also, in etiquette, an acknowledgment of his status as a consultant—an empty cloture gesture, since he had never been allowed to act like one, but still a recognition of his official position stemming from the Grand Ducal Court. The Congregation decree instructing Bellarmine to inform him cannot be construed otherwise. And, in fact, Foscarini was granted no official advance notice of the condemnation, because he was an ecclesiastic under obedience and considered to have spoken at his own risk. If the plan had been to spring the news on Galileo so as to trap him into an unwary reaction, someone else would have been detailed to it than a Prince of the Church and certainly not by Congregation decree. Bellarmine himself would not have lent his person to it, or his own house. We know from his biographers the scrupulous consideration he insisted on in all circumstances. "If any of his own personnel came to his room to speak to him, he would not let them begin until they had taken a chair. When they had concluded their business, he would remove his cap and accompany them to the stair with as much ceremony as if they were distinguished strangers." There is no doubt that, in the mind of Bellarmine, the whole transaction was conceived on a formal and dignified plane. It was, indeed, *the* audience that Galileo had been expecting all along, granted at last when it could no longer serve his purpose. It was to be followed by the inquisitorial injunction (which was a stigma of social dishonor), *only in case* the subject proved recalcitrant; in which case, then, if necessary, incarceration became the next step.

But Galileo simply submitted himself (*acquievit*). We can well imagine that he did not find it a time to protest.[2] Faced with Bellarmine

2. Galileo knew better than to argue with princes of the Church when they were not consulting him but stating their considered opinion, even in a private way. In those weeks Maffeo Barberini, who was his friend and protector, had given, in the course of a conversation, his answer about the theory of the tides, which was later to become famous (see p. 175). "When Galileo heard these words," writes Cardinal Oregius, who was a witness, "he remained silent with all his science

addressing him in his throne room, surrounded by his retinue of "black and white hounds of the Lord," he must have kept a stunned silence. But, then, why should the Commissary have sprung forward with a threatening injunction?

The document makes little sense as to form either. The instructions said "before a notary and witnesses," but the notary has not signed; nor are any officials mentioned as witnesses, as was the strict custom. Whenever the Inquisition served this type of injunction, it required the accused to sign with his own hand and then had the signature authenticated by the notary and the whole countersigned by its officials.[3]

Here we have only what amounts to an administrative minute, unsigned, casually transcribed. It was a very Catholic historian, but a distinguished one, Professor Franz Reusch, who in the 1870's drew attention to this fact. Something else is strange about it. Not only are official witnesses left unmentioned but in their place a couple of the Cardinal's servants have been brought in, who certainly were not qualified to understand or bear witness to Inquisition procedure. The location of the document in the file, as we shall now see, is no less out of order.

The dossier of the investigation of Galileo may look incomplete to those who expect to find there the story of the instigations, intrigues, pressures, and counterpressures that made up the famous affair. But it

and thus showed that no less praiseworthy than the greatness of his mind was his pious disposition." We need not doubt Oregius' word, since he was one of the three experts chosen in 1633 to decide about the *Dialogue* who found it damnable.

3. See fol. 398 of the Acts, where Galileo in 1632 acknowledges receipt of the summons to come to Rome (cf. p. 269) with a declaration written in his hand and signed. This is authenticated by five ecclesiastics of the Inquisition; then the whole is notarized by the Chancellor of the Holy Office in Florence. Even this was a substitute for a full-dress injunction, as we shall see. The attempts at getting an injunction served in due form in the trial of Vergerio in 1545–47, in the face of a defendant who refused to accept it, gave rise to all sorts of ludicrous incidents and substitute procedures. In the case of an interrogation the notary and witnesses did not have to sign, but the document had to be authenticated by the principal himself in due form: "Io N. N. ho deposto come sopra."

is not. It is simply the legal file of the material that had to go into the making of a legal decision, and as such it is fairly complete. It is the report of investigations carried out and measures taken by regular authorities. The pagination, at least the first one, was demonstrably carried out quite early, at the same time as the documents came in, and it is continuous. Hence we know that nothing is missing.[4]

The way it is built up is also quite definite and natural. Every single legal act, or official letter, was written (or started) on the first verso of a new double sheet and then incorporated and stitched into the file according to date. This, of course, left a large number of blank second pages in the context. These, too, are numbered. Some of them were used for administrative comment, forwarding notes and follow-up instructions, all in the proper time order. But in this as in any other administration of the times, there is no single letter, report, legal act, or certified copy which does not start on the first page of a new sheet. That is, with one apparent exception: the Bellarmine injunction. This most essential piece is written on space that was only accidentally available, being provided by the back pages of two other documents. Its place as well as its form emphasizes that it is only a minute.[5]

Thus, the text we have is not, and does not purport to be, an original

4. Or, rather, very little is missing, and that unconcealedly. Thus, two contiguous folios, belonging to the same double sheet, have been neatly cut out, before the first pagination, but leaving large margins to remind us of their existence. They come right after Lorini's falsified copy of the *Letter to Castelli* (fol. 346). There is another half-sheet, the first half, cut out in the same manner, to face p. 376, which contains the *propositio censuranda*. The same with pp. 431, 455, and 495.

5. These pages (fols. 378^v and 379^r), facing each other, are the verso of the blank second page of the Qualifiers' report (fol. 377) and the blank recto of what is the second half of p. 357, which belongs to Caccini's deposition. This is the way other transcriptions are set down too; cf. those referring also to papal commands, 352^v, and the one on an unnumbered sheet following 534. The procedure followed is quite regular as far as the first part is concerned (the Pope's order to Bellarmine on the twenty-fifth), for the original of that was supposed to be in the *Decreta* and here only reproduced for information. But then it slips on with deceptive casualness into the second part, dated February 26, which is the injunction itself and should have been preserved in the original.

but a mere transcription of relevant material, unsigned like all the similar ones.[6] But, then—where is the original? It clearly belongs at this place, on a separate sheet; it should be here, like all the other originals, but it is not in the file and never has been, as the continuous pagination proves. The only evidence that something happened that day is not a legal document, whether genuine or not; it is an administrative minute. It is strange that so many acute historians should have overlooked this as a starting point for their inferences. Did they suppose that the Inquisition file had been lugged around to Bellarmine's residence like a register in order to write the protocol on its back pages? The file never went out of the office; protocols made out somewhere else were incorporated into it.

That the original should have existed there is no doubt, for Bellarmine's instructions were explicit, and it was to be signed by the notary and countersigned by the recording secretary of the Holy Office and eventually by Galileo, too.[7] But that document was suppressed before reaching the file, or maybe even before being written, and the transcription substituted which purported only to be a copy. It purported that, too, with becoming modesty. The scribe remained able to state in confession or under oath that he had never falsified a document but

6. It does not even pretend to be an exact copy but only a paraphrase, as seen from the unusual abbreviations "said opinion" and also "said Galileo," which refer directly to the Congregation decree quoted immediately above but which would be out of place in an independent protocol.

7. This is not to say that all commands of the Inquisition had to be acknowledged. There are plenty of examples to the contrary. But they are on immediate matters (e.g., not to leave town until further orders). Even so, they are countersigned by qualified officials. When the Inquisitor gave them away from his headquarters, he was accompanied by his assistants as witnesses. But here, if the higher instructions were followed, we have an injunction on matters of intention to be given only in case of resistance. Hence we expect to find: "Io G. G. ho ricevuto precetto come sopra e prometto di obbedire." To say that the acknowledgment was not necessary is to say that the injunction was served without the demurring which motivated it, and then it would become a grave irregularity, to be challenged on these grounds alone.

had written down a minute that was judicially meaningless, since it lacked all the signatures.[8]

Even so, the good Father who did the job with such prudence had overreached himself. Following routine dutifully, he had first transcribed the text of the papal decree of the twenty-fifth; but had he known that the original of the decree was to be lost, as it is, to future historians, he would have cut off his hand rather than preserve the text in this place, where it was not strictly needed; for nothing can hide now the glaring contradiction between the orders and their purported execution.

If Galileo did not, explicitly, resist, there was no legitimate ground for the absolute personal prohibition of the Commissary to teach and discuss "in any manner," which goes beyond the wording of the decree and is of the type reserved for persons whose intentions were vehemently suspect. (In this case, submission became technically an abjuration.) The decree, as made out for all good believers, formally allowed the discussion of Copernicanism as a mathematical hypothesis, since Copernicus was only to be "corrected"; it forbade simply its presentation as a philosophical truth. It mentioned Galileo not at all, and great pains had been taken to keep him out of any injurious implication.

This is how Galileo himself understood it, for, two months later, he decided to counteract just such rumors as that he had been faced by the Inquisitor. Sagredo, among others, had been writing from Venice: "Those friends of ours confederated with Messer Rocco Berlinzone have done a foul job on you, spreading the rumor that you had been

8. We have said earlier, and we must emphasize it here, that the first Catholic historian, to our knowledge, to have found that there is something strange about the document is Professor Reusch. He remarks that there is no regular record at all of an injunction. What was taken for it, he adds, is a "Registratur," i.e., a note made by the notary of the Inquisition and incorporated in the Acts, as if referring to a document that is not there. Sherwood Taylor, a Catholic historian also, accepts this definition.

called to account by the Inquisition and had to go around like a whipped dog. I believe those thieves do their work against us in many parts, but God will confound their evil counsels." [9] Hence, to safeguard his personal honor, Galileo requested of Bellarmine a certificate of the proceedings and promptly received it in the following form:

We, Roberto Cardinal Bellarmino, having heard that it is calumniously reported that Signor Galileo Galilei has in our hand abjured and has also been punished with salutary penance, and being requested to state the truth as to this, declare that the said Signor Galileo has not abjured, either in our hand, or the hand of any other person here in Rome, or anywhere else, so far as we know, any opinion or doctrine held by him; neither has any salutary penance been imposed on him; but that only the declaration made by the Holy Father and published by the Sacred Congregation of the Index has been notified to him, wherein it is set forth that the doctrine attributed to Copernicus, that the Earth moves around the Sun and that the Sun is stationary in the center of the world and does not move from east to west, is contrary to the Holy Scriptures and therefore cannot be defended or held. In witness whereof we have written and subscribed these presents with our hand this twenty-sixth day of May, 1616.[10]

There is certainly no mention here of any injunction; in fact, what would have followed on it (i.e., an apology or retraction) is formally denied.

9. Of what was currently said we have also a document in a letter from Naples of Matteo Caccini (June 11): "The Congregation of the Index published a decree against the opinion of Galileo, after a consultation had taken place in the Congregation of the Holy Office in the presence of the Pope, and in this meeting Sig. Galilei made his abjuration." This misleadingly precise account is part of a letter relaying direct news from Rome; we know his contacts were excellent ("My very dear friend the Secretary of the Holy Office," he says elsewhere). Thus, it is not an idle rumor but a strongly accredited indiscretion coming straight from Dominican or allied circles. It caused Matteo Caccini to withdraw from Galileo as from a marked man, and quite a number of people to do the same.

10. The original draft of this certificate has been found in the Bellarmine file of the Secret Archive and published by Favaro (Ed. Naz., XIX, 348). It shows that the Cardinal had written originally in the middle line "but that" (*sì bene che*) and then, realizing this might not be explicit enough, had erased it and replaced it with "but that only" (*ma solo che*).

Historians *ex parte* have maintained that this is the merciful way of the Church: she wanted to protect Galileo from any public slur, out of respect for him and for the Grand Duke, and therefore released only an honorable certificate; but she knew very well he was a dangerous and obstinate character and tried to keep him on the straight path by a secret injunction. This sounds reasonable enough, and knowledgeable, and experienced. It impressed even historians from the other side, like Th. Henri Martin, so much that they forgot to ask for the exact context of the injunction. But in 1870 out came another piece of evidence, not from the yet undisclosed dossier, but from the collection of papal decrees, which had been searched by Gherardi during the few hectic weeks of the Roman Republic of 1849, when, the Pope having fled, the archives became suddenly, if too briefly, open to inspection.

This is what Gherardi discovered among the *Decreta* of the Congregation of the Holy Office:

The Lord Cardinal Bellarmine having reported that Galileo Galilei, mathematician, had in terms of the order of the Holy Congregation been admonished to abandon [*deserendam* (*disserendam,* "discuss," was the word originally written)] the opinion he has hitherto held, that the Sun is the center of the spheres and immovable and that the Earth moves, and had acquiesced therein; and the decree of the Congregation of the Index having been presented, prohibiting and suspending, respectively, the writings of Nicolaus Copernicus, of Diego de Zuñiga *On Job,* and of Paolo Antonio Foscarini, Carmelite friar—His Holiness ordered the edict of prohibition and suspension, respectively, to be published by the Master of the Palace.

This is the context. It is a document for the authorities only, a regular report on business transacted. It corresponds exactly to the instructions of February 25. Those instructions had envisaged three successive steps to be taken in the three several cases: acquiescence, objection, or obstinacy on the part of Galileo. The steps were: admonition, injunction, and prison. The report now says that admonition was met with acquiescence and goes on to other matters. If there had been an injunction, it would contain at least a mention of it. Otherwise, there should be attached a separate report by the Commissary-General.

But there is none. On the strength of this one report, the authorities could have no idea that an injunction ever was needed or had been served; and, indeed, as we shall see later, for several years, they apparently did not have the slightest idea.[11]

Nor did Galileo himself seem to be aware of it, judging from this. He would not have dared to ask Bellarmine for a certificate if he had not expected that certificate to come out absolutely favorable. We have his request, which has been found among Bellarmine's papers. It is simple and straightforward and does not demand or suggest any leniency. In his first letter to his secretary of state, a few days after the decree, he notes with satisfaction that his person has been left out of it, that Copernicanism has not been condemned as heretical but only interpretations of it, and that Copernicus has been suspended only for correction. He says (Bellarmine or Cardinal Caetani must have told him) that the corrections will cover only ten lines of the Introduction (about the agreement with Scripture) "and here and there a word, as where Copernicus calls the Earth a star." He adds: "I have, as will be seen from the nature of the case, no involvement in the matter and should not have troubled myself about it had not my enemies drawn me into it."

This is simple and explicit. It corresponds to the letter of February 6. He as learned that he must write no more theological letters; but then he would not have written them if he had not been dragged into

11. A frequent way of burying the issue is to say, or imply, that laymen have raised much ado about some ordinary short cuts in procedure and that Galileo, himself a layman, may not have understood very well what was taking place. But the judge who wrote the sentence in 1633 was certainly no layman, and we shall see him walking on eggs in the matter of that injunction. In fact, the irregularity would appear more shocking to the trained eye than it would to us. Nor did the Vatican authorities of the nineteenth century feel more comfortable about it, for (notwithstanding the promise they had given the French government when the abducted archives were brought back from Paris) they released only a few selected documents, woven into an ingenious apologia by Monsignor Marini, in 1850; and it was only much later that they decided there was more to be gained from publication than from concealment. Hence they encouraged M. de l'Epinois to publish an integral reproduction in 1877.

it; and now that the thing is decided, he does not have to pursue the matter further. His personal philosophical endeavor, which he always kept in the background, has now to be abandoned. For the rest, he holds himself free, like anyone, to discuss heliocentrism as a mathematical hypothesis and is awaiting the new edition of Copernicus as an approved textbook. He then goes on: "It may be seen from my writings and my doings here in what spirit I have always acted, and shall always continue to act, so as to shut the mouth of malice; my conduct in this business has been such that no saint could have shown more reverence for the Church or greater zeal."

This may have been said largely to appease the Grand Duke; it may be whistling in the dark; but it is certainly not the language of a man terrified by the Inquisition, told that he is under special surveillance, and enjoined never to discuss or mention the system in any way. It corresponds exactly to what the ambassador learned confidentially and in covert language from the authorities. The feeling of pride is, in fact, more genuine than one might suspect, for Galileo knew by then that his *Letter to the Grand Duchess* had been a strong, if unacknowledged, factor in the last-minute compromise.[12] Nor do his later acts belie this attitude in the least.

To this cool attitude of the scientist there come also official sanctions. Cardinal del Monte wrote an explicit letter of indorsement.[13] The Pope received Galileo on March 11 and gave him an audience which lasted three-quarters of an hour. As Galileo mentioned the persecution of his enemies, the Pope assured him that he need not fear, for he was held in such esteem by himself and the whole Congregation that

12. This we know from the Buonamici diary (see p. 313 below).
13. It should have been the Cardinal's concern, as a relative and as a Florentine, to warn the Grand Duke unofficially that, however decorous the proceedings, Galileo had not come out very well and should *not* be encouraged and shown too much favor. He wrote instead: "I can assure your Highness that Galileo has come out of this in excellent position . . . and I wanted you to know it, for it is to be expected that his enemies will not desist from their machinations, as they have not reached their intentions in this way." The same tone is in Cesi's letter: "Let them bark in vain."

they would not listen to these calumnies. He also repeatedly expressed his readiness to show his favor with deeds.

Now Bellarmine was, in his own way, a saintly and benevolent scholar. He was also the man who could retain a personal friendship with Sarpi even across the havoc of war and anathema and warn him of the danger to his life. But Paul V Borghese, according to all contemporary reports, was an authoritarian martinet, a literal, rigid mind, and a man "so averse to anything intellectual," as Guicciardini says, "that everyone has to play dense and ignorant to be in his favor." Such a Pope would not have shown signal benevolence to a suspect under inquisitorial reprimand, not even to please the Grand Duke This means that Bellarmine had stated exactly what the report of March 3 says, and no more. We would have to imagine, although it would seem rather fantastic, that Bellarmine and Father Segizi had arranged to keep the injunction a secret from the Pontiff himself.

We have thus the gravest reasons to doubt the authenticity of the minute of February 26, and this is a point to be established toward later developments. As for Galileo, to all appearances he never doubted his position then or later. As he stood, he felt unhappy but clear. His fighting temper had not left him. "He is of a fixed humor," writes Guicciardini with alarm on May 13, "to tackle the friars head on [di scaponire i frati] and to fight where he cannot but lose. Sooner or later you will hear that he has fallen over some unsuspected precipice. I hope that the season, at least, will drive him from hence."

But Galileo stayed on. He would not have it look as though he had been driven away by base gossip and intrigue. He even indulged in a little matchmaking between Prince Cesi and Isabella, the sister of his late friend, Filippo Salviati (". . . the splendor of such names and, on the side of the Prince, a grave wisdom surpassed only by a truly angelical virtue . . ."). The Grand Duke reassured him of support and, over the ambassador's protests, sent him funds. But at last the secretary of state wrote him: "Your Honor, who has had to deal with monkish persecutions, knows what is the taste of them, and their Highnesses fear that a further stay in Rome might bring you into trouble.

You have got out of this honorably; you can let the sleeping dog lie and return here. There are rumors going around that we do not like, and the monks are all-powerful; and I who am your friend and servant ought to warn you."

This was an order. Galileo left Rome on June 30, still unenlightened and unreconstructed. "Of all hatreds," he wrote, "there is none greater than that of ignorance against knowledge."

II

Many things could be said in extenuation of the mistake of the authorities which have been rarely said, while most of the defensive position takes its stand on legal quibbling. One may well say—we have stated it ourselves in the opening chapters—that this was a vast conflict of world views of whose implications the principals themselves could not be fully aware.

The opposing reasons were of majestic dimensions, stemming from the night of ages; the new developments both compelling and dangerous; the consequences still not to be grasped by us who live three centuries later. Hence an ecumenic council would appear as the proper instance before which to present the issue, either for decision or for postponement of decision. Of this, Galileo was aware. He could not suggest it under penalty of excommunication, but we know that he often said or implied as much in private. It is very true that the world situation, and the Church's own Counter-Reformation policy, made the idea of a council look exceedingly implausible. We do not presume to pass judgment on the subject. We are simply saying that, if a decision had to be taken, a council was in order. To deal with the question on an administrative level was not only an arbitrary procedure; it was an inexcusable mistake, which is the necessary premise to the graver mistake of the trial sixteen years later. Technically, it was not the eleven Qualifiers who can be accused of being wrong (they could hardly have answered anything else under the circumstances, as we shall explain later); it was the authority who put the question up to them. Yet, even so, granting the lines of procedure set down by the immovable machinery of the times, it should be said withal that a spark of understanding and leadership, the informal intervention of a higher mind inside the hierarchy, might well have saved the situation.

The drama is really more poignant in this first phase, when all is still fluid, than in the later crisis, when positions had hardened and the juridical machinery had taken over.

All was still possible in that fatal year of 1616, the year that saw the deaths of Shakespeare and Cervantes and spelled the end of the Renaissance. What Galileo was begging for was pitifully small: that the authorities should keep judgment suspended for another generation— for another few years at least. He was made to look as though the decision were the fault of his own nagging indiscretion. He was asking that the Word of God be not taken in vain, and he was maneuvered and driven and cornered, as if he were Satan himself, into tangling with Scripture to his own undoing and to that of his cause. The man who has been so persistently (and sometimes rightly) accused of vanity and conceit plays a role in this phase which appears to justify fully his words to the Grand Duke: "No saint could have shown more reverence for the Church or greater zeal."

For he certainly had come in simplicity of heart and as a true son of the Church, as the Pope could not deny. He had come not to make a scandal but to avoid it; not to raise a danger but to make one plain; not to oppose a truth but to offer it. What was taken to be his pride of mind was the urgent warning that such things would come to pass as would make pride of mind inevitable. Like the prophets of old, he had spoken of a shadow over the land, and the priests had cast him out.

He was pleading for an understanding from the highest minds, and what he met with was invincible ignorance, gilded with flattery for his "inimitable conceits"; he was begging for a hearing, and what he got was Caccini.

III

Because, if we must leave the philosophy of history and go back to facts, here are the cold facts as shown in the 1616 sentence itself. The eleven Qualifiers of the Holy Office had been requested to give a ruling on the following opinions:

I. The Sun is the center of world and hence immovable of local motion.

II. The Earth is not the center of the world, nor immovable, but moves according to the whole of itself, also with a diurnal motion.

These last words sound obscure, to say the least. They are in Italian, which caused some historians like Domenico Berti and Karl von Gebler to believe carelessly that they were taken out of the *Solar Letters*. Of course they are not. No Copernican would express himself thus.[14] Galileo might have said, with the reflexive as was done in his time (it occurs once or twice in the *Dialogue*), that the Earth moves *in* itself of a daily motion, not *according* to itself. We would have no clues to these phrases if we did not have from the secret archives the original Italian which is in Caccini's denunciation: "La terra secondo sè tutta si move, etiam di moto diurno." It makes no sense in any language, but there it stands. It is a decomposition into pseudo-Thomistic double talk (*secundum se*) of the simple statement: "The Earth turns around itself in a day"—which is, incidentally, how Aristotle himself refers to the theory.[15] But it is obviously a garbled

14. The origin of this mistake is the summary from an unknown hand that precedes the Acts in the official file and was apparently prepared as a brief for the meeting of the Congregation of June 16, 1633, that was to take a decision about the trial. It is said there actually: "having seen the two propositions from the book on the *Solar Spots,* etc." The author of the summary had been led astray by the contiguity in the file of two different documents. One of them, as we have seen (fol. 375ᵛ), was an instruction to look up the *Letters on the Solar Spots*. It follows immediately Attavanti's deposition. The next one (fol. 376ʳ) is the circular of convocation about the *propositio censuranda,* as it was sent out to the RR. PP. DD. Theologis on February 19, assigning them for the fourteenth hour ½ of Tuesday, February 23. The slip is natural in one who hastily summarizes an incomplete collection. If the file had been kept properly, the mistake would not have occurred. What is missing between the two items are the minutes of the Congregation of March 18, which started the whole proceedings. But of this important document no copy has been found anywhere.

15. Cf. *De coelo* 293 *b* 30, 296 *a* 26–29, *b* 2–3.

version of the way Colombe had described it to Caccini as he tried to translate Copernicus into "philosophically sound" language.[16] The *et etiam* left over allows us to reconstruct the original wording: "The Earth moves as a whole around the Sun, *et etiam secundum se* of a daily motion." As for Caccini, a low-comedy character and a turbulent ignoramus, he cared less about meaning than about the man in the moon. He simply repeated the words, mixing them up, as he mixed up many other things of a less innocent nature.

The eleven consultants of the Congregation, among whom we are told were several deeply versed in the natural sciences,[17] met on February 23. They had been convoked, as appears from the act of February 25, "concerning the propositions of Galileo." The *Letters on the Solar Spots* had been procured. They had available, at their wish, the book of Copernicus to which the propositions implicitly referred; they had Foscarini's pamphlet; they had, informally submitted, the memoranda

---

16. Cf. Colombe's *Discorso:* "se noi consideriamo ciascun cielo secondo sè tutto," etc. At another point Colombe ridicules the theory "which compels the Earth to go around the center according to accident and never to the center according to itself."

17. Hartmann Grisar, *Galileistudien*, p. 38. The names of these distinguished experts (some of them had indeed attained considerable fame in the theological controversies of previous years) are signed as follows on the protocol:

Petrus Lombardus, Archiepiscopus Armacanus.
Fr. Hyacintus Petronius, Sacri Apostolici Palatii Magister.
Fr. Raphael Riphoz, Theologiae Magister et Vicarius generalis ordinis Praedicatorum.
Fr. Michael Angelus Seg.[s], Sacrae Theologiae Magister et Com.[s] S.[ti] Officii.
Fr. Hieronimus de Casalimaiori, Consultor S.[ti] Officii.
Fr. Thomas de Lemos.
Fr. Gregorius Nunnius Coronel.
Benedictus Jus.[nus], Societatis Iesu.
D. Raphael Rastellius, Clericus Regularis, Doctor theologus.
D. Michael a Neapoli, ex Congregatione Cassinensi.
Fr. Iacobus Tintus, socius R.[mi] Patris Commissarii S. Officii.

"Seg." stands for Segizi, the Commissary-General of the Inquisition; "Jus." for Giustiniani, the only Jesuit on the committee, which contained a majority of Dominicans, as was the custom in matters of theology.

and briefs that Galileo had forwarded to their superiors; they had his letters to Castelli and Dini; they had at their beck and call Father Grienberger at the Collegio Romano, who was their consulting astronomer. To all this they gave no thought, nor, actually, were they supposed to. They probably had not even been informed about the issue. They looked up their schoolbooks, compared Caccini's denunciation with the texts, and came back with the answer. They did not trouble to remove the illiterate *etiam* or to try to restore a meaning.[18] To them, as to their superiors, this was something that did not sound well because it spoke of the Earth moving and the Sun standing still, and it had to be condemned as philosophically foolish and absurd.

The ship of state had sailed past the issue. It was only the backwash which hit Copernicus, causing him to be suspended *donec corrigeretur*. Foscarini, who had been an acceptable author a year earlier, was now wholly forbidden, because such discussions "gave occasion to scandal" or, as we would say today, were bad for public relations. As for Galileo, he was left untouched, his *Letters* uncensored, and his theological epistles never mentioned, although Caccini's denunciation had been specifically aimed at him and the procedure as well. The protection had worked. But the Copernican movement had been stopped dead in its tracks, with what consequences for Italian culture the next hundred years would show.

There is a logic to it all, even a considerate logic. The state hath its own reasons that reason knoweth not. Galileo's ideas and his person had been carefully left out of the issue, as we noticed above. The question submitted to the consultants was one of public order: Certain opinions are circulating, as related by an informer, and are stirring

18. That the meaning is inscrutable is comically granted by Father Olivieri (see n. 6, p. 129). They even went worse than their superiors on one point. The proposition submitted had been: the Sun is in the center and *hence* immovable; they erased the *hence* and replaced it with *wholly,* as if to give formal assurance that they were totally unacquainted with the content of Galileo's discoveries, theories, and theological letters, in which the rotation of the Sun was given outstanding significance.

a scandal. A ruling is requested, so that the correct directives may be imparted to the thought police. Only the consequences of the theories mattered on the level of public relations; that is why the only material submitted is a third-hand denunciation by an informer. The incipient scandal had to be dealt with on its own level.

As it happened, the scandal had been created by the informer himself. Deprived of guidance, the police apparatus had become the tool of its own *agents provocateurs*.

This fatal short circuit between the judiciary and the executive seems to be a constant feature of the streamlined state—or of the state which feels itself compelled to go pragmatic under the stress of emergency. The case is not unknown in our time, and even in free countries, of a politician who serves at one and the same time as disturber of the peace, prosecuting attorney, judge, jury, and detective agency. The serious trouble begins when the higher authorities find themselves in his tow.

In the Rome of 1616 the legislative decisions had come from the Council of Trent: "Petulant minds must be restrained from interpreting Scripture against the authority of tradition in matters that pertain to faith and morals." This was aimed essentially at the fundamentalist reformers who were forever protesting the word of Scripture against the Roman authorities. The book of Copernicus had come out by then, and yet no specific clause is directed against that kind of interpretation. (It must be admitted that the prelates of the Council, lawyers, literati, preachers, and executives all, who had found it difficult even to follow the arguments of their own Scholastic consultants, had never thought that "mathematics" might give them trouble.)

Thus the judiciary might well have felt some doubts. It was a "conciliar affair," as Descartes was to write with cold Gallican sense, to reconsider the whole issue. In his anomalous position as chief theologian as well as chief executive, Bellarmine made up his mind that it was a mere matter of "petulance." He had the question framed, on behalf of the General Congregation, leaving out the main issue. This question he submitted on February 19 to the Qualifiers, and he received in answer, on February 24, the echo of his own words. On the twenty-fifth, as chief executive, he drew up the decree of the General Congregation, had it passed on to the Congregation of the Index, and intrusted its execution to the Commissary of the Inquisition.

The historic responsibility, then, falls on Bellarmine alone. He was a great Jesuit, tempered in thought, dedicated mind and soul to the welfare of the Church. If his intellect had been able to grasp the issue, there is no doubt that he would have put it on the agenda of a future Council, and the new science would have had a chance to enter the circle of orthodoxy. All that was really needed in the meantime was a damper on theological excursions, and that would have been the part of discretion. But fear and suspicion were much closer to the heart of the matter, and, besides, Bellarmine did not even like to think of the next Council. He was of the anticonciliar persuasion. He felt that all had been settled and that what was needed henceforth was administrative resource. We are led back, then, to the incredible passiveness of Bellarmine's brothers in the Order, the mathematicians of the Collegio Romano, who apparently took their vow of obedience *perinde ac si cadaver* to dispense them from any intellectual responsibility, perhaps also of intellect *tout court,* according to the instructions of their General, Acquaviva; for of their personal good disposition toward Galileo there is no doubt. But they accepted the function of mere technicians of the transit instrument. Obedience and preoccupation with "scandal" had been bred into the bones of the Order, from Bellarmine down, to such an extent that the intellectual reflexes were dead.[19]

19. See Father Grienberger's remark quoted on p. 125. We shall return to this subject on p. 315. Monsignor Majocchi wrote in 1919: "The authorities simply gave Galileo a lesson in positivism." This is only too true. They virtually did—in the Comtian sense of the words. To stick to historical fact, however, it should be noted that in the arguments that Campanella had heard used against Galileo's theory, eleven of them, there is no mention at all of that which is brought up by modern Church historians, namely, that the theory was not sufficiently proved. As far as we know, only Father Grienberger used it to motivate his abstention.

The leader who fails in leadership has only himself to blame if he falls prey to a conspiracy of his subordinates. The explanations of Bellarmine's conduct in terms of scientific prudence and mature consideration turn out to be whitewash. Dini and Ciàmpoli had been mistaken in their trust; it was Caccini, the "subversive," in his minklike cunning, who had made the right bet. Ballarmine was semiconsciously frightened by a problem he had never faced: What if the Aristotelian substructure were to prove unreliable? The problem went beyond his training and his mental capacities. He decided it was no problem at all and fell back on the police for an estimate of the situation. They gave him Caccini's stuff, under the name of Galileo's propositions; it went in, was processed, qualified, came out—still with the same label—was condemned, stamped, and expedited by the General Congregation. No one had ever bothered to look at it.

VII *The Years of Silence*

I

Eight years followed in which "life went on." The old commonplace is still apt to describe an activity which has lost its clear goal while the nature of the protagonist remains unchanged. The great work in progress had been sidetracked, perhaps forever; the road was blocked ahead. "Those three most powerful operators," as he wrote, "ignorance, malice, and impiety," had won the day. But, after the first weeks of disgust and dejection, Galileo was again in harness.

There was frequent illness in those years, a painful rheumatic condition, with complications, which had plagued him recurrently. There was much thinking also on the foundations of mechanics and on profound infinitesimal questions, which carried his attention far afield to reaches he had never considered before. There were also the consolations of country life in his villa of Bellosguardo, overlooking Florence and the sweep of the Arno: the care of the olive crop and the cutting and grafting of vines, at which Galileo was enormously proud of being a renowned expert. And there was the pleasant company of his literary friends.

"His conversation," says Viviani, although he knew him only in his last years, "was full of wit and conceits, rich in grave wisdom and penerating sentences. His subjects were not only the exact and speculative sciences but also music, letters, and poetry. He had a wonderfully retentive memory and knew most of Virgil, Ovid, Horace, and Seneca; among the Tuscans, Petrarch almost whole, the rhymes of Berni, and all of the poem of Ariosto, who was his favorite author."

There was also, by now, Sister Maria Celeste, turned seventeen, who was going to become a major presence in the old man's life. In her passionate love for her father, the girl was able to draw from his visits and his letters and from the small world of her rustic convent in Arcetri the subjects for a correspondence of such bubbling freshness and grace as might have made her, had she lived under different conditions, an Italian Sévigné.[1]

In her penurious and menial surroundings Suor Maria Celeste had created an intense life all of her own.

"I cannot rest any longer without news," she writes, "both for the infinite love I bear you, and also for fear lest this sudden cold, which in general disagrees so much with you, should have caused a return of your usual pains and other complaints. I therefore send the man who takes this letter purposely to hear how you are, and also when you expect to set out on your journey. I have been extremely busy at the dinner-napkins. They are nearly finished, but now I come to putting on the fringe, I find that of the sort I send as a pattern, a piece is wanting for two dinner-napkins: that will be four ells. I should be glad if you could let me have it immediately, so that I may send you the napkins before you go; as it was for this that I have been making such haste to get them finished.

"As I have no cell to sleep in of my own, Sister Diamanta kindly allows me to share hers, depriving herself of the company of her own sister for my sake. But the room is so bitterly cold, that with my head

---

1. Some of it has been collected in an anonymous English translation (by Mary Allen Olney): *The Private Life of Galileo through the Letters of Sister Maria Celeste* (London, 1870). But much of the quality of the original is bound to be lost in any translation.

in the state in which it is at present, I do not know how I shall remain, unless you can help me by lending me a set of those white bed-hangings which you will not want now. I should be glad to know if you could do me this service. Moreover, I beg you to be so kind as to send me that book of yours which has just been published, so that I may read it, for I have a great desire to see it.

"These few cakes I send are some I made a few days ago, intending to give them to you when you came to bid us adieu. As your departure is not so near as we feared, I send them lest they should get dry. Sister Arcangela is still under medical treatment, and is much tried by the remedies. I am not well myself, but being so accustomed to ill health, I do not make much of it, seeing, too, that it is the Lord's will to send me continually some such little trial as this. I thank Him for everything, and pray that He will give you the highest and best felicity.

"P.S. You can send us any collars that want getting up." [2]

To be nearer to her, Galileo eventually moved to the little villa in Arcetri which was to be his final dwelling; and promptly she started reweaving around him the threads of his broken family life. The loss of the father's letters is an irreparable literary loss, for he told her everything, but even through the mirrored reflection in her writing we know more about his life in that period than about any other. "I keep and put aside all the letters that Your Honour writes me every day, and with much delight read and re-read them, so I leave it to you to judge whether I should not like to read also those that are written to you by such virtuous and loving persons."

Her own letters give us back the ways and sounds of Tuscan country life as scarcely any others. We see her instructing the maid, taking care of the house and the stable, keeping check on the farm. She prepares delicate dishes and sends them up to him by special courier; she makes for him preserves, sweets, canel water and rosmarine; mends his linen; picks for him the last December rose she found in a

2. Sister Maria Celeste to Galileo, November 21, 1623 (*ibid.*).

corner of her garden. "Spending my time in the service of Your Honour," she writes, "I do enjoy immensely, and I hardly notice the limitations of a nun's life, except when I hear that Your Honour is sick, for then I wish I could come and live in the house." From her we learn of his visits, of his gifts and attentions, of the time he glazed the windows of her cell with his own hands, so that she and her friends could have some daylight to work by in the winter months. "Truly this is work more befitting a carpenter than a philosopher." She comes back to ask him more serious favors, for what she resents deeply in the convent is not their poverty but the neglect of the authorities in providing spiritual assistance to such uncertain or forced vocations as she sees around her, and she asks her father to use his influence at Court in order that they may be given some better confessors than those they have, "more used to hunting hares than to caring for souls."

The epistolary activity of Galileo in those years was immense, for he kept in constant touch with his disciples, whose fame was growing, and he was never weary of assisting their thought in a vast range of subjects. Young Father Cavalieri had taken up from him the study of infinitesimals, from which was to come his *Geometry of Indivisibles*. As for Castelli, he had published his pioneer treatise on *The Motion of Water* and had been appointed chief consultant for hydraulic projects. But consulting engineers did not command high fees then. Pushed from pillar to post, ever faithful, ever cheerful, he would write from Rome: "I am eating cucumbers as the day is long, since my purse is not enough for melons, drink cold wine like a millrace, pass the dog days as I can, and the Masters preserve me in their favor." Another time he wrote: "This project of Lake Trasimeno is getting bigger as time goes on. I am in water up to my chin, but we'll let it stay there, *'exclusive,'* and the wine inside, *'inclusive.'* "

A project Galileo had long postponed offered a merciful opportunity for dull time-consuming labor. It was that of working out the tables of the satellites of Jupiter and of using them as a celestial chronometer for the measurement of longitude, which entailed much observation, much repetitive computation, and an interminable exchange of letters through embassies with the representatives of Spanish sea power, who had suddenly evinced interest in this possible new aid to navigation.

Through all this he was collecting himself. As the diver descending into the dark depths feels his strength rise from the burning of his oxygen under pressure, so the scientist's mind, as it receded into isolation, burned brighter to itself. The past compromises and loose adjustments of thought discarded, Galileo seems to be facing more decisively the full implications of his theory.

It is an inhuman wrench for the mind to tear itself loose from the instinctive world of the senses around us, so "full of a number of things," peopled with familiar substances which reassuringly go about subsisting in their own several ways as if they knew how—and to uncover instead everywhere the mysterious realization of abstract laws; to conceive of mathematical function determining each point of being in a dizzying tension between the infinite and the infinitesimal, where the lonely intellect has to feel its way with new instruments of rigorous analysis. It implies a dedication; a new feeling not only of nature but also of the divine. When the time for expression comes again, the quiet prose of the physicist will rise of itself to compelling heights, spark and crackle with contained metaphysical power. But, for many years yet, silence was in order.

Slowly and painfully, Galileo was learning to adjust to a world of absurdity, to create for himself a language of ambiguous and unseizable irony, to believe what he did not believe while thinking what he thought. "I wear a mask, but of necessity," as Sarpi had written ten years before, "because without it no one can live in Italy." Sarpi had still been able to defend Venetian sovereignty against the Curia and had been knifed for his pains in a dark alley in Venice. "I recognize the stylus of the Holy Office," he had said with a wry pun and had taken to moving about only in a gondola, well escorted. Galileo, too, now wore a mask, and it was not that of worldly expediency. It was that of the man who has to combine an ingrained respect for a holy and legitimate institution with disrespect for its judgment and with bitter sorrow for the consequnces of its action. He knew—none better than he

—the damage that had been wrought by the decree of 1616. The slow growth of public interest in astronomy, which, following the era of geographic discoveries, had spread in the preceding generation from high to low, tying up with the new idea the Italians had been forming of the importance of natural science, had just reached the point where it was ready to burst into flower. The heliocentric theory, under its ancient name of Pythagorean philosophy, had become common cultural property and common interest, an uncertain but exciting expectation voiced from many sides; it was awaiting the very type of richly endowed leader that Galileo happened to be in order to develop into a great scientific movement. The decree of the Inquisition had put a stop to all that. The "Galileist" brush fire had died out; people had turned quietly to other more conventional interests. The old man felt like a survivor, surrounded by useless and sterile respect.

He had not lost the last hope, however. Prohibitions come and go, and he knew this one to be such a departure from established practice and common sense that it could not long survive.

Prohibition in itself was an old and reasonable thing. It was the guardian of dogma. It applied to actions, to a personal "choice" on tenets (*hairesis*), and, beyond those, to instrumental arguments, to matters of policy—in brief, to all expressions which covered an intention. Supposing that Father Olivieri had been ordered to abandon the quibbles that we have painfully reproduced on page 121, he could not have protested even in his conscience. He had concocted a sophistry; it had been found no good as an instrument; let him invent another.

There was here a semantic difficulty between the old and the new. To men of the old persuasion, like Galileo, the new-fangled Jesuit word of "blind obedience" meant nothing that was orthodox, and the feeling was shared by many in the regular and secular clergy. The idea of transferring obedience to the intellectual field was quite new indeed; for it was understood that dogma was of faith, first and last, and that otherwise the intellect was bound by its own laws. Who had ever heard that one's mind, created free, must submit itself passively to the decisions of a committee of incompetents? "These," wrote Galileo later, and he must have said it many times among friends in these years, "these are the innovations which are bound to lead to the ruin of states and to the subversion of commonwealths."

Out of this certainty grew his invincible hope. Two years had not elapsed when Galileo was cautiously probing the ground. In 1618, having been requested by the Archduke Leopold of Austria for some work from his pen, he ventured to send him his most risky piece of writing (it was the memorandum he had prepared in 1616 for young Cardinal Orsini), accompanied by the following letter:

With this I send you a treatise on the causes of the tides which I wrote at the time when the theologians were thinking of prohibiting Copernicus' book and the doctrine enounced therein, which I then held to be true, until it pleased those gentlemen to prohibit the work and to declare the opinion to be false and contrary to Scripture. Now, knowing as I do that it behooves us to obey the decisions of the authorities and to believe them, since they are guided by a higher insight than any to which my humble mind can of itself attain, I consider this treatise which I send you to be merely a poetical conceit, or a dream, and desire that your Highness may take it as such, inasmuch as it is based on the double motion of the Earth and, indeed, contains one of the arguments which I brought in confirmation of it.

But even poets sometimes attach a value to one or other of their fantasies, and I likewise attach some value to this fancy of mine. . . . I have also let a few exalted personages have copies, in order that in case anyone not belonging to our Church should try to appropriate my curious fancy, as has happened to me with many of my discoveries, these personages, being above all suspicion, may be able to bear witness that it was I who first dreamed of this chimera. What I now send is but a fugitive performance; it was written in haste and in the expectation that the work of Copernicus would not be condemned as erroneous eighty years after its publication. . . . But a voice from heaven aroused me and dissolved all my confused and tangled fantasies in mist. May therefore your Highness graciously accept it, ill arranged as it is. And if divine mercy ever grants that I may be in a position to exert myself a little, your Highness may expect something more solid and real from me.

There is no mistaking the scornful irony in those words. The true meaning becomes explicit when we find again the same terms of "fantasy," "paradox," and "vain chimera" ten years later as a saving clause at the end of the *Dialogue,* but this time with the full impact of the Copernican proof behind them.

II

The skies themselves seemed not to leave the issue in peace, for soon the attention of the world was shaken by the comets of 1618, of which one has remained the most impressive in the memory of man. Coming, as it did, at the outset of the Thirty Years' War, it could appear only too justifiably a portent of God's wrath. Princes were frightened, the public was in a turmoil, and apocalyptic specialists computed anew the end of the world. Of the innumerable writings that it prompted, Pierre Bayle's *Pensées sur la comète* (which was really written about this one, although it was published on the occasion of the comet of 1680) is the only one that has survived. Much more modest, and indeed unimportant, was a discourse delivered in the Collegio Romano amid great concourse of public by a learned Jesuit, Father Horatio Grassi. But Galileo read it, and his temper began to rise. There is no misplaced gentleness in the marginal jottings on his copy. The expletives alone would make a vocabulary of good Tuscan abuse: *pezzo d'asinaccio, elefantissimo, bufolaccio, villan poltrone, balordone, barattiere, poveraccio, ingratissimo villano, ridicoloso, sfacciato, inurbano.* So these trained seals who had kept to their holes in time of crisis were now gloating about him and oraculating again. One had only to glance through Grassi's *Discourse* to realize that the good man did not even understand the working of the telescope while displaying its use so complacently. But, even before looking at the text, Galileo knew very well that the author had not come on stage amid applause to bring new ideas but simply to drive another nail, as he thought, in the coffin of Copernicanism, well assured that by this time the Man of Florence ("quello di Firenze," as they called him) was in no condition to answer back.

Moved by the helpless anger of his friend, Mario Guiducci, "consul" of the Florentine Academy, offered to write an answer himself.

Comets and new stars have always fascinated the mind which believes in a magic and miraculous order of things. It is the regularities, rather, that have been taken for granted, until the advent of scientific speculation. It seems natural enough for heaven to go round and for the Sun to rise every morning, but a comet in the skies becomes a portent of vast significance. Conversely, for the scientific mind as it had been at work since the Greeks, eternal harmony and periodicity are the true awesome portent of a higher design, and irregular events become a disturbing problem. The accepted explanation for the wise since Aristotle had been that comets are exhalations of earth vapors rising above the sphere of fire. This keeps their freakish behavior away from the harmony of the spheres. But Tycho by his measurements on the comet of 1577 had shown that they must be higher than the Moon and also that they have an orbit of some strange sort. Kepler, then, had thought he could show that the path was rectilinear. What Father Grassi was now suggesting was a compromise. He agreed that the comet was in heaven, but, following the Aristotelian distinction between earthly and heavenly matter, he insisted that its path must be circular.

As for Galileo, he found himself against almost everybody, for he held that comets are only optical effects born of earthly vapors. This was no doubt wrong, but there were serious reasons for his choice. In the matter of novae he had gone all out in favor of Tycho's and Kepler's findings, which placed the new stars in the firmament, for that was to him, as it was for Kepler, an excellent way of proving that the heavens were not fixed and unalterable. But new stars were obliging enough to stay put, as flares in the sky, whereas the comets had been shown by Tycho to have paths which were utterly aberrant from a Copernican point of view. Some were even retrograde. Newton would be able eventually to turn Halley's comet into the triumph of the new system. But Newton had not yet come; and Galileo, who had his own reasons to believe that circular paths were the only ones physically possible in outer space, thought it best to try to prove that the comets did not belong to heaven at all but were optical effects in the atmosphere. It came surely *ex parte*, but it still was a sensible effort in the manner of the Presocratics to extend physics to the heavens, and well worth a try. In fact, the connection that he inferred between comets' tails and the Sun's beams turned out to be substantially right. The real trouble with his position is that it broke the old alliance with Kepler, who was the better astronomer of the two, and brought Galileo the wrong kind of backing in astronomy.

Grassi's opinion, by contrast, may appear closer to the truth, but it was such only in appearance. It was a compromise position, and it was a purely political one. We have seen how Tycho's system had been pressed into the service of the Vatican as providing the most opportune deviation from the Copernican issue; what Grassi was doing was only mixing Tycho and Aristotle, half and half, to provide a more fashionable version of the same old brew. As for the scientific reasons, they remained so far behind that Grassi used the telescope, the means now made available for reaching new conclusions, in a way that made no sense. He assumed that telescopic magnification was in inverse ratio to distance and hence that he could prove the great distance of the comet by the small difference he found between the telescopic and the visual image.

Galileo was only too well aware of what Grassi was trying to do. But, as we follow his marginal notes, we see his anger gradually turning into a chuckle. These gentlemen apparently still labored under the impression that physical problems could be solved with a school exercise in rhetoric, adorned with the proper quotations. Well, he could ask them a few questions about their physics.

The *Discourse on the Comets* came out in June, 1619. It was signed by Guiducci, but there was no mistaking the hand behind it. Much applause and favorable comment greeted it in Rome, for the *Discourse* showed a Galileo disposed to carry on with his contributions to science while exercising his ingenuity on acceptable subjects. His old friend Cardinal Maffeo Barberini, as if to ask him to forget the old bitterness connected with the prohibition decree, sent him a Latin poem in his honor entitled "Adulatio perniciosa" ("Dangerous Adulation"). But Ciàmpoli wrote that the Jesuits "were much offended and were preparing to strike back." In fact, the year had not elapsed when Grassi came out with a Latin dissertation, *The Libra* ("Balance"), under the anagram "Lothario Sarsi Sigensano." Since he had not been attacked personally, he would not answer in person. But there was no misunderstanding his intention either. Guiducci, who had maintained a vertical rising path of the comet as born from earthy vapors, had admitted discreetly that "a further cause" might have to be found in order to explain the deflection toward the north. "Sarsi," after more than one slighting remark, comes to a halt before this admission:

What is this sudden fear in an open and not timid spirit which prevents him from uttering the word that he has in mind? I cannot guess it. Is this other motion which could explain everything and which he does not dare to discuss—is it of the comet or of something else? It cannot be the motion of the circles, since for Galileo there are no Ptolemaic circles. I fancy I hear a small voice whispering discreetly in my ear: the motion of the Earth. Get thee behind me thou evil word, offensive to truth and to pious ears! It was surely prudence to speak it with bated breath. For, if it were really thus, there would be nothing left of an opinion which can rest on no other ground except this false one. . . . But then certainly Galileo had no such idea, for I have never known him otherwise than pious and religious.

On reading these ugly provocations, Galileo must have wondered whether he had not been a fool to get himself involved in such quarrels. He might have known his motive, had he cared to ask himself. The long-pent-up bitterness had found a way out. But, if *they* were considering him as dead and buried already, he would show them. There was no decree that forbade showing up an ass. Besides, now, "Sarsi" had him on the spot. Even his most anxious friends admitted that he must step forward in person to cover Guiducci and to vindicate the honor of science. Cesi and Ciàmpoli advised the form of an open letter. Cesarini, who was intimate with the Jesuits, was willing to be the recipient. But Stelluti, another Lycean friend, wrote from Rome: "To take on the Fathers would mean never to see the end of it, for they are so many that they could face the whole world, and, even if they are in the wrong, they will never admit to defeat." Right, agreed Galileo, the Jesuits would be left out of it. But here was a straw figure, this "Lothario Sarsi" of unknown address; he was going to pelt the scarecrow with rotten eggs and tomatoes.

Yet those were times of trouble. His friend and patron, Cosimo II, had just died (1620). The protection of a strong-minded prince who had helped him unswervingly was replaced by the more uncertain favor of the widowed Grand Duchess, a very pious lady, who had assumed the regency until young Ferdinand II should come of age. There was also the trend of things in Rome. The College of Propaganda Fide was being organized for the conquest to the faith of far continents which would offset the losses to Protestantism in Europe; and with it the word "propaganda" had entered on its career. The Jesuits were gaining ascendancy even though Bellarmine had died in 1621; Loyola and Xavier were being enrolled among the saints.

Gagged and tethered, watched by malevolent suspicion in every move (Tommaso Caccini had come back and started afresh on his persecutions), beset by sickness, pressed by the hopes and angers of Florence, Galileo had to proceed with great care and deliberation. It was only two years later that he could tell his friends that the answer was on its way to the press.

III

Suddenly, in August, 1623, the news burst like a star shell over the bleak landscape: Maffeo Barberini had been elected Pope. There was rejoicing in Florence. After Paul V, a dull and savage-tempered old man, the brief reign of Gregory XV had brought only slight improvement. But Maffeo Barberini, or rather Urban VIII, as he was now, was a friend of the arts and a Lycean academic himself. It was in everybody's memory that, only three years before, following the *Discourse on the Comets,* he had written his "Adulatio perniciosa" in honor of Galileo—as if to remind him that, even through the crisis of 1616, he had always defended the new science.[3] Now that he had no longer to play a covered political game in the Curia, it was surmised, his true inclinations could not fail to come out. Happy omens confirmed it: Cesarini was made Master of the Chamber, and Ciàmpoli was confirmed in his newly won position as Secretary of the Briefs, which was equivalent to a private secretaryship in the British system. "I am fully confident," announces Rinuccini, "that this is going to be the papacy of the *virtuosi*."

Ciàmpoli was writing to Galileo: "Here there is felt a great desire for some further production of your thought; if you would resolve to commit to print those ideas that you still have in mind, I am quite sure that they would be most acceptable to His Holiness, who never ceases from admiring your eminence in all things and preserves intact his

---

3. Those lines, again, are rarely quoted; yet, quite apart from their classical distinction, they have an interest because of their unwittingly prophetic import. Galileo's discoveries of new things in the skies, and even of spots in the Sun, are brought in as an example of how greatness and glory deemed to be above the changes of fortune will eventually show their weakness and come to grief—how even hundred-eyed Argus let something escape him. "Truth is unwelcome to the mighty: The enemy is often more useful":

Cum Luna caelo fulget, et auream
Pompam sereno pandit in ambitu
  Ignes coruscantes, voluptas
    Mira trahit, retinetque visus.

Hic emicantem suspicit Hesperum,
Dirumque Martis sidus, et orbitam
  Lactis coloratam nitore;
    Ille tuam, Cynosura, lucem.

Seu Scorpii cor, sive Canis faciem
Miratur alter, vel Jovis asseclas,
  Patrisve Saturni, repertos
    Docte tuo Galilaee vitro.

At prima Solis cum reserat diem
Lux orta, puro Gangis ab aequore
  Se sola diffundit, micansque
    Intuitus radiis moratur.
   . . . .

Nil esse regum sorte beatius,
Mens et cor aeque concipit omnium,
  Quos larva rerum, quos inani
    Blanda rapit specie cupido.

Non semper, extra quod radiat jubar,
Splendescit intra: respicimus nigras
  In Sole (quis credat?) retectas
    Arte tua, Galilaee, labes.

Sceptri coruscat gloria regii
Ornata gemmis; turba satellitum
  Hinc inde procedit, colentes
    Officiis comites sequuntur.

. . . .
Fugit potentum limina Veritas,
Quamquam salutis nuntia: nauseam
  Invisa proritat, vel iram:
    Saepe magis juvat hostis hostem.

THE CRIME OF GALILEO

attachment for you. You should not deprive the world of your productions while there is time to work them out, and please remember that I am yours as ever."

When Prince Cesi came to congratulate him on his accession, Urban interrupted him eagerly: "Is Galileo coming? When is he coming?"

"He is dying to come, your Holiness," was the answer.

The scientist, on his side, wrote Cesi: "I am revolving in my mind plans of some moment for the republic of letters, and perhaps can never hope for so wonderful a combination of circumstances to insure their success."

But he took his time, for he wanted to effect his *rentrée* in style.

By the end of October the long-awaited answer to Grassi came out in Rome. It was the *Saggiatore* ("Assayer"), and it was promptly and unanimously recognized for what it was—the masterpiece of Italian polemic prose. Galileo had written his *Provinciales*. As in Pascal's case, the argument was not always meticulously fair, but it nailed the enemy to the post. Sparkling wit and destructive irony took the place of the weapons that had been forbidden. In a seemingly leisurely and impersonal excursion over the wide—too wide—field of "Sarsi's" utterances and references, Galileo went to work on learned nonsense and academic prejudice and brought forth what has remained in history as a breviary of the scientific method.

What was left of "Lothario Sarsi's" arguments was not much. We shall give here a brief passage from that polemic. It has been often quoted, but it loses nothing from repetition:

I cannot refrain from marveling that Sarsi will persist in proving to me, by authorities, that which at any moment I can bring to the test of experiment. . . . If discussing a difficult problem were like carrying a weight, since several horses will carry more sacks of corn than one alone will, I would agree that many reasoners avail more than one; but discoursing is like coursing, and not like carrying, and one hunter by himself will run farther than a hundred drayhorses. When Sarsi brings up such a multitude of authors, it does not seem to me that he in the least degree strengthens his own conclusions, but he ennobles the cause of Signor Mario and myself, by showing that we reason better than many men of established reputation. If Sarsi insists that I must believe, on Suidas' credit,[4] that the Babylonians cooked eggs by swiftly whirling them in a sling, I will believe it; but I must say that the cause of such an effect is very remote from that to which it is attributed, and to find the true cause I shall reason thus. If an effect does not follow with us which followed with others at another time, it is because, in our experiment, something is wanting which was the cause of the former success; and if only one thing is wanting to us, that one thing is the true cause. Now we have eggs, and slings, and strong men to whirl them, and yet they will not become cooked; nay, if they were hot at first, they more quickly become cold; and, since nothing is wanting to us but to be Babylonians, it follows that being Babylonians is the true cause why the eggs became cooked, and not the friction of the air, which is what I wish to prove.[5] Is it possible that in traveling post, Sarsi has never noticed that coolness is occasioned on the face by the continual change of air? And if he has felt it, will he rather trust the relation by others of what was done two thousand years ago at Babylon than what he can at this moment verify in his own person? I, at least, will not be so wilfully wrong, and so ungrateful to Nature and to God, that, having been gifted with sense and logic, I should voluntarily set less value on such great endowments than on the fallacies of a fellow-man and blindly and blunderingly believe whatever I hear and barter the freedom of my intellect for slavery to one as liable to error as myself.

As for Grassi-"Sarsi's" astronomical theories, they fare no better than the physical:

And so here we have, both Sarsi and I, expended a great amount of words in searching whether the solid concavity of the lunar orb (which does not exist), by moving in a circle (whilst it never did), drags along with it the element of fire (if perchance there be such an one) and, by way of it, the exhalations which in turn ignite the matter of the comet, which we do not know whether it is really in that place but do well know that it is not the kind of stuff that burns. . . .

4. Suidas was a late Alexandrine commentator who wrote a dictionary of philo-logical and other curiosities.
5. Someone has remarked that Suidas and Sarsi were the prophets of guided mis-siles. They were not. They were talking about eggs.

Grassi was pulverized in the public eye and went off to nurse his grudge. The Jesuits ordered him to lie low henceforth and not try to answer. This did not go without some very bitter feelings, for Grassi had only voiced the acceptable and accepted opinion of Jesuit astronomers. He himself was no discredit to the Order. He had drawn the plans for the Church of Sant'Ignazio in Rome and had even proposed, after Leonardo, the construction of a submarine boat of his own designing. His faults were only those of his confreres. They had learned their geometry from geometricians, their engineering from engineers —and their physics from rhetoricians. They imagined the combination could stand forever, because they had been taught to use normal intelligence in human affairs, and in the problems of Nature that of circus performers; for that was what their eloquence amounted to in the face of a nonpersuadable reality. But this time defeat had to be conceded. Galileo had effected his comeback and was again firmly established in the center of the literary scene.

VIII *Urban VIII*

Habituees of the mirror, famous readers, they fall in love with historical characters, with the unfortunate queen, or the engaging young assistant or a great detective, even with voice, of the announcer, maybe, from some foreign station they can never identify. . . . Why not go out together next Sunday; say, casually, in a wood: "I suppose you realize you are fingering the levers that control eternity!"

W. H. AUDEN, "THE ORATORS"

I

At the end of April, 1624, after a leisurely voyage and a stay of two weeks with Cesi at his castle in Acquasparta, Galileo arrived in Rome. He was bringing with him a delightful novelty, the first microscope (he called it simply "occhialino"), with which one could see all sorts of "horrendous things" moving about in a drop of water. He was received by the Pope with "infinite demonstrations of love" and in the course of six weeks had as many long conversations with him. Very soon, however, he realized that he was not going to get very far. He was talking no longer to Maffeo Barberini, but to Urban VIII.

Urban felt himself, with some reason, to be of the stuff of which the great Popes of the Renaissance had been made. In that critical period early in the Thirty Years' War, when the fate of the Reformation hung in the balance, he was planning a great political campaign which would change the balance of Europe. Splendor and power were going to be his insignia. On being shown the marble monuments of his predecessors, he said that "he would erect iron ones to himself." The fortresses on the northern borders, the new breastwork of Castel Sant'Angelo, the new manufacture of arms at Tivoli, the Vatican Armory taking up the rooms of the old library (where imported technicians cast guns for the fortress out of the old Roman bronze ceilings of the Pantheon), finally, the costly harbor of Civitavecchia—all were meant as manifest symbols of the desire of Urban VIII to establish pontifical power again as the vice-regency of Christ with the two-edged sword of the world.

Urban VIII was not of the old feudal nobility and did not share their medieval dreams. He came of a family of Florentine merchant princes who, like the Chigis and the Medicis, had entered the aristocracy only a few generations before. A Florentine himself, talented, bright, sharp, and realistic, he had cloaked his ambition while still a prelate in the dignified forms of conventional literary achievement, legal competence, and careful demeanor. Once in power, his latent pride and vanity were to break forth without restraint, and with them his natural temper, quick to anger and suspicion.[1]

He never lacked an adequate feeling of his own capacities. He ignored ancient constitutions, because "the sentence of one live Pope was worth more than all the decrees of a hundred dead ones." On being informed that the notables wished to erect a monument to him, which was usually done for Popes only after their deaths, he said: "Let them. I am not an ordinary Pope either."

He liked the theatrical side of Baroque production, the bustle of engineering projects, and his own ornate contributions to Latin poetry in hexameter and Sapphic verse. We have seen that he had written an ode to Galileo, the "Dangerous Adulation." But for the real ideas of science he had as little understanding as for the real forces stirring in

---

1. In this, too, he appears an epigone in the line of Sixtus V, for the latter, as Felice Peretti, had given an English visitor the impression of being "the most crooching, humble Cardinal that was ever lodged in an oven" but, once crowned with the triregnum, had broken forth as a "consecrated whirlwind" and the terror of the Curia.

war-torn Europe around him. His whole political concer*· :n and his master-plan were quite conventional: how to attach the powers to his chariot while at the same time increasing his own domains. In these very days of April, 1624, Cardinal Richelieu, still an obscure political figure, was preparing to enter the King's Council. By September, Urban would meet his full challenge with the ultimatum to raze the papal forts in the Valtelline. It was a new departure in that struggle between modern nations, rising and formidable contestants that were to play the destructive game of the Thirty Years' War to the utter frustration of theocratic power.

But in those days Urban was still dreaming of spectacular successes. It was the morning of his reign, a morning full of magnificence and confidence. Amid the turmoil of the affairs of state he found time for long audiences with Galileo.

What took place in those audiences will forever remain a matter for speculation. But from scattered data we may infer that the conversation went something like this. On being copiously complimented on the *Saggiatore* and being told by the Pope that he had had it read aloud at table, Galileo deprecated the poor merit of these feeble excursions on a perforce limited subject, whereupon the Pontiff exclaimed his wish that more such incomparable creations should flow from his magical pen. Thereupon Galileo tactfully alluded to the malice of his many enemies and to the many disadvantages under which he labored, and the Pope reassured him that, if he remained such a dutiful son of the Holy Church as he had shown himself hitherto, his enemies would bark in vain. The System of the Schools, in intelligent hands, ought to fear nothing from the new science, for it was established on natural evidence itself; and he, the Pope, could show it quite easily. He expanded on that subject.[2] The campaign against Galileo was really alarm born of the incompetence of certain people who usurped the privileges of the scholar, and it would be kept in check.

2. Cf. the dispatch of Niccolini, June 12, 1642.

Frustrated, thus, in his first approach, the scientist bethought himself of indirect pressure. Some time later Cardinal Hohenzollern, on his leave-taking audience, was moved to represent to the Pope what difficulties he had in converting German noblemen who had been shocked by the prohibition of 1616. The Holy Father was sympathetic. But he remarked that the Church neither had condemned nor would condemn the doctrine of Copernicus as heretical, but only as rash (*temeraria*), and that there was no chance that it would ever be proved wrong, for a convincing proof was impossible.[3] The statement of fact, we may observe, was less than accurate, for, in the first place, the Congregation of the Index is not "the Church," and, in the second place, it had declared the opinion *false*, not *rash;* in the third place, its Qualifiers had specified reservedly that it was "foolish and absurd philosophically and formally heretical."

Be that as it may, the Pope could, even without pronouncing himself *ex cathedra* for the first time on the subject, have had the findings corrected or reversed. He did neither. He somewhat attenuated the content and at the same time confirmed it as a juridical precedent. The main objective was lost. But those remarks left a slight opening.

Galileo in his contacts had "begun to discover new land," as he wrote. This appears to mean, from other allusions, that the prelates he consulted (Cobelluzzi, Barberini, Borghese) agreed that there had been entirely too much fuss about this affair, that it was a purely

3. This is from the letter to Cesi, January 8, 1624. We have, moreover, the following in G. F. Buonamici's memorandum of 1633: "Cardinal Zollern encouraged Galileo, telling him that the Pope had reminded him of having defended Copernicus at the time of Paul V and assured him that, were it only owing to the respect justly due the memory of Copernicus, he would never allow this opinion to be declared heretical in his time." As Buonamici's paper is inaccurate on several factual details concerning the events of 1633, this reference remains in doubt. On the other hand, the paper contains confidential statements that cannot have been communicated by any except Galileo himself (such as his conditions for going through with the abjuration); this about Cardinal Zollern ought to be one of them. The compliments to Copernicus reserved for a German audience agree with Urban's diplomacy at the time. They also dovetail with the other part of the statement above. On the Buonamici memorandum see n. 5, p. 311.

juridical matter, and that the decree could not be revised for reasons of prestige but that anyone could go and be as Copernican as he pleased, provided he gave no scandal and played the game.[4] The Roman hierarchy knew itself too well not to countenance a skeptical worldly conformism in others.

Fortified by these opinions, Galileo in the next audiences again approached the subject. He steered through many mutual deplorations on the decline of good writing toward the remark that a number of very wonderful conceits and effects of Nature were still waiting to be written about, were it only for the delight of the mind—if he understood the decree rightly to read that a free discussion of natural hypotheses was still allowed. He was assured that this was the very spirit of the decree, as everyone should know: not to restrain the mind in its ingenious conjectures but to prevent the wrong philosophical conclusions from being drawn. We Ourselves, said the Pope, have validly defended Copernicus in 1616, and he pointed out that it would expose the Church to the ridicule of the heretics if the very man who gave such a valid contribution to the reform of the calendar carried through by Pope Gregory were declared heretical in his thoughts.[5] So long as he reigned, insisted the Pontiff, the memory of Copernicus had nothing to fear. The Church knew very well how much prudence is required in this delicate matter of the interpretation of Scripture.

4. Cardinal Antonio Barberini, Sr., had cautioned against one difficulty, namely, that Copernicus had made the Earth a star. Galileo and Castelli had assured him that it could be handled. It is difficult for a modern to realize how rigid conservatism in official places could coexist with a seemingly free ferment of ideas. In 1624 the theological faculty of Paris, which held in France most of the functions of the Inquisition, condemned the anti-Aristotelian theses of three candidates, and the Parliament in consequence ordered the theses destroyed and the candidates expelled. But apart from doctoral theses, all sorts of ideas found expression. From the administrative vantage point of the authorities, "novelties" could look like a very limited local disturbance in the orderly flow of approved scholarship. On Wolynski's count, there were 2,330 works published on astronomy between 1543 and 1687 (which brings us to the time of Newton's *Principia*); of those, only 180 were Copernican (see *Archivio storico italiano,* 1873, p. 12).

5. Buonamici's memorandum (see n. 5, p. 311).

THE CRIME OF GALILEO

Surely, it was not her intention to clip the wings of Signor Galileo's subtle speculations and admirable discoveries, which were an adornment of the true faith and might also lead to remarkable improvements in engineering, as long as he was quite sure he intended to leave theology alone.

But, then, suggested Galileo hastily before the Pope could revert to discoursing of absent friends, the decree must have been misunderstood by many, for there was ill-informed muttering at home and sneering abroad that it had been the work of uninformed consultors.[6] —Nonsense, said the Pope, We Ourselves were part in it. There were then high reasons. But it was certainly a regrettable necessity, most regrettable. And, then, urged Galileo, would it not be to the benefit of the true faith if the many natural reasons for and against could be probed carefully and dispassionately so as to show that the issue, maturely examined, needed a higher decision? That, agreed the Pope, would be a good idea. To prove that all the ingenuity of man could devise in the matter of the heavens could lead to no conclusive statement was all to the benefit of obedience. Let the Signor Galileo assay theories with that exquisite balance of scruples wherewith he was wont to test the truth, and show again that "we are not to find out the work of His hands."

Better still, suggested Galileo, supposing that one took the following line, which had occurred to him while writing a poetic conceit which perhaps His Beatitude remembered from years back, a curious fantasy on the ebb and flow of the sea to which he was attached and which had been possibly too much appreciated by certain foreigners who had taken it for their own: supposing that one could produce proofs of the Pythagorean theory that imposed themselves as physically necessary, if not metaphysically. . . .

6. The source for this and the following is in the *Letter to Ingoli* and in the Preface to the *Dialogue on the Great World Systems*. There are also Riccardi's instructions to the licenser and Oregius' text, of which later. Needless to say, there is no record of the conversation, and we have only stitched together indirect references in the way that seemed the most plausible.

Urban VIII cut him short with a little lecture:[7] "Let Us remind you
of something that We had occasion to tell you many years ago, speaking as one philosopher to another; and, if We remember, you were not
willing then to offer Us any definite refutation.

"Let Us grant you that all of your demonstrations are sound and
that it is entirely possible for things to stand as you say. But now tell
Us, do you really maintain that God could not have wished or known
how to move the heavens and the stars in some other way? We suppose
you will say 'Yes,' because We do not see how you could answer otherwise. Very well then, if you still want to save your contention, you
would have to prove to Us that, if the heavenly movements took place
in another manner than the one you suggest, it would imply a logical
contradiction at some point, since God in His infinite power can do
anything that does not imply a contradiction. Are you prepared to
prove as much? No? Then you will have to concede to Us that God
can, conceivably, have arranged things in an entirely different manner,
while yet bringing about the effects that we see. And if this possibility
exists, which might still preserve in their literal truth the sayings of
Scripture, it is not for us mortals to try to force those holy words to
mean what to us, from here, may appear to be the situation.

"Have you got anything to object? We are glad to see that you are
of Our opinion. Indeed, as a good Catholic, how could you hold any
other? To speak otherwise than hypothetically on the subject would
be tantamount to constraining the infinite power and wisdom of God
within the limits of your personal ideas [*fantasie particolari*]. You
cannot say that this is the only way God could have brought it about,
because there may be many, and perchance infinite, ways that He
could have thought of and which are inaccessible to our limited minds.[8]

7. Historians usually date this idea from the conversation of 1630. But we have
seen (p. 135) that it is mentioned in Oregius' *Praeludium*, whence we have para-
phrased the statement quoted below. The passage in question, according to Berti,
occurs also in the first edition of 1629. Hence the argument dates back at least
to 1624 and probably, as Oregius implies, was used for the first time in 1616.
8. The last two sentences are those Galileo quotes as a conclusion to the *Dialogue*

We trust you see now what We meant by telling you to leave theology alone."

It was only then, probably, that Galileo was able to measure the chasm which separated this thought from that of the Pontiff; for the latter's words, taken seriously, would have implied that all investigation of Nature was bound to lead to nothing. He might have objected as he does in the *Dialogue:* "Surely, God could have caused birds to fly with their bones made of solid gold, with their veins full of quicksilver, with their flesh heavier than lead, and with wings exceeding small. He did not, and that ought to show something. It is only in order to shield your ignorance that you put the Lord at every turn to the refuge of a miracle." [9]

But this was no time to argue. He kept his peace. He must have been familiar already with that type of argument and known how diffiicult it was to cope with. From the point of view of Church philosophy, it was sound and orthodox doctrine. Robert Grosseteste had provided the epistemological part of it back in the thirteenth century. Taken on the pragmatic level, it did not make much sense, for it permitted, while not permitting, science to proceed, with the proviso that it would not be getting anywhere. For all his literary sympathies, the Pope was utterly unable to grasp the implications of the new thought. A humanist of the sixteenth century, schooled by the Jesuits in Peripatetic principles, Urban lived in a world of significant forms and sensuous substances, varied and multiple, with many wonderful names and qualities apt for the learned discourse; the paradox of mathematical physics, the bridge thrown directly from the extreme abstraction of geometry to basic monotone matter defined only by mass and measure, remained beyond his conceiving. The new "natural conclusions," he felt, had their proper place in enriching the world, not in reducing it to geometric space.

as coming from "a very high authority," and we must assume the quotation to be faithful.

9. This remark and others to the same effect are tucked away in the text so as not to appear a direct answer to the Pope's argument.

This is where his thinking was backed by the great schemes of the Renaissance and its hope in unknown harmonies. "There is nothing that is incredible," Marsilio Ficino had said. "For to God all things are possible, and nothing is impossible. There are numberless possibilities that we deny because we do not happen to know them." This was also what Pico della Mirandola had maintained, hinting at reaches of "natural magic" beyond our dreams; and Campanella, too, was supporting Galileo in the hope of results such as no scientist could ever produce. It was "Platonic theology" itself, urging man to extend his imagination beyond what he could see and test; it was Leonardo's belief in the creative power of artistic "fantasy." And this is clearly, even more than subtle Scholastic theories, the idea behind Urban's words: We cannot suppose that Nature has to be contained within the limits of our "particular fantasy," for she is all the possible as well. Moreover, in good Christian religion, no creature can "necessitate" its maker, were it even by true knowledge; and the transcendence of God makes it impossible that from this world we should ever know His ways. It was known that we are not allowed, for example, to think of space as infinite by nature, for then it would become a necessary part of the nature of God and thus lose its creatureliness.

Surely, it is written: *Dominus scientiarum Deus,* "God is the Lord of sciences." But this does not allow us to try to impose the seeming "necessities" of one science upon all the other ones, and it does not go without a certain arbitral role assigned to His vicar on earth.

All these things Sanctissimus had learned in his time. Therefore, he concluded, the Church is not doing any damage to science if she precludes a serious treatment of such ideas which would give scandal to the faithful. They cannot be really true and should be labeled "fantasy." As such, they may have their charm; and the Pope could show that he was able to appreciate it, for it was he who had restored Campanella, the incorrigible maverick Dominican, to freedom and literary activity.

Urban's thought was a late version, even as he himself was a late copy of the Renaissance Popes. No one could explain to him that, under his very reign, the Church was going to face things that his philosophy had never dreamed of. As a humanist, he felt he had given an adequately ample answer. As a lawyer, he decided the case was settled and turned to more urgent business.

II

Would he still have been able to answer thus if Galileo had produced one fresh proof, viz., Kepler's laws? He probably would have; still, doubt is allowable. But Galileo had never read Kepler's work on Mars that was in his library; it was as though he had not heard of it, although it would appear that Cavalieri was teaching it in Bologna. The irony of this incomprehensible blindness seems like a cruel sport of the gods; the more so as Kepler had come out in 1619 with his third law, the most impressive of the three to a mathematical mind. Even while Galileo was sitting there with the Pope, Kepler was publishing his *Gleanings from the Saggiatore,* in which he defended Tycho Brahe from reproaches of inaccuracy,[10] for he could not appreciate from his distant perspective the causes of Galileo's disdain of Tycho. To him the Tychonic system remained valuable, because it provided nothing but a natural transition to the truth of Copernicus; and he did not realize how effectively others were deliberately using it as a diversion to shunt astronomy into a dead end. But then, remarks Kepler, in a soothing way, it is said that, when Orpheus was deprived of Eurydice by the inexorable decrees of Orcus, he turned in his sorrow with unconsidered words against Eurydice herself. What Kepler understands

10. Kepler had entered the lists as the defender of Tycho's memory against Scipione Chiaramonti and his *Antitycho.* By defending Tycho's observations in the matter of the nova, he was playing unwittingly into the hands of the Jesuits, who needed Tycho for very different reasons. This was the beginning of a regrettable difference between the two scientists which damaged their friendship. Galileo backed Chiaramonti (on the comets if not on the nova), at least indirectly, for tactical reasons and was later knifed in the back by the latter for his pains. It was a case of what Galileo himself had warned against: "In order to defend a mistake, one is compelled to make a hundred more and in the end is left with nothing to show."

even less, living far from the Inquisition, is the explicit way in which both contestants dissociate themselves from any Copernican implication. "Could it be," he asks in gentle mockery, "that Aegle has become afraid of Silenus' forehead, after having herself daubed it with red?"

The trouble with Kepler was that truly angelic nature of his, incapable of any self-seeking thought or even of resentment. The persecutions of Tycho's kin over twenty years (Tengnagl had only recently died, in 1622) had moved him not in the least to deviate from his filial preoccupation with the honor of his master. As for his own discoveries, they could wait until someone brought them to light. "Has not God waited six thousand years to have His works explained?" [11]

In his defense of Tycho, Kepler goes over the data of the orbit of Mars from which his research started; and yet, there is not a word to remind Galileo of the book he had sent him fifteen years before, or of his laws, or of their importance. There is, indeed, not a word of reproach about his having neglected those discoveries—no appeal, no pressing reminder to the friend who was drifting away from him and who might have been called back to his sense of scientific solidarity. Thus the discoveries go unmentioned again. The two men go on as ships that pass in the night.

Left to his own devices, Galileo at this point of his Roman solicitations felt that he had a pullet in the hand which might well be worth a fat hen in the bush. To Cesi, who wrote that time and patience would help, he replied that life is short, that to play the courtier one must be young and strong, and that he could not sit around forever waiting for officials pressed by business to lend him an ear. He discussed the situation with Father Niccolò Riccardi, the new Master of the Holy Palace (Urban had surrounded himself with Florentines). The Padre Maestro,

11. The history of Kepler's laws during the seventeenth century remains most obscure. Descartes had still never heard of them when he died; nor had Mersenne, who read everything and knew everybody. Horrocks knew but did not publish anything about them in his brief life. Bullialdus was the first to announce them in France, without arousing much notice, in 1639; then Wallis discussed them; and this takes us to a time very close to Newton's adoption of them in 1666.

also called familiarly "Padre Mostro" because of his immense girth and erudition, was an old friend of his. As the chief authority in charge of licensing, he had written an enthusiastic appraisal of the *Saggiatore*. He was now giving much hope and encouragement. All these difficulties about the heavens, he averred, had been trumped up by those hard-shelled Roman curialists—speaking strictly in confidence. The truth about the heavens was that stars are moved by angels, and that was that. But many wonderful discourses could still be excogitated thereupon. In so far as he understood the words of His Holiness, they represented an explicit directive to Galileo not to deprive the world of the miracles of his discoveries and to continue adorning Italy with the splendor of his mind.

As he departed, loaded with favors, holy medals, "Agnus Dei," and pensions for his family, escorted by an orotund papal parchment of commendation for His Most Serene Highness the Grand Duke (". . . We embrace with paternal love this great man whose fame shines in the heavens and goes on earth far and wide . . ."), Galileo felt that he had not been wholly unsuccessful. He was sixty years old by now, and he had learned what one could expect from the world. Eight years of prudence had taught him the way of devious implication. If he had pulled through with the *Saggiatore,* he could hope, this time with papal favor, to mention his subject in a more explicit manner and let it quietly sink in.[12] He had confidence in the force of the truth, once it is intrusted to the pen, which, as he used to say, "is the touchstone of the mind." Copernicanism was not heretical. It was not even so wild as all that. So far so good. He now had permission to present his brief to the public. From what he understood of the authorities,

12. The *Saggiatore* was denounced to the Inquisition in 1625, and a motion was made in the Congregation to have it prohibited. But Father Guevara, General of the Theatines, gave it a favorable report, in which he explained that even the opinion of the Earth's motion, maintained with due submission, would not have appeared to him a reason for condemning it (see Guiducci's letter from Rome, April 18, 1625).

they were interested only in formal clauses of submission that would safeguard their prestige and punctilio. "If we cannot get past *that* outfit, call me Grassi," he must have said to Ciàmpoli, or the Florentine equivalent of it, for that certainly was the way he felt.[13] The *Dialogue on the Great World Systems* had been decided upon.[14]

III

He decided to try out the ground. He wrote a long-overdue reply to Francesco Ingoli's brief of 1616,[15] in which, after correcting his opponent's naïve mistakes in geometry in a good-natured and leisurely way, he took a resolutely Copernican stand: "I maintain further," he concluded after giving several cogent reasons, "that I know other facts of experience which have been hitherto observed by no one, from which, within the limits of natural and human considerations, the rightness of the Copernican system appears incontrovertible." He had prefaced the letter, however, with a careful diplomatic statement of submission: he would never say the doctrine was true—far from it—but he wished to prove to the heretics of Germany that, if in Catholic Italy the views of their great countryman had been rejected, it was not from ignorance of their great probability "but from reverence for Holy Scripture and the Fathers and from zeal for our religion and holy faith." The more valid the proofs, he added, "the clearer the beneficent conclusion that there is no trusting purely human reasoning and that we must rely

13. What he and his friends really thought of the above-mentioned outfit of consultants comes out only rarely in the letters. But the good Guiducci, who was even then being fooled by Grassi's "magnanimous" behavior, wrote, in approving the *Letter to Ingoli* (see below): "I like your idea of getting rid of such people, who are glad murderers of courtesy and charity. You ought to show them up without mercy." The Italian phrase, "che la cortesia e pietà ascrivono a lor trofei," says even more in its terseness: "who count courtesy and charity among their trophies," which implies not only kiling those virtues but setting them up stuffed.
14. See letter to Cesare Marsili, December 7, 1624; to Cesi, December 24, 1624.
15. See p. 98. Kepler had also written a reply from a copy that had reached him.

implicitly on the higher knowledge which alone can bring light to the darkness of our mind." The chuckle is almost audible. The well-worked-out submission clause hides it impeccably.

There was no question of printing the letter, but it circulated widely, was read by Ciàmpoli to the Pope, and raised no objections. Galileo had boldly tested his own interpretation of the papal directive; he was going to discuss heliocentrism not as a mere mathematical supposition but as a physical conclusion which ought to be accepted if only supernatural wisdom did not deny it. The trial balloon, from all indications, had worked well.

He was hoping now to bring the *Dialogue* to a conclusion in a couple of years, the more so as several parts of the argument had been worked out previously and needed only a recasting. But many circumstances, not the least of them illness, delayed him year after year. There seems to have been a complete intermission to the almost-finished work between 1626 and 1629. This interruption, which changed the whole timing probably to Galileo's disadvantage, was due, he implied, to his many occupations, mainly engineering consulting work. But there seems to have been also a certain amount of hesitation and discouragement. Cesi and Ciàmpoli kept pressing him. "We hear," writes the latter in 1628, "that your *Dialogue* is coming along very slowly, and we bewail the loss of such rare treasures. We cannot wait to read at least some small part. Your friends beg of you to disregard the counsels of repose and to follow the urge to glory and our exhortations. . . . Do not defraud the expectations of the world."

But Galileo knew how carefully he must organize his forces before striking. He was no Bruno or Campanella, to rush into print with generous certainties and uncertain reasons. The "immense design" was proving even more appalling as he faced it at long last, and more difficult to encompass. As the physicist's thought was grappling with its difficulties, it had to mature at the same time the foundations of that theory of motion which was to be the subject of his later *Discourses on Two New Sciences*. They were taking shape in his own mind even as he labored at his cosmological exposition. All could not but go together.

It is characteristic of Galileo that from this time on in his sixties, which is when most men conclude and crystallize their thought, his intellect was most fully mobilized down almost to the last hours of his life, reshaping, reinterpreting, reorganizing without cease the vast array of his ideas, even through the tragic times that he was to traverse, in invincibly resurging creativeness.

On October 29, 1629, he wrote to Elia Diodati, his Paris correspondent, a Tuscan *émigré* and Protestant statesman who had had a great part in the French translation of the Bible: "I have taken up work again on the Dialogue of the Ebb and Flow of the Sea, which was left aside for three years, and with God's grace I have found the right line, which ought to allow me to terminate it within the winter; it will provide, I trust, a most ample confirmation of the Copernican system."

On December 24 he was able to announce to his friends in Rome that the *Dialogue on the Great World Systems* was completed.

IX
The "Dialogue"

When shall I cease to wonder?   SAGREDO

I

The *Dialogue,* this fateful work which was to become such a "captain piece" in Western history, meanders at ease across the whole cultural landscape of the time, carrying in its broad sweep much strange material of various origin. As a composition, it looks unfinished, unpolished, at times inconsistent. This is partly nature, partly art. It has no unity except that of life itself. It is, in fact, "the story of the mind of Signor Galileo." But it is the mind of a man who knew very well where he was going. In the work there is all of him: the physicist, the astronomer, the man of the world, the littérateur, the polemicist, even at times the sophist; there is, above all, the totally expressive and expressed Renaissance man.

Galileo, like Newton, had been brought up on Archimedes and Euclid; but, unlike Newton, he was far from making an idol of the style of the pure geometricians "who utter not a single word not imposed by absolute necessity." For he holds that "the nobility, greatness, and magnificence which make our actions and enterprises marvelous and excellent do not consist only in what is necessary but also in the unnecessary; I would consider base and plebian that banquet in which food and drink were lacking; yet it is not the presence of them which can make it noble and magnificent, for much more grandeur is brought to it by the beauty of the sumptuous apparel, the splendor of the furnishings, the sheen of silver and gold which delight the eye, the harmony of songs, the performances on the scene, the pleasurable drolleries." [1] The heroic poems with their episodes, the flights of Pindar's fantasy, are his avowed models. There is a price to be paid for this—the sacrifice of straight scientific language. A modern may miss the intellectual tension of abstract developments, the tightness of the formula which brings the theory its shape. But Galileo is willing to pay that price in order to remain a man among men, a person and a force within his own culture. What is characteristic of the prose is certainly not economy; it is expression, the warmth and passion throughout, the ever returning wonder. The motto of the work might well be Sagredo's word: "When shall I cease from wondering?"

Micanzio remarked on reading it: "And who before now had guessed what the Copernican issue was all about?" He was substantially right. Adventurous notions like Digges's, wild visionary pronouncements like Bruno's, which frightened people off with their avowed heresy, technical pamphlets like the *Sidereal Message* and the *Letters on the Solar Spots*, had allowed readers to guess or piece together some important new ideas; but they had left things on the level of an emotional difference between people who had a taste for the new and those who stuck to the old. Copernicus, even had he not been prohibited, remained a book for specialists; Kepler was unreadable. Of men who had disliked the System of the Schools and had struck out at it with brilliant but inconclusive remarks, there had been many even before Copernicus. But the real movement of thought had never come to a head, and the prohibition of 1616 had swooped down at the strategic moment to check it and disperse the efforts. The cognoscenti could still applaud the high-class fencing of the *Discourse on Floating Things*

---

1. "Lettera sopra il candore della luna." It should be said that these words are written by way of ribbing Fortunio Liceti's intolerable diffuseness. But Galileo is amiably willing to admit to the same weakness.

or of the *Assayer,* but it remained good spectator fun; and they went home without being able to piece together the great puzzle that stayed disassembled by superior orders.

The *Dialogue* did exactly that: it assembled the puzzle and, for the first time, showed the picture. It did not go into technical developments; it left all sorts of loose ends and hazardous suggestions showing to the technical critic. But it was exactly on the level of educated public opinion, and it was able to carry it irresistibly. It was a charge of dynamite planted by an expert engineer.

It is Socratic in a novel way. The argument starts with a frontal attack on the science of the professors but soon is deep in the physical realities shown to us by the surface of the Moon. It follows thus the very sequence of the discussions of the early years. It moves on in a leisurely manner from one question into another, taking pot shots at casual objectives until we are far off the track, picks up with a "Where were we?" and comes back for a while to playing cat-and-mouse with Simplicio as a butt, but soon is off again in another direction, in full cry after some luckless lay figure who has brought up the needed asininity. Meanwhile the web of proof is being woven unobtrusively, until after a while the reader asks himself what kind of people could be blind to the evidence; what other opinion could be held except the Copernican?

In form as in substance, the work is a break with the academic tradition; it goes back through the dialogue form of the Renaissance to the true Platonic vein. The names of the characters are not Hylas, Philonous, or Philalethes. They address each other as "Sig. Salviati," "Sig. Simplicio mio"; they quarrel and make up; they move with their feet solidly planted on the marble floors of a Venetian palace on the Canal Grande. Their forms of address are those of Italian society of the period; the scenes and interludes of action are managed by Galileo as a man of the theater who had tried his hand successfully at comedy. Salusbury, in his translation, by Latinizing the names and using the English forms of address, has removed them to a slightly imaginary space as "Three Gentlemen of Venice"; but the life still comes through.[2]

Of the three characters, Filippo Salviati is obviously the one closest to Galileo's soul. He speaks for the author himself. Of the temper of the man and his intellectual personality, we have almost no traits in the few letters left by him. Nor does the author help us much when he says that "in him the lesser splendor was distinction of lineage and magnificence of wealth; a sublime intellect, which set no delight higher than exquisite speculation."

The known facts of his life are equally scanty. Born of Averardo Salviati in 1582, Filippo inherited, when still young, his father's senatorial rank in the Florentine nobility. He had also inherited his father's banking interests, for the Salviatis were and remained bankers and merchants, like the Medicis, like most of the great houses which had

---

2. The Salusbury translation, on which we have based our English text of the *Dialogue* (Chicago: University of Chicago Press, 1953), remains, with all its faults, better, once corrected, than any modern one could be. Although we had to modernize it and shorten the sentences, the text preserves a measure of the original spirit. It has in it the leisurely unrolling of seventeenth-century thought, with that peculiar ingenuous quality that would be lost in any imitation. Unfortunately, Salusbury is no Thomas Browne. It is a far cry from his efforts at achieving the elegance of Jacobean prose to the style of the Italian original, a masterpiece of Baroque production. The Galilean harmony is the full equal of Monteverdi and Palestrina, while Salusbury is at best a village organist. What is worse, his translating is miserably unreliable. Yet he, too, is an artist of sorts. Of facts about him we have next to nothing, yet he makes himself known to us in his Introduction more vividly than any biographer could do. Even the text shows more of his personality than should be allowable. He loves to show off his erudition, which is fair, and his exactness, which is more doubtful. He takes sternly to task Bernegger's Latin translation for each trifling mistake, thus demonstrating to his sponsors the necessity of his work; at the same time, every few pages, he takes off on flights of inaccuracy that would make one doubt of his sanity. A familiar casualness with the original was common to all seventeenth-century translators: witness Florio and Adlington; it must also be admitted that the Italian original, with its tricky adverbs and anacoluthons, might lead better men astray. But when, as here, it is a matter of a carefully reasoned argument, one wonders what the translator must have thought on rereading the nonsense that he had written down. There is a suspicion that he never did.

risen to power in the Republic after the checkmating of the feudal nobility and the razing of their towers in the thirteenth century. Filippo Salviati seems to have studied with Galileo in Padua and to have stayed with him in Venice, but the *Dialogue* is our only evidence for this. In 1611, as soon as he settled down in Florence, Galileo visited Filippo in his magnificent Villa delle Selve, which is still to be seen on the hillside above Signa, with its ample façade and terraces overlooking the valley of the Arno and its view reaching out as far as the mountains of Carrara. He came back at frequent intervals as much for the "salubrious air which was balm to his afflicting ailments" as for the company of his friend Salviati, with whom he shared an enthusiasm for burlesque poetry and low comedy, and who writes him that no one can read Ruzzante more delightfully than he and that he is being awaited impatiently by the whole company. But there is also record of long work on the satellites of Jupiter at the villa's observatory.

In 1612 they carried out the series of observations and inferences on the sunspots which are described in the Third Day of the *Dialogue*. In the same year Sagredo came to visit in his turn; later Castelli drove up to discuss hydraulics. Still in 1612, Salviati was made, on Galileo's sponsoring, a member of the Accademia dei Lincei, and he in turn sponsored the admission of Ridolfi and Castelli. In 1613 he introduced to his master a new disciple, G. B. Baliani, a Genoese patrician who seemed to be interested in problems of hydrostatics and was to become one of the most important of Galileo's correspondents. A last letter of Salviati from Genoa of January, 1614, still concerns Baliani.

But, as Salviati is leaving the scene, we are vouchsafed a brief revealing glimpse of his personality. He had left Florence in a fit of pique, after losing out in a quarrel of precedence about entering church with Bernardetto de' Medici. There is more to this than the "quaint mores" of aristocracy. The Salviatis, like the Bardis and the Pazzis, had once been contestants for primacy in Florence. Piero Salviati had been Savonarola's chief supporter against the Medici faction, as anyone who has read *Romola* knows. The shrewd and ruthless policy of old Cosimo I had put his competitors out of the running by undercutting them financially at the crucial time. There had been reconciliation and intermarriage, but the old grudge was bound to flare up, as it did in the desperate attempt of the Pazzis. Filippo Salviati set out on a long voyage which was to lead him we know not whither, for in March, 1614, death put an end to it in Barcelona. He was then thirty-two years of age.

We have no elements to appraise his personal contribution. But Salviati has been fortunate above many greater than he in that his intellectual personality comes to us through the pages of the *Dialogue* with the evidence of a poetic creation. We see him as a light, quick, serious mind, impatient of pedantry and minutiae, relying on his own razor-sharp logic and sound scientific instinct more than on an academic education, with an unfailing eye for essentials, a great respect for reason, and a laughing wit. He is the man with the gift of the gods. Galileo was no modest man himself (indeed, who was in his time?), and what he expects from others when writing about him is apt to shock our sense of understatement. But, as he puts his gifts under the invocation of a beloved shade, he forgets himself in his creation, and we face a delicately drawn silverpoint, the Portrait of the Scientist as a Young Man.

Sagredo is the Man of the World in the *Dialogue*. He has been set up as the standing portrait of a Venetian nobleman, endowed with the traditional statesmanship of his caste, attentive to new developments in science, open to argument but careful not to commit himself on theoretical issues.[3] The man who signed himself familiarly "Il Sagredo" or "Il Sag" did indeed appraise his own position thus: "I am a Venetian gentleman, nor did I ever pass myself off as a man of letters; I have had literary friendships, and I spent my protection on writers, but I do not intend to advance my fortunes or to acquire praise and reputation through my interest, however sincere, in philosophy and mathematics; I have rather identified my position with the integrity

---

3. Micanzio wrote in 1632: "How beautifully you have given life to our dear Sagredo. God help me, it is as if I heard him speak again."

of the magistrates and the good government of the Republic, to which I bent my efforts in my young years, following the custom of my fathers, who gave to it all they had of life and strength." But there was also in him a waywardness and instability which prevented him from going too deeply into anything. One is reminded at times, in the elaborate care he gives to pleasurable trifles, of Voltaire's Senator Pococurante. He was, in fact, a *bon vivant,* and this was not the least of the characteristics which endeared him to Galileo.

Born of Niccolò Sagredo and Cecilia Tiepolo in 1571, Giovan-francesco Sagredo was made a member of the Supreme Council of the Republic at the age of twenty-five as befitted his name and rank; but his varied interests, as also his love of pleasure, made him take as little as he could, after his "young years," of the heavy responsibilities of business and state which were the accepted lot of the Venetian aristocracy. His quick intelligence and good judgment made him the very listener that Galileo had always desired, the *honnête homme,* as it was later called; and his independence of mind asserted itself often, at times successfully, against his master. We know him better than Salviati from his letters. He is the faithful and resourceful friend, always ready with ideas and counsel, whether it be about a pleasure trip, a business settlement, or an experimental difficulty. He enjoys life and wants his friends to enjoy it; he is very much of a gentleman but is an outspoken, practical, and acute gentleman.

He wrote over many years on the making of telescope lenses and thermometers (he had artisans from the glassworks of Murano trying out new formulas for him); on magnetism; on the theory of light, arguing with Galileo, who maintained the idea of an agitation of the medium against that of a transmission of substance; and on sundry scientific novelties. Once in a while a melancholy feeling came over him that he had wasted his life, and he wrote in a lofty Stoic vein about the blessings of philosophy and the pleasures of moderation. But soon his bubbling nature would reassert itself, and he would write about life in Venice, "that city of all delights," wild parties in his country estate on the Brenta, and the unending difficulties in finding reliable servants.

He would send delicacies or would request Galileo's good services in finding new breeds of dogs or works of art for his collection, especially a Bronzino "at any price." He died in 1620, at the age of forty-nine. His brother Zaccaria, the hard businessman, wrote coldly that he had been carried away by a bronchitis, which was "also brought about by his infinite disorders."

As to Simplicio, it is reasonable that he should remain under an ancient pseudonym, for his name is legion. He is the average obstinate and literal-minded Aristotelian professor of the universities. Yet he is not what he might so well have been—a satire on the shrill and cantankerous opponents that had made Galileo's life miserable with their intrigues. He is the literary creation of a sunny temperament. There is a rather charming good nature in his bookishness that allows him to survive defeat after defeat and emerge patient, pleasant, willing and eager for more. He does not mind submitting himself to merciless cross-examination and having truths extracted out of him that go against all his convictions. He can get stuffy when driven into a corner and at times can lose his head. Then he will start clamoring: "This manner of thinking tends to the subversion of all natural philosophy and to the disorder and upsetting of heaven and earth and the whole universe!" But he regains his composure easily and goes on arguing. One feels that, if he had not been indoctrinated beyond repair in his earlier years, here would be a good mind.

Toward the end he loses himself quietly and unprotestingly in the thickening fog of incomprehensible novelties, only to emerge in the very last minute, summoned by his creator, to emit the Pope's opinion about the impossibility of true knowledge; his conclusion, it must be said, is lame, unprepared, and out of character. The last lines spoken on his own a few pages earlier had been only to explain his silence:

I believe, verily, Sagredus, that you are put to a stand; and I believe that I know the cause of your confusion, which, if I mistake not, rises from your understanding part, and only part, of Salviatus' argument. It is true, as you suspect, that I find myself free from the like confusion; but not for that cause which you think, to wit, because I understand the whole. No, it happens quite the contrary, namely, from my not understanding anything; and confusion is in the plurality of things and not in nothing.[4]

This is said not without grace, but it does not build up Simplicio's intellectual stature for the decisive pronouncement with which he is to conclude the discussion. Worse, it is with a repeated admission of incompetence that he prefaces his final saying:

As for the past discourses, and particularly this last, of the reason of the ebbing and flowing of the sea, I do not, to speak the truth, very well comprehend it. But by that slight idea, whatever it be, that I have formed thereof to myself, I confess that your hypothesis seems to me far more ingenious than any of all those that I ever heard besides; still, I esteem it neither true nor conclusive, but, keeping always before the eyes of my mind a solid doctrine that I once received from a most learned and eminent person, and to which there can be no answer, I know that both of you, being asked whether God, by His infinite power and wisdom, might confer upon the element of water the reciprocal motion in any other way than by making the containing vessel to move, I know, I say, that you will answer that He could, and also knew how to bring it about in many ways, and some of them above the reach of our intellect. Upon which I forthwith conclude that, this being granted, it would be an extravagant boldness for anyone to go about to limit and confine the Divine power and wisdom to some one particular conjecture of his own.

SALV.: An admirable and truly angelical doctrine, which is answered with perfect agreement by the other one, in like manner divine, which gives us leave to dispute touching the constitution of the Universe, but adds, withal (perhaps to the end that the exercise of the minds of men might not cease or become remiss), that we are not to find out the works made by His hands. Let, therefore, the disquisition permitted and ordained us by God assist us in the knowing, and so much more admiring, His greatness by how much less we find ourselves capable of penetrating the profound abysses of His infinite wisdom.

SAGR.: And this may serve for a final close of our four days' disputations, after which, if it seem good to Salviatus to take some time to rest himself, our curiosity must, of necessity, grant it to him. . . . In the meantime, we

4. *Dialogue,* p. 456.

may, according to our custom, spend an hour in taking the air in the gondola that waits for us.[5]

After five hundred pages of argument in which words have not been spared on either side, one might have expected something less perfunctory. Nor was Simplicio the man to say it. It was in the character of the obstinate logician to go down fighting and not to save himself with some theological weasel words. It would have been better, artistically and philosophically, if Galileo had followed a line that he obviously considered at a certain point [6] and had Salviati throw aside his Copernican "mask," unveiling himself in a *coup de scène* as a skeptical mystic who resigns all his science to God. We can imagine several possible reasons for the switch, all interesting, but they have to remain pure guesswork.

II

When Galileo announced to his friends in Rome that the *Dialogue* was ready, he got nothing but cheerful messages. Castelli wrote that the road was clear and that Padre Riccardi, who, as Master of the Holy Apostolic Palace, was the chief licenser, promised his ready assistance and asserted that theological difficulties could be circumvented. In another letter Castelli brought the exciting news that the Pope had admitted to Campanella in an audience that the prohibition of 1616 was a nuisance and had added: "It was never Our intention; if it had depended upon Us, that decree would not have been passed." These are not quite the empty words that historians have declared them to be, for we know that he had exerted a restraining influence at the time; but they were certainly such as to encourage the fondest hopes.[7] Ciàmpoli wrote: "You are awaited here more than any most beloved damsel."

5. *Ibid.*, pp. 471–72.
6. *Ibid.*, p. 146.
7. Especially as they were said to Campanella, whom the Pope knew very well to be a passionate anti-Aristotelian, an unreconstructed Copernican, and the author of a *Defense of Galileo* which had been printed in Germany in 1622.

Galileo arrived in Rome on May 3, 1630, and on the eighteenth he was writing: "His Holiness has begun to treat of my affairs in a spirit which allows me to hope for a favorable result." Urban VIII had again indorsed the idea of an astronomical dialogue, provided the treatment were strictly hypothetical, and had left the rest to the licensers. The diplomatic way in which Galileo presented the intention of his work to the Pontiff may be gathered from his "Preface to the Judicious Reader," which opens the *Dialogue*. Urban made only one specific restriction, namely, that the title should not be "On the Flux and Reflux of the Sea" but "On the Two Chief World Systems," for he did not want the book organized around a "necessitating" proof such as that through the tides.

After that, it was time for Father Riccardi to go to work. The bustling "Padre Mostro" went hastily over the manuscript and was not entirely reassured. He did not understand much about astronomy, but the stuff did not look to him as hypothetical as he had been told. He delegated his assistant Father Raffaello Visconti to examine it and make such alterations as were needed. Father Visconti, who was supposed to be versed in mathematics, went over the text, changed a few words here and there, and gave his approval. He had obviously understood insufficiently either the text or the papal instructions. But now the imprimatur for Rome was as good as granted.

Father Riccardi was still not reassured. The hostility of certain circles told him that this was going to mean trouble. But he could not ask the author to rewrite the book, and, besides, he could not imagine exactly how it should be rewritten. To Galileo and the ambassador Niccolini, Riccardi's cousin-in-law, who fed him pleasant Chianti and many assurances, he did not know what to say. He decided he was going to look at the text himself. As this entailed further loss of time, he agreed to pass on to the printer each sheet as soon as revised. But, in order to start, the printer needed a license, so the license was granted, while the text remained in Riccardi's hands. He insisted meanwhile that the Preface and the conclusion be rewritten so as to correspond more exactly to papal intentions. Since the license had been given for

Rome only, and the text was going to be printed under the supervision of Prince Cesi and the Lyncean Academy, he was obviously relying much more on Cesi's assistance than on his own acumen in arranging things.

By the end of June, Galileo, fearing the heat and the "unhealthy air" of Rome (there really was some malaria in the city at the time), left for Florence, with the understanding that he would be back in the autumn with a new version of the Preface and the conclusion. He knew that nothing much would be done during the summer, and he expected to be present while most of the correcting took place.

All looked well; but a few weeks after his return to Florence the grievous news came to Galileo of the death of Prince Cesi. This was an irreparable blow, for no one else could fulfil Cesi's double function of executive and mediator in the difficult enterprise. The situation soon became obscure. On August 24, Castelli, usually a temperament not given to evil suspicions, wrote Galileo urgently, "for many most weighty reasons which he did not wish to commit to paper, to have the work printed at Florence, and as soon as possible." While Galileo was wondering what this might mean, a new factor came to force his decision: the plague of 1630, which had been making fearful ravages in the north (it was the one later classically described in Manzoni's *Promessi Sposi*), showed up sporadically in central Italy, quarantine stations were set up everywhere, and communications became difficult.

Galileo had to rely now on the good offices of the Florentine ambassador. Luckily, it was no longer Guicciardini who had the post but Francesco Niccolini, a faithful friend. He and his wife (she was Riccardi's cousin) had the "Father Monster," as they called him affectionately, as a habitual guest, and now they bent their efforts on extracting a permission from him. Riccardi at first refused; then, yielding to the subtle pressure of Caterina Niccolini, he relented and sent permission to have the final revision done in Florence. The Preface and the conclusion, however, he retained in his hands, "to arrange them according to the wishes of His Holiness."

The Florentine Inquisitor, Father Giacinto Stefani, read the book, changed a few words, but found nothing wrong with it. Indeed, he was "moved to tears at many passages by the humility and reverent obedience displayed by the author." But, still, nothing could come out without the Preface and the conclusion, and Father Riccardi would not let go of them. What follows is a pitiful comedy that it would be useless to detail. From Castelli's dark allusions it is easy to infer that the Jesuits, advised by Grassi and Scheiner, had swung into action. The new opposition was far more dangerous than that of Caccini and his Dominicans. The unfortunate Father Monster, fully aware by now of the delicate situation and of the dangers to his career, was on the rack. He could not very well refuse an imprimatur he had already given, and he did not know how to withhold it. Caught between the Niccolinis on one side and Ciàmpoli on the other, squirming under summons from the Grand Duke, who was, after all, the liege lord of his family, he twisted and turned in despair, delaying, raising new problems, imposing new clauses, pretending he did not have the papers, invoking the reserved intentions of the Holy Father. He asked that still another theologian revise the text in Florence and sent pressing instructions to make sure of the hypothetical treatment.[8] Another revision by the Inquisitor himself, Father Clemente Egidii, and still another imprimatur for the text; but a year had gone by, and still the Preface and concluding statement were lacking.[9] Galileo was in despair. He could

8. The text of his instructions is reproduced on p. 343.
9. It remains a profoundly puzzling question why Riccardi, with all his fears, did nothing about the conclusion, which he retained admittedly in order to "arrange" it. There was a stylistic fault in the text that he could perceive as well as anyone. It would have been easy for him to give the conclusive argument a more adequate formal dressing, such as we have sketched out ourselves on p. 175, following Oregius' paraphrase. Later, he was to say to Magalotti (see p. 200) that there had been in the manuscript "two or three arguments invented by our Lord's Holiness himself" which had been omitted in print. This was obviously not so, for the Preliminary Commission did not sustain the charge. Riccardi was only seeking an excuse for the mental paralysis that had seized him in the face of the text. One explanation might be this: that Galileo had told him that this was exactly how the Pope had wanted it; and it is indeed very possible that Urban, who disliked pedantry, may have given him once the gist of the argument in

show any commission appointed by the Grand Duke, he insisted, that "I have never entertained any other views or opinions than those held by the most venerable Fathers of the Church"; he was willing to describe again and again, if needed, his own theories as "dreams, nullities, paralogisms, and chimeras"; but there was nothing to do against this kind of sabotage. "The months and the years pass," he exclaimed, "my life wastes away, and my work is condemned to rot."

Riccardi obviously did not dare come again before the Pope with his problem and ask for help concerning his wretched revision. He hung himself like an albatross around Ciàmpoli's neck and asked for a direct order. He got his clearance. Even so, he tarried. It was only on July 19, 1631, "dragged by the hair," as Niccolini puts it, that he surrendered the packet to the embassy.

In February, 1632, Galileo was able at last to present to the Grand Duke the first printed copy of the *Dialogue*.

---

those few words that we find in the text. Moreover, Galileo may have thought it clever flattery to couple that "admirable and truly angelical doctrine" with another, "in like manner divine," taken directly from Scripture, and may have insisted on conciseness as part of the rhetorical effect. Riccardi, patently, realized that the effect had not been obtained; but it was then up to him to submit the text to the Pope and ask for a revision, and this he never did.

X The Summons

Flectere si nequeo superos, Acheronta movebo   VIRGIL

I

The book was greeted with rapturous praise by the literary public. The edition sold out as it came from the press. Owing to persistent difficulties of quarantine, it went on sale in Rome only in June. Campanella wrote in great emotion: "These novelties of ancient truths, of new world, new systems, new nations, are the beginning of a new era. Let God make haste, and let us for our small part help all we can. Amen." Father Scheiner had known for a long while that the forthcoming *Dialogue* would not spare him.[1] He was in a bookshop when a

[1]. Father Christopher Scheiner, a German Jesuit from Ingolstadt, had considerable standing as an astronomer and had been once a friend and correspondent of Galileo. But an embittered and rather pointless priority rivalry about the discovery of the sunspots had driven them apart since Scheiner's letters to Mark Welser, published in 1612 under the nom de plume of Apelles, and Galileo's answering *Letters on the Solar Spots* of 1613. Galileo, while writing the *Dialogue,* knew that Scheiner was preparing to revive the twenty-year-old polemic with a frontal attack on the Copernicans in a forthcoming treatise entitled *Rosa Ursina.* The treatise was intended to pay back Galileo not only for Scheiner's personal grudge but also for the defeat of Scheiner's fellow-Jesuit, Horatio Grassi, in the *Saggiatore.* Galileo therefore did not refrain from tackling Scheiner's theories in advance as he was writing the *Dialogue.* This he did—apart from some pointed remarks about the Apelles letters—by singling out a little anti-Copernican treatise of Locher, a favorite pupil of Scheiner, and using it as chief target for his

friar from Siena wandered in, singing its praises. He turned pale, was seized with a fit of trembling, and said to the bookseller: "Ten scudi if you can get me a copy right away." Father Riccardi felt his heart sink. "The Jesuits," he said to Magalotti, "will persecute this with the utmost bitterness."

The letter of Magalotti (August 7) which contains this important item of information is interesting also in other more human respects: "On Monday morning," he writes, "I was in the Church of S. Giovanni, when the most reverend Father [Riccardi], having heard that I was there, came to seek me. He signified to me that it would be agreeable to him were I to give up the whole of the copies of Signor Galileo's book of *Dialogues* which I had brought from Florence, promising to return them in ten days at the farthest. I answered that I regretted infinitely not being able to comply with his wish, for, of the six copies which I had brought, five were for presentation, and his Reverence knew that they had already been presented. . . . He must know that in this particular it was impossible for me to satisfy him. At the very utmost I could only have given him my own and Monsignor Serristori's copy. He appeared sensible of the difficulty but assured me that it was only for the sake of the book and its author that he had wished to have the said copies. Then I took occasion to ask why such diligent perquisition should be made to have the books, since I was sure that if the author were written to, and given to understand the feeling of the Superiors, he would have divined that it was a case for obedience; and that, having received the permission of our Lord's Holiness and of the

destructive refutation. The device was polemically effective and quite legitimate; it even turned out to be a riposte instead of a preventive counterattack, because Scheiner's book came out earlier than the *Dialogue*. It was Scheiner, rather, who was able to launch his preventive counterattack by campaigning against the *Dialogue* two years in advance of its publication and with an adequate idea of its contents. What made the situation worse was that, as Father Athanasius Kircher admitted later (see p. 315), Scheiner was a Copernican at heart and sacrificed throughout his scientific conscience to the political convenience of his superiors. His enmity was not only that of the rival but that of the man who had "sold out" on his beliefs.

Sacred Congregation to publish the work, as anyone might see by the imprimatur in the beginning of it, it was not to be believed that he would fail to give every possible satisfaction. I also hinted that he had already been written to on the subject. To this he answered in the affirmative but without any specification. This, as you know well, was because the dealings of the Holy Office cannot be revealed, even the very smallest particle, under pain of the severest censures. He just added that what had been written and ordered was in a spirit of kindness and leniency and with no object but the glory of God and the tranquillity of Holy Church and that no damage should accrue to the reputation of the author, whom he looked upon as one of his best friends.

"Then he proceeded to disclose another reason for wishing to have these copies of the *Dialogue*. I should be ashamed to repeat it to you, for the sake of his reputation and for the inventor's, only that I know I can speak to you in confidence. It is this. Under the seal of secrecy he told me that great offense had been taken at the emblem which was on the frontispiece, if I recollect aright (I say this because I paid no great attention to the frontispiece and have not the book by me just now). This emblem, unless I am mistaken, consists of three dolphins holding each other's tails in their mouths, with I know not what motto. On hearing this, I burst out laughing and showed him plainly how astonished I was and said I thought I could assure him that Signor Galileo was not the man to hide great mysteries under such puerilities and that he had said what he meant clearly enough. I declared that I believed I could affirm that the emblem was the printer's own. On hearing this, he appeared greatly relieved and told me that, if I indeed could assure him that such was the case (now see what trifles rule our actions in this world), the result would be most happy for the author. I thought I had by me a small book written by a Portuguese doctor about a preventative for the plague which would convince him of the truth of what I was saying. He said my word as a gentleman was quite enough. But I answered that, in case this book had not the emblem on its title-page (which indeed it has not, though it is printed by Landino), I would sent to Florence for what would convince him clearly enough, and he was extremely glad to accept my offer.

"So the matter stands. Other motive for censure I do not think there is, except that already mentioned by the Master of the Sacred Palace; namely, that the book has not been printed precisely according to the original manuscript and that, among other things, two or three arguments have been omitted at the end which were invented by our Lord's Holiness himself and with which, he says, he convinced Signor Galileo of the falsity of the Copernican theory. The book having fallen into His Holiness's hands, and these arguments having been found wanting, it was necessary to remedy the oversight. This is the pretext; but the real fact is that the Jesuit Fathers are working most valiantly in an underhanded way to get the work prohibited. The reverend Father's own words to me were: 'The Jesuits will persecute him most bitterly.' This good Father, being mixed up in the matter himself, fears every stumbling block and wishes naturally to avoid bringing trouble on himself for having given the license. Besides which, we cannot deny that our Lord's Holiness holds an opinion directly contrary to this [of Galileo's].

"Now, if it is true that the original manuscript was altered, I know not what to say; but, if not, it will be easy to convince the authorities, and, once convinced, they can go no further, I should think. . . .

"But if some omission has been made through inadvertence, particularly the omissions I have mentioned, I would advise that the utmost readiness be shown to add, take away, or change, so as to save appearances. Meanwhile do not fail to send me as soon as possible some publication of Landino's, were it but an almanac, that I may be able to show it to the reverend Father, and if possible get me one which was published before the publication of the *Dialogue*."

On receiving this, Galileo must have been staggered by the monstrous hypocrisy of it all, for the suspension was already official, and it had struck him like a bolt out of the blue. On the first of the month the Inquisitor of Florence had presented himself at Landini's bookshop with orders to suspend the publication of the book and to deliver all the copies he had in stock. To this Landini was able to answer blithely that he had not one copy left. Father Riccardi had obviously been unaware that the scandal was in the open while he was trying to worm and writhe his way out of the predicament.

While letters of congratulation were still pouring in, Galileo was furiously denouncing the miserable intrigues of his enemies and warning that an unheard-of abuse of authority must have taken place somewhere. But on August 21 he received a fighting letter from Father Campanella which confirmed the bad news:

I have heard that they are having a commission of irate theologians to prohibit your *Dialogue;* and there is no one on it who understands mathematics or recondite things.

Please note that you may hold that the opinion of the moving Earth was properly forbidden, without having also to believe that the reasons alleged are good. This is a theological rule, and it can be proved, for in the Nicene Council it was decreed that "the angels may be portrayed because they are truly corporeal." The decree is valid but not the motivation, for all Scholastics say, in our time, that angels are incorporeal. There are many more grounds.

I fear the violence of people who do not know. The Father Monster makes fearful noises against; and, says he, *ex ore Pontificis.* But His Holiness is not informed, nor can he think this way. My advice is, have the Grand Duke write that, as they have put Dominicans, Jesuits, Theatines, and secular priests on this commission, they should admit also Father Castelli and myself, and if they win, *succumbemus,* etc., even in the proposition, let alone the reasons. But I am not supposed to know about it, *quia,* etc. Or you may ask for us as lawyer and attorney in the case; and, if we do not win it, hold me for an ass. I know the Pope is of great mind and when he will be informed, etc. God keep you.

Galileo must have read it with a variety of feelings, for the grand old friar was known to be an adept at getting himself into trouble. Nothing daunted by the news, however, he wrote the draft of a stiff diplomatic note, which the Grand Duke, who shared his concern, ordered promptly signed by his secretary of state and dispatched. It requested of the Pope the appointment of a mixed commission in Florence to investigate the matter. But when Niccolini, on September 5, called at the Vatican with the protest, he was met with a blast from Urban that checked his prepared statement. "Your Galileo," the Pope fairly shouted at him, "has ventured to meddle with things that he ought not and with the most grave and dangerous subjects that can be stirred up in these days."

I replied [Niccolini goes on] that Signor Galileo had not printed his work without the approval of the Vatican. He [the Pope] replied with the same fury that he and Ciàmpoli had circumvented him, especially Ciàmpoli, who had dared tell him that Galileo would be entirely guided by the papal commands and that all was well; and it was all he had known without ever having seen or read the book. He made bitter complaints against Ciàmpoli and Father Riccardi, although he said the latter had been circumvented too, for with fair words had been extracted from him first the license, and then again a permission to print in Florence without following the instructions given to the Inquisitor, and then also putting on it Riccardi's name, which has nothing to do with licenses outside of Rome. Here I came back, saying that I knew a special commission had been appointed, and since it might happen (as is the case) that there might be persons in it evilly disposed toward Galileo, I respectfully begged him to give him a chance to justify himself. Then His Holiness replied that, in these affairs of the Holy Office, nothing is ever done but to pronounce judgment and then to summon to retract. I answered: "Does it not then appear to your Holiness that Galileo should be informed beforehand of the difficulties, oppositions, and censures that are made to his work and what it is that annoys the Holy Office?" He answered violently: "The Holy Office, We are telling you, sir, does not proceed in that way and does not take that course, nor does it ever give information beforehand. It is not the custom. *Besides, he knows well enough what the difficulties are, if he wants to know them; for We have discussed them with him, and he knew them all from Ourselves.*" And as I represented that the book had been dedicated to the Most Serene Master, that it was a matter of one of his servants, and that I humbly hoped that some consideration would be shown, he said that in these things which might bring religion very great prejudice, of the worst that has ever been invented, His Highness must concur in punishing them, as he is a Christian prince, and that therefore I must write him not to become involved in this if he wants to come out of it with honor.

Niccolini was no fool, and he had realized by now that the Pope was blustering. There had been an unavowed tension in those last months between the Holy See and Tuscany, for the Grand Duke could not but side with the Hapsburgs at that turn in the Thirty Years' War which had brought the Pope to the side of France. The Pope was now scoring an unexpected advantage by threatening with the spiritual weapon that he alone could wield. But the flimsy complaints brought up were nothing that could be made to look like heresy. Niccolini took occasion from those last words to counter on his own initiative with a clear diplomatic threat:

I answered it was certain I would get orders to have to weary him still further, as I was doing, but that still I could not believe that His Beatitude would go so far as to countenance the prohibition of a book that had been already approved, without first hearing Signor Galilei.

This meant: "We stand on good ground. If you want to bring about an international incident, please go ahead and suit yourself." The Pope was aware that he had ventured on thin ice and that he was being politely told now to mind his own business—which was confusion and insubordination in his own house. But it was not easy for him to retreat. He unmasked his batteries.

He said prohibition was the least that could happen to him [Galileo], and *he had better take care he was not summoned before the Holy Office;* that he had decreed a commission of theologians and of other persons versed in different sciences, all grave men and of holy mind, who would weigh every particular, word for word, for it was a question of the most perverse business that could ever be handled. And he went on with grievances against him and Ciàmpoli. Then he charged me to inform our Master that the doctrine was perverse in the extreme; everything would be maturely considered; let his Highness not commit himself and proceed softly. . . . He added he had acted with great consideration for Galileo, by having impressed upon him what he knows and by not having referred his affairs, as he ought to have done, to the Holy Office but to a specially appointed commission. Which was something. He concluded: "I have used him better than he used me, for he deceived me."

The Pope had used the threat of the Inquisition in order to browbeat the Grand Duke, but it was clear he did not see very well as yet how it could be carried through. It was to this end, and not out of any consideration, that a special commission had been appointed.[2] If it did not discover sufficient grounds, and if the Grand Duke stood firm, the Pope might find himself in a very difficult position indeed. But the dreadful specter of heresy had been raised, and with that he had won his first round.

Niccolini's report came as a bombshell in Florence, knocking out a whole set of patient political combinations, and sent the ministers scurrying for cover. "The Grand Duke," quavers Cioli, the new secretary of state, "has read your dispatches and has come into such a violent upset of anger that I do not know what will happen next. What I know is that his Holiness will never have to blame the ministers here for giving bad advice."

II

Galileo was aghast and utterly at a loss to understand what was the matter from the roundabout messages of his friends in Rome. The secretary of state was reticent, for Niccolini's dispatches were under the seal of strictest secrecy.

What had actually happened began gradually to transpire. Certain Jesuits, apparently the only ones in the administration who could read the book and understand it, had shown the Pope that under the

2. The Pope said again a few days later that "the commission had been formed out of the ordinary to see whether it would be possible not to bring the matter before the Holy Office" (dispatch of September 18). Now, as we shall see from the report of the commission, the several enumerated counts of Galileo's transgression do not contain any reference to the Inquisition. In fact, it is admitted that they might involve merely corrections in the text. It is only because of a new document discovered by the Holy Office that the possibility of prosecution comes up. This goes far to deny the Pope's contention.

rhetorical mask the whole argument was a compelling plea for the Copernican system. While Grienberger and the old hands were looking on with mixed feelings,[3] Grassi, Scheiner, and their group had sparked the vast forces of the Society of Jesus into a purely political campaign against these novelties which threatened its hold on education, the whole carefully controlled and contained "humanistic" program on which they brought up the ruling classes—and beyond those the principle of authority itself. As Stelluti had once warned Galileo, once the Society had come in, he was never going to see the end of this business.[4] The personal vanity of the Pope had been cleverly roused when it was represented to him that his argument against the tides had been put into the mouth of Simplicio the simple, obviously to ridicule him. Nothing could have been further from the author's mind. He had simply obeyed his instructions literally by letting the Aristotelian have the last word; but he had understood this as a purely formal clause, not to be carried through artistically. Riccardi seems to have concurred in this view, since he did not request any addition to that section which he pondered over for months, searching for new ways to make it "safe."

There is no fury like a philosopher scorned. Urban VIII, as Cardinal Bentivoglio said of him, liked to lay down the law in all fields of human knowledge. Amid the chorus of respectful indorsement, this one single voice had aroused in him the sharp feeling that perhaps he was not taken very seriously as an intellectual, for indeed he could realize that Galileo, for all the proper compliments, had made his "medicine of the end" look pretty silly. "There is one argument that *they* will never answer," the Pope was to complain to Niccolini, like so many frustrated authors before and since; and, as he mentioned it, says the ambassador, his fury rose again in most unpastoral fashion. Even after

3. Torricelli's letter, September 11, 1932. See pp. 213–14.
4. "It would be a business of which you would never see the end if you picked a quarrel with those Fathers, for they are so many that they could take on the whole world, and, even if they are wrong, they would never concede it . . . the more so as they are no friends of the new opinions" (January 27, 1620).

Galileo's death, ten years later, his rancor was unabated. Niccolini describes him then as a very old man, his head sunk so low that it was on a level with his shoulders. But when the talk came around to Galileo, and he intimated that he would not countenance a monument over his enemy's grave, he was impelled to recount all that he had explained to him once, and what the other had tried to answer, "and before he was through with it a long time had gone by."

It is, however, somewhat unfair of historians to expand upon this Simplicio incident as the single motivation of the Pope's actions. The business was unpleasant enough without it. It looked as though he had been fooled successfully and in a legally airtight way. As a matter of simple truth, of course, it was he who had fooled himself by reserving decision for himself and then not having an expert advise him, by handing down instructions through Riccardi in a matter that neither of them understood, by telling Ciàmpoli several contradictory things in his changing moods, and by leaving Ciàmpoli to take a flying chance on one of his remarks. But this he could not bring himself to admit. He decided that the real cause was a conspiracy involving his closest collaborators. It was tantamount to disaffection; it was as though his own staff had silently manifested their lack of confidence in his own superior judgment. A ruler in that predicament is apt to lose his head; many horrid doubts may have come to him in the watches of the night. He had been a Pope now for nine years, his autocratic grand policy must begin to be judged by its fruits, and there was not much to show.

The Emperor of Austria himself, the mainstay of the Church, the author of the Edict of Restitution, was no longer in such a good position, and, what is worse, he was no longer a friend. The initiative in the great game had passed to his main opponent, Richelieu, who had won his most far-reaching victory, namely, the launching of Gustavus Adolphus of Sweden. He had pried apart the Austro-Spanish coalition, forcing the Italian powers into his system, so that the Pope had found himself bound in covert alliance with him—and the Swedish heretic— against the House of Austria. And right now the newly risen power in the north was beginning to frighten Rome. Even as Niccolini came in

for his audience, the Pope must have received the news that the
Swedish king had neutralized Brandenburg and been joined by the
Saxons. In another three weeks he was to hear that the only Catholic
army in the field, that of Tilly, had been destroyed at Breitenfeld. But
worse than the alarming advance of the heretic must have been the
galling awareness for Urban that all this upset was the carrying-out of
the plans of Richelieu and that infernal Père Joseph, the men who had
financed Gustavus Adolphus with five tubfuls of gold and were now
on their way to establishing the paramountcy of France in Catholic
Europe. Urban's great combinations and diplomatic maneuvers had
been in vain, as had been his attempts to carve out a domain in Italy
at the expense of his associates, and his own underhanded dealings
with the Swedes. He had quarreled with the Emperor, had been threatened and humiliated by Spain, was checkmated in Italy itself by the
Venetian Republic. And now this.

Urban VIII must have felt the issuing of the *Dialogue* at this juncture as a churlishly planned aggravation of Fate. Although harassed
by politics, he was intelligent enough to perceive that the argument
about the heavens threatened the very bases of the educational system
established since Trent; he could appreciate the reasons of incensed
Jesuits who told him that this kind of thing was potentially more
disastrous than Luther or Calvin.[5] And he himself in Maecenian vanity

5. See p. 229. The other considerations are inferred from the Pope's own words.
There is also a desperate letter of Campanella, October 22: "If I were to write to
you the reasons and interests that move them against you while they should not,
you would be staggered. *Ex arcanis eorum sacris et politicis.* But I was not admitted. . . ." They are the reasons that were set forth later in Inchofer's *Tractatus syllepticus,* where it is said indeed that it is more criminal to disbelieve the
mobility of the Sun than the immortality of the soul. How far did those reasons
weigh in the actual inception of the scandal? There is hardly a hint of them in
the contemporary documents. Even outside observers like Buonamici, Peiresc,
Gassendi, and their informants saw nothing in the crisis but the work of personal
hatreds. "Le Père Scheiner luy a joué ce tour, *ut creditur."* This opinion is echoed
on all sides. But, instead of subsiding after the trial, the antiscientific movement
gained momentum steadily in the next decades, and this shows that political decisions had taken place, at least immediately after 1632. In 1693, sixty-one years

had encouraged the author. He was in a cleft stick.

The judgment of political observers in Rome reflects his quandary. The ambassador from Modena wrote home in November shortly after the news of the death of Gustavus Adolphus at Lützen and of the uncovering of the Pope's secret alliance with the Swede: "Instead of bringing him back to his senses, these events moved him only to fury. He has lost his head to the point that he will act without the least judgment."

Precluded from satisfacory action, Urban's anger vented itself on his hapless subordinates. Riccardi was called on the carpet and anxiously protested his innocence. He was able to show that he had delivered the papers only on receipt of a clearance from Ciàmpoli. As for Ciàmpoli himself, he had nothing to show, for he had boldly used whatever words the Pope had let fall upon some undefined occasion.[6]

Riccardi managed to retain his post, but Ciàmpoli was finished. The prelate who but a few weeks before had been rated for elevation to cardinal in the next Consistory was exiled as governor to the small town of Montalto della Marca, later transferred several times to obscure posts. He was never allowed to return to Rome. His letters to Galileo in 1633 are those of a man who has made his peace with the world. "Come to see me, my persecuted Socrates," he wrote, "we shall

---

after these events, Viviani, by then a very old man, asked for permission to issue a corrected edition of the *Dialogue*. Newton's *Principia* had already come out. But this is what his friend Father Baldigiani had to tell him: "There is a general movement here in Rome against the physicists. Extraordinary meetings of the cardinals and of the Holy Office are taking place, and there is talk of a general prohibition against all authors of the new physics, including Gassendi, Galileo, and Descartes."

6. From what the Pope said to Niccolini, we can infer that Ciàmpoli had simply vouched for Galileo's argument being strictly orthodox and had begged the Pope to relieve the censors of their fears about a text that they could not understand, much less arrange to suit their scruples. The Pope must have accepted his assurances and his promises as a way out rather than have to spend his own time on the question. Ciàmpoli's play had obviously been to make the Pope feel that only those two great minds, his and Galileo's, could understand each other and that he could count on Galileo's following the spirit of his instructions.

take good care of your health here. . . . As for myself, I have found my consolation in study, and I still hope to write something whereby I may be remembered." He died in Iesi ten years later, at the age of fifty-four. When Urban VIII heard of the passing of the man in whom he had once placed so much trust, he was moved to say: "Another great person is gone."

III

If the Pope felt that he had been successfully fooled, he had considerable reasons which Galileo might have perceived well in advance. Yet Galileo seems to have refused even to consider them. He was obviously dismayed at the turn of events, but he did not cower as the man who has been found out, nor did he evince the helpless resignation of Ciàmpoli, who knew himself beyond appeal. He, like the Pope, was genuinely angry, and his anger may be clearly perceived in his letter under the words of submissive protestation. From the very genuineness of his anger we may infer that the Pope had given him something fairly substantial in the way of authorization. If these people now—and he still thought of the palace executives—did not know how to play the game according to the rules, or were swayed by puny intrigues, he would give them his mind. He had been authorized to write on Copernicanism; he had not been asked to lie but only to profess obedience; his text had been approved.[7] He had not spoken in the first person; he had let a literary character defend a position, which much more godless fictionary characters had been allowed to do. As to the thesis itself, long ago tried out in the *Letter to Ingoli,* it had had the ample written indorsement of Riccardi to the Florence Inquisitor, sent just before the printing. The text had been revised and rerevised,

---

7. Campanella had called Aristotle and the Scholastics all sorts of names, had come out boldly for the Copernican system, and had propounded new and arbitrary interpretations of Scripture, but it had been enough to protect him that he should have written at the end of his *Defense of Galileo:* "In the above discussion, I at all times submit myself to the correction and better judgment of our Holy Mother the Apostolic Roman Church."

licensed and relicensed, and then licensed again, in two cities; it had been prefaced and provided with a proper ending and even with a title by the highest authority. There they were, the five imprimaturs, "together, dialogue-wise, in the piazza of the title-page, complimenting and ducking each other with their shaven reverences." [8] What more could the strictest discipline require? His strongly rooted juridical sense made him conclude that someone here was getting out of hand; and, as it could not be the licensing authorities themselves, it must be an informal conspiracy that had momentarily captured the Pope's judgment, and he should expose it.

It cannot be maintained, as Wohlwill does, that this was simply the old man's self-delusion, for we have the same opinion reflected more or less strongly by his Roman correspondents, who were not simpletons. Old Filippo Magalotti, who had taken the place left vacant by Cesi, is explicit:

You need not fear that the commission can ask the authorities to declare the Copernican opinion damnable and heretical; even if they decided that the opinion is false, I do not believe that it would be requested to be declared such by the supreme authority; I tell you this because I am told so by the members of the Congregation of the Holy Office, which handles dogmatic matters. They say that there are in the Church controversial matters wherein the authority of the Fathers is divided, such as, e.g., the Immaculate Conception; and they all say definitely that without a most urgent necessity, or without the declaration of a General Council, such issues can never come to a head. Now this is certainly not the way things are tending, and the Padre Maestro too is of opinion that it will come to a slight arrangement of your *Dialogue* by adding or removing a few things.

Niccolini, an experienced diplomat, who should have felt uneasy about his own involvement, says the same. And yet he had faced the Pope in his anger. The archbishop of Siena, Ascanio Piccolomini, an experienced churchman, wrote on September 29:

It seems exceeding strange to me that such a recent and precise approba-

8. Milton, *Areopagitica.*

tion should be opposed by the passions of some people who might find fault only in what they conceive of the book, for the work itself ought to appease the most timid conscience. On the other hand, I will say you deserve this and worse, for you have been disarming by steps those who have control of the sciences, and they have nothing left but to run back to holy ground.

As for Castelli, he wrote: "This is the time to stand up to them and answer with the words of Copernicus to Paul III: *Illos nihil moror.* . . ." And later: "I have said openly that if the Inquisition were really called in, and if this holy and supreme tribunal did not proceed in the manner that is due, it would work damage to the reputation and reverence owed to it, and that, if they prosecuted a man who had written so modestly, reverently, and reservedly, it would mean that others would henceforth write brutally and resolutely."

The consensus of the correspondents is: "There is nothing they can do to you. But things are out of hand for a while, because the Pope has made an impulsive move. Sit tight, do not yield more than you have to, but do not irritate them." We have from more than one source the same colloquial expression: "*They* have gone off half-cocked, and now they feel they have to run the tilt; when they come back, it will be time to talk." But there was also nervousness around, because it was realized that they had to deal with a spoiled amateur of absolute power who was playing by ear.

As most of those who have the responsibility of advice feel themselves constrained to "pussyfooting," it is like a breath of fresh air to have the uninhibited opinion of the good friar of Venice, Fra Fulgenzio Micanzio:

But what miserable sect can that be to which anything that is good and founded in Nature by necessity appears contrary and odious? The world is not limited to a single corner; you shall see your work printed in many places and languages.[9] . . . My worry is that I may see myself deprived of

9. This reassurance is repeated in several letters: "Il suo dialogo andrà in molte lingue, e sbattasi chi vuole" (August 5, 1631).

the thing I hoped for most, your other dialogues that were coming [i.e., the *Two New Sciences*]; if they are stopped because of this, I shall send to a hundred thousand devils these hypocrites without Nature and without God.

In Rome itself there were many who were not at all impressed by all this talk of heresy. A still obscure young scientist by name of Torricelli (a discovery of Ciàmpoli) turned to Galileo right in the turmoil of those September days. He wrote, shyly introducing himself as "Copernican by conviction, by profession and sect Galileist." He had defended the thesis of the book with Father Grienberger, who was his friend, he said, and who expressed only mild disapproval.

IV

The sane people, the "cautious optimists," turned out to be wrong. They had not yet realized that the authorities had gone off the deep end. But there was one man at least who should have entertained fewer illusions, and that was Galileo himself. He knew best what the book meant, and what the Pope had meant on his side, and what an abyss divided the two conceptions. Once the Pope's eyes had been opened, Galileo had everything to fear. Yet, strangely enough, he is the "fightingest" of them all. He is sure he can convince the authorities if they but give him a chance; he privately asks, as Campanella had suggested, for a discussion *in concilio Patrum*. He wants to go over the book point by point with any committee which may be appointed. Yet "unworldliness" is not the word that describes him; and he knew the value of discretion. Even his enemy Piero Guicciardini had granted him that.

To expatiate on hybris as has so often been done is no explanation. Galileo thought his personal position juridically sound, but he knew it to be politically weak. The infinite deliberation he displayed in bringing out the *Saggiatore* is the best proof. Then why, in an old man of worldly experience, this venture, this—as it turned out—truly insensate gamble? If he had only wanted to publish his ideas, he could easily have played safe. The man who had composed the *Saggiatore* knew he could write rings around the censors (even the judges at the trial were unable to find fault with the pamphlet). There was one obvious and quite easy way that he was, in fact, compelled to consider later—but it was then too late. He could have concluded the *Dialogue* by having Simplicio, or perhaps better Sagredo, produce triumphantly out of a hat the Tychonic system, which had never been discussed, and have Salviati, tongue in cheek, admit himself vanquished; this would have allowed him to conclude more convincingly with the Pope's wisdom. The Church would have indorsed this, for it was as good as the hard-working Jesuit Riccioli could invent in 1657 to refute Galileo officially in his *Almagestum novum*.

Moreover, if he had wanted to look utterly innocent, Galileo could have sacrificed what he knew perfectly well to be an untenable, if enticing, theory on circular fall [10] and himself produced Riccioli's "crushing physicomathematical argument," which would have confused the trail completely. Riccioli made a fool of himself with it, as Borelli did not scruple to show in 1668, notwithstanding the still rigid prohibitions; yet he was universally applauded as a champion of the faith. All the more easily could Galileo have clowned with such devices, since the rest of the *Dialogue* left no doubt as to where reason lay. His vanity, which was great, would have found its profits therein, for he would have been complimented by all and sundry, including the hypocrites, while the scientific-minded would have read between the lines. He and his friends might have sat back to enjoy the joke on the authorities. The book would have penetrated freely and quietly to destroy gradually the established teachings of Church philosophy, while Galileo's position remained secure for his lifetime.

He might have done this; he might have done even less, viz., had Salviati step forth to offer himself the "medicine of the end"—and yet he had refused to do it and still did. He gambled everything on speaking the truth unequivocally. It was a reckless gamble, but it was a generous one. Galileo knew very well that he was working a surprise coup. He had been sufficiently warned on his theory of the tides, as

10. *Dialogue*, p. 178.

the Pope said to Niccolini, and the Pope was right. But he expected the argument to be so irresistible as to checkmate his enemies, bring even the authorities to a grudging acceptance, and so to save Catholic science in this perilous crisis. After all, they had scrutinized it; they could not very well admit they had not understood a word of it. No sane man will run his head into the stone wall of logic once he has been shown the wall. The old illusion of 1615 took long to die in the scientist's mind. And this time, too, he did have written permission. He knew, beyond doubt, that he had disregarded the Pope's explicit intentions. But he was strong in his certainty that he had not disobeyed the edicts of the Church. He obviously thought—as Ciàmpoli did, for that matter—that he had to contend with the fancies of a vain and headstrong but brilliant personality who was still, for all his pontifical robes, the old Maffeo Barberini whom he had known and loved. There is scarcely an intelligent man who will not believe that people in power cannot take themselves seriously all of the time and who will not naïvely extend to them his sympathy in the hope of a shade of refreshing complicity in return, of a trace of humor.

Galileo had far more positive grounds than these wistful ones, however, for his hope; these should be spelled out, since no one seems to have noticed them. In 1616, at least so Buonamici says, it was the *Letter to the Grand Duchess* which had provided Maffeo Barberini with the grounds he needed to withstand a proclamation of heresy.[11] No one had acknowledged it openly; discreet silence had prevailed among the parties. But Galileo knew by this that Barberini's bark was worse than his bite. He was in a way entitled to hope for a second stage of the same coy performance. He was even more entitled to expect it, in that Barberini, as Pope Urban VIII, had shown himself not ungenerous intellectually or a narrow-minded fanatic. He had, two years previously, saved Campanella, notwithstanding the old communist's infinite philosophical indiscretions (which included avowed Coperni-

---

11. Or at least Galileo was sure it was so, which amounts to the same thing in this case. It is his version of the story that has been preserved in Buonamici's diary, of which more on p. 311.

canism), and gotten him out of the jail of the Spanish Inquisition in Naples, where he had rotted for years as the result of a truly devilish persecution plot.

Galileo had, thus, grounds to think that he could force Urban's hand ever so little, while appealing to Barberini's judgment; and, beyond the first moment of spite, he expected understanding and magnanimity. It was reasonable of him to hope, if only to hope, that the Pontiff, under the impression of the *Dialogue,* would become his secret ally and, while pretending aloofness, would quietly move to extricate the Church from her scientific impasse. Even if that were too much to expect, he had certainly the right to expect a measure of intelligence or, at least, discretion in these men who were intrusted with steering the Christian Republic—or, at the very least, diplomacy.

Shall we call this self-begotten blindness, conceit born of applause and flattery? Shall we call it deluded trust in one's fellow-men, a trust certainly strengthened by their liberal compliments but shown at its best in Galileo's patient and unremitting attempts at reasoning with them? These and similar psychological motives have been presented to satiety. What should be considered more seriously are the political factors.

As we stated at the outset, Urban VIII and his court may be considered much less the oppressors of science than the first bewildered casualties of the scientific age. They did not have the least idea of the momentum of the new type of thinking. Only one group of men could, or should, at least have guessed: and those were the Jesuit astronomers. They were more than half-convinced that Galileo was right—we would know this from Father Kircher even if we did not have any other sources. Galileo had plenty of information about their thought, and he kept expecting that, whatever their personal feelings, their duty to the Faith would cause them to interpose a word of advice. It was they, and no one else, whose obligation it was to prevent the Pope from making a fool of himself. But the vast apparatus of indoctrination and constriction that their Order had devised was now working to its own undoing. Following "like unto corpses" the corporate political will of their Society, they shut their eyes, their ears, and their minds. The power of discipline fed back into the complex steering machinery in a circuit of self-destruction.

Thus, beyond the failure of the evaluating mechanism, we are led back to that "political will" of which the Jesuits had become the spearhead but which was shared in various measure by all the hierarchy; and here the pattern becomes visible at last. Galileo had once thrown down the challenge, and now he was going to pay for it. The original challenge went far back in time. He had become a danger when he started writing in Italian and when he decided to bypass the universities and vested intellectual authority and reveal his mind to enlightened public opinion. This was traditional enough as a move. Had not Dante had recourse to vernacular for reasons not very dissimilar from his own? But, then, Dante had remained in the eyes of the authorities a very suspicious character, and so, clearly, was he.

In short, this man was a troublemaker. The scientist as an isolated specialist had not been understood as a social danger, which he might well be considered to be, even to the present day. It was Galileo, the Renaissance figure who wanted the scientific awareness spread to the whole advancing front of his civilization, from its expressive and technological capacities and its critical activity to its philosophical reflection, who appeared as a dangerous novelty-monger.

"If," writes Joseph de Maistre patronizingly, "if he had not written, as he had promised not to; if he had not tried to prove Copernicus by way of Scripture; if he had only written in Latin. . . ." Three untruths and one unhelpful suggestion. The proper balanced formula. We may still pick up gingerly the one suggestion. There is that typical "prudence" in it. If he had written in Latin, he would have left it to someone else like Foscarini or Bruno to tell the facts in the vernacular and take the consequences, for such things were not to be kept under a bushel. As to himself, true enough, he would have risked at most being put on the Index, for, in sum, what could it matter? Of the writing of unreadable tomes there is no end.

Let us try, standing under the correction of better-informed authorities, to put some substantive content into the frivolous Maistrian *if*'s.

If he had waited another century or so for his superiors to understand; *if* he had not inevitably collided with the monopoly of the most powerful organization within the Church, self-charged with controlling the flow of new ideas; *if* he had not felt he had to go over their heads, urgently, to the responsible minds in what still remained the fundamental entity, the *Ecclesia,* the Community. . . . Why, surely.

He had laid himself wide open instead. Those who still refer to the Preface of the *Dialogue* as a miserably ineffectual piece of hypocrisy seem to be overlooking that he was saying specifically what had to be said both ways, and so carefully said, that even the inadvertent italicizing of it could become explosive, as Magalotti reported wryly:

"There is no want of such as inadvisedly affirm that the decree was not the production of sober scrutiny but of an ill-informed passion, and one may hear some mutter that consultors altogether ignorant of astronomical observations ought not to clip the wings of speculative minds with rash prohibition. My zeal cannot keep silence when I hear these inconsiderate complaints. . . . I was at that time in Rome and had not only the audience but applauds of the most eminent prelates of that court; nor was the decree published without previous information given me thereof. Therefore, it is my resolution in the present case to give foreign nations to see that of this matter as much is understood in Italy, and particularly in Rome, as transalpine diligence could imagine. . . . I hope that by these considerations the world will come to know that, if other nations have navigated more than we, we have not studied less than they; and that our returning to assert the Earth's stability and to take the contrary for a mathematical fantasy proceeds not from lack of acquaintance with others' ideas thereof but (had we no other inducements) from those reasons that piety, religion, the knowledge of the Divine Omnipotence, and a consciousness of the incapacity of man's understanding dictate to us."

This is the formal cover that was needed in order to write the book at all. It had to pretend to be like so many authorized books, an empty and noncommittal exercise in philosophical rhetoric, an arrangement of Japanese flowers—in brief, some kind of work of art. The Master of the Holy Palace had found the presentation "just right" and insisted that it be not altered further.

A mere cover it was, though, a flimsy veil of convention which stood by tacit agreement. As is the rule in such matters, whoever touched it made a fool of himself. In the clear, for the "Judicious Reader" (*Discreto Lettore*) to whom those words were addressed, it made excellent sense: "Since the authorities have chosen to get themselves into a jam, and refuse to realize it, it is for us, the Italian believers, to extricate them quickly and inconspicuously so as to save their face, before our faith suffers humiliation at the hands of its enemies." (Once the veil of convention was torn, once the book was malevolently scrutinized, it became impossible to construe the Preface otherwise, as was to be ragingly pointed out by the experts for prosecution.)

The audience with Bellarmine is underlined in that text, challengingly, with the quiet pride that becomes the acknowledged consultant. At the hour of what he knows to be scientific victory, Galileo is generously throwing the mantle of his intellectual prestige around the authorities so as to cover their past incompetence and obduracy. And this, more than anything else, more than what was said about his theological "meddling," his derogatory tongue, his infernal telescope —this was what could not be forgiven.

V

The fourth act of the tragedy had started. On the first of October the Inquisitor of Florence appeared at Galileo's house and served him with a formal summons, on the part of the Holy Office, to present himself in Rome within thirty days. Galileo realized at last with terror the full gravity of the situation; he took to his bed in unfeigned sickness. In a letter to Cardinal Francesco Barberini, Urban's nephew, he begged to be spared the winter voyage, fearing that, in his condition, he would not terminate it alive. "I curse the time devoted to these studies in which I strove and hoped to move away somewhat from the beaten path. I repent having given the world a portion of my writings; I feel inclined to consign what is left to the flames and thus placate at last the inextinguishable hatred of my enemies."

He still suggested, however, that a revision of his book might appease the authorities, and he asked that a commission be appointed in Florence to supervise it. But, he concluded, "if neither my great age, nor my many bodily infirmities, nor the depth of my grief, nor the hazards of a journey in such a condition are considered sufficient reasons, by this high and sacred tribunal, for granting a dispensation, or at least a delay, I will undertake the journey, esteeming obedience to be worth more than life."

With this Galileo was not only trying for a last intercession; he was also giving notice to his protectors that he would not try to escape, as he might well have done, for he had received among others, it seems, a message from Francesco Morosini. Magnanimously forgetting the break that had occurred between them twenty years before, when Galileo left Padua, the old statesman had offered him the inviolable sanctuary of Venetian territory. We know that several of his friends were urging him to do just that, and it would appear that even Niccolini—very privately—inclined to the same advice. But at that juncture the fight seemed to have gone out of the old man. He was no Sarpi, to organize his defiance within great and recognized issues of power policy. He had held up to then in his own mind, not much caring, two incompatible frames of reference which had grown out of the contradiction of the times —for he was deeply a man of his times. Now the precarious security had been shattered, and he found himself suddenly a helpless displaced person, an old man, broken and sick, "struck from the book of the living," in need of some kind of protection and comfort. The pallid specter of fear, a craving for acceptance and forgiveness, and the humiliation of begging were besieging the man who had hitherto been a joyous and whimsical warrior.

What had happened in Rome, unfortunately, made the last attempt at a compromise worse than futile. In fact, the Pope was given the letter by Cardinal Barberini, and he annotated curtly: "Business settled in last Congregation. No further answer needed. See from Assessor whether orders have been carried out." But Galileo was still in the dark concerning the latest events. If he had known, he might have reconsidered his decision to deliver himself up.[12]

On September 11 Niccolini had received a very agitated Padre Riccardi, who had again advised prudence and submissiveness, for the *Dialogue,* it appeared now, had really been a signal piece of disobedience. He had tried, he said, to get Campanella and Castelli on the Preliminary Commission but had failed; he would still do all he could. "But, above all, he told me, under the seal of absolute confidence and secrecy, that there had been found in the books of the Holy Office that, sixteen years ago, it having been heard that Galileo entertained this opinion and spread it in Florence, *he had been summoned to Rome and forbidden by Cardinal Bellarmine in the name of the Pope and the Holy Office to discuss this opinion, and that this alone is enough to ruin him utterly.*"

The situation had changed, and obviously in a sense that no one had foreseen; for, when Urban made his scene before Niccolini on the fifth, he had shouted that "Galileo should take care not to be summoned by the Holy Office." Expatiating on Galileo's crimes, he had accused him of coaxing a permission out of the licensers and of sundry minor transgressions which really implied only laxness on the part of the censors and administrative short cuts on the part of the author; but it was clear that, if he thought of referring the case to the Inquisition, he did not yet see exactly how it could be done.

It was with that end in mind that the Preliminary Commission had gone to work, and the results had been gratifying. What they had found in the acts of the Inquisition was the injunction of February 26, 1616, on the part of the Commissary-General (p. 134) with the clause "not to teach in whatsoever manner" that no one had suspected before

---

12. Cf. Buonamici's memorandum: "He obeyed against the opinion and advice of his truest friends, who would have had him go abroad, write an apology, and not expose himself to the impertinent and ambitious passion of a monk [i.e., the Commissary-General of the Inquisition]."

and least of all the Pope himself, who had told Galileo to go ahead and write about Copernicus.

This was what Riccardi, in great agitation, confided to Niccolini on September 11. Something new had been added which made the prosecution possible. It was also—but this he did not say—what saved his head and deflected the storm on Galileo. Fright turned him henceforth into a man of perfidious counsel.

The Preliminary Commission had just then, after five sessions, which took about a month, submitted to the Pope a three-page memorandum on the Galileo affair.[13] The three following indictments were outlined against the author: (1) Galileo has transgressed orders in deviating from the hypothetical treatment by decidedly maintaining that the Earth moves and that the Sun is stationary; (2) he has erroneously ascribed the phenomena of the tides to the stability of the Sun and the motion of the Earth, which do not exist; and (3) he has further been deceitfully (*fraudolentemente*) silent about the command laid upon him by the Holy Office, in the year 1616, which was as follows: *"To relinquish altogether the said opinion that the Sun is the center of the world and immovable and that the Earth moves; nor henceforth to hold, teach, or defend it in any way whatsoever, verbally or in writing, otherwise proceedings would be taken against him by the Holy Office, which injunction the said Galileo acquiesced in and promised to obey."*

Then follows the remark: "It must now be considered what proceedings are to be taken, both against the person of the author and against the printed book." Yet the nature of these proceedings is not

13. Ed. Naz., XIX, 324. It is amusing to note that the scribe had written "Campanella" and then erased it to replace it with "Galileo." This *lapsus* ought to show that the great utopian had caused considerable comment in the Commission with his request to be consulted. No one had forgotten his *Defense of Galileo,* published in Germany in 1622. In fact, he had been threatened. He wrote to Galileo on October 22: "They had their committee, with many invectives against the new philosophers, etc. And I was named too." It did nothing to improve the atmosphere. What with Sarpi and Campanella and the "German mathematicians," it was plain in Rome that Galileo did not have the right kind of friends.

in any way discussed in the document, but it now refers "as to fact" in five counts to the historical events, from the time when the *Dialogue* was submitted in Rome in 1630 to its publication in Florence in 1632. A sixth count considers that the following points in the *Dialogue* itself must be laid to the author's account:

a.   That, without orders and without making any communication about it, he put the imprimatur of Rome on the title-page.

b.   That he had printed the Preface in different type and rendered it useless by its separation from the rest of the work; further, that he had put the "medicine of the end" in the mouth of a simpleton and in a place where it is hard to find; that it is but coolly received by the other interlocutor, so that it is only cursorily touched upon and not fully discussed.

c.   That he had very often in the work deviated from the hypothesis, either by absolutely asserting that the Earth moves and that the Sun is stationary, or by representing the arguments upon which these views rest as convincing and necessarily true, or by making the contrary appear impossible.

d.   That he has treated the subject as undecided and as if it were waiting for explanation, while he has really given it.

e.   That he contemns and maltreats authors who are of a contrary opinion and those whom the Holy Church chiefly employs.

f.   That he perniciously asserts and sets forth that, in the apprehension of geometrical matters, there is some equality between the divine and the human mind.

g.   That he had represented it to be an argument for the truth that the Ptolemaics go over to the Copernicans but not vice versa.

h.   That he had erroneously ascribed the tides in the ocean to the stability of the Sun and the motion of the Earth, which do not exist.

The two first points are miserably revealing of the search for any kind of motive. The Special Commission, however, by no means draws the conclusion, from all these errors and failings, that the *Dialogue* should be prohibited but says: "All these things could be corrected, if it is decided that the book to which such favor should be shown is of any value."

Immediately after, there follows the seventh count, stating again ("as to fact") that "the author has transgressed the mandate of the Holy Office of 1616, 'that he should relinquish altogether the said opinion,' etc., down to 'and promised to obey.' "

Even as an exploratory report, the paper is strangely inconclusive. After listing the author's several transgressions, it suggests that a corrected edition of the book might be enough of a sanction, as though the violation of the injunction of 1616, if true, were not in itself a damnable enough crime. Since the majority of the members were bitterly opposed to Galileo, it is clear that the juridical situation must have looked to them extraordinarily embarrassing.

There were undoubtedly two major stumbling blocks: one was that the book had been licensed; and the other, as Magalotti had said, that there was no way of declaring the Copernican doctrine formally heretical. (This was also how Father Guevara had understood the rules when he declared in 1625, after the publication of the *Saggiatore*, that the Earth's suggested motion is by itself not blameworthy.)[14] The case was admitted to be very far from clear, but—said rather doubtfully—there was enough to have the Holy Office look into it, if this was what was desired.

It was not much, but it was enough for the Pope's needs. On September 15 he informed the ambassador that he could do no less than hand over the affair to the Inquisition.[15] At the same time the strictest secrecy as to this information was enjoined on both ambassador and sovereign, with a threat that otherwise they would be proceeded against according to the statutes of the Holy Office. He should not

14. Cf. Ed. Naz., XIII, 265.
15. In fact, one wonders why the authorities did not insist on this point: that as soon as the injunction was discovered, it being clear that Galileo had infringed it by writing the book, he was liable to immediate arrest. This is very far, however, from what Francesco Barberini implies in his letter to the Nuncio of September 25 (see p. 290) or from what was said to Niccolini. Much more consideration is shown in this phase in which feelings are high than in the later one. It is as though the authorities felt that they were venturing onto unsafe ground and that Galileo might rebel and move to safe territory.

have spoken, he stressed, but he was doing it out of regard for his Highness. What he meant, of course, was that he wanted to offer the Grand Duke a chance to disassociate himself from the scabby sheep before he was struck by the dishonoring summons. The insistent requests of Niccolini for reconsideration His Beatitude evaded with what he was pleased to consider a humorous anecdote.

On September 23 the General Congregation pronounced that Galileo had transgressed the injunction of 1616, and on October 1, as we have seen, the official summons was served on him at Arcetri.

Niccolini soon received the news of the event and of Galileo's despair and set out again indefatigably to help. He pleaded with the prelates of the Holy Office the ailments of the old man and the difficulties of a two-hundred-mile journey in the worst season. They "only heard what he had to say and answered nothing." He went to the Pope himself. "Your Holiness incurs the danger," he said, "of his being tried neither in Rome nor in Florence, for I am assured that he may die on the way."

"He must come," was the Pope's reply. "He can come by very easy stages, in a litter, with every comfort, but he really must be tried here in person. May God forgive him for having been so deluded as to involve himself in these difficulties, from which We had relieved him when We were a cardinal."

Niccolini then made bold to remark that, if there was any fault, it was with the licensers, whereupon Urban went off again into a tirade against Riccardi and Ciàmpoli. "But he should have known better," he concluded, "than to get himself into such a tangle [*ginepreto*] of questions which are of the most delicate and pernicious kind there is. Now he must come." He added, "between his teeth," says the Ambassador, something to the effect that there might be, among the judges of the Holy Office, some who had already been in the Preliminary Commission. This referred, as came out later, to the three consultors who had been asked to report on the book.

Niccolini had not even obtained a delay. On the nineteenth of

November Galileo received a second summons. This time he sent in a certificate signed by three doctors:

. . . We find that his pulse intermits every three or four beats. . . . The patient has frequent attacks of giddiness, hypochondriacal melancholy, weakness of stomach, insomnia, and flying pains about the body. We have also observed a serious hernia with rupture of the peritoneum. All these symptoms, with the least aggravation, might become dangerous to life.

The Holy Office answered with a papal mandate which said that such evasions were not going to be tolerated and that in case of further delay a commissioner escorted by a physician would set out to bring Galileo back as a prisoner in irons (*carceratum et ligatum cum ferris*). If danger to life made a postponement advisable, he must be brought back as soon as he could travel, but still as a prisoner and in irons.[16]

This time the Grand Duke himself advised Galileo to go. History has branded him a weak-kneed ruler who handed over his protégé to persecution. Yet he should be granted considerable extenuation. He was not the king of France or the Venetian Senate; he was himself a protégé—a princeling caught between the House of Austria, his suzerain, and the Papal States, his neighbor. He could not expect protection from the Emperor in such matters concerning orthodoxy, as Cosimo I had had in the contest concerning his coronation (it had nearly come to a war with Pius V). Tuscany was in an exposed position on the southern border of the Empire and might have to take on the Papal States alone. In his own house the young man of twenty-two had to contend with the pious alarm of his dowager mother; as a ruler, he had to consider the possible repercussions of a conflict with the monks among the superstitious populace. He found no help in his ministers, who were furious at this sudden upset of their delicately calculated

16. All statutes and laws impeding the free action of the Inquisition, directly or indirectly, were null and void *ipso jure* (see Farinacci, *De haeresi quaestiones 182*, No. 76).

moves and countermoves on the diplomatic chessboard and were all for washing their hands of the ill-omened astronomer.[17] He did not. He offered Galileo his own litter for the voyage and his own embassy in Rome for a residence and, against the advice of his secretary of state, gave orders to Niccolini to go all out in his defense.

Galileo, on his side, after the first shock, had fully recovered his fighting spirits. He was for "having it out" with the ecclesiastical authorities on the whole issue, including the dangerous theological subjects that he had obediently left alone for so many years and that were now again brought out against him.

In a strong letter to Elia Diodati in Paris, written on January 15, after the final summons of the Inquisition and shortly before leaving for Rome—a letter probably intended as a kind of intellectual testament intrusted to the Protestants in case he were to be silenced forever —he comes back squarely to his position of 1615 as outlined in the *Letter to Castelli*. The pretext is given by some recent anti-Copernican tracts of Froidmont and Morin on which Diodati had asked his opinion, but what he is expressing in no uncertain terms is what he thinks of the Pope himself:

As to Froidmont, I could have wished not to see him fall into, in my opinion, a grave though widespread error; namely, in order to refute the opinions of Copernicus, he first hurls scornful jests at his followers, and then (which seems to me still more unsuitable) fortifies himself by the authority of the Holy Scripture, and at length goes so far as to call those views on these grounds nothing less than heretical. That such a proceeding is not praiseworthy seems to me to admit of very easy proof. For if I were to ask Froidmont, who it is that made the Sun, the Moon, the Earth, and the stars, and ordained their order and motions, I believe he would answer, "They are the creations of God." If asked who inspired Holy Scripture, I

17. Objectively, it no doubt looked bad, even at the time. Grotius, writing to Vossius in 1635, speaks of the Grand Duke surrendering "in craven fear" (*socordi metu*) and suggests that a way should be found to remove Galileo to Holland. (His own experience in escaping from well-guarded fortresses made him confident on this point.) Galileo himself thought he should have been better protected. His later work he pointedly dedicated to the French ambassador, Noailles, as a patron.

know he would answer, "The Holy Spirit," which means God likewise. The world is therefore the work and the Scriptures are the word of the same God. . . . Nothing ever changes in Nature to accommodate itself to the comprehension or notions of men. But if it be so, why, in our search for knowledge of the various parts of the universe, should we begin rather with the words than with the works of God? Is the work less noble or less excellent than the word? If Froidmont or anyone else had settled that the opinion that the Earth moves is a heresy, and if afterward demonstration, observation, and necessary concatenation would prove that it does move, into what embarrassment he would have brought himself and the holy Church.[18]

The one who had lost his head was, rather, Urban VIII. He felt around him a chill little wind of criticism. It had been said of him for a long time that he had sacrificed the interests of the Church to his personal ambition, to his vanity, to the cupidity of his relatives, and to the interests of the House of Barberini. The ambassador of Modena in Rome was writing in those very days to his prince: "These rulers want to aggrandize their family; they love wealth; they lust for

18. The rest of the letter is important:
"Many years ago, when the stir about Copernicus was beginning, I wrote a letter of some length in which, supported by the authorities of numerous Fathers of the Church, I showed what an abuse it was to appeal so much to Holy Scripture in questions of natural science, and I proposed that in future it should not be brought into them. As soon as I am in less trouble, I will send you a copy. I say 'in less trouble,' because I am just now going to Rome, whither I have been summoned by the Holy Office, which has already prohibited the circulation of my *Dialogue*. I hear from well-informed parties that the Jesuit Fathers have insinuated in the highest quarters that my book is more execrable and injurious to the Church than the writings of Luther and Calvin. And all this although, in order to obtain the imprimatur, I went in person to Rome and submitted the manuscript to the Master of the Palace, who looked through it most carefully, altering, adding, and omitting, and, even after he had given it the imprimatur, ordered that it should be examined again at Florence. The reviser here, finding nothing else to alter, in order to show that he had gone through it carefully, contented himself with substituting some words for others, as, for instance, in several places, 'Universe' for 'Nature,' 'quality' for 'attribute,' 'sublime spirit' for 'divine spirit,' excusing himself to me for it by saying that he foresaw that I should have to do with fierce foes and bitter persecutors, as has indeed come to pass."

power; but, when a decision is at hand, they do not have the guts to go out and take serious risks. They look arrogant enough, but then they cut a pitiful figure." Urban was in truth not unaware of his predicament; he knew his people were murmuring, and those months had brought nothing that could spell hope for the future on the chessboard of international politics. Early in the game, in his sanguine debuts, he had felt, not without reason, modern and farsighted in staking the newly rising French nation against the traditional power of Spain and Austria; as he surveyed the situation, he could hardly feel that it had been a successful gambit. He had been used by Richelieu instead of using him; he had alienated Austria for no profit and had given scandal by his undercover alliance with the Swede. The King of Spain in his anger had gone so far as to challenge him in Consistory, through Cardinal Borgia, to be reminded of "his more pious and more glorious predecessors" and to stop these unseeming collusions with heretical power; he had had to move swiftly to crush a political plot in his own Curia. He had begun to see enemies everywhere.

"The Pope lives in fear of poison," writes a diplomatic correspondent. "He has gone up to Castel Gandolfo and shut himself in; no one is admitted without being searched. The ten miles of road are heavily patrolled. He is in great suspicion that the preparations made in Naples might be aimed at him, that the fleet of the Grand Duke of Tuscany may any day set sail against Ostia and Civitavecchia. The garrisons and lookouts on the coast have been reinforced." This nervous apprehension corresponded less to actual dangers than to a deep sense of failure. With the eclipse of French power following the death of the Swedish king, the illness of Richelieu, and the alignment of England against the Netherlands, he realized that his elaborate game was up and that it was only a matter of time until he would be forced back into the Hapsburg orbit, which was indeed to happen three years hence. And if he had only known, just at a time when France was again to be decisively on its way to victory. Bad luck without a break, all mistimed and mischanced.

And if he brought down his gaze from grave world perspectives to this annoying learned fuss about the planets, he could discern in a small version the same story all over again. He had tried to play the big-hearted Renaissance prince and to take science under his mantle, and here he stood outwitted by Galileo as he had been by Richelieu. Galileo, while offering himself as an ally, had mobilized lay thought against the intellectual authority of the Church and created a scandal. But at least he, Urban, could do something there. He could break his back and humiliate that gang for all to see. He was going to make a terrific intervention. Here was an occasion to recoup his prestige and reaffirm his position as head of the Faith. He was going to show those Florentines that there were limits to their impertinence. He had banged his fist publicly upon the table and ordered the *ad hoc* Commission to produce a case against that man on the double-quick. The Commission doubled up and produced a case, or at least what could look like one. But there was uneasiness all around.[19]

VI

Absolutely elsewhere, in a Hyperborean corner of the New World that no one in Rome had even heard of, in those very days, an unknown and faintly absurd young cleric named Roger Williams, sitting in the wigwam of Chief Massasoit, was preparing his case against another—minuscule and preposterous—theocratic state: "The STATE

19. Notwithstanding the unexpected boon of the injunction of 1616 that the Commission had dug up, which provided a legal handle for the prosecution, the Pope toned down his language considerably after the report. In the first interview with Niccolini on September 5 he had spoken of "la più perversa materia che si potesse mai avere alle mani," "dottrina perversa in estremo grado," which terms would apply only to grave heresy. Later it becomes "un gran ginepreto, del quale poteva far di meno, perche son materie fastidiose e pericolose" (September 18); "materia gelosa e fastidiosa, cattiva dottrina.... fu mal consigliato.... era stata una certo Ciampolata cosi fata" (February 27, 1633). Apparently, as Magalotti had foretold, the Holy Office had raised difficulties about a prosecution on dogmatic grounds, and he had fallen back on the political.

RELIGION of the World," he wrote, "is a POLITIC invention of men to maintain the CIVIL STATE . . . GOD requireth not an UNIFORMITY of RELIGION to be INACTED and INFORCED in any CIVIL STATE; which inforced UNIFORMITY sooner or later is the greatest occasion of CIVILL WARE, RAVISHING of CONSCIENCE, PERSECUTION of CHRIST JESUS in his servants, and of the HYPOCRISIE and destruction of millions of souls. . . . It is the will and command of GOD, that a PERMISSION of the most PAGANISH, JEWISH, TURKISH, or ANTICHRISTIAN CONSCIENCES and WORSHIPS, bee granted to ALL men in all NATIONS and COUNTRIES; and they are onely to bee FOUGHT against with that SWORD which is onely (in SOULE MATTERS) ABLE to CONQUER, to wit, the SWORD of GODS SPIRIT, the WORD of GOD. . . ."

Half the world away from there, and also from Rome, in Marco Polo's fabulous city of Cambaluc, which had been discovered only lately to be the same as Peking, Father Adam Schall von Bell, S.J., known in China as T'ang Jo-wang, on whom the Emperor had conferred the titles of "Most Profound Doctor [*tung kwan hsiao*], Superintendent of the Imperial Stud, High Honorable Bearer of the Imperial Banquet, and Exploring Teacher of the Mysteries of Heaven," was having to struggle not only against the intrigues of court officials but with his own authorities in the Vatican. Sharp letters from Rome had reminded him that, as director of the Imperial Bureau of Astronomy in charge of the calendar, he was indorsing with his authority all sorts of "superstitious excrescences" connected with alleged miraculous events in the heavens.

The imperious Jesuit, more used by then to rebuking the Emperor than to begging permission from his superiors, had to plead patiently that his own position remained undeviatingly scientific but that it was wise to give some leeway to ancient superstitions. Miracles in the sky, he said, could come in very useful, in so far as it was he who had the authority to interpret them. And, after all, he suggested, if we are to believe in the miracle of Joshua, why should we not let the Chinese

The Summons

believe in the significance of comets, the more so if we can turn their credulity to good political use? [20]

VII

Galileo was coming in to Rome to meet his fate. After twenty-three days on the road, which included a painful quarantine, on the thirteenth of February he reached the embassy, where a warm bed was ready for him, and he was cared for by the ambassador's wife, Caterina Niccolini, "queen of all kindness." He was allowed to stay there undisturbed for several weeks, visited by one or another prelate of the Inquisition in a noncommittal way. Monsignor Boccabella, the former Assessor, was very friendly; Monsignor Serristori, helpful. The Commissary-General was not to be seen, but Galileo paid his respects at the Holy Office and was introduced to the new Assessor, Monsignor Febei. Otherwise, he waited. "We find a wonderful pleasure," wrote Niccolini, "in the gentle conversation of the good old man." And on the nineteenth: "I think we have cheered up the old gentleman by showing him all that is being done for his cause; yet at times he comes back to finding this persecution very strange. I told him to show a will to obey and to go very softly."

Through these engaging words we can see a Galileo not at all cowed but vigorously annoyed, still amazed, and willing to remonstrate with the authorities high and low. This is confirmed by a letter of Galileo

20. This plea found acceptance eventually, but the rest of Schall's policy did not fare so well. Matteo Ricci, Schall, and Verbiest, the founders of the Chinese mission, as well as their French successors, had been so deeply impressed by Confucianism that they considered it a part of the Old Dispensation. They worked out a theological compromise which accepted both names and rites from Chinese worship. This line ran at last into categoric condemnation from the Holy Office: "Falsa est, temeraria, scandalosa, impia, Verbo Dei contraria, haeretica, Christianae Fidei et Religionis eversiva, virtutem Passionis Christi et Crucis ejus evacuans." The Dominicans had paid back their old rivals, as Father Navarrete's book on Jesuit excesses admits not without satisfaction. What was lost in the scuffle was only the Chinese Empire.

himself to his brother-in-law: "We [Niccolini and Galileo] hear at last that the many and serious accusations are reduced to one and the rest have been dropped. Of this one I shall have no difficulty in getting rid, once the grounds of my defense have been heard."

A dispatch of Niccolini five days later is more explicit:

> As far as I can learn, the main difficulty consists in this—that these gentlemen here maintain that in 1616 he was ordered neither to discuss the question nor to converse about it. He says, on the contrary, that those were not the terms of the *precetto*, which were that that doctrine was not to be held or defended.

So the secret communicated in dread secrecy to the Grand Duke alone on January 15 was out, and Galileo was scoffing at it. If it was Bellarmine's notification that made the trouble, they might not know that he had a copy of it in Bellarmine's own hand, which allowed him to call their bluff at any time; for the rest, he felt he had the law on his side so positively that he was for challenging the authorities on all this fuss, if Niccolini had not restrained him. This is, in itself, enough to prove conclusively, if further proof were needed, that Galileo was utterly unaware of any action taken on that day of February, seventeen years before, except the statement on the part of Bellarmine.[21]

We have said "if further proof were needed," because all Galileo's behavior since 1616 is proof enough in itself. He could not possibly have "forgotten," as early as 1618, a command *nec quovis modo docere* coming from the Inquisitor in person, when he wrote the letter on tidal motion to the Archduke Leopold; and no one but an utter fool could have written what he did, including the *Letter to Ingoli,* up to the *Dialogue* in 1630, with such a Damocles' sword over his head; nor

21. All the allusions, by the Pope as well as by the officials, referred to "an injunction by Bellarmine." There was certainly intentional inaccuracy here, as otherwise the surprise scene prepared for April 12 (see p. 259) could never have taken place. But it would seem that the Pope himself was taken in by this version (see pp. 305–06).

is it conceivable that a man of his sense would not have asked in his papal audiences to have the injunction lifted as a preliminary to any encouragement to write.

Thus, it was a completely clear and reassuring picture that was in the minds of the two friends as they discussed the issue at the embassy in those early days of March, 1633. The signs were encouraging. The grim Senior Inquisitor himself, Cardinal Desiderio Scaglia, had read the *Dialogue* with the help of Castelli and had the points cleared up one by one for him; the monsignors of the Holy Office dropped comforting hints. Both friends expected that, now "the tilt had been run" and obedience shown, the case would be gradually allowed to drop. The Grand Duke was aready putting pressure on the Pope to have Galileo sent back home.

It was, therefore, a very dismayed Niccolini who heard from the Pope on March 13 that Galileo was going to be summoned to the Holy Office as soon as the trial came around on the agenda. To Niccolini's expostulations, the Pope answered that there was no way out. "May God forgive Galileo," he said, "for having intruded into these matters concerning new doctrines and Holy Scripture, where the best is to go along with common opinion; and may God help Ciàmpoli too concerning these new notions, because he has a leaning toward them and is inclined toward new philosophies."

He added that Signor Galileo had been his friend, that often they had dined familiarly at the same table, and that he was sorry to subject him to these annoyances, but that it was a matter of faith and religion. I think I remarked that when he was heard he would be able, without difficulty, to give all explanations requested. He answered me that he will be examined in due time but that there is an argument to which they have never yet given an answer, and that is that God is all-powerful, and, if He is, why should we try to necessitate Him? I said that I did not know how to speak on those matters, but that I thought I had heard Galileo saying that he was willing not to believe in the motion of the Earth, but that as God could make the world in a thousand ways, so it could not be denied that He could

235

have made it in this way too. He grew angry and replied that we should not impose necessity upon the Lord Almighty; and, as I saw him working himself up to a fury, I avoided saying more that might have hurt Galileo. I just added that anyway he was here to obey, to cancel or retract whatever he would be told in the interest of religion, and that I did not know enough of this science and did not want to get myself into some heresy by talking about it. And so handling it lightly, for I was taking good care to steer wide of the Holy Office, I went on to other business.

This last passage is revealing. One has to appreciate the fine blend of caution, cool contempt, and intellectual freedom that those men brought to their dealings with the super state. It has not proved easy to duplicate in our times. In a dangerously close play, acting with familiar ease, Niccolini had conveyed to the person on the sacred throne how little he thought of him, while preserving intact the formalities owed to his position. The Pope had winced, and Niccolini knew the Grand Duke would like to hear about it. The Grand Duke let him know in return that he was "thrilled." The tone of the correspondence in those times remained diplomatic throughout. What those men really thought was something else again. It has been vividly expressed for them by their senior, Francesco Guicciardini, in his autobiographical notes—but this is part of another story.

As for the memories of past friendship, they were polite conversation. The Pope's feelings had really changed into an enduring rancor. We can see it if we take a brief glimpse at what was to come. A year later, after the sentence, when Galileo petitioned from Arcetri that he be allowed to move into Florence for medical treatment, the answer was: "Sanctissimus refused to grant the request and ordered that said Galileo should be warned to desist from handing in supplications, or he will be taken back to the jails of the Holy Office." This time the Grand Ducal Court gasped: "Incredible"; "Unheard of." "But, then," as one of them writes, "anything that comes from the Inquisition is bound to be most new and unprecedented." Old Nemesis, however, was to catch up with Urban VIII, the lover of novelties; for what posterity remembers of the incident is Galileo's letter to Diodati, July 25 of that year 1634: "This period has been further darkened for me by great loss. During my absence, which my daughter considered most perilous for me, she fell into a profound melancholy which undermined her health, and it came at last (two months after my return) to a crisis of which she died after an illness of six days, just thirty-three years of age, leaving me in desperate grief. And by a sinister coincidence, on returning home from the convent, in company with the doctor who had just told me her condition was hopeless and she would not survive the next day, as indeed came to pass, I found the Inquisitor's Vicar here, who informed me of a mandate of the Holy Office at Rome that I must desist from asking for grace or they would take me back to the actual prison of the Holy Office. From which I can infer that my present confinement is to be terminated only by that other one which is common to all, most narrow, and enduring forever." [22]

VIII

What Niccolini extracted from the Pope that day of March 13 was a promise that the accused would be assigned comfortable rooms, with the assistance of a servant who could come and go instead of being isolated in a cell or *secreta* as was the procedure.

He did not tell Galileo about the impending trial. There would be time enough for that. But he set out to visit the prospective judges one by one, spending the name of the Grand Duke freely. To Cardinal Barberini he represented "the poor state of health of the good old man, who for two nights continuous had cried and moaned in sciatic pain; and his advancing age and his sorrow." All he received were assurances of the greatest possible consideration.

Even in his prudent seclusion, however, Galileo could feel that the going had become hard. The fair-weather friendships, the facile admiration, and the ornate compliments had evaporated; influential

22. See also his letter to his brother-in-law, April 27, 1635: "I suffer much more from the rupture than has been the case before; I have no sleep, my pulse intermits, the most profound melancholy has come over me. I loathe myself, and I hear my little daughter perpetually calling me. . . ."

people were turning a cold shoulder. No one of his acquaintances dared approach the authorities in his favor, except old Buonarroti, whose letter has been preserved; and his supplication did not weigh much. Even the ministers in Florence were trying to get rid in some inconspicuous way of the luckless mathematician. Cioli wrote the ambassador that he should not commit himself too deeply and that, anyway, the administration could not be financially responsible for Galileo beyond the first month of his stay. The ambassador wrote back with cold scorn that it made no difficulty, that henceforth he, Niccolini, would be glad to meet the expenses out of his own pocket.

When Galileo was told on April 8 what was awaiting him, he took it with astonishing spirit. Here at last were ten cardinals on a bench who would have to listen and stand reason. This was going to be a "showdown"; he announced that he would tackle the whole issue, from theology to physics. The so-oft-told tale of intimidation and surrender has obliterated in history this very real struggle unto the last. The legendary "Eppur si muove" that Galileo is supposed to have murmured after the sentence would have been a mere emotional escape; whereas there is true and tragic grandeur in this invincible hope, at the very gates of the Inquisition from which so many had not returned, of moving men whom he had always known to be "unmovable and unpersuadable."

It was Niccolini who had to tell him that this was not the way things were going to be. The merit of his case was being decided without a hearing, and he had better not try to maintain anything at all "but to submit to whatever he may see they want in that business of the motion of the Earth."

This was the final blow for the old man. "He fell into the deepest dejection and since yesterday has sunk so low that I am greatly concerned for his life. We are all trying to ease him and comfort him, and to work for him through our connections, because truly he deserves everything good; and all this house of ours, which loves him extremely, is stricken with great sorrow."

VRBANVS VIII. BARBERINVS PONT. MAX.

Urban VIII in the Year of His Accession to the Pontifical Throne

Cardinal Francesco Barberini

As nephew to Urban VIII, and his closest collaborator, he held the position currently called of "Cardinal-Master," which was replaced after him by the post of Secretary of State. He tried to save Galileo from recanting.

Ascanio Piccolomini, Archbishop of Siena

He was Galileo's friend, who harbored him for five months after the trial.

Joannes florent. Ponti

Ciampolus a Secret: fieis

Supios pm.

1627

Eques Octaui Leonus

Roman' pictor fecit

Giovanni Ciàmpoli

This portrait, by Ottavio Leoni, was made in 1627, at the height of Ciàmpoli's career, when he was Secretary to Urban VIII, and five years before his downfall.

XI

The Inquisitors' Plight

Hora novissima
Tempora pessima
Sunt: Vigilemus.

I

The problem confronting the Inquisition was far from simple. With the personal injunction that had been discovered in the file, they had enough, as the poor Father Monster said, to "ruin Galileo utterly" if they wanted to. This was clearly the original idea of the procedure as seen by the Preliminary Commission and suggested vividly in Riccardi's indiscretions. The injunction provided a legal handle for the Holy Office. Otherwise the charges were vague and difficult to substantiate. This seems to have remained the feeling during the early phase of Galileo's stay in Rome. "The charges," he wrote, as we remember, "have gradually been allowed to drop, except one." So much he had gathered from his informal conversations with Monsignor Serristori and other officials.

Was this only a trap, laid in order to encourage him to pronounce himself more freely on scientific subjects? It could not but work poorly. It is a custom to credit the Inquisition with all sorts of hypocritical ways, but then also one can suppose anything. We have run into this kind of supposition already in the case of the first trial. Historians have descanted upon the duplicity of the Curia which allowed Galileo to carry on his efforts until the end of February, 1616, while the decision had fallen several months before. We have found that it was not so and that Bellarmine himself had never tried to deceive.

It might be better to start with a concrete question: Why did those officials give away so informally a secret which had been previously guarded with jealous care—with such care, indeed, that the Pope had not even allowed Niccolini to transmit it to the Grand Duke in a dictated report but exacted from him the promise that he write the dispatch in his own hand? The secret had a purpose, and the damage and risk of this informal disclosure could not be ignored. Most of all, the surprise effect on the defendant was lost for the interrogator; and, in case it were decided to sentence Galileo to prison on the injunction alone, there were now witnesses, Niccolini and his friends, ready to divulge that he had been sentenced on the strength of a command which he asserted had never taken place and which could not be shown to bear his acknowledgment.

Once the question is raised, there seems to be only one reasonable answer: The authorities were genuinely worried about the injunction, which certainly did not look very good, and those weeks of pause were spent in trying to get Galileo in an unguarded mood to confirm it. He could guess that they were probing the ground; a whole month passed in these perplexities.

The decision reached apparently, as we shall see from the course of the proceedings, was that, since the Pope had requested a sentence, the injunction would be considered valid, although they had managed to extract no confirmation of it from Galileo. It was needed for getting around the licenses, in order to have a case at all. But it was to be retained only in the capacity of a "b factor," as engineers impolitely call it, of undefined weight. The case itself should rest on the question of merit. Otherwise the sentence would not achieve its aim as a deterrent on public opinion.

But here the difficulties began. To raise the question of merit meant to bring into the foreground again the responsibility of the licensers, who had given in so many words permission to present the Copernican opinion and even to maintain it on purely physical grounds. The embarrassment is clearly to be perceived in the indecisive report of the

Commission, which tries to find safe grounds in such ridiculous charges as that the Preface had been printed in different type; that the Roman license was abusively mentioned, since the book had been transferred to the Florence licensers; etc.

Nothing really would do except the theological crime. But how to prove it? It might be said that this, in principle, need not embarrass the Inquisition, which, like all secret state police, was entitled to do exactly anything. It was the image of absolute power whence it sprang. Its action was in principle *extra ordinem,* for it was an emergency tribunal which had created its own administrative law and could change it at will. Moreover, it was the guardian of "revealed truth" as a whole, that is, not only Scripture and dogma but the whole "deposit of the Faith" as it has come down to us through tradition and belief. Like all living things, the Church will not admit an outside definition of her contents. Thus, in principle, the powers of the Holy Office were discretionary. This principle was fearfully abused by the Spanish Inquisition. But there was a rationale behind it, with inherent limits that we should see.

II

And, first of all, there is the fact that the Church is not an impersonal power like the Roman praetor but the mother of the faithful.[1] The irreconcilable apostate, the social virus, she has to eliminate. All the others she does not punish; she "penitences." Willingness is assumed, the correction is supposed to be welcome, and indeed the penitential life that is offered to the culprit is the very same that the judging monks have elected for themselves in free vocation. He must be made

1. It may be illuminating to note how specifically, except for this, the Roman Church continued the Roman Empire. It had inherited from it on one side the science and rigor of Justinian's *Institutions,* on the other the figure of the Emperor, ruling directly through a group of freedmen of undefined responsibility. The cardinals had, of course, a status that put them far above the freedmen, but they too might have to run for their lives, as the Barberinis did after the death of Urban VIII.

to see himself as the Church sees him. What counts is the union of wills. With the evolution of the Church into a state, the metaphysical requirement of a union of wills remains; but it gets admittedly a bit strained at times. In a theological state, man is not innocent until proved guilty. Much the reverse, he is presumed guilty, and God or the authorities alone can know how much. This was the assumption not only in Rome but also, about the year 1630, in Boston. Today, it is the Russian condition. We must, if anything, admire the cautiousness and legal scruples of the Roman authorities in that civilized period.

What the individual does on his own, so runs the logic, can lead him only to disaster, and indeed this has been proved again and again. That is why guidance is needed. Man, the "timid, staring animal" man, is the least able to know what he is doing or why or whither it may lead him. What he should have ready in his soul is a willingness to childlike submission. In front of the Tribunal of the Inquisition a person was not supposed to *prove* his innocence; at best he could find himself innocent after scrutiny. It would have been bad form to expect it, for sin is man's condition, and to be called to account meant that one's noxiousness had already been long and carefully weighed. It was only awaiting exact evaluation. The best that one could expect, as an equivalent of acquittal, was a warning. The very fact of being called before the court was social disgrace.[2]

We have tribunals of orthodoxy in our own time, and the state of mind with respect to them has been well described by a Russian historian who went through the Yezhov purge: "I could not claim to be an orthodox Marxist, because the continual alterations in the party line made a consistent attitude of orthodoxy incompatible with scientifically founded convictions. But in my historical work I always tried to remain within the bounds of official instructions, to use the 'classical heritage' of Marxism to the full, and to conform with the intentions of Soviet policy. I had been regarded as a loyal Soviet scholar. Neverthe-

---

2. "Etre cité a ce tribunal n'est pas une recommandation, et en sortir, même par la porte d'un acquittement, ne sera jamais un titre de gloire" (Grimaldi).

less, I was prepared for arrest. Why? Because, like all other Soviet citizens, I carried about with me a consciousness of guilt, an inexplicable sense of sin, a vague and indefinable feeling of having transgressed, combined with an ineradicable expectation of inevitable punishment." [3]

This goes to show how much less fearsome the Inquisition really was than its modern counterpart. In an age of social stability, which had not yet codified the dynamics of dialectical change, one knew at least what the general line was; it had never changed for generations, and people had learned to know where essentials lay. If we go through the list of fifty-one questions that was set up by the Italian Inquisition in the sixteenth century to test orthodoxy, we can see that they all bore on pretty fundamental aspects of faith or morals. In fact, the best testimonial in favor of the Inquisition is the resolute confidence of Galileo and his friends that there was no case at all against him.

On the part of the Holy Office itself, we have corresponding scruples which kept it hunting over the scale for a correct definition of Galileo's transgression, in the zone that goes between "error" and "heresy." This element of uncertainty rests on a subtle but very real distinction. Something that is not essential to the faith may not be a heresy *ex parte objecti,* as Bellarmine had said, but it may become a heresy *ex parte dicentis* when maintained in such a way that he who utters it has set his will against that of the Church. This becomes a matter of intention, however, and what happens in the secret of a man's soul is not easy to determine.

At that very time the Puritans of Boston were quite sure that they could know whether a man was of the elect and so worthy to be a citizen of the Republic of Regenerate Saints. In the mind of the Roman authorities, with many centuries of experience behind them, holiness was less easy to identify. A man had to have run his mortal course, and very concrete miracles had to come from his intercession above,

---

3. F. Beck and W. Godin, *The Russian Purge and the Extraction of Confession* (1951).

before he was recognized as one of the elect. On earth all was very uncertain. What counted was behavior. The rest had to be left to God and the secret of the confessional.

The Holy Office knew it best of all. The very amplitude of its powers, which set it apart from the other Congregations (for it was not merely administrative as they were, but it was supreme court, judge, jury, and law-enforcer all in one), compelled it to be careful. Heresiology is no more of an exact science today than it was at the time of Athanasius. But, since a definition there has to be, it can come only operationally through form, procedure, and precedent. Heresy admits of no degree; but in practice propositions are of many kinds. They can be heretical, close to heresy, erroneous, temerarious, or simply offensive to the pious soul. To determine the exact degree is a juridical problem, based strictly on the consensus of the texts and on the weight of "grave opinion" in their interpretation.[4] In so far as there is no direct and proclaimed heresy involved, a qualification is always subject to revision and hence to reasonable (if submissive) question.

III

The present-day apologetic version, then, which settles the Galileo incident by charging the censors of 1616 with a "grave and deplorable error in using an altogether false principle as to the proper interpretation of Scripture"[5] is at best an evasion of the problem. The eleven wretched men, who have to bear a blame that should properly fall on the judges of 1632 and on certain others, were average officials who looked up their books and condensed in two paragraphs the "grave

---

4. See Aquinas *Quaestiones quodlibetales* ix. 16, about the rule of faith: "It is certain that the judgment of the universal Church cannot possibly err in matters pertaining to the Faith; hence we must stand rather on the decisions the Pope judicially pronounces than by the opinions of men, however learned they may be in Holy Scripture." This, we may notice, applies specifically to dogmatic questions or to traditions which are no longer historically verifiable—in general, to things which cannot be discussed *de facto*.

5. J. Wilhelm, in *Catholic Encyclopedia* (New York: Appleton, 1910), art. "Galileo."

opinion" of established teaching. They had been asked categorically, and this was the answer. In the lack of any new weighting which should have been supplied by Grienberger and Bellarmine, it is difficult to see what else they could have done.

We have seen, for instance (on p. 99), from the learned pen of Father Hontheim: "Scripture and tradition speak again and again of the fire of hell, and there is no sufficient reason to take the statement metaphorically." This, then, is the consistent criterion of interpretation as of today, and the Qualifiers did not deviate from it. If he had not been allowed by the Pope in 1757 to understand the motion of the Sun allegorically, Father Hontheim would still today be in duty bound to believe the Ptolemaic position.

In fact, his colleagues still do believe what amounts to almost the same. Father Agostino Gemelli, a well-known physiologist in his own right and late Rector of the Gregorian University, stated in the press in 1953 that the increased belief in the occurrence of conscious life in other planets or galaxies that is noticed in present-day cosmological speculation can come only of an ignorance of theology; for theology, while leaving a completely open field to scientific speculation, is able to affirm categorically in advance of facts that there are not and cannot be any beings endowed with soul anywhere in the universe except on the Earth. This type of qualification, however individual, has considerable theological grounds to support it, of a more stringent nature indeed than those concerning the mobility of the Earth. It would probably be ratified if necessary, as the exclusion of evolutionary theories has been, and hang like a Damocles' sword over the heads of such astrophysicists as are willing to abide by Church rulings. A sacramental and dogmatic institution like the Church does not surrender its basic cosmological tenets at the behest of public opinion, or it would become an ethical culture society. At best it will decide to wait until its own mind is made up.

In other words, from the point of view of interpretation, the findings of 1616 were no mistake at all. They only became a mistake once they were declared to be such. But mistakes come and go, and this is not the point that hurt. It was the rash and unprecedented tampering with the underlying mechanism of change that created the crisis.

The issue becomes clearer if we take, not a present-day author, but the Vatican astronomer Settele, on whose repeated request Galileo's work was removed from the Index in 1822. Up to that date he had had to believe "with a true assent, internal and sincere," if not absolute, that the immobility of the Sun was tolerable since 1757, while Galileo was still wrong for suggesting it. The day after, he was allowed to change his mind. Well, of course, this is a caricature. Of course, the Church accepted perfectly well that he should have been a "Galileist"; in fact, she was herself persuaded by his reasons. She indorsed, in other words —as she had always indorsed—the idea that a man is entitled to entertain opinions that have been declared false and even to prove them right, so long as it is with the proper external submission. But that was exactly Galileo's position in his letters to Castelli and to Dini, in his *Letter to the Grand Duchess,* and in his behavior in 1632. He himself had inherited it from the doctors of the thirteenth century who had opposed the decision denying the existence of the antipodes.[6] The legal situation never had changed by one jot.

There are in the Church controversial matters in which the authority of the Fathers is divided or insufficiently expressed. There are, in fact, any number of them. On such issues, as Magalotti had learned in the Holy Office, the policy was that "without the declaration of a General Council, or without the most urgent necessity, they can never come to a head." That the cosmological question was of this kind was not only admitted tacitly (as Descartes remarked, Copernicanism was taught without objection); it had been proved by the *Letter to the Grand Duchess.* The forty pages of that letter, bristling with venerable texts, present an impressive counter-battery of opinions of the Fathers on the subject. No one had acknowledged it openly, but it had given pause

6. It is remarkable that throughout his pleadings this precedent never comes up. Even Copernicus, who referred to the point, ascribed the opinion to Lactantius, an individual. They knew that great administrations, like pretty women, will never admit to a mistake.

to Caetani and to Barberini himself, as Galileo knew, and had caused them to have the decree of 1616 proclaim heliocentrism only "false" and to proclaim it so only *in forma communi*. It had been put into a kind of limbo from which it would have taken "some extravagant resolution," as Magalotti said, to move it to the formal status of heresy, for dogmatic truth is not manufactured overnight; it takes a vast and gradual convergence of opinion throughout Catholicity on the subject, and the Pope only makes it irrevocable by his pronouncement. It had been the wisdom of the Church to commit her word through the ages only on supernatural subjects which could not be challenged by any new discovery.

As for what concerned Nature or society, any slow change of opinion would eventually register. The trouble was that no legitimate change had ever been imagined that would not be slow. As we said in an earlier chapter, the Earth had already been half-allowed to move "imperceptibly" after Cusanus; if it gained only a mile of speed a day, in less than two centuries it would be revolving inconspicuously and comfortably on its orbit, with no one to object. The world was a static affair, and knowledge even more so.

IV

Thus, when Bellarmine told Galileo that he must give up the opinion, he was not expecting an "absolute assent" but only obedience. "Galileo acquiesced and promised to obey." He pledged, in other words, not to commit his personal affirmation. He was not forbidden to entertain it in his mind as "mathematical" or "probable" or to discuss it quietly with his peers.' With time that brings all things, respectful pressure

7. We have the jurisprudence on it. In 1651 Father Caramuel Lobkowitz asked the Congregation for directives concerning cases of conscience submitted to him by people who were disturbed by Galileo's sentence. The answer was: "The Congregation did not deal with doctrine, but by order of the Pope prohibited [certain] actions by positive law." The authorities had nothing to object to the Father's own summing-up: "When an opinion is thus forbidden, it is stated not that it is improbable but that it is not probable." This seems to have clarified the situation entirely.

of educated minds might cause a change which would eventually register in official decisions. (It actually did in 1757.) The Jesuit mathematicians themselves, if left far in the background, were willing to be parties to the invisible conspiracy. It was Father Grienberger himself who stated that, if Galileo had not incurred the displeasure of the Company, he could have gone on writing freely about the motion of the Earth to the end of his days. Grienberger's judgment can hardly be suspected of heresy.

Galileo's crime lay in having perceived that change in the "new things" of science could not be so slow as expected. Catholicity did not have world enough and time to make up its mind at leisure, as was the case concerning papal infallibility. He saw "prematurely" (a term which in our fast-shifting times has forced its way even into police language) what ordinary minds like the Vatican astronomers could realize and communicate only a century too late. But his formal position was as correct as theirs. He had with great care established his intention as strictly pious and submissive and had surrounded himself with the legal guaranties required. It was his bad luck and nothing else to run into a coalition of forces which decided that he must be liquidated.

But how to make him out as a heretic? Readers of American history may find an interesting parallel here with Governor Winthrop's problem in the case of Anne Hutchinson. In both cases there was only one way—to prove a criminal intention—and it was less easy to do in Rome than in the somewhat highhanded Bay State Republic. To go after men's minds was an unrewarding job, and not recommended, for who would 'scape whipping? The Commissary-General had to proceed gingerly. There was actually no such thing as a "thought crime" in his book, although heresy is theoretically defined as such. There was only identifiable acts of the will—what was currently called the "sowing of tares." Whatever evil intention there was had to be proved.

Now, Galileo, as we have seen, had taken great care to submit and check the intention with the Pope himself and then have it repeated back by the Master of the Holy Palace. He had been explicitly allowed to prove, if he could, that "it is impossible to get away from the Pythagorean doctrine, except for the reasons of Divine omnipotence dictated to him by our Lord's Holiness." He had been given by the Pope the proper title for the book which involved a comparison between the "Great World Systems." He had had his text prefaced, concluded, revised, and licensed. The simple fact, and the Commissary knew it, was that His Beatitude had changed his mind about the instructions after the book had come out. Even dogmatic almightiness could hardly turn that into an incrimination of the author. All he was entitled to do was suspend the book. Acute frustration was bound to result. Wrote Campanella desolately in his last letter to Galileo: "It seems fate that, the more we strive to serve our Masters, the more harshly they turn against us and maltreat us. God's will be done."

Such, then, was the predicament. If the trial could be based only on the injunction, they had a case. If the trial had to be based on the book, they had only the beginning of a case and must trust luck to bring it to a conclusion.

The heart of the matter was that the Pope had thought he could use Galileo for his purposes. He had found himself outwitted and serving Galileo's purposes instead. It was a very imponderable business—a situation which did not involve a demonstrable act of the will. But, still, intention is part of a contract. This contract had turned out to be a deal with one man's wits matched against the other's; and he needs a flameproof suit who plays a lone hand of poker with theocracy. Dissimulation of aim could become criminal, and there certainly had been dissimulation of a kind. It was a delicate matter, however, to make the charge stick unless the defendant committed mistakes during the interrogation. Once the trial was on, there would always be the risk that it would turn against the Master of the Holy Palace. We have seen these hesitations reflected in the report of the Preliminary Commission and in the long weeks of probing. The text appeared too well protected; charges against it could not be substantiated, as Niccolini writes.

Finally, there was only one thing to do. And that was to break precedent. Three experts for the prosecution had been chosen from among the members of the Preliminary Commission, as the Pope announced to the ambassador "between his teeth." Two at least were enemies of Galileo—Inchofer and Pasqualigo. And they were not of the Holy Office. It was their assignment to tear the veil of established convention and prove that the defendant had really "held" the doctrine he claimed only to discuss.[8]

It can hardly be maintained that this was not a breaking of precedent. Dozens of publications were held up or condemned every year for holding the most grievously erroneous views. But, in so far as their authors had submitted in advance to the judgment of their superiors, no question was made of their intention, and they were not even troubled in their careers. We have seen the case of Campanella and that of Bellarmine himself. Galileo was exactly in the same position, and he had been discussing a doctrine considered simply "false." It was only after the success of the *Dialogue* that it suddenly became "the most perverse and pernicious matter that could be thought of." For that reason, a "novelty" indeed was needed in order to trap him. Once his evil intention was established a priori, it was a matter of maneuver to get him off the safe track and make him fall into either an admission or an untruth. In his eagerness to shy away from admission, there was a good chance that he might slip into the deeper chasm. This device does not bear a pretty name in the practice of the courts, but nothing better had been found to serve the intentions of His Beatitude.

To conclude, then—and this may help us over several strange features that will follow—the trial was conceived from the first as dictated by Reason of State, and as such above law and custom. All the outward show of regularity did not deceive anyone. Reason of State was held to justify many things; it led James I to sentence

---

8. A report from experts was in order. All that ought to have been needed for a regular prosecution was to establish that Galileo had violated the injunction "not to teach or discuss, in whatsoever way." It was easy to establish that. But, as we shall see, the Consultors went further and showed that Galileo "held" the opinion, so as to bring him into collision with Bellarmine's instructions.

Balmerino, his innocent secretary, rather than face up to Bellarmine's rightful accusation of duplicity. It led authorities in Rome to trump up charges against a scientist and indefatigably to persecute his memory for three centuries after his death. It led Bismarck to alter the Ems dispatch, and the Japanese to strike at Pearl Harbor. It has led present-day powers to do such things as Tamerlane himself would have boggled at. There is no question here; all this is in order. Provided, of course, it succeeds. What made Galileo "find this persecution very strange," as Niccolini says, is that he was given all sorts of juridical make-pretense, as we still are given today, but never, then or later, a clear and authoritative explanation of what that Reason of State could be. He knew what the Pope had said but admitted it made no sense to him, as it made none to the ambassador. In the explanations that were given after his time, artful confusion has continued to prevail. Many writers seem to believe that by taking the famous injunction for granted, with adequate persistence, they may get history to accept it. They have not been wholly unsuccessful. But it does no credit to their inventiveness. It may be said that Reason of State will stand being officially explained only after a long lapse of time. True enough. Three centuries have passed, and we are still waiting.

XII The Trial

Judex ergo cum sedebit
Quidquid latet apparebit...

"DIES IRAE"

I

On the twelfth of April, 1633, the first hearing took place before the Commissary-General of the Inquisition and his assistants. The Commissary's name was Father Vincenzo Maculano, or Macolani, da Firenzuola, which caused him to be currently called "Father Firenzuola" from the name of his home town. We know very little of this man whose career was to lead him later to the purple. He was, like all Inquisitors, a Dominican friar, but he had been singled out by the Pope (at least according to the talk of the town) not so much for his theological zeal as for the technical and administrative capacities he had shown in supervising the fortification of Castel Sant'Angelo. Urban VIII was no fanatic, and he liked to have humanists and executives in his entourage.

Galileo had officially surrendered to the Holy Office on that morning, for it was a standing rule that the accused were to be held imprisoned and in strict seclusion until the end of the trial. Out of consideration for his state of health and also for the Grand Duke's prestige, he was exceptionally allowed quarters in the Inquisition building itself, which was located close to the Vatican.

According to procedure, the defendant was put under oath and

257

asked whether he knew or conjectured why he had been summoned.[1] He answered that he supposed it was on account of his last book. He was shown the book and identified it as his. They then passed on to the events of 1616. He said that he came to Rome in that year, and *of his own accord*, he specified,[2] in order to know what opinion it was proper to hold in the matter of the Copernican hypothesis and to be sure of not holding any but holy and Catholic views. These were soft words, but he had been advised to keep to the safe and submissive side. He was then asked about the conferences he had had with several prelates prior to the decree, and he explained that they had been due to the desire of those prelates to be instructed about Copernicus' book, which was difficult for laymen to understand. He could be glad now of his precaution to have put his arguments down in writing. The Inquisitor then asked what happened next.

A.: Respecting the controversy which had arisen on the aforesaid opinion that the Sun is stationary and that the Earth moves, it was decided by the Holy Congregation of the Index that such an opinion, considered as an established fact, contradicted Holy Scripture and was only admissible as a conjecture [*ex suppositione*], as it was held by Copernicus [*sic*].

Q.: Was this decision then communicated to him, and by whom?

A.: This decision of the Holy Congregation of the Index was made known to me by Cardinal Bellarmine.

Q.: Let him state what Cardinal Bellarmine told him about said decision, and whether he said anything else on the subject, and what.

A.: The Lord Cardinal Bellarmine signified to me that the aforesaid opinion of Copernicus might be held as a conjecture, as it had been held by Copernicus, and His Eminence was aware that, like Copernicus, I only held that opinion as a conjecture, which is evident from an answer of the same Lord Cardinal to a letter of Father Paolo Antonio Foscarini, provincial of the Carmelites, of which I have a copy, and in which these words occur:

1. See fols. 413 ff. of the Acts in Volume XIX of Favaro's National Edition of Galileo's *Works*. The questions are in Latin; the answers, in Italian.

2. It had become current, as we have seen from Riccardi's disclosures on p. 222, to say that he was summoned to Rome in 1616. Notwithstanding his denial here, it reoccurs in the official summary (see p. 304).

"It appears to me that Your Reverence and Signor Galileo act wisely in contenting yourselves with speaking *ex suppositione* and not with certainty." This letter of the Cardinal is dated April 12, 1615. It means, in other words, that that opinion, taken absolutely, must not be either held or defended.

This was neat. It was surely not the time to try to correct their obstinate preconceptions about Copernicus, if those preconceptions could be turned to some use. But Galileo was now requested to state what had been decreed in February, 1616, and communicated to him.

A.: In the month of February, 1616, the Lord Cardinal Bellarmine told me that, as the opinion of Copernicus, if adopted absolutely, was contrary to Holy Scripture, it must neither be held nor defended but that it could be taken and used hypothetically. In accordance with this I possess a certificate of Cardinal Bellarmine, given on May 26, 1616, in which he says that the Copernican opinion may neither be held nor defended, as it is opposed to Holy Scripture, of which certificate I herewith submit a copy.

Q.: When the above communication was made to him, were any other persons present, and who?

We can see Galileo suddenly getting suspicious. This was the first intimation that something more might have taken place on that day, for Riccardi, Serristori, and the Pope himself had mentioned only Bellarmine, and he was confident he knew exactly what Bellarmine had said. But Bellarmine had been dead these thirteen years, and he had only this piece of paper. He tries to be careful.

A.: When the Lord Cardinal made known to me what I have reported about the Copernican views, some Dominican Fathers were present, but I did not know them and have never seen them since.

Q.: Was any other command [*precetto*] communicated to him on this subject, in the presence of those Fathers, by them or anyone else, and what?

At this point the old man is becoming frankly scared. The Commissary is looking at a document in front of him; Galileo has no idea what the document may contain, and this is the mysterious Inquisition. He is afraid of falling into a trap; he is afraid of contradicting openly.

We see thoughts racing through his mind. Was Bellarmine's *precetto* something else, juridically, than what he thought it to be? He must have gone over it with Niccolini and his canonist friends. Could the whole decree be construed as a disguised bill of attainder? Had some words escaped his memory that made it a special command *ad personam?* Did anyone else make a move on that day? Could the presence of those Dominicans have meant something?

A.: I remember that the transaction took place as follows: The Lord Cardinal Bellarmine sent for me one morning and told me certain particulars which I had rather reserve for the ear of His Holiness before I communicate them to others.[3] But the end of it was that he told me that the Copernican opinion, being contradictory to Holy Scripture, must not be held or defended. It has escaped my memory whether those Dominican Fathers were present before or whether they came afterward; neither do I remember whether they were present when the Lord Cardinal told me the said opinion was not to be held. It may be that a command [*precetto*] was issued to me that I should not hold or defend the opinion in question, but I do not remember it, for it is several years ago.

Q.: If what was then said and enjoined upon him as a *precetto* were read aloud to him, would he remember it?

A.: I do not remember that anything else was said, nor do I know that I should remember what was said to me, even if it were read to me. I say freely what I do remember, because I do not think that I have in any way disobeyed the *precetto*, that is, have not by any means held or defended the said opinion that the Earth moves and that the Sun is stationary.

The Inquisitor now tells Galileo that the command which was issued to him before witnesses contained: *"that he must neither hold, defend, nor teach that opinion in any way whatsoever."* Will he please to say whether he remembers in what way and by whom this was intimated to him.

3. No one has cared to go into this cryptic remark. Yet the fact that it implies information reserved for the Pope ought to mean that Bellarmine had told him of Maffeo Barberini's moderating intervention in the General Congregation in 1616. The "particulars" therefore were a brief account of the proceedings that were not disclosed and are alluded to in Buonamici's diary.

A.: *I do not remember that the command was intimated to me by anybody but by the Cardinal verbally;* and I remember that the command was "not to hold or defend." It may be that "and not to teach" was also there. I do not remember it, neither the clause "in any way whatsoever" [*quovis modo*], but it may be that it was; for I thought no more about it or took any pains to impress the words on my memory, as a few months later I received the certificate now produced, of the said Lord Cardinal Bellarmine, of May 26, in which the order [*ordine*] given me, *not to hold or defend* that opinion, is expressly to be found. The two other clauses of the said command which have just been made known to me, namely, *not to teach* and *in any way,* I have not retained in my memory, I suppose because they are not mentioned in the said certificate, on which I have relied, and which I have kept as a reminder.

Q.: After the aforesaid *precetto* was issued to him, did he receive any permission to write the book that he has acknowledged was his?

The old man has stood his ground desperately, but he is obviously terrified. He has thought it better to concede that the notification in audience may have been some kind of command. He no longer knows where he stands, and this is no time to cite the Pope's ill-advised encouragements or to implicate the authorities. It might all fall back on his head. The only thing is to duck.

A.: I did not ask permission to write the book, because I did not consider that in writing it I was acting contrary to, far less disobeying, the command not to hold, defend, or teach that opinion.

[There follows a factual account of the negotiations concerning the printing.]

Q.: When asking permission to print the book, did he tell the Master of the Palace about the *precetto* which had been issued to him?

A.: I did not happen to discuss that command with the Master of the Palace when I asked for the imprimatur, for I did not think it necessary to say anything, because I had no doubts about it; for I have neither maintained nor defended in that book the opinion that the Earth moves and that the Sun is stationary but have rather demonstrated the opposite of the Copernican opinion and shown that the arguments of Copernicus are weak and not conclusive.

With this the first hearing was concluded. The very last statement is a poor job, for Simplicio's peroration could by no manner of means be construed as a "proof"; but by then Galileo was more dead than alive. His name below the proceedings is signed with a shaking hand. It cannot be said, however, that he lost his presence of mind. The statement that he had not told Riccardi about the *precetto* because he did not think it necessary may sound embarrassingly like Junior not telling Nurse what Mummy had told him to tell her, but it is not so at all. If we accept Galileo's undeviating position, that Bellarmine had simply notified him of the imminent decree, it would have sounded rather silly on his part to go and solemnly remind Riccardi that he

Signatures of Galileo on the Protocols of the Trial

The first signature comes after the interrogation of April 12 above. The second is to be found at the end of the protocol of April 30 (see p. 276), when he has regained some assurance.

hoped he knew a decree had been issued in 1616. Riccardi would have answered jokingly: "I trust this is what your conversations with His Holiness have been about, or else what are we doing here?" [4]

4. That there *had* been a personal element in Bellarmine's convocation was obvious, but it has nothing to do with the case in point. The whole proceedings of 1616 had been taken *in causam Galilaei mathematici* and that was why Bellarmine had summoned him: to inform him by allusion of the considerations which were behind the published decree. He must have told him at the same time of the moderating action of Barberini on the Pope, as we can infer from Galileo's reserved statement at the interrogation, and only then explained to him that the forthcoming decree made it mandatory that the Copernican doctrine be "neither defended nor held" (although the book of Copernicus was expected to come out again after correction). It meant: "Before talking about it again, it is a good

It was quite another matter if there had been a formal injunction of the Inquisition in 1616 not to teach, defend, *or in any way discuss* the theory, for that involved a suspicion of heresy, or at least resistance, and would require an elaborate rehabilitation before the author could write again. And surely, even then, the Pope was at fault, for he should have known; the instructions of February 25, as we have seen (p. 133), prescribed, in case of recalcitrance, an injunction, and even arrest, and the report of Bellarmine on March 3 should have reflected those events. It actually did not, and that is the important point. So the Pope could not know. It was Galileo, he said, who should have come and told all in due obedience. Now he was under the odium of "having been found out."

All this is ridiculous and pitiful, of course. It was no time to be playing at Nurse and Mummy. A great and rigid authoritarian administration with a thought police which is supposed to know all should at least keep its records straight. Before granting permission to write the book, the Pope should either have remembered or have had his memory refreshed, or someone from the Inquisition might have told him.

---

thing to make sure one has given it up as a commitment. Since you represent that commitment in the public eye, we are telling you in advance of publication. Please be careful." The Cardinal must have added: "We know too well your pious sentiments not to trust, etc." Translated into a statement for public use, it becomes exactly Bellarmine's certificate. These simple facts had better be spelled out, to eliminate the confusion raised on this point by Berti, Gebler, Scartazzini, and others. Thus it was quite true that the whole content of the communication had remained impersonal and implied no more than the words of the decree. The Pope knew them well, and as he understood them he had not found it necessary to give Galileo special dispensation when he approved, in 1624 and in 1630, of his discussing the ideas hypothetically. What he had done was to issue a directive interpreting the policy of 1616 in the light of the requirements of 1630, which involved the writing of a book by Galileo under his high supervision. To assume that the Pope did not know about the summons would have been ridiculous, since he himself, as a cardinal, had sat in on the Congregation *in causam Galilaei* of February 24, 1616, which ordered the summons, and had obviously been informed, although he was not present on March 3, of Bellarmine's favorable report. Whatever personal intimation there may have been in Bellarmine's summons had thus been explicitly revoked by his directives of 1624 and 1630.

Worse: as a party to the secret deliberations of the Congregation of 1616, the Pope could not possibly have forgotten, if the injunction really took place, that he and the other members had been secretly directed to handle Galileo as a dangerous character; yet he had publicly favored and encouraged him in 1624, and now he was acting injured innocence, because there was no mention of an injunction in the *Decreta*.

About all of this Galileo was still in the dark. So far as he knew, all might have been in order, some kind of injunction might have been mysteriously made out in due form, and he might have been hanging himself by obstinately refusing to admit it. Yet he felt it safest to cling to what he knew. He remembered nothing else; he had never acknowledged anything else, except a simple notification not to hold or defend.

The Inquisitor had been dragging him along on an equivocal term. When he said *precetto*, he implied from the start a personal prohibition (see p. 259). For Galileo, it meant only the notification from the Cardinal. It is the text of that notification that seems to him to be challenged, until the Inquisitor asks insistently whether he remembers being addressed by anyone else. But he does not go beyond that, and down to the very end—that is, until the sentence—Galileo is never told that it *was* someone else and that it was the Commissary-General of the time. Hence his answer has to remain correspondingly indefinite. Was this done so he should not be able to deny explicitly that the Commissary had ever spoken? Was it in order to create the equivocation so cleverly exploited in the summary, as we shall see later? Was it because it was a principle never to disclose the charges? In any case, it is only when he understands that he is really being asked about a "command" that he replies anxiously: "It may be that a command was enjoined on me, but I do not remember." From that moment, he is on his guard. He is obviously trying to remember whether anyone said anything that he had better admit. He does not have a lawyer who could ask what kind of injunction they are talking about.[5] But, as the

---

5. Counsel for accused was excluded since the Council of Valence in 1245, on the grounds that "lawyers delayed the proceedings with their noise [*strepitus*]."

Inquisitor returns five times to the question of who had addressed him and tries to draw him out in various ways, Galileo answers again and again: "No one except Bellarmine."

In so doing, he has foiled the whole maneuver. For it had been clearly the Inquisition's intention to extract out of him, were it in a moment of bewilderment or fright, the admission that there *had* been a special command by the Commissary enjoined on that day. Such an admission in a signed protocol would have been a substitute for all the irregularities of the injunction. From that moment, the document of 1616 would have become fully legal. As it was, instead, Galileo had re-established consistently the fact that Bellarmine had informed him only of the contents of the coming decree; and thus the text of the decree remained the only legal directive to be considered both by him and by the censor. The injunction, on the other hand, if assumed valid, would have been a directive to the censor to suppress all and any writings of *this* particular person in the matter of Copernicus, or to prosecute them if published.

II

Where Galileo instead had walked into the delayed-action trap in his very attempt to play safe was in the last statement in his interrogation. To say that he had demonstrated the opposite of the Copernican opinion sounded very much like an attempt to fool the judges. It is not impossible that he should have reserved just such a line of argument, relying on some geometrical legerdemain and on his persuasive capacity. To say, however, that this was "why" he had not told about the notification made it worse. Like so many prisoners under questioning, he was protesting too much. It worked to his undoing, for five days after the audience the results of the official examination of the text came in, and they were not such as to make his plea look good. Three

There was an official called *advocatus reorum* who functioned, however, only *in camera* if he did at all. The accused was never told the charges until the sentence.

Counselors of the Inquisition, Augustinus Oregius (the Pope's theologian), Melchior Inchofer, and Zacharias Pasqualigo, delivered their reports, which came to the same conclusion: The author had not only "discussed" the forbidden view; he had maintained and taught and defended it, and there was a "vehement suspicion" that he was inclined to it and even held it to this day. Inchofer and Pasqualigo gave a long list of passages which could leave no doubt. On the whole, their quotations were correct, in that they were faithful to the sense.

We shall summarize Inchofer's seven-page report, which is the most explicit.

1. The accused does teach, for, as St. Augustine says, what is teaching except to communicate knowledge? Now Galileo certainly does so and has done so since his pamphlet on the sunspots. It is of a teacher to hand on to his disciples first those precepts of a science which are easiest and clearest, so as to enlist their interest, and to present the science as a new one, which attracts curious minds wondrously. Moreover, defendant makes it appear as though a number of effects which have been already truly and authoritatively explained otherwise could be solved only by the motion of the Earth.

2. He does defend. One may be said to defend an opinion even if he does not refute the contrary one; all the more, then, if he tries to destroy that utterly. In law this is called an impugnation.—Copernicus only proposed a more convenient method for computations [this interpretation is, as usual, due to Osiander's Preface], whereas Galileo tries to confirm and establish it as a doctrine and with new reasons, which is twice to defend.—Because, if the intention had been disputation and intellectual exercise, he would not so proudly and arrogantly traduce and ridicule Aristotle, Ptolemy, and all the truths he will not acknowledge. And, if he does so in writing, there is no doubt he must have done it much more in conversation.

3. He does hold. He does so on two counts, through necessary conclusions and also through his assertiveness, for we need not consider valid the occasional pretended protestations that he interposes in order not to appear to go against the decree. As for the reasons given in his Preface, it is certainly not the "mutterings against Church Consultors" which could have

moved a serious man to undertake such a work; and I did not come across a single publication of ultramontane authors in which this matter of the decree is as much as mentioned, not to speak of the Consultors. It is sure that of Catholics no one would have dared. And then, if this was the motive, why did he not undertake really to defend the decree and the Holy Congregation? But this is so far from his thoughts that he goes on to arm the Copernican opinion with new arguments that no ultramontane ever suggested, and he does so in Italian, surely not the language best suited for the needs of ultramontane or other scholarship but the one most indicated to bring over to his side the ignorant vulgar among whom errors most easily take hold.

4. The author claims to discuss a mathematical hypothesis, but he gives it physical reality, which mathematicians never do. Moreover, if defendant had not adhered firmly to the Copernican opinion and believed it physically true, he would not have fought for it with such asperity, nor would he have written the *Letter to the Grand Duchess,* nor would he have held up to ridicule those who maintain the accepted opinion, and as if they were dumb mooncalves [*hebetes et pene stolidos*] described them as hardly deserving to be called human beings.[6]

Indeed, if he had attacked some individual thinker for his inadequate arguments in favor of the stability of the Earth, we might still put a favorable construction on his text; but, as he holds all to be mental pygmies [*homunciones*] who are not Pythagorean or Copernican, it is clear enough what he has in mind, especially as he praises by contrast William Gilbert, a perverse heretic and a quibbling and quarrelsome defender [*rixosum et cavillosum patronum*] of this opinion.

This last sentence affords a rewarding glimpse into the ways of thought of the thought police. The good Jesuit never stops to consider whether the magnetic phenomena discovered by Gilbert might not be highly relevant, as in fact they are, to a discussion of physical prin-

6. "I have met with such arguments that I blush to rehearse them, not so much to spare the shame to their authors, the names of whom might remain perpetually concealed, as because I am ashamed so deeply to degrade the honour of mankind" (*Dialogue,* p. 291).

ciples.[7] For him, the only point is that Gilbert is a perverse heretic, and hence guilt by association is established. "Quibbling" and "quarrelsome" are hardly apt descriptions of Gilbert's scientific style; they are stock adjectives from Inchofer's Scholastic equipment, roughly equivalent to the present-day "subversive."

But if, intellectually, this expert is the *homuncio* whom Galileo had sized up well in advance, he is otherwise shrewd and competent enough. He pins down the quarry. His report in its relentless animus is well worthy of the hand that wrote the *Tractatus syllepticus*. The defendant is shown to have transgressed not only the questionable injunction but Bellarmine's direct notification "not to hold or defend."

One cannot but wonder what had happened to the previous deliberations hinted at by Monsignor Serristori: "All points have been allowed to drop, except one." Such helpful hints could have come only from the Commissary's office, and Galileo had seized on them for guidance in preparing his defense. The injunction alone provided a legal point,

7. This Gilbert episode has a weird sequel that is worth recounting, were it only to show by one example among many how Galileo's person goes on forever being ground between the upper and the nether millstone. In the 1840's, Arago, then the great authority in French astronomy, wrote some comments about the affair. He stood, needless to say, for Science. But, being also a pillar of the state, he thought he had to strike an impartial note. After making out Galileo to be not much of a scientist (the Encyclopedist preconception, carried on by Delambre and Chasles), he remarked that he was even less of a moral character, witness his cowardly surrender before the authorities and the "base envy" he evidenced with respect to Gilbert. Now here is the relevant passage in the *Dialogue*: "Yes, I am wholeheartedly for Gilbert's magnetic philosophy, and I think that those who have read his book and tried his experiments will bear me company therein. . . . I extremely praise, admire, and envy this author that an idea so stupendous should have come into his mind touching a thing handled by infinite great intellects and hit upon by none of them. I think him, moreover, worthy of extraordinary applause for the many new and true observations that he made, to the disgrace of so many fanciful authors who write what they do not know." Needless to say, Arago had never read the *Dialogue*, as no one in France had done; he thought he could trust the word of some Inchofer of his time abouts its contents. There seem to have been a great number of such agents around, judging from the revolting lies they managed to accredit even among Protestant scholars.

and Niccolini could confirm it, for Galileo knew himself triply protected against a trial of mere intention: by the Pope's authorization, by the explicit instructions to the licensers, and by the license itself. The first day of the questioning had not belied it, for the Commissary had insisted on nothing but the injunction. Hence Galileo had understood this to be still the dangerous point and felt that he was easing the task for any leniently disposed judge by making a stand on the injunction and by abounding otherwise in the sense of pious conformism. And, now that the reports had come in, it turned out that he had only been making a noose to hang himself.

Does this again imply Machiavellian duplicity on the part of the authorities? We have tried to show in the previous chapter what the situation seems to have been. The search for the point of indictment had led to a long-drawn-out fumble between different conceptions; and, as the first scene comes to a close, we see those conceptions embodied in two factions which are still far from agreeing on a common line. The Dominicans of the Inquisition, no longer the ruthless ones of a generation before, were still trying to handle the affair on a restrictive legalistic basis; but they had against them the will of the Pope and the plans of a curial group allied with the Jesuits, of whom men like Inchofer were the spearhead, who were pressing for judicial slaughter. The hints dropped by the officials, which were intended to help Galileo, had led him astray. The Jesuit faction had outmaneuvered its opponents and sprung its trap.[8]

8. On opening the proceedings, the authorities had to take two possibilities into account: either the defendant acknowledged the injunction, and then he was technically guilty of relapse and could be sentenced on that alone, but he could be conceded extenuating circumstances; or he denied it, and then he could be further prosecuted (a) for evasion and (b) for "holding" the condemned opinion. By sticking strictly to the letter of his instructions, Galileo might have contended that, however much he had erred in the language, he had never deviated from a hypothetical discussion. On this point it would have been difficult to break him down except by torture, which was against the rules for a man of seventy, and more, in his condition. But there was enough to make out vehement suspicion if required. Actually, through his last denial, the defendant had put

This was in truth legal "railroading," as we have said, for in those times it was well understood that a man could go quite far in playing "double truth" and yet stay within judicial orthodoxy, as long as he covered himself with explicit clauses of submission—and an official license. At most he could have been asked to rewrite in a "problematic" form.[9] One-half of the existing literature could otherwise have been condemned by such methods.

We must insist on this point, because Inchofer's report may look to the modern reader more objective than it really is. To demonstrate that Galileo considered the Copernican argument as convincing for human reason was to hit him below the belt, for that was exactly what he had been supposed to do under the Master of the Palace's written instructions of July 19, 1631: "Signor Galilei will have to add as a peroration the reasons from divine omnipotence dictated to him by Our Lord's Holiness, which must quiet the mind, even if there were no way out of the Pythagorean arguments [*ancorchè da gl'armomenti Pitagorici non se ne potesse uscire*]." That was why the Preliminary Commission, although summoned by the Pope in his anger, had found itself compelled to conclude lamely: "The faults that we have found might be corrected, if the book is deemed worth publishing." How little, how miserably little, correction could entail technically is shown by what happened more than a century later, in 1744.

---

himself into a worse position than that. At this point, as we have indicated, there appeared two opposing factions among the judges. This sketch may help us infer which course may have been advocated by either.

9. As matter of curious precedent, this was exactly the solution suggested by the Jesuit General Acquaviva to Bellarmine when the latter's *Controversies* were being put on the Index in 1590; not to retract any of his opinions but simply to change over the chapter headings from the negative to the problematical form: "Whether, etc." Yet Bellarmine's opinions had been declared erroneous by the Pope himself and not by a secondary Congregation, as was the case with helio-centrism. What had drawn the attention of Inchofer in the *Dialogue,* from the juridical point of view, were the few strictly affirmative passages, one of them a small marginal heading: "The Sun does not move."

In that year a Pope of great sense, Benedict XIV (still affectionately known in Italy as "Papa Lambertini"), gave permission to print a revised edition of the *Dialogue,* although Galileo and Copernicanism itself were and remained under condemnation. Now in this "revised" edition *not one word* of the text has been altered, and only a few marginal headings expunged or modified by the insertion of an *if* which makes them into "probable" statements. Such was, and had always been, the formal meaning of the command not to "hold" an opinion. It had a mile-long jurisprudence behind it. Galileo had some right (if the story is true) to challenge the cardinals on the day of his sentence to show him what could be wrong with his book. But the Consultors' report had driven him to break on the rock that he had tried to avoid by steering the discussion around to real issues. As he lay there, day after day, in the building of the Inquisition, racked with acute sciatic pains and intestinal trouble, for all that he had fine rooms and Niccolini's own majordomo to attend him, he might as well have been confined like anyone else in the dark holds of the Castle.

III

Weeks passed, and nothing happened. The judges were deliberating. The Inquisition was always slow. But in this case we can guess why it was being slow. The Inquisitors had a clear case already, and they did not know what to do with it. In the exploratory phase they had been worried about the rather shaky personal injunction which was the keystone of the case as it had been handed to them. Now they could feel they had gotten past that, for the defendant's denials, in the light of the Consultors' report, made as clear an incrimination as anyone could need to put the machinery into gear—if this was what was really wanted. The Inquisition had been built into a dreadful apparatus in order to make terrifying examples whenever needed, so that no one should feel secure. Once the procedure had been turned on, a man was virtually at their mercy. This time they had been requested by the Pope to oblige with a political performance and a "limited example."

It would be like administering a shampoo with a Bessemer converter. Some of the judges at least were balking at this point—perhaps even, at last, the Pope himself.

We know this from what followed, which does credit to all concerned. Cardinal Francesco Barberini, who was himself one of the ten judges, had put discreet pressure on the Commissary to find a way out. One day the Commissary walked into Galileo's room and sat down with him. It was Ivanov coming to Rubashov. The story is told in a letter written to the Cardinal, which was unearthed by Pieralisi in 1833:[10]

In compliance with the commands of His Holiness, I yesterday informed the Most Eminent Lords of the Holy Congregation of Galileo's case, the position of which I briefly reported. Their Eminences approved of what has been done thus far and took into consideration, on the other hand, various difficulties with regard to the manner of pursuing the case and of bringing it to an end. More especially as Galileo has in his examination denied what is plainly evident from the book written by him, since in consequence of this denial there would result the necessity for greater rigor of procedure and less regard to the other considerations belonging to this business. Finally, I suggested a course, namely, that the Holy Congregation should grant me permission to treat extrajudicially with Galileo, in order to render him sensible of his error and bring him, if he recognizes it, to a confession of the same. This proposal appeared at first sight too bold, not much hope being entertained of accomplishing this object by merely adopting the method of argument with him; but, upon my indicating the grounds upon which I had made the suggestion, permission was granted me. That no time might be lost, I entered into discourse with Galileo yesterday afternoon, and after many and many arguments and rejoinders had passed between us, by God's grace, I attained my object, for I brought him to a full sense of his error, so that he clearly recognized that he had erred and had gone too far in his book. And to all this he gave expression in words of much feeling, like one who experienced great consolation in the recognition of his error, and he was also willing to confess it judicially. He requested, however, a

10. The text of the letter will be analyzed later on (see p. 318).

little time in order to consider the form in which he might most fittingly make the confession, which, as far as its substance is concerned, will, I hope, follow in the manner indicated.

I have thought it my duty at once to acquaint your Eminence with this matter, having communicated it to no one else; for I trust that His Holiness and your Eminence will be satisfied that in this way the affair is being brought to such a point that it may soon be settled without difficulty. The court will maintain its reputation; it will be possible to deal leniently with the culprit; and, whatever the decision arrived at, he will recognize the favor shown him, with all the other consequences of satisfaction herein desired. Today I think of examining him in order to obtain the said confession; and having, as I hope, received it, it will only remain to me further to question him with regard to his intention and to receive his defense plea; that done, he might have [his] house assigned to him as a prison, as hinted to me by your Eminence, to whom I offer my most humble reverence.

> Your Eminence's most humble and
> most obedient servant,
> FRA VINC⁰. DA FIRENZUOLA

ROME, April 28, 1633

One wonders what the initial conversation between the two may have been like. It makes one regret that the tape recorder was not in existence; for, this once at least, it was Galileo who had something on the Commissary. He had received in October a letter in which Castelli reported a meeting with Firenzuola, whom he had known for a long time, he said, as a competent military engineer and "a decent person." Castelli had gone to Firenzuola when the first trouble was stirring and, as between monks, had talked to him as vividly and "heretically" as he knew how. "I told him I had no scruple in holding firmly that the Earth moves and that the Sun stands still and that I saw no reason for prohibiting the *Dialogue*. The Father told me that he was of the same opinion and that these questions should not be determined with the use of the authority of Holy Writ. He even told me he intended to write on the subject and would show it to me."

Thus, Galileo knew that the reluctant dragon who had been ordered to devour him held really the same opinion that he did; and there must have been much curious sparring between the two on the lofty subject of theological interpretation. After "many and many arguments and rejoinders," The Commissary must have felt that he was getting nowhere and told him the facts bluntly, somewhat like this:

"My dear Signor Galileo, you do not seem to realize your position. You insist on talking about your text, while I have not asked you about it. You still want us to believe both the rightness of your thought and the purity of your intention, allowing at most that you misunderstood the instructions. You think you can make a stand on Bellarmine's certificate. But the Holy Office cannot be defied like that. It is desired from high quarters, as you realize, that we should make an example, and we are going to. The question is: How far do you want to push us?

"You may quote the licenses again. You may try to allege that the injunction we have was—shall we say—well, lacked your signature. You are going to say that you were encouraged by high quarters to discuss the doctrine and that one cannot discuss it without teaching the contents. But don't you see that in that case you compel us to go into your motives? Don't tell me that your intention is not in question. It is. And I am very much afraid that it might come out, God forbid, that you were, and are, a Copernican. Please—you are not talking to Firenzuola now; you are talking to the Commissary. That you held, as I was saying, the opinion all along and that you do even now—with dissimulation and pertinacity in the face of your inquirers—hold it. I might just as well tell you that this is the way it looks, now that the experts' report upon your book has come in. This would be quite enough in itself. For Cardinal Bellarmine left you in no doubt about the Church's intentions; you promised to obey and then chose to disregard them. You did try to outwit us and affirm your will, which has become contradictory to that of the Church on theological matters. May I add that you further used the freedom you had been given to slip in a couple of propositions which directly deny the transcendence of the Divine Mind. You know what that is called, don't you? A real procedure *de vehementi,* once started, cannot be so easily checked. We shall have to go through the routine of rigorous questioning, by regrettable means if necessary, and the admission will come out. After that there is only our mercy, which means perpetual incarceration in the prisons of the Holy Office. Nobody wants that.

"If you would only understand, you ought to see that a plea of disobedience is still your best bet. Admit it. Plead forgetfulness, complacency, pride, vanity, conceit—choose your own out of the catalogue of venial sins—and we shall have no need for inquiring further. You will get off with a light spanking, and everybody, please believe me, will be much the happier."

Whatever the words, this was the gist of it, as is clearly indicated in the letter, and it was well said. It was the stroke of lightning that rent the veil of Galileo's obsolete Renaissance convictions. He had been introduced to the modern state.

When he was called in two days later, April 30, he was asked whether he had anything to say. He spoke as follows:

In the course of some days' continuous and attentive reflection on the interrogations put to me on the twelfth of the present month, and in particular as to whether, sixteen years ago, an injunction was intimated to me by order of the Holy Office, forbidding me to hold, defend, or teach "in any manner" the opinion that had just been condemned—of the motion of the Earth and the stability of the Sun—it occurred to me to reperuse my printed *Dialogue*, which for three years I had not seen, in order carefully to note whether, contrary to my most sincere intention, there had, by inadvertence, fallen from my pen anything from which a reader or the authorities might infer not only some taint of disobedience on my part but also other particulars which might induce the belief that I had contravened the orders of the Holy Church.

Being, by the kind permission of the authorities, at liberty to send about my servant, I succeeded in procuring a copy of my book, and, having procured it, I applied myself with the utmost diligence to its perusal and to a most minute consideration thereof. And as, owing to my not having seen it for so long, it presented itself to me, as it were, like a new writing and by another author, I freely confess that in several places it seemed to me set forth in such a form that a reader ignorant of my real purpose might have had reason to suppose that the arguments brought on the false side, and which it was my intention to confute, were so expressed as to be calculated rather to compel conviction by their cogency than to be easy of solution.

Two arguments there are in particular—the one taken from the solar spots, the other from the ebb and flow of the tide—which in truth come to the ear of the reader with far greater show of force and power than ought to have been imparted to them by one who regarded them as inconclusive and who intended to refute them, as indeed I truly and sincerely held and do hold them to be inconclusive and admitting of refutation. And, as an excuse to myself for having fallen into an error so foreign to my intention, not contenting myself entirely with saying that, when a man recites the arguments of the opposite side with the object of refuting them, he should, especially if writing in the form of dialogue, state these in their strictest form and should not cloak them to the disadvantage of his opponent—not contenting myself, I say, with this excuse, I resorted to that of the natural complacency which every man feels with regard to his own subtleties and in showing himself more skilful than the generality of men in devising, even in favor of false propositions, ingenious and plausible arguments. With all this, although with Cicero "avidior sim gloriae quam sat est," if I had now to set forth the same reasonings, without doubt I should so weaken them that they should not be able to make an apparent show of that force of which they are really and essentially devoid. My error, then, has been—and I confess it—one of vainglorious ambition and of pure ignorance and inadvertence.

This is what it occurs to me to say with reference to this particular and which suggested itself to me during the reperusal of my book.

After this declaration, the defendant was dismissed; but he came back after a moment (*post paullulum*), asking to be allowed to make a supplementary statement:

And in confirmation of my assertion that I have not held and do not hold as true the opinion which has been condemned, of the motion of the Earth and stability of the Sun—if there shall be granted to me, as I desire, means and time to make a clearer demonstration thereof, I am ready to do so; and there is a most favorable opportunity for this, seeing that in the work already published the interlocutors agree to meet again after a certain time to discuss several distinct problems of Nature not connected with the matter discoursed of at their meetings. As this affords me an opportunity of adding one or two other "days," I promise to resume the arguments already brought in favor of the said opinion, which is false and has been condemned, and to confute them in such most effectual manner as by the blessing of God may be supplied to me. I pray, therefore, this holy Tribunal to aid me in this good resolution and to enable me to put it in effect.

By enlisting the co-operation of Galileo, the Commissary had obtained the admission he needed, and with it he had regained the initiative over his opponents.

IV

Historians have wept unrestrained tears over this final self-degradation of the great man. Nothing apparently would have satisfied them except his being roasted at the stake in Campo di Fiori, as Bruno had been thirty-three years before. In fact, it was a rational move, and it would have obtained for Galileo all that he really wanted—the circulation of the *Dialogue*. No doubt it was bitter to him. He skipped it in his first statement and then drove himself back to say it. He knew he had to say it. It was what Niccolini had advised, much earlier in the game, and what he suggested again now.[11] In an age which laid so much more weight than ours on formalities, everyone knew the difference between due form and intention. Kepler himself, the blameless and fearless Kepler, had thought well in 1619 to send to his bookseller in Italy a letter to be shown to the authorities, so they would not prohibit his *Harmonice mundi*. Although a fervid Protestant, he avowed himself to be "a son of the Church" and added: "As much as I have been able to understand of the Catholic doctrine I not only submit to but indorse it with my reason, and I have tried to show it in several passages of this work." The censor must have raised his eyebrows in

11. Dispatch of May 22. Niccolini, after seeing the Pope, is suddenly afraid again that it may come to the prohibition of the book, unless it is decided to have him write an apology, "as I suggested to His Beatitude." This means that, in his recent deal with Galileo, the Commissary had intimated that a corrected version would be allowed.

wonderment over such a peculiar "son of the Church," but what Kepler lacked was only pratice in the proper language. Anyway, on the Index forthwith did he go.

Moralist historians do not seem to notice that their perspective is that of believers in another religion. They would have Galileo behave like Jerome of Prague or like a prophet of Bruno's strange un-Christian God. They forget that he was a member of the Apostolic Roman communion and had to submit in some way. Quite apart from the personal inconvenience of being burned at the stake, it would have been a sin of diabolical pride on his part to push the Vicar of Christ into committing a crime.

He had gambled and lost. He was not a religious visionary being asked to renounce his vision. He was an intelligent man who had taken heavy risks to force an issue and to change a policy for the good of his Faith. He had been snubbed; he had nothing to do but to pay the price and go home. The scientific truth would be able to take care of itself.

He had realized at last that the authorities were not interested in truth but only in authority. They did not expect him to change his mind. They wanted, most illegally, to kill it; and he was going to consider his own interests henceforth. In this new clarifying spirit of mutual disrespect, he proposed a deal *in extremis*. But it was too late. The reigning faction had decided it was not going to be outsmarted again.

His suggestion was allowed to drop. But, in any case, the dangerous passage had been negotiated: from now on, the Commissary was empowered to carry on interrogations only *pro forma*. True to his promise, Firenzuola released the prisoner in the custody of the ambassador, who was surprised and overjoyed to see him arrive back at the Villa Medici. "It is a fearful thing," he wrote to the Grand Duke, "to have to do with the Inquisition. The poor man has come back more dead than alive."

The next interrogation on May 10 had been obviously prearranged in the tête-à-tête, for Firenzuola, on opening it, informed the defendant, according to the rules, that eight days were allowed him to present a defense if he wished to submit one; and Galileo handed it in at once. It was as follows:

When asked if I had signified to the Reverend Father, the Master of the Holy Palace, the injunction privately laid upon me, about sixteen years ago, by the order of the Holy Office, not to hold, defend, or "in any way" teach the doctrine of the motion of the Earth and the stability of the Sun, I answered that I had not done so. And, not being questioned as to the reason why I had not intimated it, I had no opportunity to add anything further. It now appears to me necessary to state the reason, in order to demonstrate the purity of my intention, ever foreign to the practice of simulation or deceit in any operation I engage in.

I say, then, that, as at that time reports were spread abroad by evil-disposed persons to the effect that I had been summoned by the Lord Cardinal Bellarmine to abjure certain of my opinions and teachings and also to submit to penitence for them, I was thus constrained to apply to his Eminence and to solicit him to furnish me with an attestation, explaining the cause for which I had been summoned before him; which attestation I obtained in his own handwriting, and it is the same that I now produce with the present document. From this it clearly appears that it was merely announced to me that the doctrine attributed to Copernicus, of the motion of the Earth and the stability of the Sun, must not be held or defended; but that, beyond this general announcement affecting everyone, there should have been ordered anything to me in particular, no trace thereof appears in it.

Having, then, as a reminder, this authentic attestation in the handwriting of the very person who informed me of the command, I made no further application of thought or memory with regard to the words employed in orally announcing to me the said order not to hold or defend the doctrine in question; so that the two articles of the order—in addition to the injunction not to "hold" or "defend" it—to wit, the words "not to teach it" and "in any way whatsoever"—which, I hear, are contained in the order enjoined on me, and registered—struck me as quite novel and as if I had not heard them before, and I do not think I ought to be disbelieved when I urge that in the course of fourteen or sixteen years I had lost all recollection of them, especially as I had no need to give any particular thought to them, having in my possession so authentic a reminder in writing. Now, if the said two articles be left out, and those two only be retained which are noted in the accompanying attestation, there is no doubt that the injunction contained in the latter is the same command as that contained in the decree of the Holy Congregation of the Index. Hence it appears to me that I have a reasonable excuse for not having notified to the Master of the Holy Palace about the command privately imposed upon me, it being the same as that of the Congregation of the Index.

Now, if so be my book was not subject to a stricter censorship than that made binding by the decree of the Index, it will, it appears to me, be sufficiently plain that I adopted the surest and most becoming method of having it guaranteed and purged of all shadow of taint, inasmuch as I handed it to the Supreme Inquisitor at the very time when many books dealing with the same matters were being prohibited solely by virtue of the said decree. After what I have now stated, I would confidently hope that the idea of my having knowingly and deliberately violated the command imposed upon me will henceforth be entirely banished from the minds of my most eminent and wise judges; hence those faults which are seen scattered throughout my book have not been artfully introduced with any concealed or other than sincere intention but have only inadvertently fallen from my pen, owing to a vainglorious ambition and complacency in desiring to appear more subtle than the generality of popular writers, as indeed in another deposition I have confessed; which fault I shall be ready to correct with all possible industry whenever I may be commanded or permitted by Their Most Eminent Lordships.

Lastly, it remains for me to beg you to take into consideration my pitiable state of bodily indisposition, to which, at the age of seventy years, I have been reduced by ten months of constant mental anxiety and the fatigue of a long and toilsome journey at the most inclement season—together with the loss of the greater part of the years to which, from my previous condition of health, I had the prospect. I am persuaded and encouraged to do so by the faith I have in the clemency and goodness of the most Eminent Lords, my judges; with the hope that they may be pleased, in answer to my prayer, to remit what may appear to their entire justice the rightful addition that is still lacking to such sufferings to make up an adequate punishment for my crimes, out of consideration for my declining age, which, too, humbly commends itself to them. And I would equally commend to their consideration my honor and reputation, against the calumnies of ill-wishers, whose persistence in detracting from my good name may be inferred from the necessity which constrained me to procure from the Lord Cardinal Bellarmine the attestation which accompanies this.

The world will long remember the touching appeal for mercy. What it seems to have forgotten is that it concludes what amounts to a very strong defense, so confident and prompt indeed that one is led again to imagine some previous helpful hints from the Commissary himself. Galileo goes as far as he dares in calling his accusers a pack of liars. The expressions "not to teach it" and "in any way whatsoever" had struck him as "quite novel" and as "not heard . . . before." So they were indeed—and to the Pope himself for that matter. (The accused still had no word of a specific injunction by Father Segizi as separate from Bellarmine's command.) He ventured to suggest coolly that they be soft-pedaled henceforth. There is no mistaking the intimation. After politely granting that he might possibly have forgotten the full command, he goes on to dismiss that possibility in the sentence that we have italicized (in the original: "Che poi, stante che 'l mio libro non fusse sottoposto, etc.," which amounts to: "Enough of that nonsense") and proceeds from there to reaffirm his perfect regularity. Such a defense, clearly, could be effective only within the frame of the extra-judicial settlement that the Commissary had offered. It was there only to complete the record, and it must have been made clear that it would be acceptable.

XIII

The Problem
of the False Injunction

Inter hos judices vivendum, moriendum,
et quod durius est, tacendum.

I

What can be the conclusion concerning that famous injunction of 1616? It is, and will remain to the end, the kingpin of the case. With it, from the legal aspect, the trial stands or falls. It came to our notice how everything connected with it was being surrounded all along with a screen of vague, reticent, or misleading language so as to protect it from indiscreet curiosity.

Some curiosity is therefore in order. We are going to review the evidence, starting from the two critical documents that we gave in chapter vi. One of them is the injunction; the other is Bellarmine's certificate.

Friday, the twenty-sixth [of February]. At the palace, the usual residence of the Lord Cardinal Bellarmino, the said Galileo, having been summoned and being present before the said Lord Cardinal, was, in presence of the Most Reverend Michelangelo Segizi of Lodi, O.P., Commissary-General of the Holy

We, Roberto Cardinal Bellarmino, having heard that it is calumniously reported that Signor Galileo Galilei has in our hand abjured and has also been punished with salutary penance, and being requested to state the truth as to this, declare that the said Signor Galileo has not abjured, either in our hand, or the

Office, by the said Cardinal, warned of the error of the aforesaid opinion and admonished to abandon it; and immediately thereafter, before me and before witnesses, the Lord Cardinal being still present, the said Galileo was by the said Commissary commanded and enjoined, in the name of His Holiness the Pope and the whole Congregation of the Holy Office, to relinquish altogether said opinion that the Sun is the center of the world and immovable and that the Earth moves; nor further to hold, teach, or defend it in any way whatsoever, verbally or in writing; otherwise proceedings would be taken against him in the Holy Office; which injunction the said Galileo acquiesced in and promised to obey. Done at Rome, in the place aforesaid, in the presence of R. Badino Nores and Agostino Mongardo, members of the household of said Cardinal, witnesses.

hand of any other person here in Rome, or anywhere else, so far as we know, any opinion or doctrine held by him; neither has any salutary penance been imposed on him; but that only the declaration made by the Holy Father and published by the Sacred Congregation of the Index has been notified to him, wherein it is set forth that the doctrine attributed to Copernicus, that the Earth moves around the Sun and that the Sun is stationary in the center of the world and does not move from east to west, is contrary to the Holy Scriptures and therefore cannot be defended or held. In witness whereof we have written and subscribed these presents with our hand this twenty-sixth day of May, 1616.

We showed then that the first document looks gravely irregular both as to form and as to its place in the file; that the instructions of the Congregation to Bellarmine, as well as Bellarmine's subsequent report on what he had done that day, agree with his certificate and *not* with the injunction; and that there was in fact no allowable ground for an injunction as things stood.

We have seen further that in his most carefully considered piece of writing, the Preface to the *Dialogue,* Galileo deliberately mentions the famous audience as a signal distinction. He is actually calling the authorities to witness against the rumors that had been spread of a secret recantation. This would have been to provoke them foolishly if he had not been quite assured that things stood, in fact, so.

The natural supposition is that the record was hastily fabricated in 1632 when the authorities were trying to get a case against Galileo. Since it was certain, however, that no new sheet had been inserted, Wohlwill suggested that the regular record had been fraudulently altered by deleting the last lines and by tacking a new ending onto it.[1] He supported his contention with a mass of evidence derived from inspection of the manuscript with a magnifying glass. The paper being in bad condition and corroded by the ink, that evidence remained very controversial. Gebler and then Favaro, also from direct inspection, held out for the authenticity of the document. It is true that Gebler's conclusion (Favaro refrains from drawing any) is hardly more flattering: the text was concocted, with careful deliberation and malice prepense, on that very day it was dated, February 26, 1616, and planted in the file in order to trap the unsuspecting scientist the moment he proceeded to discuss the Copernican system "in any way whatsoever."[2]

1. Wohlwill's contention is that the original document, as indicated by the spacing of the text (fol. 378ᵛ), faint traces of erased letters, and other clues, ended, after Bellarmine's words, with the simple concluding statement that would be logically expected: "cui praecepto idem Galilaeus acquievit et parere promisit." This conclusion was carefully deleted and a sequel inserted, concerning the intervention of the Commissary, beginning with the words "et successive ac incontinenti" ("and immediately thereafter") and going on to the blank recto of the next sheet, fol. 379ʳ (see Appendix II of the second volume of his *Galilei,* p. 298).

2. We have indications that Galileo himself inclined to this opinion. In his letter to Peiresc he says: "If some power would bring to light the slanders, frauds, stratagems, and trickeries that were used eighteen years ago in Rome. . . ." This means something definite. Very definite, indeed, in the light of his subsequent words in that same letter (quoted *in extenso* on p. 351): "Against one wrongfully sentenced while he was innocent, it is expedient, in order to put up a show of strict lawfulness, to uphold rigor." Galileo is saying here something new with respect to what he had said in 1616. He wrote at that time to Picchena that he had "incredible tales to tell him about the workings of those three most powerful operators, ignorance, malice, and impiety, such that he dared not intrust to writing." But what he meant then, obviously, were the intrigues which had brought about the prohibition of 1616 and his being accused of blasphemy. (Of these "slanders"

Thus the matter stood for decades; it seemed suspended pending new evidence. This came eventually, not from any document, but from new physical means of analysis. In 1927 Laemmel, with the co-operation of the Vatican authorities, submitted the doubtful page first to soft X-rays and then to the much more rigorous test of the Hanau ultraviolet lamp.[3] The result left no doubt on one point at least: the pages had never been tampered with. Wohlwill's laborious inferences fell to the ground. They had never been very plausible to begin with, except on the surface, for Wohlwill had never stopped to consider that the document (we have seen earlier it is in the form of an unsigned minute) would hardly have been worth that amount of fuss. It would have been easy for anyone who wanted to do away with an early version to cut off the two pages containing it, as has been done elsewhere in the file and with no thought of concealment (fols. 342 and 343). He would still have had available in the right place a blank page, 377^v, quite sufficient if used properly, on which to effect a new transcription.

Having settled that particular point, Laemmel thought he could draw the conclusion that the whole text had been added in 1632 when it was badly needed. But his reasons are curiously uninformed and of hardly any logical value. What could it mean, for instance, that the handwriting seems different on the second page? The supposedly altered text begins in the first one.

Against such arguments, one has to stand on Gebler's findings, confirmed recently by Jauch: the text is in exactly the same hand as other neighboring and certainly genuine documents; hence, it was written

he had been cleared by the Inquisition.) The net result of the intrigues was the decree itself. Now he declares himself innocent of ever having violated the decree (as he is accused in the sentence) ; hence he ought logically to accuse the tribunal of sheer arbitrariness in what had become a trial of intention. Instead, he mentions "frauds, stratagems, and trickeries" going back to 1616. This ought to mean forged evidence, about which the authorities had to put on "a show of strict lawfulness."

3. H. Laemmel, *Archiv f. Gesch. d. Mathematik*, Vol. X (March, 1928).

at or about the same time. To this we can add a clinching argument: the contemporary pagination shows that the original, if there ever was one, never got into the file; and therefore the decision to replace it with a falsification must have been taken then and there.

Still, there is something that remains hard to explain. The operation is curiously botched. The lack of an original alone might be construed as a mishap, for an inserted double sheet may drop out, but the wrong substitute job in the wrong place is painfully lasting evidence. A regular judge would have had to throw out the injunction on that evidence alone; even the judges of 1633 did not dare rely too much on it.

Should one see here plain cynical disregard for regularity? We would doubt it very much. Regularity was a fetish with the administration, and any such detectable irregularity always entailed a risk for its author. It would almost look as though the thing had been done by someone not in full control of events and having to make shift with what he had. Even so, from a Commissary-General able to arrange things at his will, one might expect more resourceful solutions. For instance, leaving the pagination open and referring to the injunction with seeming casualness but convenient explicitness somewhere else. A later investigation could then only have accused the archivist of negligence for losing the original.

So there might remain a point of doubt. Let us check our conclusions as they stand by assuming the opposite to be true, namely, that things happened as written and that Galileo really stands guilty of violating his instructions. We would then have to say that the protocol was accidentally lost as soon as made out; that the official doing the pagination never noticed its absence; that someone noticed it soon afterward; and that it was deemed sufficient to insert a transcription which can only have been done from memory, for, if the original had been available somewhere, it would have been put back into place. It does not sound very convincing.

Thus we are led back perforce to our version, and the question why the operation was carried out so and not otherwise turns out to be simply a statement of the Commissary's best judgment, based upon what he thought could be done and could not be done. The straight fact that emerges is that it was not held to be quite essential to have the protocol—or, rather, that, following Bellarmine's audience, it was deemed better to have no protocol at all rather than an authentic version of that audience. And so we may be led to conclude that the Commissary simply decided to do without one. Regularity has its limits. But, it would seem, falsification has too.

We know that there had been a strong tension in 1616 between the higher authorities who had decided on diplomacy and the Dominicans, bent at that time on repression. Vatican quarters several times hinted to Guicciardini that "the monks" were relentless. We may then reconstruct as follows: The Commissary, as he watched the scene (we know he was present), was disgusted with the easy way in which Galileo was let off, and he decided to omit the protocol, although his instructions were clear, and the witnesses already designated, obviously by the Cardinal himself. On going back to his office, he told his assistant to arrange a more helpful minute of the proceedings. "And," he may have added, "make it stiff, just in case. What they don't know doesn't hurt them; when trouble arises, it is we who have to take it on." Or it may be, of course, that the assistant, Father Tinti, did the job on his own initiative. But it seems very unlikely. This theory would have the merit of explaining naturally why the protocol was omitted from the pagination as well as accounting for the other facts in the case.[4]

4. We should mention here a variant derived from an independent study of the documents and personally communicated by Professor C. Jauch. His idea is that the minute was written in advance of proceedings by officials who took the "second degree" for granted and then let the text stand in the record, even though events had gone otherwise. The idea is quite plausible. In that case, however, the text would have been easy to make out as a regular, if false, protocol, which it is not. Moreover, the names of the witnesses from the Cardinal's household, obviously designated by the Cardinal on the spot, could not have appeared, and the signature of a couple of the regular Inquisition officials would have been the natural thing, in addition to making it look more legal. Finally, we would expect to find in the text the clause: "the said Galileo having demurred," whose very lack in the actual document is so revealing. A man inventing the situation

To look at that silent sheet now, after three centuries, gives one a strange feeling, as though it were trying to tell us something. The first part, which reproduces the papal decree, is dealt out with well-practiced smoothness. As soon as it comes to the injunction, the lines get closer, and the writing becomes less legible, as though the writer were unconsciously trying to duck.

The falsification as such is, then, beyond doubt—truly, by modern standards, an exceedingly modest one. Father Segizi would never have dared forge a protocol. He had done a little something, the least he could do, in order to provide a toehold for prosecution if that were needed. It was as much as, on the other side, Lancelot Andrewes proved quite willing to do when he altered the text of Father Henry Garnet's letters in order to implicate him in the Gunpowder Plot.[5] Our contemporaries cannot expect their authorities to be so considerate. Today, over one-half of the globe, the suspect is asked to forge the accusation documents himself, and to do it thoroughly, by inventing all the lurid details that can make his confession convincing and comprehensive. He is supposed to disavow, dishonor, and damn himself with all the fervor of progressive citizenship, if he is to take his last walk to the basement at peace with his conscience.

Going back to Galileo, we can see that the course of events agrees with our previous conclusion. For not only, as we have shown, did Galileo feel completely confident that the officials were mistaken when the matter was finally revealed to him (and that would have been rather the time for him to grovel) but those very officials demonstrated, by their manner of handling the procedure of injunction when it was really necessary (viz., in order to summon Galileo to Rome), the elaborate context of rules in which such an act is framed. Here was a man who had patently fooled them, who was now subtly evading and

 ante factum would not have omitted that clause, whereas, trying to arrange what had actually happened, he would have tried to keep down lies to the strict minimum necessary.

5. Cf. Lingard, *History of England* (3d ed., 1825), Vol. IX, Appendix, Note D, pp. 433-35.

challenging them; and yet a whole contraption had to be worked out in order to have something that would serve for an injunction without a previous refusal to motivate it.

II

How this was done is a fascinating little story—and a short course in procedure—all by itself. It is provided by Francesco Barberini in two letters to the Nuncio in Florence, both of September 25, 1632, when Galileo was to be summoned to appear in Rome after the publication of the *Dialogue*. The first letter said:

> The Florence Inquisitor is instructed to tell him that he must be pleased to come to Rome and exhort him thereto, explaining to him that he might with his presence repair many things and give and receive satisfaction. If he promises to do so, there is no need to go further; but if perchance he should refuse to come, or make difficulties, let the Father have a notary in readiness who will then enjoin on him the command [*facci precetto*] to come to Rome.

On reading the draft, which is in the hand of Benessi, a papal secretary, Barberini had this section struck out and replaced by the following, which was much more drastic:

> [He] shall notify him of a *precetto* to present himself, etc., and he shall be made to promise to obey said *precetto* in the presence of witnesses, so that, if he refuses to obey, in any case they can be examined.

This altered version was signed and dispatched, but immediately afterward Barberini must have received the actual text of the Inquisition orders, sent out two days previously, for he wrote on the same day a second letter:

> His Holiness has ordered that the Inquisitor should signify to Galileo, in the presence of a notary and of witnesses (not however qualified in his presence as such), that the will of the Congregation is that he should come to Rome for the whole month of October; if he declares himself willing to obey, he should be made to acknowledge in his own hand the communication and his intention to obey; this acknowledgment, once he has departed,

shall be certified and authenticated by the notary and witnesses. If Galileo refuses to acknowledge or to come to Rome, then the Father Inquisitor shall make out the injunction in due form.

We have thus three degrees of the same action described; and it was the intermediate one that was adopted. Now we should consider that the proceedings of 1632 were being taken *ab irato* and by authorities who knew, as is said in the same letter, that Galileo was not respecting the suspension and was "thinking of sending" his book abroad (there are instructions to stop it at the border). Furthermore, we must suppose they assumed that he had violated the injunction of 1616. Yet they could not bring themselves, even at this point, to serve a regular injunction complete with the clause *sub poenis*. Benessi's early draft corresponds exactly in form to Bellarmine's instructions in 1616. It is full of soft words, which shows that it was assumed at the papal secretariat that the affair had to be handled with kid gloves and on the same level of social consideration as in 1616. Then there is a change of mind, but the authorities never go as far as the third degree, which is the strict regular injunction. They could not, apparently, because Galileo, however suspicious his thoughts, had always been regular and submissive; and the best they could do was to lay a trap. (But, then, had he or had he not violated the injunction of 1616 in their eyes? We are left with the same curious question.) Therefore, they evolved an intermediate procedure, whereby they could get a signed acknowledgment without serving the injunction. It was only if he refused that the Inquisitor was supposed to step forward and say: Very well, this is it, now, and these here are the witnesses. In this case, of course, a further refusal to acknowledge and submit would have meant rebellion, warranting immediate arrest. We have thus the three degrees mentioned in the decree of February 25, 1616, confirmed and spelled out in detail.

We have, indeed, more. These men, who had no sense of the ridiculous, had elaborately restaged the whole operation of 1616, including the deceit, but this time taking all the precautions to make it foolproof. Galileo was asked politely to state his acquiescence in writing. He did. Then, as soon as the commission was beyond earshot, the assistants, who had previously been in the next room, apparently under the pretense that they had come just for the outing, bore down on the paper, which was frantically signed, countersigned, sworn to, and then validated by the Secretary of the Inquisition. Galileo still thought that what he had given was a written assurance, but they had now, without a refusal to motivate it, what could serve for an injunction in case it were needed.[6] Clearly, the *extra ordinem* had its limits—and also a curious shape of its own in their minds.

III

In the light of these later events it appears all the more incongruous that in 1616, when all was still clear, the Commissary should have sprung forward brandishing his threat *incontinenti*, as soon as Bellarmine had considerately informed Galileo that his theory had been found wrong, without even giving him the time to declare his acquiescence to the new ruling.

These problems really all reflect to the credit of the institution. In fear of its own absolute and unlimited powers, it had framed for itself such a rigid set of rules that, when the need came for cutting corners, it could not do so by merely stretching the interpretation. As a result, certain officials, who held the view that when a job has to be done it has to be done, did not shrink from altering the records without the acquiescence of their superiors. That they were not above such methods is well known; there is quite a number of precedents. The following is taken from a formal protest to the Cardinal Legates of the consuls of the city of Cordes in Languedoc in 1306:

Item, seeing that the processes and books of the said Inquisitors are deservedly suspected by us, both by reason of change or burning or cancellation of writings in the said books, and also by reason of confessions extracted by the Inquisitors uncanonically and by force of torture, and written down (as it is said) otherwise than the matter stands in truth, and seeing also that this is reported in the district of Albi and in the regions round, there-

---

6. A puzzle remains: why this fumble between three versions of the same act? We may begin to guess some reasons further on.

fore, we, the consuls of the city of Cordes, beseech and request you to inform yourself on this matter. Moreover, since it is publicly reported that certain witnesses, through whom you may gain clearer information concerning the alterations and burning and cancellation and injustice of the said records and processes, have at the command of those Inquisitors sworn certain prejudicial oaths, to wit, that they will not reveal that which they know of these matters, under pain of being condemned as relapsed heretics and burned—therefore the said consuls beseech and request, etc.

How widespread these conditions were is shown by the vain summons of Pope Clement trying to recall the Inquisitors to order. Things had changed considerably for the better since that time, and the central organs had enforced regularity. But it would appear that someone, at times, still took the law into his own hands.

To maintain that Bellarmine himself was a party to the deceit ought to be out of the question.[7] The operation seems to begin and end in the office of the Commissary-General of the time, Father Michelangelo Segizi, among those implacable Dominicans to whom Guicciardini alludes, "fired with holy zeal" like their own Lorinis and Caccinis and no more scrupulous, like them convinced that mathematicians are a tool of the Devil, who thought it an excellent precaution against the Adversary to put in this pretended registration. No one need be deceived by it if he did not want to, they thought; and, meanwhile, here was a trap to snare the Evil One in case of need. As it happened, it was

---

7. If needed, there would be evidence to help us. We have noted earlier how irregular the choice of witnesses is. It would be passing strange that in Bellarmine's own palace, with "a number of Dominicans standing around" as we know from Galileo's deposition, two servants of the Cardinal's household should have been commandeered by the Inquisitor himself to witness a secret injunction, instead of the ecclesiastic officials that procedure imposed. No one could have chosen and commanded them except the Cardinal. And he knew too well, as everyone did, that Inquisition procedure admitted of no lay witnesses to its acts. He had emphasized thus to Galileo, who was present, that no injunction was implied; that this was his regular private audience and not a visit of the Inquisition; and that, since Galileo had acquiesced, it was going to be handled formally like any public act, be it a notification or the granting of a title.

Pope Urban and the Congregation who were to be snared in it.[8] Fouché, well versed in the ways of Old Nick, used to teach: *surtout pas de zèle.*

If the document was actually predisposed in 1616, it might throw some light upon the insistent rumors that went around then of secret measures. Echoes come back from the diplomats' suspicions: "The monks are all-powerful"; "One of these days we shall hear that he has fallen over some incalculable precipice [*qualche stravagante preci-*

---

8. Some historians who want this ancient quarrel to be patched up and to have everybody live happily ever after have advanced a curious compromise suggestion. It is implied by Favaro, apparently, and made explicit by J. J. Fahie. The idea is that the Commissary pounced upon some bewildered question that came to Galileo's lips the moment Bellarmine had finished speaking (e.g., "What, not even discuss the theory?") and interposed quickly an explanation that it was not to be discussed in any way whatsoever. Subsequently, without either Galileo or Bellarmine (both declared to be present) having taken note of it, the event was set down as an injunction. The learned authors do not seem to have realized that this saves nobody's face. An injunction that escapes the notice of the enjoinee is a fraudulent injunction. Even only to omit the last threatening clause *sub poenis, etc.,* would make it such. We have seen from the other cases of regular injunctions that elaborate formalities were taken to make them explicit. The compromise that is suggested amounts thus to another variant of the act of forgery. Also, we have Galileo's explicit and repeated declaration, under very dangerous circumstances, that no one except Bellarmine said a word to him. He does not remember, he specifies, whether those Dominican Fathers were still in the room when the Cardinal spoke to him. Apart from this, it is absurd. To suppose that Galileo was abruptly told that what Bellarmine had just explained to him was no longer valid, that he was no longer allowed a discussion *ex suppositione*—and that he did not even notice such words coming from the Commissary of the Inquisition, makes no sense at all. The theory had to be mentioned because it has been adopted by Fahie, who is among the very few reliable English authors on the subject whose work is currently available. We think our supposition is, on the whole, more charitable to all concerned. A strange note is struck by Father Brodrick in his *Bellarmine* (II, 370). After admitting the "discrepancy" between the two documents, which he explains through the "fussiness or excess of zeal" of the Commissary, who spoke or tried to speak out of turn (we have seen what this explanation is worth), he concludes: "The writer of the other report [the injunction] and the purpose for which it was intended are not known." This last sentence is hard to believe, but it stands there in black and white. It presents again as much of a mystery, written in our own time, as the whole of the proceedings of three centuries ago.

pizio]." The kind of men who were capable of organizing the denunciations that we have seen, and the report on the proceedings that we shall soon see hereafter, can be credited with exactly anything. And they seem to have also implied it beyond the bounds of discretion. Some good brother must have gone around in guarded exultation, saying darkly: "Just wait and see." [9]

It might still be asked, finally: Why did Galileo in person never pronounce himself explicitly on the subject? He was the man to know. Well, we do have a fairly explicit statement from him—as explicit as he could make it without contempt of court. It is to be found in Buonamici's memorandum (see p. 311). He told the judges that he would not recite the formula of abjuration, even at the risk of dire penalties, *if it contained anything implying that he had ever deceived his censors and specifically in the matter of extorting a license.* And in fact it does not, although the sentence was built upon this specific accusation, and hence a penitential admission was in order. But, if he does *not* admit that he did "artfully and cunningly" refrain from telling about the injunction, then Galileo is saying as clearly as he can, in the face of the authorities, that the injunction never existed. And this ought to answer the question.[10]

9. Those who used to maintain with Wohlwill, Cantor, Gherardi, Scartazzini, and others that the document was fabricated only in 1632 pointed to the fact that Galileo had come under the attention of the Inquisition apropos of the *Saggiatore,* and also of the *Letter to Ingoli,* and that the injunction would have been then brought up against him. This is no doubt a point. The Vatican authorities insist that the document has been there since 1616, and we incline to agree. It ought to imply, however, this: that the Inquisitors realized that either piece did not allow them to go beyond a pointed reminder; that this would have spoiled the game and allowed Galileo to retreat without damage; and that they decided to give him enough rope to make a solid noose for himself. That is, if the Inquisitors bothered to look up the file at all, which is the point where doubt is allowed.

10. Since Monsignor Marino Marini, almost all ecclesiastic historians have lamented his denials in the first interrogatory and considered them "childish evasions unworthy of such a great man." It is indeed plausible to suggest that Galileo at that point desperately refused to admit what might incriminate him and claimed that, "if it was so, he had lost all memory of it"; although, if he lied, he showed great consistency and adroitness in maintaining his point throughout the interrogations.

Even a century ago the question was hardly open to doubt. M. de l'Epinois, writing in 1877 as an accredited apologist for the authorities, was willing to grant that the document is "a note for a protocol which probably never was written," and, starting from there, the case for the defense becomes hard to maintain. The best that this reputable scholar could do, in fact, was to ask why Galileo did not speak out: "After the trial, how could he not be revolted at the thought that he had been faced with a forgery, and how could he keep silent on this point? How can it be that, in the nine years which followed, this man so vehement in his expressions did not vent his indignation in letters to the Grand Duke and to his friends at home and abroad against the odious abuse of justice and the crime of the base falsifier of whom he had been the victim?"

It is still conceivable that M. de l'Epinois may not have known the letters we quoted above, which express the victim's feelings in no uncertain terms. But he could not be unaware (having published the record himself) of the famous incident of 1634 we recounted on page 237, when Galileo, having asked for some easements on grounds of illness, was notified by the Pope that, if he was ever again heard of, he would be taken back to Rome and jailed for good. It is under those circumstances that the author asks why he did not indict formally the Holy Office for a fraud to which he was the only surviving witness. Now really. Even published after his death, such a document would have called down implacable persecution on his family, which depended largely (as most of that class did) on ecclesiastical benefits or protection. When Galileo wrote, "If only *some power* would bring to light . . ."; when he said and repeated that he had been gagged forever—he meant it. If M. de l'Epinois had nothing better to suggest, it would have been wiser of him to have kept silent.

Buonamici wrote what was understood to be so in the embassy cir-

But here the motivation would be reversed. The sentence had fallen, with the judges reserving the right to "moderate, commute, or take off" the imposed penalties. It would have been, therefore, in Galileo's interest to be co-operative, as we have seen at modern trials, and to make as ample a confession as possible.

cle. It follows that it was clearly established among all concerned, with the possible lone exception of the Pope himself, who may still have stood there in the solitary unawareness of despots, that Galileo's trial was based on a judicial forgery, although it could not be stated explicitly without bringing about a diplomatic crisis.

XIV

Change of Course

Nil inultum remanebit   "DIES IRAE"

I

Be that as it may, there was good cheer at the Villa Medici in those weeks of May, 1633. It was clear to Galileo after his release that the worst was over. The answers to his letters in those weeks give evidence of an optimism among his friends and relations which is positively chirping. They expect the case to die out quietly. Cardinal Capponi writes from Florence that the favorable issue of the trial had been a foregone certainty. Guiducci, Aggiunti, and Cini send in their congratulations. Archbishop Piccolomini asks when he can send a litter to convey his friend to Siena.

Sister Maria Celeste writes that she had been so stunned with joy at the good news that she was seized with a violent headache that lasted for a day and a night. This was one of the very few intimations of her anxieties. She had helped her father's friends to remove all the papers from the house for fear of an Inquisition raid and had braced herself for the worst, as she "cried to God without ceasing." But her correspondence all through the ordeal is sheer intelligence of the heart.

"My beloved Lord and Father," she writes, "your letters have come like the *zoccolanti* [the wooden-shod friars] not only in a pair, but like them with much noise, giving me a more than ordinary emotion of

299

pleasure. As to your return, God knows how much I desire it, nonetheless it will be good for your health to stay a little while with the Lord Archbishop in Siena and enjoy the many exquisite pleasures he can provide you, before coming back to this your dear hovel, which truly laments your long absence; and in particular the wine barrels, one of which, envying the praise you give to the wine of those countries, has spoiled her wine, and the same would have happened with the other, except that we noticed it in time and sold the wine to a tavern through Mattio the shopkeeper. By way of punishment we drew them up in the loggia and knocked their bottoms off, as is the sentence of the more experienced wine-bibbers in these parts.

"The potted oranges have been damaged by a storm, and we have transplanted them in the earth until you tell us what must be done. The broadbeans are wonderful, from what Piera [the maid] tells me, and there will be about five bushels of them.

"Your little mule has become so haughty that she will be ridden by none, and she bucked even poor Geppo, but nicely, so he wasn't hurt. She disdains to be ridden by others, and no one can get her past the village, being without her true master.

"I have bought six bushels of wheat, so that as soon as it gets cooler, Piera can go about making bread. She says that her desire for your return is so much greater than yours, that if they were put on a balance, yours would just go high up in the air. Of Geppo I need not even say."

Niccolini was the only one whose happiness was not unclouded. In an audience of May 21 he had heard that the trial would probably be concluded by the Congregation Thursday week. "I very much fear," he writes in his dispatch, "that the book will be prohibited, unless it is averted by Galileo's being charged, as I proposed, to write an apology. Some salutary penance will also be imposed on him, as they maintain that he has transgressed the command issued to him by Bellarmine in 1616. I have not yet told him all this, because I want to prepare him for it by degrees in order not to distress him. It will also be advisable to keep it quiet in Florence, that he may not hear it from his friends there, and the more so, as it still may turn out for the better."

He had been told that in ten days it would be over. But weeks passed, and complete silence continued to reign.

II

What was happening was that the case, being concluded (*expedita causa*), had been sent up for decision to the higher authorities; and there, obviously, a crisis had arisen.

It had gone up in the form of a report which summed up the proceedings to date and which has been preserved for us, although unsigned, so that we shall never know its real author.[1] It is the *chiusura d'istruzione,* as such documents are still called today. This indecent

---

1. It has been shown by Wohlwill that the summary was sent up *without* the documents of the trial (*Galilei,* II, 337ff.), and his conclusions are now confirmed by the analogous procedure followed in the trial of Giordano Bruno. The acts of that trial are lost, but the summary was recently discovered (A. Mercati, *Il Sommario del processo di Giordano Bruno* ["Studi e Testi Bibl. Apost. Vat." (1942)]). The fifty-nine-page document, equally unsigned and very similar to that of Galileo's trial, is addressed to the Assessor and, through him, to Bellarmine for decision (1597). The proceedings that followed were, first, the conclusions extracted by Bellarmine and the Commissary, consisting of eight heretical propositions, then a decree of February 4, 1599, in which Bruno was ordered to recant the propositions. After this, it becomes a matter of personal negotiation. Bruno recanted; then, obviously in a severe nervous breakdown, he challenged the authority of the Holy Office, appealing directly to the Pope. Such a move was natural in itself, and we have Galileo at least talking about it; but Bruno's memorandum simply reaffirmed his theses, which were certainly heretical, and he was given forty days to retract them again. Then after a visit of the authorities in his cell, where he refused to retract, and a last attempt by his fellow-Dominicans, on January 20, 1600, the Pope signed the decree handing him over to the secular arm. As to the summary that we are discussing in Galileo's trial, it should be noted that L'Epinois, writing in defense of the authorities, agrees substantially with Wohlwill on its role in the procedure. The question is therefore beyond controversy.

and fascinating piece of judicial skulduggery has rarely been reproduced, and yet it is an essential part of the story. The judge who later
wrote the sentence, as we shall see, went back to the original documents; but this report is apparently all that the Pope and the Congregation had to go on as they decided about the future course of the trial.

We give here the first two pages. The remarks in italics are ours.

AGAINST GALILEO GALILEI

In February, 1615, Father Nicolò Lorini, Dominican of Florence, forwarded here a letter of Galileo which was being circulated in that city and
which, following the positions of Copernicus, contained many propositions
that were either suspect or temerarious. Said Father informed that the letter
was written to contradict certain sermons delivered by Father Caccini on
Joshua X, to the words "Sun do not move." (*This is inaccurate as to time
but of little consequence.*)

The letter is to Father B. Castelli, a monk of Montecassino, at the time
mathematician in Pisa, and it contains the following propositions:

That in Holy Scripture there are many propositions false as to the strict
meaning of the words. (*This is Lorini's careful forgery carefully highlighted.*)

That in natural disputes it should be given the last place. (*This is artfully
truncated.*)

That Scripture, in order to accommodate itself to the incapacity of the
people, has not abstained from perverting some of its essential dogmas,
in attributing even to God Himself conditions very far from and contrary
to His essence. (*This is the only direct quotation, and it is artfully lifted in
order to bring into evidence the word "perverting," which had again been
forged into the text by Lorini [see p. 45].*)

That in a way, in natural matters, the philosophical argument must prevail over the sacred.

That the command of Joshua to the Sun should be understood as having
been made not to the Sun but to the *primum mobile,* if one does not hold
the Copernican view. (*This is capable innuendo, as the reasons are left out
and the statement made to look disrespectful.*)

Notwithstanding all diligence, it was impossible to secure the original of this letter. (*This is not so. The original had been forwarded by Galileo on February 15, 1615, but had never found its way into the file.*)[2]

Examination was made of Father Caccini, who testified, in addition to the above, that he had heard other erroneous opinions uttered by Galileo:

That God is an accident, that He laughs, weeps, etc., and that the miracles said to be made by the Saints are not true miracles. (*This is a falsification. Even Caccini had not directly said that Galileo had uttered these opinions* [*see p. 46*].)

He named some witnesses, from whose examination it appeared that such propositions were not assertive on the part of Galileo and his pupils, but only disputative. (*This is again a falsification. Attavanti had stated explicitly that Galileo had never had anything to do with certain theses that he, Attavanti, as a theological student, had mentioned disputatively* [*see p. 49*].)

Having found further in the book on sunspots published in Rome by said Galileo the two propositions, etc. [Here follows the Latin text of the Qualifiers.] (*This is a false statement which may still be due possibly to carelessness* [*see p. 147*]. *The propositions were taken from Caccini's denunciation.*

2. This incident affords us one opportunity of scrutinizing the Inquisitorial policy. As soon as he heard that Caccini was going to Rome, Galileo wrote in haste his first letter to Dini and inclosed a copy of the *Letter to Castelli* "lest by inadvertence some words be altered." The *Letter* reached Dini on February 21, and he gave it to Prince Cesi, who promptly had "a great number of copies made," as he writes on March 7, and handed over to several people; he gave one personally to Bellarmine. It was unavoidable routine for the Cardinal, after having read it, to forward it to the Inquisition file that he himself had started on the suspect with so much forethought four years earlier. Thus we know that the *Letter* reached the Inquisition in early March. Now Father Segizi, the Commissary, on specific orders of the Congregation of February 25, had written to the Archbishop of Pisa requesting him to secure "in a skilful manner" an authentic copy, and the Archbishop had answered on March 7 that he was trying but that it was difficult because he had "to pretend to be friendly and interested merely in the subject." On March 22 he was to answer that he had failed and that "the easiest way ought to be to get a copy from Galileo himself." Hence, a copy arriving directly from Galileo about or after March 10 is sure to have received full attention. But the Inquisitor, instead of having it placed straightway into the file, obviously had it compared first with Lorini's version. As this last looked more toothsome and profitable, he must have destroyed the authentic copy.

*It certainly aggravated the case to say that they had been taken from a
printed work by the defendant.*)

They were qualified as absurd in philosophy;

and the first, as formally heretical, because expressly contradicting Scripture and the opinion of the Saints; the second, as at least erroneous in faith,
considering true theology.

Therefore on February 25, 1616, His Holiness ordered Cardinal Bellarmine to summon before him Galileo (*this leaves it implied that Galileo came
to Rome under summons in 1615, which he had denied explicitly*) and to
command him [*facesse precetto*] to abandon and not discuss in any manner
said opinion of the immobility of the Sun and the stability [*sic*] of the
Earth. (*This is false. The instructions to Bellarmine did not include the
clause "not to discuss in any manner" [see p. 133].*)

On the twenty-sixth following, by the said Lord Cardinal in the presence
of the Father Commissary of the Holy Office, notary, and witnesses, said
command was intimated to him [*gli fu fatto il detto precetto*], which he
promised to obey. Its tenor is that "he should wholly abandon said opinion,
nor further hold it, teach it, or defend it in any manner whatsoever; otherwise proceedings would be taken against him by the Holy Office." (*This is a
deliberately misleading account of the actual document, since the injunction
above is described in the acts as delivered by the Commissary and not by
the Cardinal.*)

No need to go on.

What has been done here deserves to be called in modern terms a
"slick job." Whoever read this document could have no idea of the
contradiction between the orders of the Congregation and their alleged
execution in Bellarmine's residence as reported in the documents; he
could not suspect that the defense had a strong point here. In fact, he
was prevented from understanding Galileo's defense at all; and the
further material was so arranged, including the *in extenso* reproduction
of Galileo's calculated admission on April 30, to cause him to conclude
that the defendant had pleaded guilty to a minor transgression, mainly
in order to escape the accusation of heresy.

But there is something even more remarkable. Why, on what
grounds, did the analyst have to exhume here, among so many data

omitted, just the forgotten blasphemous nonsense that Caccini had planted into the file and which had dropped out of the case since the time it had been ignored and thrown out of court by the Inquisitors of the previous generation? There is no mistaking the care with which it is highlighted. It is also ascribed to Galileo directly and in person, which even Caccini had not dared to do. True, the analyst concedes that it was declared to have been uttered only disputatively, but the extenuation as it stands becomes the knife blade capably inserted below the fifth rib. For now, sixteen years later, Galileo had in fact maintained that his Copernican position had been purely disputative. By digging up the disallowed precedent, the accuser is suggesting this: "Defendant regularly invokes the disputative position whenever it suits him; but, whereas it might be imagined from the present case that his main interest is astronomy, we can show from his past that his intention is, and has always been, pure irreligion and blasphemy."

The general idea is clearly to cut out the juridical defense and to underline the defendant's last plea, whereby he throws himself on the mercy of the court. And then we are struck by a strange uniformity. This is the nth time, since Riccardi's earliest disclosure, that the injunction is constantly misrepresented as a command by Bellarmine alone. The Pope himself had described it thus to Niccolini on February 27, and we suppose in good faith. No mention is made anywhere of the intervention of Father Segizi. The only outsider to know otherwise was the defendant himself, for he had been able to guess it, at least, in the audience of April 12—but under the oath of absolute secrecy that covered all the proceedings, so that it could not reach the Pope through Niccolini. There is no fortuitousness involved here, as might have been supposed previously: the writer of the abstract was working on the actual documents; and yet he carefully misrepresents the events in the same way. Further on in the summary a full page is given to the first interrogation, with much picayune detail about the account of previous events connected with the licensing, obviously to convey the impression of an irregularity hidden inside them (there was none, as the sentence tacitly admitted later). But the essential phase

305

of the questioning, when Galileo was stringently asked five times whether he remembered a statement delivered "by someone else"—and denied it—is brazenly fixed in one sentence: "He admits the injunction, but on the strength of the certificate, in which the words *quovis modo docere* are not registered, he says that he has no memory of them." Two lies in three words, a maximum of effortless efficiency. We have evidence, therefore, of a definite line of policy, followed consistently up to the time when the decision fell. Why is not entirely clear. Then comes the sentence, written probably by one of the cardinals on the Board acting as Judge-Extensor, which ignores the report and works out the case on a parallel but different line.

In one thing at least they agree: in deriving the whole merit of the case from Lorini and Caccini.

Caccini and Lorini. The machinery went on humming to the pitch set seventeen years before. It had been nimbly set by scoundrels, liars, and forgers of solidly established reputation, to which an imposing section of the clergy, both regular and secular, prelates, archbishops, cardinals even, were ready to bear witness. Father Maraffi, a Dominican authority entitled to bring judgment on the men of his Order, had put it in no uncertain terms at the very outset of the affair: "We should not open the door for every impertinent individual to come out with what is dictated to him by the rage of others and by his own madness and ignorance." The door had been thrown wide open and kept open. Certain Eminentissimous Lords of the Congregation seemed to feel at home only within the orbit of thought of their police informers, and beyond it the case appeared very obscure. History has indorsed this unassuming appraisal of their own mental capacities.

Someone else was obviously doing all the thinking, who had taken over from where the scandalous pair and their associates had left off in 1616. But what took place exactly? On this we have only a few leads. From Firenzuola's letter we know that the Pope and the Congregation allowed him to pursue the compromise line he had suggested but that several members at first "found this idea too bold." Since it cost nothing at least to try, it shows again in this second phase that the faction pressing for rigorous punishment was well represented inside the Congregation as well as outside, wherever certain disparate elements could work hand in glove. They must have had considerable latitude of action.

The *affaire Galilei*, which looms so large in the eyes of posterity, was really a very secondary problem for the authorities at that time, beset as they were by a multiplicity of ordinary and extraordinary business that looked far more important to them. Even for the Florentine secretariat of state, it was coupled with other minor difficulties with the Inquisition, such as the well-forgotten Alidosi case. As for the Pope, he had granted it only the most inadequate attention. Riccardi had never been able to talk about it when he was trying to extract a permission. Later, troubles had piled up for the Holy Father such as would have given an ordinary man a nervous breakdown. To the bad news from abroad had been added, as we have said, after Cardinal Borgia's challenge in Consistory, the discovery of a cabal aimed at establishing the Spanish faction in power in Rome; and Urban VIII had had to stamp it out with drastic measures. He was "living in fear of poison." It was rumored that one of the reasons for his displeasure against Galileo, never admitted, was that the luckless one had been negotiating about his method for longitudes with the Spanish Admiralty.

In all these affairs of high policy it was the Jesuit staff that held the threads. To think that the Pope was really informed about the details of the case would be not to know the ways of top executives: in his crowded schedule of appointments, pressures one way or the other were most of what he got to hear. It was the Assessor and the Commissary who were intrusted with the continuity of the case; and the Commissary-General of the Holy Office was, he too, an executive beset by a vast number of cases and problems running concurrently. Under these conditions it is quite possible that the Pope may never have known at all how things stood. The only documents that he surely saw, as far as we can make out, were the early report of the Preliminary Commission and then the summary of the interrogations. It is significant that both manage to gloss over cleverly the events in Bellarmine's palace.

III

We are left, then, with the question: Was the Commissary, Firenzuola, a major party to the conspiracy? As far as blurring out the action of his predecessor went, we might see his motivation. He would be theoretically at least coresponsible for the incredible abstract. But it does not bear his explicit signature. To credit him with its direct authorship implies a degree of duplicity for which there is no warrant. That he was trusted by Castelli may mean little, for Castelli had always been a trusting soul; but he was apparently trusted also by Francesco and Antonio Barberini, whom Niccolini in his turn considered reliable. Those three men were in a position to know who was what.[3]

It should also be noticed that the document is a hasty, sloppy, and inferior, although shrewd, compilation, such as a competent Commissary-General would not make himself responsible for. It is in the anonymous hand of the same secretary who wrote down the interrogations, of which we have the original. But who did the dictating? It ought to be, in good reason, the prosecuting attorney, "The Magnificent Carlo Sinceri, Doctor of both laws, Proctor Fiscal of this Holy Office," as he is mentioned in the sentence. His name makes him a most inviting candidate for this piece of character assassination.

But, saving the more-informed advice of canonist experts, we would not leave out of this the Magnificent's direct superior, namely, the

---

3. We must admit that there were ugly rumors against the Commissary, as shown by some remarks of Peiresc; but they are third hand. There is also, inevitably, the other question: Supposing that Barberini had not trusted him, to whom else could he have addressed his request? Firenzuola was the man in charge. This, however, would be spinning out suppositions. From all that we can feel, Firenzuola was saying what he thought. This was also the impression of Niccolini: "The Commissary shows an intention to have this case settled and to have it die out quietly" (May 1).

Assessor of the Holy Office. We have said previously that above the Commissary-General there was an Assessor of high ecclesiastical rank. We know from the Bruno trial that it was normal for the Assessor to approve and hand on the final report. His name was Monsignor Paolo Febei of Orvieto; he had succeeded just in that spring the friendly Monsignor Boccabella. He had listened politely enough to Galileo when the latter called on him; but earlier, when Niccolini had submitted the medical certificate of sickness, he had indicated in true Vatican manner, "by movements of the head and also by noises," that he considered it worthless. In a word, he was one of "them." That is all we know. And, we may notice, the Assessor was the only official in the Inquisition who was not a Dominican. His office had been set up in that way for purposes of check and control. He may very well have played a key role in this conflict. Above him there were only the cardinals of the Board.

The chief powers in the Congregation itself seem to have been Desiderio Scaglia, the senior professional Inquisitor among the cardinals[4] (we have seen that he had gone over the *Dialogue* personally, and Niccolini pinned some vain hopes on him); Guido Bentivoglio, who held the title of Chief Inquisitor; and Marzio Ginetti, who presided at the time in his capacity as Cardinal-Vicar. Francesco Barberini, as "Cardinal-Nephew," was Secretary ex officio.

There are two stray pieces in the puzzle for whose reliability no one could vouch but which ought to go on the record. One of them is a passage out of Guido Bentivoglio's later *Memorie:* "God knows how much I regretted to see this Archimedes in such a sorry pass, and all by his own fault, for having wanted to bring into print the new opinions about the motion of the Earth against the true accepted sense of the Church. It is these opinions which brought him before the Holy Office here in Rome, where I was filling at the time the office of Supreme Inquisitor-General, and where I tried to help him out as much

---

4. We know he was that already in 1624 from a letter of Giovanni Faber to Cesi on the trial of Marcantonio de Dominis.

as I could." This attitude seems to be borne out by another passage in the same memoirs, where the Cardinal takes the Pope to task for wanting to legislate in all matters, even philosophical.

The other piece is from a go-between. Many years after the events a certain Canon Gherardini wrote a brief *Life of Galileo*. It was published first by Targioni and begins as follows:

"I came to know Signor Galileo in the year 1633, when I lived in Rome. As I had a close acquaintance with one of the chief ministers of the Holy Office, I offered my assistance, which indeed could not go beyond giving him some helpful hints to guide him. I was prompted to do this by the official himself [Bentivoglio? Barberini?], who not only was moved by the urgent pressures of Galileo's protectors but also wanted to counteract in part the evil intention of another personage who had great authority in that Tribunal and wanted to save him from an impending and far too severe humiliation.

"Galileo professed himself grateful for my services, but, either because he did not think enough of his helper or because he suspected some deceit or because he trusted too much in his innocence, he was not willing to listen to certain suggestions of that prelate, whose name I could not reveal to him without indiscretion; and it is perhaps this forced silence of mine which caused him to disregard the warnings, from which came the consequences that everyone knows. Even so, they were less than had been feared by those who had known the origin of such fierce persecution. In a word, the wound was small if we consider the force behind the dart; and it was an effect of the protection with which the Grand Duke had surrounded him."

That there actually were implacable elements among the judges is shown by the Commissary's letter. By elimination they can be tentatively located (besides Scaglia) within a group of three: Ginetti, the president; Gessi; and Verospi—all of them Romans and prejudiced against Florentine influences. They may be considered to be "the Pope's faction" in this affair. Of Verospi, the Pope had told Niccolini reassuringly that he "knew about mathematics," but that might well be taken in a sinister sense. As for the helpful prelate, it might be

Bentivoglio, or Francesco Barberini, or Zacchia. The "evil intentions" certainly went far, for the decision, harsh as it is, bears the documentary mark of a compromise (see n. 10, pp. 329-30). There were obviously forces which wanted the *Dialogue* burned as the work of a confirmed heretic, and Galileo confined for the rest of his days in the holds of Castel Sant'Angelo, which had never been the Pope's intention. They had left no means untried. They were the same who had spread the rumors that those dolphins on the imprint were a sinister Masonic symbol and that Galileo had astrologically predicted the death of the Pope in 1630. Their apologetic manifesto is the Jesuit Inchofer's *Tractatus syllepticus*.

It should be mentioned that we have what looks like Galileo's own inferences at the time, for what they are worth, from the Buonamici memorandum.[5] They point bitterly to the Commissary himself. According to that paper, Firenzuola was a black soul who engineered the proceedings in alliance with the Jesuits out of "monkish hatred" for Father Riccardi. This seems too pat, and, besides, the search for someone on whom to fix the blame while exonerating the hierarchy

5. See Ed. Naz., XV, 343. G. F. Buonamici, of whom more later, writes in September, regretting Galileo's sudden departure which prevented him from submitting the text of a memorandum that he has sent to correspondents abroad. The paper had therefore been agreed on and probably also the line to be followed. As it stands, however, it is an odd mixture of talk of the town, inaccurate personal reconstruction, and factual data that can come from none other than Galileo himself. These have proved valuable. (Nor should the obviously wrong account of the interrogations be held against it, because that was a point where Galileo could not help, being under oath of silence.) Otherwise the intention is too clear not to have to be discounted. It is significant, however, that he too remarks that this sudden reconciliation of the Jesuits with the Dominicans after the quarrel *de auxiliis* made them into strange bedfellows.

The memorandum was dismissed as apocryphal by T. H. Martin and Gebler and maintained to be such by G. Guasti in the *Archivio storico italiano* (1873). These doubts are no longer possible since Favaro's National Edition, which not only authenticates the document but shows its repercussions at home and abroad. The question of its reliability is another matter. But the fact that Buonamici himself did have important confidential information from Galileo is established beyond doubt.

has its obvious motives. But the choice of Firenzuola as the villain shows at least that Galileo for a time had drawn the worst conclusions from what he had seen of his behavior.

We say "for a time," and it must have been under the impression of those last days, when he felt he had been double-crossed in the deal he had made with the Commissary. Earlier, he had written his brother-in-law that he trusted his promises more than those of anyone he had met so far, and his impression was confirmed by Niccolini. In after years, as new information reached him, he concluded that the operation had been master-minded by the Jesuits alone.[6]

6. Quite independently of these impressions, it is difficult to see, on the face of it, how the Commissary-General could be exonerated entirely. Too many elements come straight from his own desk. On no one else did it devolve to "discover" the injunction, to inform the Pope, to brief the Preliminary Commission, to organize the trial, and to report its course to the Congregation. He had, in fact, to run the show. So much is implied in his letter to Barberini. If one or the other move took place without his consent, they all finally had to come to his knowledge.

But how much was the result of his own planning? All we can say is that several stages are discernible in the proceedings. The early campaign which aroused Urban VIII took place outside, and it ended up in the report of the Preliminary Commission. When the affair was handed to the Commissary, there was a sudden lowering of tension in the exploratory phase, which tended to minimize the case, and in fact to drop it altogether, had it not been for the injunction. We can conceive that the Commissary was on the spot, for it was hard for him to admit that his predecessor had forged a record. Loyalty is strong in the great services. Then comes the report on the *Dialogue* which is the work of the Consultors appointed by the Pope (under whose influence we do not know), and with it the anti-Galileo faction has a new powerful weapon. The Commissary steps in, helped by Barberini, and, in the absence of the Pope, who is at Castel Gandolfo, negotiates an extrajudicial settlement. This holds until about the middle of May, when, the Pope having returned to Rome, the case is sent up to the Congregation. Galileo's defense, which was really supposed to conclude the trial, had taken place on May 10. At that point, however, the case seems to have been taken entirely out of the hands of the Commissary. We say so because he had expected to conclude the case himself in his own way, and he did not; because the summary of the trial should have been along his lines, and it was not. It is as though the Proctor Fiscal and the Assessor had confiscated the case, arranged it as best they could so as to get an unfavorable decision, and handed it on for sentencing, because the sentence obeys the higher instructions but disregards many of the falsifications of the summary. We have to say "as though," because, in the absence of

Those who knew the Commissary speak of him as a practical, sensible man and a decent soul. We might even suppose this: That he went along at first with the proceedings, expecting them to turn eventually against the Master of the Holy Palace, whom he disliked, according to insistent rumors, and who certainly was on the spot; and that, when the Consultors' report came in, he suddenly realized that Galileo was in a grave position (notwithstanding the fact that he had successfully denied the injunction) and rushed to get him out of it before it was too late. But who will ever know? He remains an undecipherable figure, wrapped in the hood of his Order and the mystery of his service.

IV

One remaining piece of the puzzle ought to be of interest. It is provided by a lone page of Buonamici's diary. G. F. Buonamici was a friendly "intelligencer" who was in close contact with Galileo during that period and performed many services and informal errands on his behalf. As soon as Galileo was sent back to the embassy on May 1, he came to visit; and Galileo must have gone over the whole situation with him, for, on returning home, he started under the date of May 2 a careful account of the affair, going back to the events of 1616. It is there that we learn of Maffeo Barberini's moderating intervention in the Congregation under the influence of the *Letter to the Grand Duchess*, of his sensible remarks to Cardinal Hohenzollern in 1624, and of other such things that Galileo had never disclosed before. But the story breaks off at the end of the first page in the middle of a sentence, and the next pages are gone. There must have been good reasons for disposing of them. From the general tone, it can be inferred that the sequel was a reconstruction of the intrigues against Galileo as the lat-

---

further documents, it is impossible to decide how far the Commissary himself may have obeyed, or connived, or compromised, or been overruled. We have thus even less than before the right of branding the Commissary with infernal duplicity, although many will still say that he, as the "black-and-white hound of the Lord," had to consider first the *salus Ecclesiae* and only in the second place his conscience.

ter could see them at this point and of the successful settlement of the affair up to date. The logical conclusion in this happy mood ought to be an account of Galileo snatched from the jaws of death by the strong intervention of his sponsors, of the Pope and of Francesco Barberini and not last of the Commissary, who had just made the deal with him. We should remember that on that day it seemed that even the *Dialogue* had been saved pending correction. Iniquity stood reproved, and the two men must have felt free to discuss the influences which had been at work.

Later, in July, Buonamici composed his memorandum to be sent abroad, of which we have spoken already, and it was of course in the blackest mood. Galileo was then in the state of a man who has been hit with a blackjack and does not know what happened. Everyone had betrayed him. But in this account meant for the public, it was wise to leave out the hierarchy entirely, for they had Galileo at their mercy. This explains why the sequel of the diary was torn off as a precaution against informers. It must have contained a very different and compromising version. It was decided in the later document that all the guilt of the executives could be concentrated on the Commissary, whom they no doubt at that point considered a party to the Dominican-Jesuit plot. Once the documents are seen in the proper light, the accusation loses much of its weight.

One thing can be concluded for certain: that an extremely capable outfit of "hypocrites without Nature and without God," as Micanzio calls them, was operating effectively inside the hierarchy. Some of them were undoubtedly fanatics like Inchofer; others, mere power politicians. Some were even scientific renegades like Scheiner (at least if we believe Father Kircher), who had chosen to commit the Church to what they knew to be ultimate discredit for the sake of personal revenge and of currying favor with the authorities. The rest is lost in the mists of time. Were the events even contemporary, it would be hard to reconstruct them. The working of great administrations is mainly the result of a vast mass of routine, petty malice, self-interest, carelessness, and sheer mistake. Only a residual fraction is thought. To try to look into them is as unprofitable as to stare at the wall of Plato's cave.

As to Galileo, he had no doubts at all. He never thereafter deviated from cold implacable contempt for his judges, and he took considerable risks to express it. He repeatedly speaks of a masterly conspiracy of "hatred, impiety, fraud, and deceit" which would startle the world if he could tell. And he might have known a few things which we do not. One statement at least we have through his correspondence, and it is "straight from the horse's mouth." In a conversation which he expected would remain confidential, Father Grienberger said: "If Galileo had only known how to retain the favor of the Jesuits, he would have stood in renown before the world, he would have been spared all his misfortunes, and he could have written what he pleased about everything, even about the motion of the Earth." [7]

Unnumbered tons of learned and ingenious apologia have flowed from the presses since that day to obliterate that phrase from the memory of posterity, and they have in a large measure succeeded. But then one opens the records, and there it is.

7. Galileo's letter to Diodati, July 25, 1634. After the Galileo trial in 1633 the venerable Father Athanasius Kircher confided himself to Peiresc: "He could not hold himself from admitting, in the presence of Father Ferrant, that Father Malapertius and Father Clavius himself did not really disapprove of the opinion of Copernicus; in fact, that they were not far from it themselves, although they had been pressed and ordered to write in favor of the common doctrine of Aristotle, and that Father Scheiner himself followed only by order and through obedience" (letter to Gassendi, September 6, 1633). Peiresc admits that this casts an extraordinary sinister light on the figure of Scheiner, whom he had tried himself to reconcile with Galileo.

XV

The Sentence

Quomodo sedet sola civitas plena populo; ecce facta est quasi vidua domina gentium.

LAMENTATIONS I

I

The Acts of the investigation, represented by the inquisitional abstract we have reproduced in the preceding chapter and by the report of the experts, were sent up for decision to the Holy Congregation in early May, 1633, but had to wait for the return of the Pope from Castel Gandolfo. The affair was on the docket for the first meeting in June but was twice postponed. So that it is only under the date of June 16 that we find the decision entered in the *Decreta:*

Sanctissimus decreed that said Galileo is to be interrogated on his intention, even with the threat of torture, and, if he sustains [the test],[1] he is to abjure *de vehementi* [i.e., vehement suspicion of heresy] in a plenary assembly of the Congregation of the Holy Office, then is to be condemned to imprisonment at the pleasure of the Holy Congregation, and ordered not to treat further, in whatever manner, either in words or in writing, of the mobility of the Earth and the stability of the Sun; otherwise he will incur

---

1. The text says *et si sustinuerit*. Some, reading *ac* instead of *et* (the manuscript is in bad shape), have translated: "as if he were to sustain torture." It is a forced translation, and, besides, the *et* has been generally accepted. Hence, it means: "and if he sustains it," which does not refer to torture (otherwise it would be *cum*) but to the examination itself.

the penalties of relapse. The book entitled *Dialogo di Galileo Galilei Linceo* is to be prohibited.[2] Furthermore, that these things may be known by all, he ordered that copies of the sentence shall be sent to all Apostolic Nuncios, to all Inquisitors against heretical pravity, and especially the Inquisitor in Florence, who shall read the sentence in full assembly and in the presence of most of those who profess the mathematical art.

The Commissary's deal with Galileo had been overruled.

What the Commissary had outlined in his letter to Barberini, as we remember, was this: "It will only remain [after the confession] to interrogate him with regard to the intention and enjoin him formally; that done, he might be granted his house as a prison, as your Eminence suggested." [3] The statement might have been more explicit, but the general idea can hardly be misunderstood. The Commissary had suggested a settlement out of court. Once he had the confession he needed, he would receive the defense plea, also prearranged, as we saw; he would go *pro forma* through an examination of intention in which the defendant would repent and reaffirm his obedience; and after that he would enjoin on Galileo to go home and stay home, avoid writing about cosmology, and perform salutary penitential recitations.

This is also how Niccolini understood it from what the Commissary told Galileo, for he wrote: "He seems to be of intention to have the case quashed and silence imposed on it." The last clause here means clearly that the Commissary's plan involved no public sentence or abjuration. The Congregation's role would be limited to authorizing the settlement and suspending the book pending its correction. It was planned, in other words, to deal with the case on the general lines laid

2. There are here in the Gherardi manuscript the words *publice cremandum* fore, which are struck out and replaced with *prohibendum fore*. Hence, the first decision had been to have the book burned in the public square by the executioner, as was done in cases of confirmed heresy; after discussion it was toned down to a prohibition of the book.

3. This is what we can make out of the passage: "non mi restarà altro che interrogarlo sopra l'intentione e dargli le diffese; e ciò fatto, si potrà habilitare alla casa per carcere, come accennò V.E." We understand here *diffese* in the sense of the more correct *diffide*.

down for the second stage ("demurring") in Bellarmine's instructions of February, 1616. This time, and justifiably, there would be all the steps that Bellarmine had certified had *not* taken place in 1616: there would be a retraction in the hands of the Commissary, for Galileo had disobeyed rashly; there would be a formal injunction, personal restriction for a while, and salutary penances.

This in turn implies something fairly definite. If the Commissary intends to serve *now,* with its proper corollaries, the injunction that is supposed to have been served in 1616, it ought to mean that he believes that it was never served. Otherwise his plan would be as pointless as a twice-told tale and certainly derogatory to the dignity of the court.

We notice, at this point, that there is no mention of that first injunction in the letter—and yet it has been the whole subject of that critical session of questioning which had taken place. For Firenzuola, the "crime" is beginning to shape up only now, with the defendant's unfortunate behavior in the interrogations. It is as though the writer and Barberini were tacitly agreed that the earlier crime is to be disregarded. It might help us understand why Barberini later refused to sign the sentence. We noticed, also, that the defense plea, which had certainly been agreed on in the interview, as it had to fit with the confession, is a straight challenge of the old injunction as "never heard before." It would not carry far with a court that stuck by its documents.

If we follow the hypothesis, we might even imagine with some plausibility the "grounds" on which the Commissary persuaded the cardinals to let him try. The actual words of the letter are disingenuous enough: "This proposal appeared at first too bold, not much hope being entertained of accomplishing this object by adopting the method of argument with him; but, on my indication of the grounds upon which I had made the suggestion, permission was granted me." This has always been understood to mean that several of the judges wanted rigorous punishment and would have liked to stop the pacifying attempt. For how could they have doubted that Galileo would agree with any "argument" that could let him off? His answers in the first questioning indicated not an arrogant heretic but a helpless and frightened man. The question that has never been answered is rather: How did Firenzuola manage to give pause to these implacable men and win at least their temporary assent? By telling them that the defendant had aggravated his position by refusing to acknowledge the injunction? Hardly, for in the afternoon of that same day he was to tell him quietly to go ahead and impugn the injunction in his defense. By showing them what might happen now that he had been caught lying about his intention? They knew it as well as he, and they apparently did not mind. Some of them even looked forward to it.

Still, the fact is that he gave them reasons that took the ground from under their feet. This ought to mean that he did as a last resort what he hoped he would never have to do and admitted that the records left by the previous Commissary, of blessed memory, did not look too good. He intimated (nothing need be stated in those circles) that, especially after the interrogation, he did not feel he could insist too much on the injunction of 1616; that this, however, left the road open to a settlement by serving one now; and that it would be better for everyone's prospects in Purgatory to let that old injunction go back to whence it came, so long as it had not yet been revealed to the public.[4] It was enough, apparently, of a surprise effect to carry the court, at least for that day.

This last part of the story, of course, is only inference. What is certain from the letter is that a settlement had been worked out on the basis of a new injunction to replace the old one. We assume that this was the Commissary's own policy. What happened after that? We can only carry on again with inferences. We have really nothing to go by, except a passage in the Buonamici memorandum, and the explanation there is obviously fumbled.[5] But, however much Buonamici may

---

4. Only four men on the outside know about it at that point, viz., Galileo, Niccolini, Cioli, and the Grand Duke; they could be trusted to keep it quiet.

5. Buonamici places at this late date the discovery of Ciàmpoli's release note: "They turned then the prosecution against the Father Monster, who excused himself with having had direct orders from H.H., and, as the Pope denied it with irrita-

have misplaced this or that event in the telling (he apologizes for not checking his manuscript with Galileo), he was expressing the point of view of the embassy circle, whose members knew more than we do. We had better therefore not disregard the main line of his reasoning, and it is this: The Jesuits had moved to the attack in 1632, finding this an excellent tactical opportunity both to ruin Galileo and to damage the Dominicans, with whom they had an old grudge since they had been bested in the quarrel *de auxiliis*. The Dominicans had found themselves compelled to join forces, for they were in a delicate position as the licensers. Someone still hoped (maybe it was the Commissary) to make Riccardi the individual scapegoat. Hence the Commissary chose the right moment to check the pro-Jesuit cardinals, who were pressing for a heresy trial, and negotiated a settlement with Galileo. But that faction came back with a threat, perhaps to try Ciàmpoli and thus put the Pope himself in an embarrassing position. At this point the change of course took place. The Dominicans had been beaten in their attempt at preserving control of theological policy.

II

We now resume the all-too-well-known chronicle of events.

When the case came up for decision, the Pope and the Congregation decreed, as we have seen, a full-dress sentence *de vehementi,* complete with rigorous examination, public abjuration, and "formal prison." The defendant had been led to admit that his intention had been wrong because of conceit. It was now resolved not to accept his plea and to

tion, produced a note from Ciàmpoli which said that H.H. (in the presence of whom the note was assertedly written) gave orders for the approval of said book; seeing then that the Father Monster could not be involved, and in order not to look as though they had run the tilt for nothing, etc."

This is obviously wrong as to dates, for the discovery of Ciàmpoli's note and the exculpation of Riccardi had taken place months earlier (see p. 210). Ciàmpoli was already in disgrace, and the very fact that nothing worse happened to him shows that the Pope saw his own responsibility involved more than he cared to admit.

consider his intention contrary to the Church (i.e., criminal). Apparently the résumé submitted to the judges had eased the job not only by its commissions but also by its omissions, which nullified whatever defense Galileo had put up.

The threat of torture was only a formality, since it would have been an infringement of the rules to apply effective torture to a man of Galileo's age and health (in Rome it was rarely applied anyway) ;[6] but it meant that the interrogation could go as far as the *territio realis,* or the showing of the instruments of torture. This question, however, is

---

6. We have in the Acts, although it has little to do with the case, an interesting report from Desiderio Scaglia himself at the time when he was still a provincial Inquisitor in Milan (1615). It is of a very routine character, but it gives a complete outline of the procedure as it was later used in our case: "I understand the Bishop of Sarzana complains that I give orders to the Vicar of the Holy Office in Pontremoli to come to tortures and sentences without communicating with the Ordinary on the merits of the proceedings, against the form of the Clementine *Multorum de hereticis.* I can reply that said Rev. Bishop is badly informed, because I never gave such orders. When the Vicar of Pontremoli sends trials or summaries here, I take the opinion for the expedition from the Consultors of this Holy Office, and then I write to him the resolution that has been made and the decree that has been formed so he may carry out in the tortures and sentences there what has been found right here, with the proper participation of the Ordinary there." Here at least is an Inquisitor more law-abiding than Bernard Gui, who openly scoffed at the Clementine Decretal.

In any case, the application of torture, or even of *territio realis,* was accompanied by circumstantial formalities, as we know from the *Sacro Arsenale.* If it was applied in this case, we would have to suppose that the whole protocol of June 16 is falsified, as Wohlwill suggested (*Ist Galilei gefoltert worden?*). Later, he revised some of his inferences (cf. *Galilei,* II, 321 ff.). We give only his last conclusion as it stands: "On the sheet that is considered authentic on good grounds, the pagination is correct; the decree [of relegation to Siena], which is here in its proper place, is also in the usual handwriting. On the sheet which is suspect because of its contents, the pagination is interpolated in a completely different handwriting; the decree, which is here absolutely out of place, is of an unknown hand." That is all. It might be something. Later (1907), Favaro decided that it is not enough, and we incline to stand by Favaro. We say this simply because, whatever the state of the Acts, it seems very improbable that more was done to Galileo than the protocol implies.

a minor point, although it has become the subject of song and legend. The *et si sustinuerit*, which leaves open frightening possibilities in the the case of the defendant's *not* sustaining the test, may also be considered a necessary formal clause. The really serious point, which a modern might fail to appreciate, was that of a solemn abjuration, which was a social dishonor and a brand of infamy in the Catholic society of the time.

In the light of this all the physical easements and comforts granted the prisoner, of which so much has been made, show up as frivolous amenities directed mainly at the Grand Duke and at public opinion, which was getting clearly resentful of all this excess of authority. They are not even so exceptional as all that. Prior to the regime of Gian Pietro Carafa, it had been current practice of the Italian Inquisition to release prisoners not considered dangerous in the custody of their families or even of themselves. A powerful personage like Cardinal Morone could be thrown into the dungeons of the Castle, in order to give an example; but when Ulisse Aldovrandi, the naturalist, who had abjured heresy in Bologna, was ordered to Rome for his sentencing in 1549, he spent three years there visiting the monuments and came home, like many others, with his sentence remitted. The Italian branch of the Holy Office, even at its strictest, had been nothing to compare to the Spanish or even to the Languedocian.

It should be clear that we are trying not to inject any extraneous standards into the appraisal of the crisis. The proceedings that we have described fall short of the normal standards of the Roman Inquisition, which were high. In the central organs at least we know that procedure had been meticulous, and judgment correct. The terrifying apparatus had been there for very adequate reasons, namely, holy terror; but it had never been used casually or brutishly, and it was not now.

In the Galileo trial the Inquisition was suborned into a command performance by an unscrupulous group of power politicians; even so, the behavior of the judges compares most favorably with that of the famous Justice Jeffreys, or with Henry VII's judges in a treason trial;

better still, with Cecil's judges in the Gunpowder Plot. Yet that was lay procedure.[7] The Inquisition must be compared to a military tribunal or a people's court in times of revolution. It is an organ of repression conceived for situations of emergency. There was a time when the corporate religious unity of Christendom, the communion of those who pray, was conceived to be at least as important as territorial or political unity is thought to be today. In the light of that idea, such men as Peter Martyr, Torquemada, and Ghislieri appear as scrupulous judges and as ardent compassionate souls.

Cardinal Newman once wrote, in a strange blend of ancient and modern feelings: "Contrasting heretics and heresiarchs I had said: the latter should meet with no mercy; he assumes the office of the Tempter, and so far as his error goes, must be dealt with by the competent authority, as if he were evil embodied. To spare him is a false and dangerous pity. It is to endanger the souls of thousands, and it is uncharitable toward himself. I cannot deny that this is a very fierce passage; but Arius was banished, not burned; and it is only fair to myself to say that at no time of my life could I even cut off a Puritan's ears." Such thoughts are unwittingly justified by H. C. Lea himself, the great denouncer of the Inquisition, who finds himself strangely in accord with Loyola on this one point: "Had it existed in Germany in good working order, Luther's career would have been short. An Inquisitor like Bernard Gui would have speedily silenced him. . . . In France the University had taken the place of the almost forgotten Inquisition, repressing all aberrations of faith, while a centralized monarchy had rendered the national Church in a great degree independent of the papacy. In Germany there was no national church; there was subjection to Rome, which was growing unendurable for financial reasons, but there was nothing to take the place of the Inquisition, and a latitude of speech had become customary which was

7. The Abbé Morellet, who was certainly not prejudiced in favor of the Inquisition, writes: "When M. de Malesherbes read my *Inquisitors' Manual*, he remarked: Such facts and such procedures may seem new and incredible to you, but the jurisprudence is no more than our own criminal jurisprudence as it stands."

tolerated so long as the revenues of St. Peter were not interfered with."

It is all a matter of optic. Voltaire could dedicate his life to avenging the wrong done to Calas, but the ferocity of lay penal law which aroused Beccaria left him unconcerned. Today, when juridical safeguards have been exterminated in one half of the world and are gravely threatened in the other, it might behoove us not to feel overly virtuous in reading of these ancient errors. The Curia of Urban VIII stand out as great gentlemen compared to their modern lay counterparts. Caccini rides again among us, and his name is legion. He is no longer an itinerant monk; his place is in the senates of great nations. Electronic computers are slowly closing in on the citizen's uncertain course. Deviations from what is considered the essential orthodoxy have never, of course, escaped punishment since the beginning of history; but, once search converges on the "thought crime" in its double aspect of something theoretically intangible and concretely dangerous, the way of the inquirer is bound to become again and again that of the Inquisitor. A man may be belabored without defense by investigating committees, deprived of a living, or at best kept, as happened in Inquisition surveillance, under *praeceptum non discedendi* or *non accedendi,* which may mean that he is cut off from his family, his friends, or his future, without any reason whatsoever having to be given by the authorities. We have come very close indeed to inquisitional conditions without realizing it and without even the moral justification. Even less could the Catholics of the seventeenth century have reproved them. But still they found the Galileo trial very strange.[8]

8. Writes Cini from Florence on March 26: "In the house of Orazio Rucellai, where all the nobility meets, there is not one who would not give of his blood to see you vindicated of these indignities. They hope that Cardinal Scaglia will read your *Letter to the Grand Duchess.* Everyone exclaims, 'Let them *read* the *Dialogue* for once! Has the book been read? Has it really been considered?' "

Later comments become sharper: "Si aulcun la pouvoit avoir meritee [la prison] pour l'edition de ses *Dialogues,* ce debvoient être ceux qui les avoient chastrez a leur poste, puisqu'il avoit remis le tout a leur discretion. ... je pense que ces Peres peuvent aller à bonne foy, mais ils auront de la peine à le persuader au monde" (Peiresc to Dupuy, May 30, 1633, and Holstein, June 2, 1633). Peiresc

As to the causes of this extraordinary reversal to a crime of intention, which dismayed the public, the mind loses itself in conjecture. It had taken place on the return of the Pope from Castel Gandolfo, and it bears the mark of his decision. One plausible reason of policy is clear, namely, that it was considered essential to take action, not against the doctrine, but against the man. We have seen why. We cannot see, however, why the effect could not have been reached by a more correct procedure. Once they had the defendant's admission of partial guilt, it was possible to put the whole weight on that (according to the Commissary's suggestion), which made a clear-cut case, and then to mention the contradiction of Scripture as an aggravating circumstance. It would have spared the authorities the odium of a rigorous examination and of the suspicion of torture on a man of seventy.[9] This line, however, would have led to punishment but not to abjuration. This is where the mendacious inquisitional abstract possibly turned the scales, by blackening the figure of the accused. It is as though the Pope had decided that what he really wanted was not simply repression but humiliation. It was his enemy's mind that had to be shamed, and his name dragged in the mud.

III

Two days after the decision had fallen, Niccolini was again ushered into audience. He had come to ask for a speedy release as implied by the Commissary, and he was not a little taken aback when the Pope informed him that the case had been concluded and that within the next few days the defendant would be summoned to hear his sentence before the Holy Office. To the ambassador's urgent pleas for clemency, the Pope replied that they really could do no less than prohibit the

said it again a year later, in more diplomatic language but no less explicitly, in a long letter addressed to Francesco Barberini himself. He pointed out that this unprecedented behavior could not but damage the prestige of the Church. See also the remarks of Descartes quoted on pp. 342 and 345.

9. Cf. L. Garzend, "Si Galilée pouvait, juridiquement, être torturé," *Revue des questions historiques,* XLVI (1911), 353 ff.

opinion, because it was erroneous and contrary to Scripture, dictated *ex ore Dei;* as to Galileo's person, he would, according to usage, be imprisoned for a time, because he had transgressed the mandate issued to him in 1616. "However," added the Pope, "after the publication of the sentence We shall see you again, and we shall consult together so that he may suffer as little distress as possible, since it cannot be let pass without some demonstration against his person." In reply to Niccolini's renewed pressing entreaties, he said that "he would at any rate be sent for a time to some monastery, like Santa Croce, for instance; for he really did not know precisely what the Holy Congregation might decree, but it was going along unanimously and *nemine discrepante* in the sense of imposing a penance."

This was said diplomatically. We know that there was at least a certain amount of "discrepancy," since three cardinals out of ten eventually refused to sign the sentence. But nothing was left for Niccolini except to go and break the news to the accused as gently as he could. He did not mention the prison sentence, for he still hoped it would be remitted.

The final phase of the trial now proceeded strictly according to the rules laid down. On the evening of Monday, June 20, 1633, Galileo received a summons from the Holy Office to appear the next day. In this final hearing the accused was to be questioned under threat of torture about his intention, that is, as to his real conviction concerning the two systems. On the morning of the twenty-first Galileo appeared before the Commissary. After he had taken the usual oath, he was asked whether he had any statement to make, and he answered: "I have nothing to say."

Interrogated as to whether or not he holds or has held, and how long ago, that the Sun is the center of the world and that the Earth is not the center of the world and moves, "and also with a diurnal motion," he answered:

A long time ago, i.e., before the decision of the Holy Congregation of the Index, and before the injunction was intimated to me, I was indifferent and regarded both opinions, namely, that of Ptolemy and that of Copernicus, as open to discussion, inasmuch as either one or the other might be true in Nature; but after the said decision, assured of the wisdom of the authorities, I ceased to have any doubt; and I held, as I still hold, as most true and indisputable, the opinion of Ptolemy, that is to say, the stability of the Earth and the motion of the Sun.

Being told that from the manner and connection in which the said opinion is discussed in the book printed by him subsequently to the time mentioned—nay, from the very fact of his having written and printed the said book—he is presumed to have held this opinion after the time specified, and being called upon to state the truth freely as to whether he holds or has held the same, he answered:

As regards the writing of the published dialogue, my motive in so doing was not because I held the Copernican doctrine to be true, but simply, thinking to confer a common benefit, I have set forth the proofs from Nature and astronomy which may be brought on either side; my object being to make it clear that neither the one set of arguments nor the other has the force of conclusive demonstration in favor of this opinion or of that; and that therefore, in order to proceed with certainty, we must have recourse to the decisions of higher teaching, as may be clearly seen from a large number of passages in the dialogue in question. I affirm, therefore, on my conscience, that I do not now hold the condemned opinion and have not held it since the decision of the authorities.

Being told that from the book itself and from the arguments brought on the affirmative side, it is presumed that he holds the opinion of Copernicus, or at least that he held it at that time; and that therefore, unless he make up his mind to confess the truth, recourse will be had against him to the appropriate remedies (*remedia juris et facti opportuna*), he replied:

I do not hold and have not held this opinion of Copernicus since the command was intimated to me that I must abandon it; for the rest, I am here in your hands—do with me what you please.

Being once more bidden to speak the truth, otherwise recourse will be had to torture, the old man repeated dully:

I am here to submit [*fare l'obbedienza*], and I have not held this opinion since the decision was pronounced, as I have stated.

In the protocol of the trial the concluding sentence follows immediately after this last response of Galileo's: "And as nothing further could be done in execution of the decree [of June 16], his signature was obtained to his deposition, and he was sent back to his place." If Galileo had maintained so much, and no more, in his first interrogation, instead of saying that he had really intended to defend the Ptolemaic system, he might have been better off. The Commissary, on his side, had been as sparing as he could. The whole thing had taken less than an hour and was handled as a mere formality. If he had confronted Galileo, one by one, with the passages excerpted by Pasqualigo and Inchofer from the *Dialogue,* he would have had him on a cruel spot, even without recourse to the trestle and the rope. Worse, he might have brought out passages (see p. 224) noted by the Preliminary Commission, which went considerably beyond the overworked issue of Copernicanism and which might have been reasonably defined as at least *proxima haeresi;* and Galileo, as the inceptor of those thoughts, would have found himself worse than a heretic and very close indeed to the position of a heresiarch. But the dangerous issue of heresy had been settled. In fact, the sentence had been written out already on that assumption, for it was ready and signed within twenty-four hours.[10]

10. A point might be raised, under the correction of experts in inquisitional procedure. There was no more questioning about the injunction; it had not even been mentioned in the decree of June 16. One wonders why. There were two points on which Galileo had been officially found insincere, as later declared in the sentence. One of them was the injunction; the other, the intention. For the injunction, of course, the document itself was enough to establish the truth without further ado. Also, Galileo had pleaded forgetfulness, which is hard to challenge. But forgetfulness is hardly an excuse in such matters. The sentence says: "You represented that we ought to believe that you had forgotten," and goes on to other matters without insisting—but, as it comes out later, without accepting the excuse. We submit that a man could hardly be "absolved" in the end unless he confessed. It would have been logical, were it only for regularity, to ask Galileo to "recollect" in a hurry. But the subject is never touched upon, either

IV

One wonders what Galileo's thoughts must have been in those stunned hours of the night as he lay there in the Inquisition building, uncertain of what the morrow would bring in the way of a sentence.

As he measured the extent of the spectacular repression for which he had been made the pretext, he could measure for the first time the depth of the catastrophe. That his own career as a public figure was finished, he had known for a long time. But he guessed now that this was the end of the whole scientific movement in Italy and, worse, of Florence herself. Although research went on in Florence after Galileo's death in the "Accademia del Cimento," the decay could be noticed within a few years: "I have sat among their learned men," writes Milton in *Areopagitica*, "and been counted happy to be born in such a place of philosophic freedom as they supposed England was, while they themselves did nothing but bemoan the servile condition into which learning amongst them was brought; that this was it which had damped the glory of Italian wits, that nothing had been there written now these many years but flattery and fustian. There it was that I found and visited the famous Galileo, grown old, a prisoner of the Inquisition." [11] His city had lost her freedom on the field of Gavinana a century before; now she had lost her intellectual life at the hands of the Holy Office. We can date back to that day, indeed, the time when Florentine civilization, which had carried the world since the thirteenth

---

in the decree or in the questioning. Yet, intention or no intention, the matter of transgression of an injunction is of the kind that should not go unmentioned in the Congregation and its *Decreta,* as indeed it had been discussed in that of February 25, 1616. Many curious things must have happened in that sitting of June 16, which, we may remark, had been twice postponed notwithstanding pressures from both sides. There must have been a hot fight of some kind, but probably with bashful and total silence being preserved in the delicate matter of that command.

11. This decay of culture in Italy was used as an argument by Leibniz—but in vain —to try and persuade the Curia to release the *Dialogue* (cf. his letter to Magliabechi, October 30, 1699). The *Dialogue* was released from the Index only in 1822.

century, practically vanished from history. As he was able to realize it, Galileo must have rued his own fateful imprudence and the hour when he obtained permission to print his work;[12] and he must have called himself again and again the curse and destruction of his own motherland. As for the fate of science itself, his concern was justifiably less.

V

On the next day, Wednesday, June 22, 1633, in the morning, Galileo was conducted to the large hall used for such proceedings in the Dominican convent of Santa Maria sopra Minerva, built in the center of Rome out of the ruins of an ancient temple to the Goddess of Wisdom. Clad in the white shirt of penitence,[13] he knelt in the presence of his assembled judges while the sentence was read to him:

Noi, Gasparo del titolo di S. Croce in Gerusalemme *Borgia;*
    Fra Felice Centino del titolo di S. Anastasia, detto *d'Ascoli;*
    Guido del titolo di S. Maria del Popolo *Bentivoglio;*
    Fra Desiderio *Scaglia* del titolo di S. Carlo detto di Cremona;
    Fra Antonio *Barberino* detto di S. Onofrio;
    Laudivio *Zacchia* del titolo di S. Pietro in Vincula detto di S. Sisto;
    Berlingero del titolo di S. Agostino *Gessi;*
    Fabricio del titolo di S. Lorenzo in pane e perna *Verospi,* chiamati
        Preti;
    Francesco del titolo di S. Lorenzo in Damaso *Barberini;* e
    Martio di S. Maria Nuova *Ginetti,* Diaconi,

12. That feeling stayed with him. Two years later Father Fulgenzio Micanzio writes: "Please do not go on reviling and cursing the *Dialogue.* You ought to know it is wonderful."

13. This detail has been hotly contested by L'Epinois, who claims that the whole etiquette of the Holy Office was against wearing a shirt on this occasion, and Gebler feels compelled to accept his reasons. It is too bad, but we have the word of a witness, G. G. Bouchard, writing on June 29: "come reo, in abito di penitenza." The conclusion, from what L'Epinois himself contributes, would be that Galileo was actually treated as a pronounced heretic. What he was spared was the second half of the trip on the Inquisition mule, which Bruno had to take, from the Minerva to Tor di Nona and then to Campo dei Fiori.

by the grace of God, cardinals of the Holy Roman Church, Inquisitors-General by the Holy Apostolic See specially deputed against heretical pravity throughout the whole Christian Commonwealth.

Whereas you, Galileo, son of the late Vincenzo Galilei, Florentine, aged seventy years, were in the year 1615 denounced to this Holy Office for holding as true the false doctrine taught by some that the Sun is the center of the world and immovable and that the Earth moves, and also with a diurnal motion; for having disciples to whom you taught the same doctrine; for holding correspondence with certain mathematicians of Germany concerning the same; for having printed certain letters, entitled "On the Sunspots," wherein you developed the same doctrine as true; and for replying to the objections from the Holy Scriptures, which from time to time were urged against it, by glossing the said Scriptures according to your own meaning: and whereas there was thereupon produced the copy of a document in the form of a letter, purporting to be written by you to one formerly your disciple, and in this divers propositions are set forth, following the position of Copernicus, which are contrary to the true sense and authority of Holy Scripture:

This Holy Tribunal being therefore of intention to proceed against the disorder and mischief thence resulting, which went on increasing to the prejudice of the Holy Faith, by command of His Holiness and of the Most Eminent Lords Cardinals of this supreme and universal Inquisition, the two propositions of the stability of the Sun and the motion of the Earth were by the theological Qualifiers qualified as follows:

The proposition that the Sun is the center of the world and does not move from its place is absurd and false philosophically and formally heretical, because it is expressly contrary to the Holy Scripture.

The proposition that the Earth is not the center of the world and immovable but that it moves, and also with a diurnal motion, is equally absurd and false philosophically and theologically considered at least erroneous in faith.

But whereas it was desired at that time to deal leniently with you, it was decreed at the Holy Congregation held before His Holiness on the twenty-fifth of February, 1616, that his Eminence the Lord Cardinal Bellarmine should order you to abandon altogether the said false doctrine and, in the event of your refusal, that an injunction should be imposed upon you by the Commissary of the Holy Office to give up the said doctrine and not to teach it to others, not to defend it, nor even discuss it; and failing your acquiescence in this injunction, that you should be imprisoned. And in execution of this decree, on the following day, at the Palace, and in the presence of his Eminence, the said Lord Cardinal Bellarmine, after being gently admonished by the said Lord Cardinal, the command was enjoined upon you by the Father Commissary of the Holy Office of that time, before a notary and witnesses, that you were altogether to abandon the said false opinion and not in future to hold or defend or teach it in any way whatsoever, neither verbally nor in writing; and, upon your promising to obey, you were dismissed.

And, in order that a doctrine so pernicious might be wholly rooted out and not insinuate itself further to the grave prejudice of Catholic truth, a decree was issued by the Holy Congregation of the Index prohibiting the books which treat of this doctrine and declaring the doctrine itself to be false and wholly contrary to the sacred and divine Scripture.

And whereas a book appeared here recently, printed last year at Florence, the title of which shows that you were the author, this title being: "Dialogue of Galileo Galilei on the Great World Systems"; and whereas the Holy Congregation was afterward informed that through the publication of the said book the false opinion of the motion of the Earth and the stability of the Sun was daily gaining ground, the said book was taken into careful consideration, and in it there was discovered a patent violation of the aforesaid injunction that had been imposed upon you, for in this book you have defended the said opinion previously condemned and to your face declared to be so, although in the said book you strive by various devices to produce the impression that you leave it undecided, and in express terms as probable: which, however, is a most grievous error, as an opinion can in no wise be probable which has been declared and defined to be contrary to divine Scripture.

Therefore by our order you were cited before this Holy Office, where, being examined upon your oath, you acknowledged the book to be written and published by you. You confessed that you began to write the said book about ten or twelve years ago, after the command had been imposed upon you as above; that you requested license to print it without, however, intimating to those who granted you this license that you had been commanded not to hold, defend, or teach the doctrine in question in any way whatever.

You likewise confessed that the writing of the said book is in many places drawn up in such a form that the reader might fancy that the arguments brought forward on the false side are calculated by their cogency to compel conviction rather than to be easy of refutation, excusing yourself for having fallen into an error, as you alleged, so foreign to your intention, by the fact that you had written in dialogue and by the natural complacency that every man feels in regard to his own subtleties and in showing himself more clever than the generality of men in devising, even on behalf of false propositions, ingenious and plausible arguments.

And, a suitable term having been assigned to you to prepare your defense, you produced a certificate in the handwriting of his Eminence the Lord Cardinal Bellarmine, procured by you, as you asserted, in order to defend yourself against the calumnies of your enemies, who charged that you had abjured and had been punished by the Holy Office, in which certificate it is declared that you had not abjured and had not been punished but only that the declaration made by His Holiness and published by the Holy Congregation of the Index had been announced to you, wherein it is declared that the doctrine of the motion of the Earth and the stability of the Sun is contrary to the Holy Scriptures and therefore cannot be defended or held. And, as in this certificate there is no mention of the two articles of the injunction, namely, the order not "to teach" and "in any way," you represented that we ought to believe that in the course of fourteen or sixteen years you had lost all memory of them and that this was why you said nothing of the injunction when you requested permission to print your book. And all this you urged not by way of excuse for your error but that it might be set down to a vainglorious ambition rather than to malice. But this certificate produced by you in your defense has only aggravated your delinquency, since, although it is there stated that said opinion is contrary to Holy Scripture, you have nevertheless dared to discuss and defend it and to argue its probability; nor does the license artfully and cunningly extorted by you avail you anything, since you did not notify the command imposed upon you.

And whereas it appeared to us that you had not stated the full truth with regard to your intention, we thought it necessary to subject you to a rigorous examination at which (without prejudice, however, to the matters confessed by you and set forth as above with regard to your said intention) you answered like a good Catholic. Therefore, having seen and maturely considered the merits of this your cause, together with your confessions and excuses above-mentioned, and all that ought justly to be seen and considered, we have arrived at the underwritten final sentence against you:

Invoking, therefore, the most holy name of our Lord Jesus Christ and of His most glorious Mother, ever Virgin Mary, by this our final sentence, which sitting in judgment, with the counsel and advice of the Reverend Masters of sacred theology and Doctors of both Laws, our assessors, we deliver in these writings, in the cause and causes at present before us between the Magnificent Carlo Sinceri, Doctor of both Laws, Proctor Fiscal of this Holy Office, of the one part, and you Galileo Galilei, the defendant, here present, examined, tried, and confessed as shown above, of the other part—

We say, pronounce, sentence, and declare that you, the said Galileo, by reason of the matters adduced in trial, and by you confessed as above, have rendered yourself in the judgment of this Holy Office vehemently suspected of heresy, namely, of having believed and held the doctrine—which is false and contrary to the sacred and divine Scriptures—that the Sun is the center of the world and does not move from east to west and that the Earth moves and is not the center of the world; and that an opinion may be held and defended as probable after it has been declared and defined to be contrary to the Holy Scripture; and that consequently you have incurred all the censures and penalties imposed and promulgated in the sacred canons and other constitutions, general and particular, against such delinquents. From which we are content that you be absolved, provided that, first, with a sincere heart and unfeigned faith, you abjure, curse, and detest before us the aforesaid errors and heresies and every other error and heresy contrary to the Catholic and Apostolic Roman Church in the form to be prescribed by us for you.

And, in order that this your grave and pernicious error and transgression may not remain altogether unpunished and that you may be more cautious in the future and an example to others that they may abstain from similar delinquencies, we ordain that the book of the "Dialogue of Galileo Galilei" be prohibited by public edict.

335

We condemn you to the formal prison of this Holy Office during our pleas-ure, and by way of salutary penance we enjoin that for three years to come you repeat once a week the seven penitential Psalms. Reserving to ourselves liberty to moderate, commute, or take off, in whole or in part, the aforesaid penalties and penance.

And so we say, pronounce, sentence, declare, ordain, and reserve in this and in any other better way and form which we can and may rightfully employ.

Then come the signatures. They are only seven, as Cantor was the first to observe in 1864. Three judges did not sign: Francesco Bar-berini, Borgia, and Zacchia. It may well be that Caspar Borgia's reasons were political, for he had exchanged hard words with the Pope as head of the Spanish faction, was not on speaking terms with him, and probably saw no reason to do him this favor. But for Francesco Barberini and Laudivio Zacchia no extraneous motives could be found, even by diligent apologists. They simply did not sign that sentence. Physical absence on that day is not a sufficient explanation. The infer-ence ought to be that they found it "an excess of authority and an injustice," in the words of a learned French priest, Abbé Bouix, who studied the question. On the other hand, Bentivoglio, known to be rather friendly to Galileo, had signed. For all we know, however, his signing may have been part of a bargain in favor of the accused. We may see, on the other hand, how Barberini, whose solution had been flatly rejected, had good reason not to sign.

After the sentence had been read, Galileo was presented with the formula of abjuration. But at that point the proceedings lost some of their mechanical solemnity, if we are to believe Buonamici, and there is good reason to do so, since he saw Galileo soon after the event and was told facts, such as his talk with the Commissary, which only later research discovered again. "As Galileo saw himself constrained to what he would never have believed possible, the more so as in his talk with Father Firenzuola he had never had a hint of such an abjuration, he begged the cardinals that, if they insisted on proceeding against him in such a manner, they should at least leave out two points and then have him say whatever they pleased. The first one was that he should not be made to say that he was not a good Catholic, for he was and intended to remain one despite all his enemies could say; the other, that he would not say that he had ever deceived anybody, especially in the publishing of his book, which he had submitted in full candor to ecclesiastical censure and had it printed after legally obtaining a license."

An eighteenth-century version of Buonamici's memorandum (the above is from a copy corrected in his own hand) carries the following sequel: "He added that, if Their Eminences wished it, he would build the pyre [for the book, obviously] himself and touch the candle to it, and make public declaration thereof and bear the full expenses as well, if they would give him any good ground against his book." This may be an insertion of the copyist, but it does not sound like one. It rings true somehow. It might have been added by Buonamici himself to a second version after the death of Galileo.

Having won out on his two points, Galileo now dutifully knelt again and read aloud the corrected version of the formula:

I, Galileo, son of the late Vincenzo Galilei, Florentine, aged seventy years, arraigned personally before this tribunal and kneeling before you, Most Eminent and Reverend Lord Cardinals Inquisitors-General against heretical pravity throughout the entire Christian commonwealth, having before my eyes and touching with my hands the Holy Gospels, swear that I have always believed, do believe, and by God's help will in the future believe all that is held, preached, and taught by the Holy Catholic and Apostolic Church. But, whereas—after an injunction had been judicially intimated to me by this Holy Office to the effect that I must altogether abandon the false opinion that the Sun is the center of the world and immovable and that the Earth is not the center of the world and moves and that I must not hold, defend, or teach in any way whatsoever, verbally or in writing, the said false doctrine, and after it had been notified to me that the said doctrine was contrary to Holy Scripture—I wrote and printed a book in which I discuss this new doctrine already condemned and adduce arguments of great cogency in its favor without presenting any solution of these, I have been pronounced by the Holy Office to be vehemently suspected of heresy, that is to say, of having held and believed that the Sun is the center of the world and immovable and that the Earth is not the center and moves:

Therefore, desiring to remove from the minds of your Eminences, and of all faithful Christians, this vehement suspicion justly conceived against me, with sincere heart and unfeigned faith I abjure, curse, and detest the aforesaid errors and heresies and generally every other error, heresy, and sect whatsoever contrary to the Holy Church, and I swear that in future I will never again say or assert, verbally or in writing, anything that might furnish occasion for a similar suspicion regarding me; but, should I know any heretic or person suspected of heresy, I will denounce him to this Holy Office or to the Inquisitor or Ordinary of the place where I may be. Further, I swear and promise to fulfil and observe in their integrity all penances that have been, or that shall be, imposed upon me by this Holy Office. And, in the event of my contravening (which God forbid!) any of these my promises and oaths, I submit myself to all the pains and penalties imposed and promulgated in the sacred canons and other constitutions, general and particular, against such delinquents. So help me God and these His Holy Gospels, which I touch with my hands.

Having recited, he signed the attestation:

I, the said Galileo Galilei, have abjured, sworn, promised, and bound myself as above; and in witness of the truth thereof I have with my own hand subscribed the present document of my abjuration and recited it word for word at Rome, in the convent of the Minerva, this twenty-second day of June, 1633.

I, Galileo Galilei, have abjured as above with my own hand.

This, for once, was receipt of an injunction in due form.

Two days after the ceremony was over, Galileo was released in the custody of the ambassador and went back to the Villa Medici. Wrote Niccolini: "He seems extremely downcast over the punishment, which came as a surprise; for as to the book, he showed little concern over the prohibition, which he had long foreseen."

VI

It must be said that the Judge-Extensor, whoever he was, had made the best of a bad job. The sentence shows the hand of a competent jurist. He has discarded the official résumé and worked over the original sources. They are, inevitably, Lorini and Caccini forever, but at least the facts are presented correctly. It looks even as though the magistrate had consulted the original of the *Letter to Castelli* instead of Lorini's copy, for otherwise those words "false" and "perverting," forged into it by Lorini, would have seemed too good not to be used. The judge goes on from there, piling up grounds for crime of intention assiduously, and even sideswipes the Pope in his zeal, for he defines as a "grievous error" that very policy of indeterminate discussion which had received papal indorsement.

The text of the Qualifiers is there, indeed, published for the first time. He needs it for those words, *"formaliter haeretica,"* applied to the immobility of the Sun. Unfortunately, it is only the opinion of eleven learned gentlemen, without papal indorsement. But he must make shift with what he has.

The famous personal prohibition of 1616, the cynosure of the case, is not glossed over. It is revealed at last to the world, and the proceedings connected with it also disclosed, just enough to imply, even at a little risk, that Galileo had always had bad intentions (a neat job). It has to be there, because it is the only thing that can get the judge past the licenses. Once it is there, it might as well be used for a bit of innuendo and to make Galileo out in the public eye as a perversely rash and obstinate character; but the judge is obviously not comfortable about it. Instead of dwelling on it as the basic point of incrimination (which it ought to be),[14] he manages to shift the center of gravity quickly to the Bellarmine certificate, where he feels on firmer ground.

---

14. The Pope had said to Niccolini that some kind of prison sentence was inevitable *because of the injunction.* Which was reasonable enough.

In good logic either the injunction was not true, in which case Galileo was guilty at most of impertinence, or it was to be considered true and based on an article of faith; and the inescapable question for an Inquisitor would be: *an sit relapsus*—carrying with it something more than vehement suspicion. The word "malice" is there in all letters and is not taken back in what follows. But the contradictory orders of the Pope and the operations of Galileo's enemies had brought about proceedings based on a kind of three-valued logic whereby Galileo was brought to trial as though the injunction were true and was then sentenced as though, in a way, it were not very serious. A couple of imaginary (or rather faked) factors had been multiplied by each other to give an arbitrary real culpability. The acrobatics of the text were bound to give it away as soon as it came under the inspection of dispassionate jurists.[15]

The shift of ground is effected in the curious "but" section, which we are going to quote again in context. Although prepared by a previous "declaration of His Holiness," dexterously slipped in to blend with the precedents,[16] it remains a judicial mare's nest:

15. C. J. Jagemann, in his book on Galileo which appeared in 1784, having nothing to go by except the text of the sentence published by Riccioli (the Acts were published only in the nineteenth century), surmised that there had never been a special prohibition and suspected Riccioli of having invented the passage where it is mentioned. The fact is that the authorities did not dare have the sentence scrutinized in Florence. Guiducci writes on August 27 that, after it was read to the assembled public by Father Egidii, the local Inquisitor, he and others asked to peruse it but were refused. Father Egidii must have acted on orders, because he personally would have liked nothing better than to have the text taken apart by Cardinal Capponi and his circle. He was the man who had granted the license, and his personal feelings were strong. During the trial he had let Galileo know that he was praying "night and day" for him. After the sentence, we have his reply to a lost Inquisition letter: "I receive the sharp reprimand of your Lordship concerning my faulty service in licensing the *Dialogue*. I might have quite a number of things to say, but, since you judge the fault to be mine, I prefer to accept it in full humility."

16. The text reproduces, no doubt literally, Bellarmine's certificate (official documents avoid verifiable misstatements), but it tends to imply here that the decree of the Congregation was of dogmatic importance, which it was not. All decrees

. . . And all this you urged not by way of excuse for your error but that it might be set down to a vainglorious ambition rather than to malice. But this certificate produced by you in your defense has merely aggravated your delinquency, since, although it is there stated that the said opinion is contrary to Holy Scripture, you have dared to discuss and defend it and argue its probability; nor does the license artfully and cunningly extorted by you avail you anything, since you did not notify the command imposed upon you.[17]

Two points are made: (a) (*stressed*) Bellarmine's certificate aggravates the case, because it does mention the contradiction with Scripture; (b) (*added quickly*) as to the licenses, they are no good because of the injunction that you maliciously pretend to forget.

The insistence on the first point is really extraordinary. How could the certificate "aggravate" what is already declared in the previous sentence to be malice, unless it showed that the Pope had made a fool of himself with his highhanded instructions? The ominous roll of the big drum is obviously there to divert attention from the concluding sentence, which has to mention *a* command; and it is hoped that the reader, carried along by the whole sixteen lines preceding, will take the personal prohibition as an integral part of Bellarmine's notification—as, indeed, had been not hinted but brazenly affirmed in all

began with *Sanctissimus decrevit* or *mandavit,* but they were really Cabinet orders. In order to commit the Pope's sacred authority, the decrees had to carry the formula: "SS. confirmavit et publicare mandavit." Even so, it was not equivalent to a formal declaration *ex cathedra.* In fact, we know that Paul V wanted to declare the Copernican doctrine heretical and that he was restrained by Maffeo Barberini and Caetani. It was brought out later that the importance of the pronouncement had been further attenuated by having it issued, not by the Holy Office, but by the secondary Congregation of the Index. Hence, the doctrine could still be considered "undecided" (cf. Abbé Bouix, *La Condamnation de Galilée*).

17. The original Italian (Inquisition proceedings were always in the language of the accused) is: "Ma da detta fede, prodotta da te in tua difesa, restasti magiormente aggravato, mentre dicendosi in essa che detta opinione è contraria alla Sacra Scrittura, hai non di meno ardito di trattarne, di difenderla e persuaderla probabile; nè ti suffraga la licenza da te artefitiosamente e callidamente estorta, non avendo notificato il precetto ch'havevi."

previous informal statements. The ambiguity had to be kept whirling on a pinpoint. But now the judge has re-established the ground under his feet. "What is really damning," he thunders, "is this paper which you brought here in your defense."

The situation *ex parte objecti* has been carefully ignored, and we have instead a configuration of heresy *ex parte dicentis*, trying to look as though it had been there all the time.

If there had been a counsel for appeal—but there was not even a court of appeals—it might have been asked; "And why, pray, is this impersonal note, which simply repeats the terms of a public decree and which is superseded anyway by explicit papal instructions to the contrary, so much more serious than a stringent personal prohibition to write in any and whatsoever way? Would you mind *showing* us that prohibition? It begins to sound a little like the Donation of Constantine." [18]

From that point on, in fact, the injunction is lost sight of. The sentence goes downhill in a formal mumble about "seeing and considering all that has to be seen and considered" and comes to a conclusion based on the theological points alone, which are juridically the weakest. The accused is actually sentenced for suspicion of heresy, namely, suspicion of having "believed and held" (this is strictly within Bellarmine's "hold or defend") a doctrine never proclaimed heretical but simply found wrong by some cardinals, as the respectful Descartes was to write; [19] and for having believed and held that said opinion may be

18. There was a widespread notion in the Middle Ages that the sovereignty of the Pope over Rome and its territory had its origin in a charter of the Emperor Constantine to Pope Sylvester. Dante still believed it. The idea had had strong and not always tacit encouragement from official quarters in Rome, and it was allowed to drop only after a decisive exposé by Lorenzo Valla (1440). When the people of Ancona, in the fourteenth century, received an ultimatum from the Holy See about certain disputed territories, they replied blandly that the title was theirs and that it could be found registered on the back of the Charter of Constantine.

19. "Il aura sans doute voulu établir le mouvement de la terre, lequel je scay bien avoir esté autrefois censure par quelques cardinaux; mais je pensois avoir ouy

considered open to discussion, which the Congregation implied it was, up to a point, and the Pope subsequently said that it actually was so, and even empowered his Master of the Holy Palace to confirm it officially.

If we compare the sentence—and the decree of the Congregation which determined it—with the report of the Preliminary Commission, we find that the picture has changed a good deal. It remains withal what a serious sentence should be—a mirror of the truth. From it, jurists were able to conclude two centuries ago what we have derived from the documents of the Secret Archive. The injunction was really the only thing that could invalidate the official and quite specific permission; but, rather than stand the ground of the injunction to the last, the judge is led to disavow Riccardi's written instructions to the Inquisitor in Florence as they stood in the Acts:

I remind you that it is the intention of Our Lord's Holiness that the title and subject should not be on the flux and reflux but absolutely on the mathematical consideration of the Copernican position concerning the motion of the Earth, so as to prove that, except for the revelation of God and of Holy Doctrine, it would be possible to save the appearances with this position, solving all the contrary arguments that experience and Peripatetic philosophy could advance, so that the absolute truth should never be conceded to this opinion, but only the hypothetical, and without Scripture [May 24, 1631]; the author must add the reasons from divine omnipotence dictated to him by His Holiness, which must quiet the intellect, even if it were impossible to get away from the Pythagorean doctrine [July 19].

Any superior court would have had to reverse the sentence and order the defendant freed and proceedings started against the Master of the Holy Palace. We may guess now why the facts about the injunction had to be constantly misrepresented, and even to the Pope himself, by the people who were determined to "railroad" Galileo into an Inquisition trial. We can see also, in retrospect, why Galileo was so confident

dire, que depuis on ne laissoit pas de l'enseigner publiquement, mesme dans Rome: et je confesse que s'il est faux, tous les fondemens de ma philosophie le sont aussi" (letter to Mersenne, end of November, 1633).

in the face of the storm that there was not the shade of a legal case against him. To get one, he reasoned, it would take not only false documents but also the Pope's going-back on his word; either of these actions was to him beyond the bounds of the conceivable. As a matter of fact, the authorities had managed to achieve both. Even for the zinc-lined curialist stomach, it had taken quite a bit of juggling to get it past.

VII

Through his proceeding the judge has simply highlighted the careful equivocation which had been laid in the groundwork of the whole case by the Index prohibition of 1616. Through the prudent suggestion of Maffeo Barberini himself, the decree had been organized as a flexible weapon. To the public (in case the authorities might have to change their mind) the official text presented only the statement that the new ideas were wrong and unscriptural. That was the flat of the sword. But, whenever it suited them, the authorities had in reserve the cutting edge provided by the Qualifiers, the *formaliter haeretica* applied to the stability of the Sun. (The Earth was allowed to move somewhat *à la rigueur,* provided the Sun did too; such is the comic conclusion of their wisdom.) Now you see it, now you don't.

But you cannot have it forever both ways. If the authorities had been bold enough to stick by their dubious injunction, they might have sentenced Galileo on clear if limited grounds. By flourishing the prohibition itself, they brought out the cold query: "Which heresy are you talking about, anyway?" This query was promptly raised from the Gallican camp, at least privately. Descartes writes to Mersenne in 1634: "As I do not see that this censure has been confirmed either by a Council or by the Pope, but proceeds solely from a committee of cardinals, it still may happen to the Copernican theory as it did to that of the antipodes, which was once condemned in the same way." [20]

20. In 1642 Gassendi remarks that, in the absence of papal ratification, the negation of the Copernican theory is not an article of faith; and ten years later the good Jesuit Riccioli, who was obviously getting nervous notwithstanding his own monumental refutation of Galileo, reproduces his statement word for word in the

Once raised, the question had only one answer. And, as the mass suggestion of blind obedience induced by the Jesuits began to subside, it became clear, and most of all to the authorities themselves, who were by now eager to get themselves out of a jam, that there had been no heresy whatever involved. What a baker's dozen of cardinals sitting in executive committee may decide cannot become a matter of faith and salvation. Since the Pope had cozily refrained from ever pronouncing himself *ex cathedra* on the subject, he had never been entitled to brandish the sword forged for the extermination of heretical pravity.

If Galileo, standing in the hall of the Minerva, had raised this point, he would have brought the roof crashing down on his head. Yet he would have had the whole of jurisprudence on his side.

But he had to keep his peace,[21] and the rest of the Catholic world

Almagestum novum. Everywhere theologians were already preparing to cushion the fall. Father Fabri, a French Jesuit, wrote in 1661, while defending the geocentric passages of Scripture: "If ever any conclusive reasons are discovered, which I do not expect, I do not doubt that the Church will say that they are to be taken figuratively." Father Caramuel Lobkowitz wrote in 1676 in his *Theologia fundamentalis* that, if it ever should be proved wrong, "it never could be said that the Church of Rome had been in error, as the doctrine of the double motion of the Earth had never been condemned by an Ecumenical Council or by the Pope speaking *ex cathedra.*"

21. Another one who thought it better to keep his peace, although far from Rome, was Descartes. (It is true that Richelieu was hardly more liberal than the Pope on that point.) He decided that a challenge to the authorities was not worth the trouble and gave up writing about cosmology. He wrote to Mersenne on January 10, 1634: "Vous savez sans doute que Galilée a esté repris depuis peu par les inquisiteurs de la foi, et que son opinion touchant le mouvement de la terre a esté condamnée comme hérétique; or je vous dirai, que toutes les choses, que j'expliquois en mon traité, entre lesquelles etoit aussi cette opinion du mouvement de la terre, dépendoient tellement les unes des autres, que c'est assez de savoir qu'il y en ait une qui soit fausse pour connoistre que toutes les raisons dont je me servais n'ont point de force; et quoique je pensasse qu'elles fussent appuyées sur des démonstrations très certaines et très évidentes, je ne voudrois toutefois pour rien au monde les soutenir contre l'autorité de l'Église. Je sais bien qu'on pourroit dire que tout ce que les inquisiteurs de Rome ont decidé n'est pas incontinent article de foi pour cela, et qu'il faut premièrement que le concile y ait passé; mais je ne suis point si amoureux de mes pensées que de me vouloir servir de telles exceptions, pour avoir moyen de les maintenir; et le désir que j'ai de vivre au repos et

with him. For the Pope, not unlike that Queen of Spain who told her husband, "I can make princes of the blood without you, but what you can make without me has quite another name," was able to turn the Copernican opinion into a heresy by infallible pronouncement at any time; and that would have settled the question for good.

He did not, and that leaves the Galileo trial as a curious inconclusive oddment in history. Such thundering theological persecution combined with dogmatic timidity, this dragging and kicking a man for suggesting his scientific conviction while they dared not formally assert the contrary, left the authorities twice stultified in the end. They could not very conveniently broadcast the real motives, which were that Galileo had taken to writing in Italian and that he had made them look foolish, or that the political meaning of it was that the Jesuits had evened up a score with the Dominicans by way of the new game of cosmological football. They never revoked the sentence of formal prison, and the last recorded words of the Congregation in 1638 are: "Sanctissimus refused to grant anything [*nihil concedere voluit*]"; on the other hand, they never revoked the small pension that the prisoner had been granted in happier days. The whole performance is in tune with the magniloquent papal arches of the period, leading into a dump that was once a road, or with those imposing Baroque gateways of the Campagna Romana, unexpectedly opening out from a drowsy walled-in road onto a field of thistles. It, too, has that persuasive Roman air of having a purpose, where none is visible.

Roman society hardly took notice of the whole affair, except for the usual pious conversational sighs about the wickedness of new philosophies. There were more absorbing subjects to talk about, in that summer of 1633, such as Bernini's enormous and magnificent black baldachin with the twisted columns which had just been inaugurated in St. Peter's. As for the Eternal City itself, anonymous and unseizable,

de continuer la vie que j'ai commencée en prenant pour ma devise 'bene vixit qui bene latuit,' fait que je suis plus aise d'être delivré de la crainte que j'avois d'acquerir plus de connoissances que je ne désire, par le moyen de mon écrit, que je ne suis fâché d'avoir perdu le temps et la peine que j'ai employée a le composer."

it had never been much impressed with the action of its authorities and it intimated again as much through its official spokesmen, Pasquino, Marforio, and the Foot, whose age-long diplomatic immunity had never been questioned, due to their being of stone.[22] The idea of a man having to promise that the Earth would not move if he could help it was too interesting not to be taken up. More explicit was a note which, some time later, was found inserted right up under the tail of that absurd and most decorative elephant supporting an obelisk, which still turns both its backside and its worried gaze toward the monastery of the Minerva. The note said in good Latin: "Fratres Dominici, his ego vos habeo" ("Brothers of St. Dominic, this is where I hold you"). The words came, as it were, from the heart.[23]

22. Pasquino and Marforio (so the people have called them for no assignable reason since the Middle Ages) are two pieces of ancient statuary stuck in a street near Piazza Navona and facing each other. The Foot is the last remnant of a colossal imperial statue of the time of Constantine. Pasquino and Marforio are the Martin Marprelates of Rome, although often good-humored and easygoing. Most satirical flyleafs and anonymous tracts took the form of a dialogue between the two characters. We have given a sample in the epigraph to chapter vi. Marforio usually acted "straight man," and Pasquino was, as Rabelais calls him, the "marble doctor."

23. There ought to be more of the affectionate legend in this than of the truth, for the elephant was not set up until 1657, as the inscription on the pedestal shows. That inscription, however, is quite a good unintended joke in itself. It suggests in ample Latin hexameters that, even as it takes an elephant to carry the weight of the wisdom of mysterious Egypt, it takes a strong mind to carry the weight of true science. The elephant looks as though he could not make up his mind to stay or go.

XVI *Aftermath*

I

The abjuration itself is not at all the surrender and moral disgrace that self-appointed judges have made it out to be. Galileo knew exactly what he could say and what he could not say without committing the mortal sin of perjury, for he was better trained in moral theology than we are. That was why, as we know from Buonamici, he had stood firm on refusing two points even at the risk of the stake. He was never going to say that he had deceived anyone during the negotiations for the license or that he had ever deviated from Catholic orthodoxy. These would have been acts of the will. The rest was not.

His real statement then amounted to this: "If the Vicar of Christ insists that I must not *affirm* what I happen to *know,* I have to obey. I herewith declare that at no point should my will have consented to my knowledge. Not even God can prevent my reason from seeing what

349

it sees, but by His Vicar's explicit command I can withdraw my public adhesion from it to avoid scandal among the faithful. You most illegally condemn my truth and want submission. I give you submission and keep my truth. As to that matter of a 'judicial injunction,' it is your lie, not mine, that you ask me to recite, and let it be on your own heads. On this I can stand—that my will was not and will never be consciously contrary to that of the Holy Apostolic Church. For the rest, obedience compels me to say publicly whatever you please."

This is very different from what a modern reads into it. It is illuminating that Castelli, who had been tortured from afar by the thought that his master had consented to commit perjury, breathed more freely when he read the formula. This did not prevent him from thinking of the judges what he thought and even writing it on the spot, although he had to be careful about spies:[1] "My brother was sentenced on the deposition of a witness who testified falsely for a doubloon and a dinner. And yet it is among such judges that we must live, that we must die, and, what is yet harder, we must keep silent. *Inter hos judices tamen vivendum, moriendum, et, quod durius est, tacendum.* Keep me in your grace."

To have recanted was not considered a moral degradation. It was a deliberate *social* degradation, and it was as such that it broke the old man's heart.

II

It did not break his spirit, as time was to show, for, although despairing that he would be allowed to publish, he was to go on from there to his greatest scientific achievement, the *Two New Sciences*.[2] It did not

1. Castelli, at the time "Father Mathematician of His Holiness," intrusted with Galileo's defense by the Grand Duke, had been ordered off to Brescia, on his Benedictine vow of obedience, before Galileo arrived in Rome, and was allowed to return only after the latter's departure.
2. When the Duke of Noailles, ambassador of the King of France, insisted on visiting Galileo as a prisoner, he could not be refused, and on their meeting he accepted the dedication of the coming work. The manuscript was smuggled out of Italy by Prince Mattia de' Medici and ultimately printed by Elzevir in Holland.

even check the ironic and caustic flashes which broke out at times and drove his enemies to fury, even though they knew he was gagged and helpless in the face of their triumphant refutations. He made no mystery of what he thought of his judges and their judgment, nor did he feel that this scornful appraisal made him insincere in his submission and withdrew him from the communion of the faithful. He went on praying and asking his friends to pray for him. He had even planned a pilgrimage to Our Lady of Loreto to repeat the one he had made after 1616, and only his health prevented him from performing it. But to men like Peiresc he could write:

I do not hope for any relief, and that is because I have committed no crime. I might hope for and obtain pardon, if I had erred; for it is to faults that the prince can bring indulgence, whereas against one wrongfully sentenced while he was innocent, it is expedient, in order to put up a show of strict lawfulness, to uphold rigor. . . . But my most holy intention, how clearly would it appear if some power would bring to light the slanders, frauds, stratagems, and trickeries that were used eighteen years ago in Rome in order to deceive the authorities! . . . You have read my writings, and from them you have certainly understood which was the true and real motive that caused, under the lying mask of religion, this war against me that continually restrains and undercuts me in all directions, so that neither can help come to me from outside nor can I go forth to defend myself, there having been issued an express order to all Inquisitors that they should not allow any of my works to be reprinted which had been printed many years ago or grant permission to any new work that I would print. . . . a most rigorous and general order, I say, against all my works, *omnia edita et edenda;* so that it is left to me only to succumb in silence under the flood of attacks, exposures, derision, and insult coming from all sides.[3]

This makes his position clear. He had sworn before Christendom that he would never consent to any heresy; but he considered himself in no way bound to recognize as of the faith the arbitrary and wilful

3. Letters to Peiresc, February 22 and March 16, 1635. He had known about the reserved orders to the provincial Inquisitors from Micanzio in Venice. On September 8, 1633, the Pope had further reprimanded the Inquisitor of Florence for giving permission to reprint some past works.

decision which broke all Church constitutions. They had forced on him a dishonoring obligation; he was not going to honor the extorted promise. They wanted to destroy him and "extirpate even his memory." He was going to fight back with all the means at his command. Within a month of his leaving Rome, a copy of the *Dialogue* was on its way to Matthias Bernegger in Strasbourg, through trusted intermediaries, so that a Latin translation was ready for the European public in 1637.

There is no clearer sign of the anarchic situation brought about by the authorities through their travesty of legality than the resistance of the public to the prohibition.[4] Pious believers who would never have touched a Protestant tract, priests, monks, prelates even, vied with one another in buying up copies of the *Dialogue* on the black market to keep them from the hands of the Inquisitors. A friend writes scornfully from Padua that Messer Fortunio Liceti has handed in his copy to the authorities, with the clear implication that he would be the only one to do that. As Micanzio says, most readers would face the "greatest indignations" rather than part with a copy, and the black-market price of the book rises from the original half-scudo to four and six scudi (almost a hundred dollars in our currency) all over Italy.

4. Ascanio Piccolomini must be singled out as a man who was not impressed by pontifical thunderbolts. When Galileo, after his sentence, was intended to spend a long period of penitence in the monastery of Santa Croce in Gerusalemme, Piccolomini, with the help of Cardinal Barberini, obtained custody over him for five months, with strict orders to see no one. As soon as Galileo had arrived in Siena as his guest, he forthwith proceeded to open the archiepiscopal palace to a steady stream of visitors. It was there that the French poet Saint-Amant saw the scientist "dans un logement tapissé de soye et fort richement emmeublé," at work together with Piccolomini on his theory of mechanics, with papers scattered all around the room, "et ne se pouvoit lasser d'admirer cez deux vénérables vieillards, etc." The inevitable informer wrote in anonymously: "The Archbishop has told many that Galileo was unjustly sentenced by this Holy Congregation, that he is the first man in the world, that he will live forever in his writings, even if they are prohibited, and that he is followed by all the best modern minds. And since such words from a prelate might bring forth pernicious fruit, I herewith report them, etc."

This degenerates into an undignified chase reminiscent of the Keystone Cops: as soon as the *Discourses on Two New Sciences* is licensed in Olmütz by the bishop, and then in Vienna, obviously under direct imperial orders, by the Jesuit Father Paullus, the other Jesuits start in hot pursuit after the book. "I have not been able," writes Galileo to Baliani in 1639, "to obtain a single copy of my new dialogue which was published two years ago in Amsterdam [it should have been "Leiden"]. Yet I know that they circulated through all the northern countries. The copies lost must be those which, as soon as they arrived in Prague, were immediately bought up by the Jesuit Fathers, so that not even the Emperor himself was able to get one." The charitable explanation would be that they knew what they were doing. Some one at least may have understood that Galileo's work in dynamics went on quietly establishing the foundations of the system that he had been forbidden to defend. But they were like that gallant man of whom Milton speaks who thought to pound in the crows by shutting the park gate.

There is perforce no longer any question here of spiritual authority or obedience but simply of administrative abuses by a thought police whose decrees are ignored and dodged by each citizen as he can, in a manner that cannot but remind one of the "lawbreaking" under the Volstead Act. We know that Galileo regularly went in for confession and received communion. This shows that he was absolved by his spiritual counselor for ignoring the potential excommunications of Rome.

We realize the story at this point might look passing strange to a modern Catholic, especially one from Anglo-Saxon countries, who, being used to the strict separation of church and state, can hardly imagine what his reactions would be were his church endowed with secular as well as theological authority. To such an onlooker, Galileo might appear as a crypto-Protestant who is driven gradually to rebellion but does not have the courage to come out in his true colors. This is an error in perspective. Galileo belongs to a very specific type, the anticlerical Catholic, such as is common even today in countries where the resistance to the encroachments of the priesthood in temporal matters has to come from a Catholic population; a community obedient in matters of doctrine but ready to challenge the Pope acting as a sovereign, as their ancestors did who had to fight the armies of the Papal State. How far resistance and disobedience could go even inside the Counter-Reformation system is shown by the passion of the Jansenist controversy a few years later, down to the razing of Pont-Royal. Had Galileo lived in the generation of Pascal, he, too, probably, would have been driven into the Jansenist camp by the action of the Jesuits. But his figure, poised between two eras, should be seen more rightly in the perspective of the sixteenth century, to which his youth belongs.

Like Erasmus, like Copernicus himself, who lived and worked unconcernedly among the tidal currents of the early Reformation, he belongs to the ecumenic, ancient, and easygoing "Christian Commonwealth"; he cannot bring himself to see the Protestants as "pestilent heretics," segregated in the outer darkness, but rather as intemperate reformers, riding a wave of political change in their own countries, who would eventually find their way back to the Mother Church once their aims were achieved.

How much of a Catholic, indeed, was Franceso Guicciardini, who wrote that he would have dearly loved to have Luther exterminate the whole Vatican system with its "reign of infamous priests," had it not been that his personal career was involved in it? How much of a dissenter, on the other hand, was Father Paul Sarpi, Galileo's bosom friend, the excommunicate, the implacable fighter for Venetian sovereignty? He was driven beyond the pale, yet he did not break loose. Sir Henry Wotton's hopes of bringing him over into the Protestant camp came to nought. "I have come to the conclusion," writes Diodati sorrowfully back to Paris, "that it will never come to his blowing up the works [*qu'il ne soit jamais pour donner le coup de pétard*]." Both as a Venetian patriot and as a believer, Sarpi could never bring himself to sever his tie with sacramental apostolic Catholicity, and he kept to it even beyond excommunication. His last words on his deathbed were: "Esto perpetua." They certainly refer more to the Ecumenic Church than to the Most Serene Republic. No doubt he, like Galileo, considered that a time would come when sobered Protestantism would be reunited sacramentally with a chastened pontifical authority in a world of free states.

In Galileo himself there was nothing of the little old Irishwoman in the story, who refused an Ulsterman's proffered umbrella in a downpour, saying: "Thanks very much, and ye're a kind soul; but what good could be comin' to me of a Protestant umbrella?" Galileo's letters to Bernegger and Diodati, the best of his later years in their quiet dignity and frankness, bespeak the trust he laid in men whom he considered the bearers of the future. Had not France, Diodati's adopted country, set up with the Edict of Nantes a symbol of this coming era of reconciliation? Many must have felt that way in Italy during that somber close of the Thirty Years' War. The dedication of the *Discourses on Two New Sciences* to the Duke of Noailles is in itself an act of legacy to the French "ultramontanes," now that the Italian republics were no more.

Thus Galileo's resignation and acceptance could still remain unyielding both in scientific certainty and in what he knew to be the unalterable content of his faith. Although he had been ordered not to write or converse in any manner about cosmology, at the risk of being treated as a relapsed heretic, and the local Inquisitors watched his visitors and correspondence through their informers, he could write in 1641 to Francesco Rinuccini with thinly disguised irony:

To be sure, the conjectures by which Copernicus maintained that the Earth is not at the center all go to pieces before the fundamental argument of divine omnipotence. For since that latter is able to effect by many, aye, by endless means, what, so far as we can see, only appears practicable in one way, we must not limit the hand of God and persist obstinately in anything in which we may have been mistaken. But, as I hold the Copernican observations and conjectures to be insufficient, so much more do those of Ptolemy,

Aristotle, and their followers appear to me delusive and mistaken, because their falsity can clearly be proved without going beyond the limits of human knowledge.

There was enough of undisguised "intention" here to have caused him to be hauled in again by the Inquisition and end his days in its dungeons. After all, he had formally declared under "rigorous questioning" that he believed Ptolemy to be right.

Nineteenth-century scholars found this letter regrettable and undignified, which again goes to show how far a mere century or two of impunity can corrupt judgment. If, let us say, in 1951 a Russian scientist had written that he repudiated all Morganite-formalist-cosmopolitan-reactionary genetics, in obedience to the directives of the party, which is infallible in its leadership of the rising masses in their struggle, but that he was quite sure at least that Lysenko is beneath notice—if he had written thus, we would describe it as irresponsible heroics. The style that it was (and is) wise to adopt under similar conditions can be seen in a letter from Rome of Carlo Rinuccini to Galileo in August, 1633. After some chatty references to the ambassadress' night concerts in the garden, he goes on as if casually: "Wonderful things and musics are being prepared, and a great personage, who is at the head of it, has told me that he will come and sing whenever I like, so long as I can promise some conversation too. Your Excellency can see from this how many would put on your clothing and then speak for themselves. Well, I shall say no more." This is obviously a message in code, and this is how things had to be said by people mindful of their personal safety. One wonders who that great personage could have been.

Far from following his example, we see Galileo in 1641, already blind and near death, but not beyond the reach of Urban's undiminished rancor,[5] writing to Fortunio Liceti, not to a friend this time, but

5. After Galileo's death in January, 1642, the Grand Duke wanted to erect a monument over his grave in Santa Croce. But the Pope warned him that he would consider this a slight to his authority. Galileo's body was to remain for almost a century laid away in the basement of the bell tower.

356

to an important pedant whom he had already provoked with his ironic criticism:

Now your Honor may see what a hard task it will be for those who want to make the Earth the center of the planetary circles. A place which could be, as it were, a center to all planets except the Moon befits more the Sun than anything else. This is not to say that the centers of the planets must a priori tend exactly to its center; rather, they appear *hinc inde* located around the Sun, but with anomalies infinitely smaller than those which they would have around the Earth.

The man who wrote this may well, for all we know, have muttered the legendary "Eppur si muove" right in the hall of abjuration. The Commissary-General, we trust, would have done his best not to hear.

On June 30, 1633, Galileo was released in the custody of Archbishop Ascanio Piccolomini in Siena. After five months it was intended that he should go to the Charterhouse of Florence. This was later commuted, and he was allowed to move to his own little farm in Arcetri, where he was to face the remaining eight years of his life, and oncoming blindness, under perpetual house arrest.

Index

Bañes, Domingo, 88
Barberini, Cardinal Antonio, 172,
173 n., 308, 331
Barberini, Cardinal Francesco,
220 ff., 225 n., 237, 272, 290, 308,
311, 314, 325 n., 331, 336, 352 n.
Barberini, Cardinal Maffeo, 36, 96,
97 n., 126, 131 n., 135 n., 162, 164,
169–183, 216–217, 251, 260 n.,
262 n., 312 n., 313, 340 n., 344;
see also Urban VIII
Barclay, W., 85
Bardi, Giovanni, 125 n.
Basil, St., 91
Bayle, Pierre, 89, 89 n., 160
Beccaria, G. B., 325
Beck, F., 247 n.
Bellarmine, Cardinal Robert, 20,
22 n., 26, 27 n., 28, 28 n., 43,
47 n., 51–52, 53, 53 n., 79–114,
84 n., 88 n., 97 n., 107 n., 108 n.,
109 n., 119 n., 126 ff., 133–152,
137 n., 164, 220, 234, 234 n., 243,
247, 249, 254 n., 255 ff., 261 n.,
263 n., 270 n., 274 ff., 281 ff.,
285 n., 293 n., 294 n., 300 ff.,
301 n., 319, 332 ff., 340 n.; see
also Controversies; De Ascen-
sione mentis in Deum; The
Lament of the Dove
Bellay, G. J. du, 124
Belli, G. G., 124
Benedetti, G. B., 63
Benedict XIV, Pope, 271
Benessi, M., 290–291
Bentivoglio, Cardinal Guido, 207,
309–310, 311, 331, 336

"Berlinzone, Messer Rocco," 4 n.,
139
Bernardino of Siena (St.), 43
Bernegger, Matthias, 188 n., 352,
355
Berni, Francesco, 154
Bernini, Giovanni, 346
Berti, Domenico, 147, 175 n., 262 n.
Bismarck, Otto von, 255
Boccabella, Monsignor, 233
Bonaventure, St., 54
Boniface VIII, Pope, 85
Bonsi, Cardinal, 27 n., 97 n., 120 n.
Borelli, G. A., 215
Borghese, Cardinal Scipione, 122 n.,
172
Borgia, Cardinal Gasparo, 230, 307,
331, 336
Borromeo, Cardinal Federigo, 98
Boscaglia, G., 38
Bouchard, G. G., 331 n.
Bouix, Abbé, 336, 340 n.
Bovillus, C., 16
Bracci, Braccio, xxiii
Brahe, Tycho de, xxv, 10, 32,
35 ff., 35 n., 178, 178 n., 179
Brewster, Sir David, xix
Brodrick, J., 50 ff., 50 n., 107 n.,
294 n.
Bronzino, Agnolo, 192
Browne, Thomas, 188 n.
Bruno, Giordano, 7, 26 ff., 74, 114,
182, 186, 218, 277, 278, 301 n.,
331 n.
Bullialdus, 179 n.
Buonamici, G. F., 131 n., 143 n.,
172 n., 173 n., 209 n., 216, 216 n.,

Congregation of the Holy Office, 27, 27 n., 44

Congregations, 27, 27 n.

Conjunction, 73

Constantine, Emperor, 342 n.

Constitution of the World; see *Dialogue on the Great World Systems*

Conti, Cardinal, 25–26, 130

Contra Gentes (Aquinas), 49

Contro il moto della terra, 10

Controversies (Bellarmine), 89–90, 95, 270 n.

Copernicus, Nicolaus, xxiv–xxv, 1 ff., 19, 19 n., 22–23, 40, 47, 47 n., 50 n., 52, 53, 63 ff., 69 n., 75 ff., 92 ff., 119, 119 n., 126 ff., 131 n., 139 ff., 159 ff., 172 ff., 172 n., 194, 194 n., 202, 211, 211 n., 212–214, 218, 228, 229 n., 250 n., 258 ff., 262 n., 302 ff., 315 n., 327, 328, 344, 344 n., 346, 354, 355

Coresio, G., 38

Cortona, Bishop of, 47

Cosimo II, 2, 36, 126

Cosmology, Aristotelian, 55 ff.

Council of Ephesus, 89 n.

Council of the Supreme, 133 n.

Council of Trent, xx, 46, 54, 105, 150, 209

Council of Valence, 264 n.

Counter-Reformation, 41 n.

Cremonini, Cesare, xxvii, 27, 27 n., 55 n.

Cristina of Lorraine, Grand Duchess, 38, 102

Cusanus; *see* Nicholas of Cusa

"Dangerous Adulation"; *see* "Adulatio perniciosa"

Dante Alighieri, 45 n., 54 n., 111 218, 342 n.

De Ascensione mentis in Deum 91 n., 94 n.

De auxiliis, controversy, 87

De haeresi quaestiones (Farinacci), 227 n.

De revolutionibus orbium, 131

Decreta, 128, 133, 137 n., 141, 264, 317, 329 n.

Defense of Galileo, 194 n., 211 n., 223 n.

Delambre, J. B. J., 268 n.

D'Elci, A., 38

Demisiano, 10 n.

Descartes, René, 59, 60, 73, 74, 150, 179 n., 209 n., 325 n., 345 n.

Dialogue of the Ebb and Flow of the Sea, 183

Dialogue on the Great World Systems, xiv, xiv n., 2, 4, 8 n., 18 n., 20, 22, 35, 58 ff., 73 n., 75, 76 n., 114 n., 119 n., 123, 126, 135 n., 147, 160, 174 n., 175 n., 176, 181–183, 185–198, 188 n., 193 n., 199 ff., 209 n., 215 n., 224, 229 n., 234–235, 253, 254, 267 n., 268 n., 270 n., 271, 273, 277, 284, 290, 309 ff., 312 n., 318, 325 n., 329, 330 n., 331 n., 333, 335, 340 n., 352

Dianoia astronomica (Sizi), 9–10

Dictionnaire historique et critique (Bayle), 89 n.

Foscarini, Paolo Antonio (*cont.*),
104, 108, 130, 131 n., 141, 148,
218, 258
Foucault, Jean Bernard, 126
Fouché, Joseph, 294
Francis of Sales, St., 108 n.
Friars, reputation of, 110
Frisch, Ch., 112 n., 114 n.
Froidmont, 228–229
Fuligatti, J., 92 n.

Galilei, Galileo; *see* Galileo
Galilei und die Katholische Kirche
(Müller), 9 n., 14 n.
Galilei und seine Zeit, 5 n., 37 n.
Galilei, Vincenzio, xxvi, 332, 337
Galilei (Wohlwill), 301 n.
Galileists, 36, 44, 46 ff.
Galileistudien (Grisar), 148 n.
Galileo: see *Dialogue on the Great
World Systems;* see also *Discorsi*
(1638); *Discourse on the
Comets; Discourse on Floating
Bodies; Discourses on Two New
Sciences; Letter to Castelli; Let-
ter to the Grand Duchess; Letter
to Ingoli; Letters on the Solar
Spots; Message from the Stars;
Nuncius sidereus; On the Flux
and Reflux of the Sea; On Mo-
tion; On the Two Chief World
Systems*
Galileo e Fra Tommaso Caccini
(Ricci-Riccardi), 110 n.
Gallamino, Cardinal, 27 n., 46
Gallanzoni, A., 28 n., 98 n.
Garnet, Henry, 289

Garzend, L., 326 n.
Gassendi, 209 n., 315 n., 344 n.
Gebler, Karl von, xix, 131 n., 147
262 n., 285, 286, 311 n., 331 n.
Gemelli, Agostino, 249
Geometry of Indivisibles (Cava-
lieri), 156
Gessi, Cardinal Berlingero, 331
Gherardi del Testa, 141, 142 n.,
295 n., 318 n.
Gherardini, Canon, 310
Ghisilieri, Federico, 120
Giese, Tiedemann, 19 n.
Gilbert, William, 267–268, 268 n.
Ginetti, Cardinal Marzio, 309, 331
Giraldi, 95
Gleanings from the Saggiatore
(Kepler), 178
Godin, W., 247 n.
Goethe, Johann Wolfgang, 60
Grand Duchess Dowager; *see* Cris-
tina of Lorraine
Grand Duke; *see* Cosimo II *and*
Ferdinand II
Grape, simile of, 76
Grassi, Horatio, 160 ff., 166–168,
181, 181 n., 197, 207; *Saggiatore*,
166, 171, 180, 180 n., 187, 199 n.,
214, 225, 295 n.
Gravina, 108 n.
Gray-Morgan Majority Report, xix
Grazia, V., 38
Gregory XV, Pope, 164, 173
Grienberger, Father Christoph, 20,
28, 97, 100, 125, 125 n., 149,
151 n., 207, 214, 249, 252, 315
Grimaldi, 246 n.

Sarpi, Paolo, 47, 47 n., 81, 144, 157, 221, 223 n., 354
Sarzana, Bishop of, 322 n.
Sassetti, Cosimo, 20
Savonarola, Girolamo, 43, 189
Scaglia, Cardinal Desiderio, 235, 309, 310, 322 n., 325 n., 331
Scartazzini, 262 n., 295 n.
Schall von Bell, Johann Adam, 232, 233 n.
Scheiner, Christopher, 22, 197, 199, 199 n., 207, 315 n.
Schmid, Franz, 99 n.
Schönberg, Cardinal, 19 n.
Scientific method, 113
Scorriggio, Lazzaro, 131
Segizi, Michelangelo, 134, 144, 281, 283, 289, 293, 303 n., 305
Seneca, 154
Serrarius, 41
Serristori, Monsignor, 200, 233, 259, 268
Sertini, 9 n.
Settele, L., 250
Sfondrati, Cardinal, 27 n., 44, 50 n.
Sforza, Duchess, 122 n.
Shakespeare, William, xxvi, 74, 146
Sidereal Message, 5, 186
Simplicio, 58, 193
Sixtus V, Pope, 47 n., 87, 95, 95 n., 117, 170 n.
Sizi, Francesco, 9–10
Socrates, 16, 114
Soldani, G., 95
Sommario del processo di Giordano Bruno, Il (Mercati), 301 n.
Somnium Scipionis, 92

Spheres, celestial, 71
Stahlman, William D., 71
Starry Message; see Sidereal Message
Stefani, Giacinto, 196
Stelluti, C., 163, 207
Sterne, Laurence, 2, 9
Stoics, 55 n.
Stunica, Didacus à, 26 n., 97, 130, 131, 141
Suárez, Francisco, 84 n., 85, 90
Suidas, 167 n.
Superstate, theory of, 85
"Supreme Good," 59
Sylvester, Pope, 342 n.
System of the World; see Dialogue on the Great World Systems

Taberna, Cardinal, 27 n.
T'ang Jo-wang; see Schall von Bell, Johann Adam
Targioni, 310
Taylor, Sherwood, 139 n.
Teller, Edward, xvi
Tengnagl, 179
Theologia fundamentalis (Lobkowitz), 344 n.
Theory of Physical Reality, The, 113 n.
"Threefold Wedge for a Triple Knot"; see Triplici nodo triplex cuneus
Tiepolo, Cecilia, 191
Tinti, Father Giacomo, 148 n., 288
Tocsin to the King, 84
Torricelli, Evangelista, 207 n., 214
Tractatus syllepticus, 311

Library of Congress Cataloguing in Publication Data

De Santillana, Giorgio, 1902-
The Crime of Galileo.
(Time Reading Program)
Reprint. Originally published: New York:
Time Inc., 1955.
1. Galilei, Galileo, 1564-1642. I. Title.
II. Series.
QN36.G2D4   1981   520'.92'4 [B]   81-2585
ISBN 0-8094-3627-2 (pbk.)   · AACR2
ISBN 0-8094-3626-4 (deluxe)

QB
721.4
.L48
1994

Library of Congress Cataloging-in-Publication Data

Levy, David H., 1948-
    The quest for comets : an explosive trail of beauty and danger
David H. Levy.
        p.   cm.
    Includes bibliographical references and index.
    ISBN 0-306-44651-0
    1. Comets--Popular works.   2. Comets--Research--Popular works.
I. Title.
QB721.4.L48   1994
523.6--dc20   94-2741
                                                              CIP

ISBN 0-306-44651-0

© 1994 David H. Levy

Plenum Press is a Division of Plenum Publishing Corporation
233 Spring Street, New York, N.Y. 10013-1578

Printed in the United States of America

With love and affection, this book is for

My brothers and sister, Richard, Joyce, and Gerry;

My in-laws Larry and Audrey;

My nephews and nieces Jeff, Marci, Wendy, Robby,
Ali, Billy, Debbie, Michael, and Daniel

ℂ   𝔇

Preface

I *looked forward so much to those weekly dinners with Lonny Baker.*
At Tucson's Flandrau Planetarium, she was in charge of the lecture
series "Eyes on the Universe," which featured a different astronomer each Tuesday evening. Our plan was to meet before each
lecture for dinner, and tonight was especially important, for Martin
McCarthy, a famous Jesuit astronomer, was talking about "Gregory,
Galileo, and Galaxies," a religion and science lecture about creation
versus the Big Bang. Nothing could keep me from this lecture.

Nothing, that is, except a clear and moonless night.

For the past 19 years, I had been among the world's thousands
of keen amateur astronomers, organizing my life to accommodate
my true vocation—searching the night sky for comets, hoping to
discover one never spotted before. Although I had devoted 917
hours with my eye at the eyepiece and every dime I could scrape
together to further my quest, although I had moved from cloudy
Montreal to the Arizona desert southeast of Tucson, although I
had observed every known comet I could find, I had yet to find
one of my own.

The clouds in the early evening of Tuesday, November 13,
1984, promised Lonny and me a leisurely meal. We met at a
Chinese–Mandarin place, and ordered our favorite dishes—no

peas, no MSG, Lonny insisted. But as dinner went on, I sensed that the clouds were getting thinner, and Lonny could see that instead of concentrating on her words, I was looking past her out the window. "David," Lonny said, "it must be clearing up outside." "Uh huh," I replied absentmindedly. "You're going to stand me up, aren't you?" she demanded. "You're going to go home and hunt for comets, aren't you?" "Oh no!" I protested, gamely snapping to attention. "We are going to finish dinner. *Then* I am going to stand you up, go home and hunt for comets."

As we left the restaurant, she for her lecture and me for my telescope, Lonny gave me an ultimatum: "You'd better find me a comet tonight!"

Setting up the telescope for comet hunting is pretty easy. All I really have to do is make sure the cover is off. With the telescope's slow, deliberate motion across a portion of sky, comet hunting is not like a star party, where people line up to look at an object. When that happens, the sky is asked to be a servant, showing off Saturn, the moon, or some galaxy on cue. It's the opposite with comet hunting. When I start a session, I have only a vague idea of what I may find in the next hour or so as I move the telescope forward for a few minutes across a region of sky, then backward through the next sector. Whether I find a star cluster or a galaxy, a red star or a bright double star, is really up to the sky, not me. The sky is the master, my telescope the receiver, and I am the watchman.

After some 30 minutes had gone by, a faint fuzzy object appeared in the field of my moving telescope. It had the appearance of a galaxy, I thought, and a quick check of an atlas confirmed my suspicion. Like a fish thrown back into the water, the object was gone, and I was on my way. The next object was a planetary nebula, the remnant of an outburst in an ancient star—interesting, but not my quarry.

Next came a pretty cluster of stars, number 6009 in the *New General Catalogue,* but my attention was drawn to a fuzzy object in the same field of view, a bit to the south. It was a striking sight, the beautiful cluster and the faint fuzzy spot; my first reaction was,

"Why have I never seen such a thing? It should be pictured in all the astronomy books." Another atlas check confirmed my growing suspicion: The cluster belonged there; the faint fuzzy spot did not. Within a few minutes, I was sure that the object was moving very slowly in the direction of the cluster. A comet! My heart rate soared.

It was a comet all right, but was it already known? I called Brian Skiff, an observer at the Lowell Observatory some 300 miles away in Flagstaff. The 5 minutes before his return call seemed like an eternity. By now I was quite agitated. "David," Brian finally said, "You've found a new comet."

I have always wondered what the difference between a successful search program and a failed program would be. That night gave the answer: a single field of view. Over 900 hours at the eyepiece, field after field had failed to show me this holy grail.

I was thrilled beyond words, but now I needed wits more than feelings. I sent a telegram to Brian Marsden, director of the Central Bureau for Astronomical Telegrams (CBAT), the clearinghouse for astronomical discoveries. Included were the comet's position, direction and rate of motion, and brightness. With an independent discovery by Massachusetts amateur Michael Rudenko the following evening, the comet was announced as Comet Levy–Rudenko 1984t, the twentieth comet found or recovered in 1984. It was the first of a series of discoveries from my backyard.

Whether they curve round the sun in orbits ranging from a few years to two centuries or come in just once and then back away, tail first, into the space beyond the planets, comets offer a sense of mystery and romance. They may also hold some interesting secrets about the history of the solar system. But comets cannot be studied if they haven't been found. Each clear night a band of us night watchmen of the sky, spread out in backyards and roadsides all over the world, scans the sky in an intense competition. For us, hunting comets is sport, art, and passion. It is by far the slowest of all sports. It demands time—not time set by the hunter but by the sky itself. The moon acts as a referee, brightening the sky and limiting the period available for searching. The game is especially competitive just after a full moon, when a sky that has been too bright for hunting is suddenly thrust for 1 or 2 hours into darkness, and comet hunters all over the world rummage through it in a scramble for new comets. Two weeks later an almost new moon opens the morning sky for another inning as we sleepy searchers peer through telescopes to see if anything new has appeared.

In summer 1989, having just discovered my fifth comet from my backyard, I joined the asteroid and comet survey being conducted by Eugene and Carolyn Shoemaker at Palomar Mountain. Here was a totally different kind of search. For seven nights each month, I was part of a team photographing the sky through Palomar Mountain's 18-inch Schmidt—a camera telescope. Carolyn scanned films that we took, sometimes as many as 60 a night. By fall 1993, we had found 12 new comets together, 9 of which were periodic, bound to the Sun in short orbits. Combined with my own visual search, I now have 19 comets to my credit. With 30 comets, Carolyn's name is on more comets than anyone else's in history.

Carolyn's husband, Dr. Eugene Shoemaker, is a geologist who studies our neighboring asteroids and comets. Through many cloudy night conversations, I have become impressed with the single-mindedness of his path through life. He ended a controversy and launched the new science of astrogeology by proving that Meteor Crater in Arizona was the result of an impact by an asteroid from space. During the sixties and seventies, he worked with the space program, studying craters on the moon and other solar system bodies—craters, he correctly thought, that came from impacts of asteroids and comets. For his current work at Palomar, Shoemaker has switched from studying the bull's-eyes to the bullets, those objects in space before they hit anything else.

Comet impacts are the substance of this book, but comet hunting is its soul. This 200-year-old tradition is as much competitive sport as science, and its history is filled with drama, strange coincidences, hoaxes, and fun. The story of my own first comet is just one example. After I finished sending my telegram, I remembered that Lonny was still at the planetarium. I called her just as she was about to leave. "Well David, did you find me a comet tonight?" she asked. "Yup." Lonny giggled. "Where?"

I told her it was in Aquila, the constellation of the Eagle, and she laughed again. Then I said that it was moving a minute of arc per hour to the north. Lonny stopped laughing. "You're serious, aren't you?" The next day the local paper told the story on its front page. The piece did not focus on the newly found fuzzy world, whose existence was not deemed newsworthy. What did make news, the paper thought, was that I had broken a dinner date to do it.

Acknowledgments

*F*ew *things mean as much to me as comets do. To write about them clearly and sensitively, I have tried to merge the personalities, the* science, and the events into a single story that includes the poetry of the comet hunt as well as the reality of the story of comets and the major role they played in the history of Earth and its life. Part of the book is autobiography, and for the chapters about Gene Shoemaker and comet impacts, part is biography. And the comets themselves have much to tell. The result is intended to present a feel for what comets are like and what the people are like who work in the comet field.

To accomplish this, I am grateful for all the assistance I received. Linda Greenspan Regan at Plenum was helpful and encouraging throughout the growth of this book. Steve Edberg, Daniel Green, Brian Marsden, and Sandy Sheehy gave invaluable reviews and comments. Gene and Carolyn Shoemaker gave a large amount of their time for interviews and were helpful in many ways. Norman MacKenzie of Queen's University provided important suggestions for the material about Seneca; and L. Bean, Roy Bishop, Clark Chapman, Eleanor Helin, Tim Hunter, Peter Jedicke, Joe Marcus, David Morrison, Jean Mueller, Donna Donovan-O'Meara, David Rabinowitz, Jim Scotti, and Wieslaw Wisniewski were helpful with other parts of the manuscript. Kelly Beatty and Steve O'Meara, from *Sky and Telescope* magazine kindly let me use material from my "Star Trails" column, and they were helpful in many other ways as well. Finally the *Journal of the Royal Astronomical Society of Canada* is publishing my Ruth J. Northcott memorial lecture, "The Art of Comet Hunting," which contains some passages from this book.

Contents

The Quest
for Comets
An Explosive Trail
of Beauty and Danger

The Terrible Swift Sword
Pleasures and Perils of a Comet

The sky above Quebec's Jarnac Pond was inky, the night silent except for the occasional croak of a frog and the hoot of an owl. I could see more stars than I could count, and the Milky Way arched right overhead. I was 14, and for the past 2 years I'd been increasingly drawn to astronomy. "You are going to sit on the dock all night long? *Until dawn?*" My astonished grandparents couldn't believe my plan. On that lazy afternoon of August 12, we were watching clouds pass by and talking about the very bright meteor we had seen the previous evening. I had read in a book how, each August 12, the Earth's orbit intersects the orbit of a comet called Swift–Tuttle, and over a very long time, dust from that comet had spread all along the orbit, resulting in the Perseid meteor shower.

It seemed so simple. Although the meteors, most no larger than a speck of dust or a pea, would be on parallel paths when they entered the atmosphere, they would appear to radiate from a single point in the sky in the constellation Perseus. With great excitement, I somewhat precociously explained to my grandparents that the sight of meteors coming from a radiant was due to an effect of perspective—just like looking down a railroad and watching the tracks converge. But then came the punch line: As Perseus rose higher, we would see more meteors; the shower would be

Periodic Comet Swift–Tuttle. (Photograph by David Levy using his 8-inch Schmidt tele-scope from his backyard, November 18, 1991; 5-minute exposure.)

strongest just before dawn. That meant, I insisted, that I was going to stay up all night.

For the rest of my family, staying up late to look at the stars was no surprise. My parents had learned to navigate their sailboat by the stars, and we often spent evenings looking at Saturn through my small telescope. As night fell on August 12, I began my vigil. Grandma and Grandpa sat with me on the dock for a short while, relaxing on deck chairs in the warm evening, but clouds prevented much observing at first. Knowing my reputation for being somewhat klutzy, grandpa had built a makeshift fence on the dock so I wouldn't fall into the lake and drown. As the night went on, the clouds gradually dissipated, and I was absolutely thrilled to see the prediction come true. With each passing hour, the number of meteors increased. One of them appeared to split in two, others left beautiful sparkling trails. Alone on the lake that night, I was treated to a personal show of fireworks in the sky. When dawn finally came, I had logged 112 meteors.

Thirty years of Perseid meteors have passed since that August night, some were truly memorable. In 1966 I was part of a team of observers that spotted 906 meteors. Bright moonlight interfered with some of these observations, and clouds ruined others. In the early 1980s, observers around the world started paying more attention to the meteor shower, for its parent comet, last seen in 1862, was due back. Would the comet's return be accompanied by a large increase in the numbers of meteors?

THE TERRIBLE SWIFT–TUTTLE

When Lewis Swift discovered his first comet on July 15, 1862, he doubted that he had a new one. Instead he thought it was the already known Comet Schmidt, which had passed close to the Earth on July 4 of that year and was rapidly fading. Swift was using a 4-inch refractor telescope from his home in Marathon, New York, near the college town of Ithaca. But three nights later, Horace P. Tuttle saw the same comet from the small balcony attached to the refractor dome at Harvard College Observatory just as he was preparing to join the Union army fighting the Civil War. Finally realizing that his comet was a new one, Swift rushed to try to get credit for it. "I received a letter from Mr. Swift, an amateur astronomer, at Marathon N.S.," wrote G. W. Hough, assistant at Dudley Observatory, "in which he stated he had observed a comet on the 15th and 16th of July; but presuming it to be Comet II.1862 he gave no public notice of the observation."[1] It appears that Thomas Simons also discovered the comet on July 18 in Albany but did not get his name on it. In England it was called Rosa's comet for the observer who first saw it from Rome on July 25.[2]

The 1862 appearance was a memorable one. The comet was as bright as the north star, easily visible to the unaided eye. "The last time I saw the comet," codiscoverer Tuttle wrote, "was on the night of the 17th of September, after I had entered the federal army and gone to camp. It was then about six degrees [about 12 diameters of the full moon] from Antares and just visible to the naked eye."[3]

Just 4 years later, Giovanni Schiaparelli, an astronomer later famous for his observations of Mars, floated the remarkable idea that meteor streams are residue from comets. As an example, he showed that the orbit of the famous Perseid meteor shower was analogous to that of Swift–Tuttle. So not only did Swift and Tuttle have a bright comet to their credit, but they also had the one whose debris would fall in a meteor shower every August.

HORACE TUTTLE'S ORBIT

Once Horace Tuttle's comet became noteworthy, Horace Tuttle became famous, too. But like amateur astronomers throughout time, he had to sandwich in his observing between less lofty duties. Shortly after his comet discovery—it was his fourth—in 1863, he became acting paymaster in the Union Navy.[4] In 1864 Tuttle's ship, the Catskill, was anchored off Charleston, SC to blockade Charleston and Wilmington. From the Catskill's deck, Tuttle saw the comet that had been found by Ernst Tempel as it passed from Auriga into Taurus. As the ship swayed, Tuttle must have found Comet Tempel difficult to watch as it dashed repeatedly through his telescope's field for a few seconds at a time.

Later in 1866 Tuttle shared a comet find with Tempel. Remarkably Periodic Comet Tempel–Tuttle is the mother comet of the November Leonid meteors, the shower that appears to originate in the constellation of Leo the lion. Although Tuttle holds the distinction of having discovered the source comets of two major meteor streams, he wasn't quite so exemplary in other fields.

In 1869 while serving as paymaster aboard the monitor ship *Guard*, he somehow left the ship's books with a mysterious loss of $8800.90—a tremendous discrepancy at the time. Eventually the navy, realizing it had never received the thousands of dollars it claimed Tuttle owed, ordered him to Washington for courtmartial. Stung by a growing embezzlement scandal, the military had just sentenced an army paymaster to life in a penitentiary, commuted to 5 years by President Grant. Tuttle's fear that the same thing might happen to him did not however prevent him from using the Naval Observatory's 26-inch refractor to recover Periodic Comet Encke on January 23, 1875, 3 days into his courtmartial. Three weeks after the comet recovery, the court found Tuttle guilty of embezzlement. Because of doubts regarding his lawyer, and perhaps because of his comet discoveries, Tuttle's sentence was light: a dishonorable discharge from the navy, approved by President Grant.[5]

SWIFT–TUTTLE'S ORBIT

More than 900 comets have passed by since the first recorded comet almost a thousand year before Christ. Most comets come by on wide paths, or orbits, that take them round the sun and then back into deep space, not to return again for thousands of years if ever. But some 200 comets do return in periods of two centuries or less. Although Halley, the most famous of these periodic comets, orbits the sun in about 76 years, other periodic comets have different periods. Until 1992 we were not sure how long the period of Swift–Tuttle was.

Once people who calculate orbits have determined that a new comet is periodic, they predict the time of its next return visit. As that time approaches, astronomers with photographic telescopes, or telescopes with electronic detectors called charge-coupled devices or CCDs, try to locate the comet far out in space.

Computing the orbit of a comet is a little bit like watching an airplane flying above you. Imagine that you are looking low in the sky as the plane speeds along. For the purpose of this analogy, your eyes are closed except for one brief instant when you see the plane over a tree and for a second instant when the plane is over an apartment roof. From these two observations, you will have a poor idea of which direction the plane is headed, for it could have gone from point *A* to point *B* by any number of curved arcs instead of a straight line. However if you open your eyes for a third instant, now seeing the aircraft over a house, you have a far better idea of the plane's path. Ten, thirty, or a hundred positions of the plane at various instants will give you a progressively more accurate idea of the path.

But comet orbits are huge; that of Swift–Tuttle takes it almost 50 times the distance between the Earth and sun. A small uncertainty about the positions of the comet when it nears Earth can result in an error of years in predicting the comet's return more than a century later. The elements of an orbit are explained at the end of this book.

In 1902 William T. Lynn, a British astronomer and inveterate writer of letters to astronomical publications, wrote a one-page memoir about Periodic Comet Swift–Tuttle. In it he made an almost off-the-cuff suggestion: "It is possible that the second comet of 1737 may be identical" with the comet that Swift and Tuttle had discovered in 1862.[6] The 1737 comet was found from Beijing by Father Ignatius Kegler, a Jesuit priest. Since Kegler observed the comet for hardly more than a week, we have only a rough idea of its orbit, and Lynn evidently considered his estimation to be hardly more than a conjecture. But we would not know if the two were the same comet until it went to the depths of the solar system beyond the planet Neptune and then returned once more.

When Periodic Comet Swift–Tuttle finally did return, astronomers tried to calculate the details of its next pass and to their amazement, one of the calculations showed that on July 11, 2126, this comet might come much closer to Earth than ever before– perhaps disastrously close. In fact for a few months, some astronomers worried that this large comet would hit the Earth in the largest explosion in 65 million years, destroying most life forms. What comes next is the story of the process leading to that brief period of fright.

Using the positions of Periodic Comet Swift–Tuttle at many instants during its flyby in 1862, in 1973 Brian G. Marsden, director of the International Astronomical Union's CBAT, projected that the comet would loop beyond the orbit of Pluto and return between 1979 and 1983, most likely in 1982. However he was troubled by the last observations of the 1862 appearance, made from the Cape Observatory in South Africa, an observatory in the southern hemisphere that can see a large region of sky never visible from northern observatories. These observations did not fit the path that the comet had earlier appeared to be taking. It was almost as if the airplane's "pilot" had deliberately changed direction—not by much but enough to threaten the accuracy of the orbit Marsden had computed.

What if the comet did have a pilot capable of making such changes? Not a real pilot, of course, but, say, that as the comet rounded the sun, its surface started erupting, with jets of gas or dust spewing forth like steering rockets on a spacecraft. In the science of celestial mechanics, these eruptions are called nongravitational forces, since they can cause lane changes that have nothing to do with the gravity of the sun or the planets that traditionally define the comet's orbit. These forces can be strong enough to push the comet around slightly, changing its course in ways that are very difficult to calculate.

If these forces are too strong, the comet's orbit cannot really be pinned down without observations from at least two passages around the sun. Thus in 1973, Marsden spent several weeks looking at orbits of other eighteenth-century comets that could have been in fact early appearances of Swift–Tuttle. (Later we see that Edmond Halley did much the same thing to show that some comets were actually early appearances of the comet of 1682, the comet that would later be named Halley.) The first possibility was Wargentin's comet in 1750. Although it was within a few degrees from where Swift–Tuttle might have been on that previous pass had the 1862 orbit been correct, Marsden noted that this comet was moving ten times too rapidly. Marsden then suggested that Kegler's comet could be the one. Trying to connect the 217 observations of 1862 with Kegler's week-long view in 1737, Marsden came up with a prediction that the comet could return to perihelion—its closest point to the sun—around November 25, 1992. But instead of the 120-year period suggested by the 1862 appearance, if the comet was indeed Kegler's, the period must be more than 10 years longer.[7] That discrepancy alone prompted Marsden to doubt the connection. However if he were right—if Comets Kegler and Swift–Tuttle were the same—then it could not possibly return in 1981.[8]

It didn't. However most astronomers doubted the connection Marsden had tried to make, assuming instead that the comet had somehow slipped by without being detected.

SWIFT–TUTTLE RETURNS

On August 12, 1991, my friend Peter Jedicke and I were observing Perseids from a mountaintop in southern Vermont. Unlike the beautiful lakeside night almost 30 years earlier, this night was mostly cloudy. However we were impressed by the number of meteors we could see through holes in the clouds. One really bright meteor raced across the sky, its glow lighting up the cloud from atop like a searchlight beam. But that was nothing compared with what happened a few hours later on the other side of the world:

A group of observers near Japan's Kiso Observatory got the impressive rate of 352 meteors in a single hour of observing.[9] The next day, I happened to be visiting Marsden in his office at the Harvard–Smithsonian Center for Astrophysics. I had rarely seen him so excited about an observation. Looking like a kid on Christmas morning, he wondered if it were possible that his 18-year-old prediction just might come true. Was this hail of meteors spotted from Japan a vanguard? Was Swift–Tuttle on its way at last?

Despite a full moon that washed out the sky during the week of the Perseid shower in August 1992, observers tried to see what activity there was. On a beautiful clear night in Montreal, I spotted a paltry two meteors, but then another burst emerged—this time at precisely the moment the Earth crossed the plane of the comet's orbit. Despite these hints, Marsden was now starting to become shy about his prediction. Would the comet appear at all? "September maybe, but . . . nah! it won't come!" Marsden confided, "I got cold feet."

Nevertheless Marsden admitted later, "Another computation I made on July 25 gave T (or time of perihelion) = 1992 Dec. 11."[10] Later he added, "Perhaps it was that, with the exception of Kohoutek, no professional astronomer seemed to share my faith in it . . . or perhaps it was just that the day of reckoning was almost here."[11]

The answer came at last on September 26. Observing from Nagano, Japan, Tsuruhiko Kiuchi, an amateur astronomer using 5-inch diameter binoculars, spotted the comet on a path that would return it to perihelion only 17 days later than the date Marsden had predicted almost two decades before, and only 1 day off his July calculation.[12] By the following day, Jeremy Tatum from British Columbia had confirmed the sighting and had provided accurate measurements to show that this definitely was Periodic Comet Swift–Tuttle. "Things can be as exciting on paper or computer screen as at the eyepiece," Marsden said. "My whole prediction for P/Swift–Tuttle [P/ is an abbreviation for periodic comet] back in 1973 was done by paper and computer (before they had screens!), although it did take someone at the eyepiece to get the final proof."[13] Comets Kegler and Swift–Tuttle were indeed one and the same.

SWIFT–TUTTLE'S FUTURE

With observations now spanning three centuries, Marsden set out to determine whether other past appearances, like the comet of 69 B.C., might have been Swift–Tuttle—and also to predict what the next return to perihelion in 2126 would be like. "Whenever perihelion passage occurred between late June and early September," Marsden had written in his now-famous 1973 paper, "the comet should have become at least as bright as in 1862, and one would expect this to happen during one revolution out of every five or six; near collision with the Earth would take place if the comet were at perihelion in late July."[14]

When Marsden calculated the orbit forward to 2126, he came up with a perihelion date of July 11. Were the Earth and Swift–Tuttle on a collision course? What about those nongravitational forces? These could easily cause a delay. It did not take much computer time for Marsden to determine what might happen if the comet reached perihelion during a particular 3-minute period on July 26. A couple of weeks after perihelion, the mighty comet's nucleus, as large as 10 kilometers across, could crash into the Earth on August 14. Shortly after Marsden made that calculation, I wrote to congratulate him on being written up in *Time* magazine for his successful prediction. "Yes," an excited Marsden wrote back, "we've been getting a bit of *Time* exposure—and we may get more when we remark on the distinct possibility that P/S–T will become the 'mother of all Perseids' and hit us when it returns in 2126!"[15]

Even though the chance for a collision was almost nonexistent, reporters inundated Marsden with questions. "Life has been one big press conference ever since the middle of August," Marsden noted, hoping that the publicity would inspire astronomers to continue to make careful observations of the comet as it moved away from the sun.[16]

With the casual remark on Circular 5636 in October 1992 that Periodic Comet Swift–Tuttle may hit the Earth on its next return, quite a few astronomers have wondered if Marsden had perhaps gone a bit far by suggesting that there were a one in 10,000 chance of a collision. Not so, he says:

> My message was to astronomers and the need for them to observe the comet during the next several years. The observations in 1862 showed that Swift–Tuttle behaved in a very peculiar fashion—something of the kind I have never seen before in nearly 40 years of computing orbits. I regret the probability figure; that was not on the IAU circular and was rather forced out of me by reporters. The fact is that, even if Swift–Tuttle doesn't get us next time, it will have ample opportunity to do so in the more distant future, and it is the largest object we know of that has the potential to strike the Earth.[17]

By the end of 1992, Marsden reported that comets that appeared in 69 B.C. and A.D. 188 were actually early appearances of Swift–Tuttle. With the comet's orbital history now going back more than 2000 years, Marsden could now state with great certainty that the comet would return to perihelion pretty close to July 11, 2126, and there was now no chance of a collision with Earth. The scare was over—at least until 3044, when an even closer approach is predicted. Unless some new comet with our name on it rounds the sun in some surprise attack, Periodic Comet Swift–Tuttle is the largest comet on an orbit known to intersect the Earth's orbit. Thus there is some chance—albeit a remote one—of a comet hitting the Earth sometime within the next several hundred thousand years. Although the comet is only 15 kilometers in diameter, the speed of its impact would create a crater at least 200 kilometers wide, destroy the ozone layer, send up a pall of dust that would block sunlight for months, and destroy most species of life on Earth.

When the comet returns in 2126, we may get a special show anyway—from both the comet and its associated stream of Perseid meteors. Instead of its usual hundred or so meteors per hour for a few hours that night, the sky should blaze with a spectacular fireworks as thousands of meteors hit the atmosphere. Perhaps someone will then remember how, back in 1992, we thought for a while that it might be all over for us.

WHAT ARE COMETS MADE OF?

An ordinary comet has three parts—a nucleus, a coma, and often a tail. The nucleus is the source of everything we see in a comet—the dust and gases that form the coma and tail. Although observers have detected a few comet nuclei, our most dramatic view came in March 1986 when three camera-laden spacecraft—the European Space Agency's *Giotto* and two Soviet *Vegas*—sped by Halley's comet as it crossed the plane of the Earth's orbit on its way out of the inner solar system. The spacecraft recorded what looked like a large potato some 8 kilometers wide and 15 kilometers long—a really small object to generate a coma hundreds of thousands of kilometers across and a tail several million kilometers long. As some of the solar system's tiniest members, comet nuclei produce comas and tails that are among its largest and most beautiful features.

The three Halley spacecraft also confirmed what Harvard's Fred Whipple had proposed in 1950: A comet nucleus is like a snowball with dust mixed in. Instead of being a dirty snowball however, Halley's comet contains so much dust that it is better called, as astronomer Mark Sykes suggests, an icy mudball. The snow is not pure water ice but a mixture of frozen gases, including carbon monoxide (CO), hydrogen cyanide (HCN), and other ices containing carbon and sulfur.

When a comet is far from the sun, the nucleus is all there is. But as it nears the sun, the comet's ices—from water and other materials—begin to change into gas in a process called sublimation. We see a comet in two ways: Its dust particles scatter light from the sun, and ultraviolet light ionizes the gases and causes them to fluoresce. Comet Halley's nucleus loses material at a rate per orbital revolution that if spread all over the nucleus, would be 1 meter thick. In fact even when close to the sun, most of the nucleus is quiet except for active areas that are the primary source of material in the coma.

The coma is the atmosphere of material that surrounds the comet's nucleus. Gas streams from active areas at high speeds— several hundred meters per second—and carries dust particles with it into the tenuous cometary atmosphere. Most comets form comae when they get as close to the sun as the asteroid belt, well beyond the orbit of Mars. As Periodic Comet Shoemaker–Levy 9 has so dramatically shown after its encounter with Jupiter in 1992, a comet can have more than one nucleus and coma.

The coma and nucleus together make up a comet's head; material that streams away from the head is called the tail. The sublimated gases form a gas or ion tail, which generally points nearly in the direction opposite the sun, and the dust follows the comet at a more leisurely pace, often curving away slightly. As the dusty material blows away, the comet orbits the sun more slowly and forms a curved tail as the more distant particles lag further behind.

Comets are surrounded by large hydrogen clouds, as was found in January 1970 when Comet Tago–Sato–Kosaka became the first to be studied by a spacecraft. The craft discovered a huge cloud of atomic hydrogen gas emitting ultraviolet light. Depending on the size and activity of the comet and its distance from the sun, the hydrogen envelope can be 1–10 million kilometers long.

℃ *2* ☽

When Beggars Die

*M*aybe the Roman empress Calpurnia was right, comets can indeed bring calamity—but as we now know, only if they actually strike the Earth. For most of human history however, comets portended major disasters, such as the demise of a head of state, as Calpurnia reminded her husband in Shakespeare's *Julius Caesar*:

> When beggars die there are no comets seen,
> The heavens themselves blaze forth the death of princes.[1]

BROOM STARS AND BUSHY STARS

We are fortunate that comets in ancient times received such attention, for whenever one appeared, both its track across the heavens and its physical appearance were recorded. During the war between two Chinese kings, Wu-Wang and Chou, around 1059 B.C., a comet with an eastward-pointing tail dominated the morning sky. The scribes' detailed account is the first known record of a comet. Chinese recorders eventually noted two types of comet, the *po* and the *hui*. The *po*, or bushy star comet, generally meant a comet with a large fuzzy coma or atmosphere, usually without a tail, the *hui*, or broom star comet, had a tail. The Greek philosopher Aristotle called them fringed and bearded stars, respectively.

In recent years, we have had a cacophony of bushy star comets, one of which I was fortunate enough to discover in May 1990. At first Comet Levy 1990c moved almost imperceptibly among the stars of Pegasus, then in the northeast morning sky, as it closed in on Earth and sun. But as Comet Levy got closer, it brightened rapidly and picked up speed. By the middle of August, Comet Levy was parading elegantly across the summer sky, looking like a fat fur ball as it moved alongside the Milky Way. Although Comet Levy had a tail, it was not easily visible except in photographs. We couldn't see the tail at its best because it pointed away from the Earth.

The best recent example of a broom star comet was Comet West, which punctuated the morning sky like a huge exclamation mark in March 1976. I will never forget the frigid morning that my friend Carl Jorgensen and I drove south of Montreal's city lights to see what we thought might be a fairly bright comet. As we approached our observing site, I looked toward the east, but our view was blocked by trees. As soon as there was a break in the roadside forest, I looked eastward and saw the comet with its long tail pointing upward. "My God!" I exclaimed, "it's magnificent!" Still properly keeping his eyes on the road ahead, Carl agreed, sort of. "We'll get a good view," he promised. "We'll get to the site and see it through the binoculars." "No," I cried, barely able to keep from leaping out of the moving car. "It's right there!" "We'll see it soon," Carl said. "O.K." Carl drove another hundred yards and then casually looked to his left. "My God!" he finally agreed, and almost drove the car off the road.

What if I had been an astronomer in ancient Rome and this magnificent stranger had appeared in the familiar night sky? Even knowing it was a ball of ice and dust flung by gravitational forces into its orbit around the sun, I was almost incoherent with awe. Like most modern comet observers, Carl and I were elated to see this broom star comet. It was far brighter than we had expected. We sketched it and photographed it, remaining at our roadside site until the brightening dawn drowned out its light. Seeing this ghost from space was an emotional high, but although the presidency was being fought over in the United States that year, no one suggested that this spectacular comet had been sent to announce that President Ford would lose. Nor did anyone, as far as I know, blame Halley's comet in 1986 on the fall of Baby Doc Duvalier in Haiti or of Ferdinand Marcos in the Philippines.

THE HEAVENS BLAZE FORTH THE DEATH OF PRINCES

Over the thousands of years of recorded history, comet study has been free of superstition for only the last two centuries. The first book of *Chronicles* describes what could be a comet—the comet of 971 B.C. appeared around that time—that protested an ill-advised census King David had ordered. The biblical passage is read every year at the Passover seder: "And David lifted up his eyes, and saw the angel of the Lord standing between the earth and the heaven, having a drawn sword in his hand stretched out over Jerusalem."[2]

Caesar's wife Calpurnia may have seen a comet, but not *before* her husband Julius was murdered on the Ides of March 44 B.C. at the foot of Pompey's statue. Two months later, a bright comet with a tail perhaps 12 degrees long—half the length of the Big Dipper—was reported moving north to south. This comet is one of the best known from ancient times, but not because it was exceptionally bright or long-lasting. According to Plutarch, "Among the divine portents there was also the great comet; it appeared very bright for seven nights after the murder of Caesar, then disappeared." Calpurnius Siculus went further, blaming the comet for the civil war that followed: "When, on the murder of Caesar, a comet pronounced fatal war for the wretched people."[3]

In Roman Times, comets were known for what they meant rather than for what they are. Rather than objects to be admired or studied, comets were seen as messages, and in the social disruption following Caesar's death, people would see a comet playing a big role. In a beautiful treatise called *De Cometis,* a part of his

Quaestiones Naturales, Lucius Annaeus Seneca also wrote of the comet of 44 B.C. When it came to astronomy, Seneca had few equals in the ancient world, but he was no match for the treacherous politics of his era. Born around 4 B.C., Seneca lived during some of Rome's worst times, during the reigns of emperors as cruel and incompetent as Caligula, Claudius, and Nero. Seneca was Nero's tutor, and when Nero, at age 17, became emperor of Rome, Seneca had considerable power in the government of the state. For 10 years the arrangement worked, then Nero murdered his mother Agrippina in 59 A.D. and coerced Seneca into excusing this heinous act. Seneca spent the last years of his life with his friend Burrus trying to limit the excesses of Nero's madness. In 63 A.D. Burrus died, and Seneca tried to resign from politics. Feigning that he still respected Seneca, Nero refused his resignation.

Although Seneca then abandoned his wealth to live in poverty, he knew his end under Nero's tyranny was near. He desperately tried to praise Nero wherever he could: "There is no reason to suppose," he intoned,

> that the recent one [comet] which appeared during the reign of Nero Caesar—which has redeemed comets from their bad character—was similar to the one that burst out after the death of the late Emperor Julius Caesar, about sunset on the day of the games to Venus Genetrix.[4]

The soothing words didn't work. In the year 65, Nero accused Seneca of participating in a plot against him and ordered the scholar to prepare for death. According to custom, this gave Seneca his choice of demise. He chose to cut his wrist and bleed to death. Apparently his luck ran out after the comet appeared.

Still Seneca had at least completed *Quaestiones Naturales*, his seven-book opus on natural philosophy, some 5 years earlier while his position was in turmoil and his life in jeopardy. The last section is called *De Cometis*. "No man is so utterly dull and obtuse," Seneca began, "with head so bent on earth, as never to lift himself up and rise with all his soul to the contemplation of the starry heavens, especially when some fresh wonder shows a beacon-light in the sky."[5] *Quaestiones Naturales* was lost for more than a thousand years; its discovery in the twelfth century allowed scholars to understand the ideas of other Greek and Roman scholars about comets. Seneca's insight into comets is remarkable for its time.

> Blind to all the celestial bodies, each asks about the newcomer; one is not quite sure whether to admire or to fear it. Persons there are who seek to inspire terror by forecasting its grave import. But by my honour, no one could embark on a more exalted study. . . .[6]

Seneca perceived comets as an object of study rather than a superstition. Seneca follows with a summary of cometary thought up to his time. He noted that before Posidonius, who was a Greek scholar from Byzantium, Epigenes identified one type of comet "with hair on all sides" (the bushy star of the Chinese); the other "extends a loose kind of fire in one direction" (the Chinese broom stars). Unfortunately little is known about Epigenes. Even when he lived, possibly in the fourth century B.C., is uncertain. Epigenes insisted that the comets "with hair on all sides" were stationary among the stars. Either Epigenes or Seneca may be confusing these with a different kind of sky surprise called a nova. From time to time, a star may undergo an outburst, becoming very much brighter. These outbursts, called novae, are not really new stars but old ones undergoing brief increases in brightness.

One of the liveliest aspects of Seneca's writing is the vigorous way that he refutes those who disagree with him. "It requires no great effort," he sniffs, "to strip Ephorus [who lived around 340 B.C.] of his authority; he is a mere chronicler." Seneca accuses Ephorus of careless reporting: The Greek astronomer "asserts that the great comet [possibly the one of 373 B.C.] which, by its rising, sank Helice and Buris, which was carefully watched by the eyes of the whole world since it drew issues of great moment in its train, split up into two stars; but nobody besides him has recorded it."[7] Perhaps this is so, but other comets have been widely observed to split, including Periodic Comet Biela in 1846; Comet West in 1976, which broke into four parts; and Comets Levy and

Shoemaker–Holt, seen in 1988, and Periodic Comet Shoemaker–Levy 9 in 1993. For an earlier example, Byzantine records show that around 822 A.D., "A comet was seen in the sky as a sort of two moons joined together brightly, and moreover separated by different attachments."[8] Comet splitting is not uncommon.

Seneca believed that comets are formed "by very dense air, and since the most sluggish air is in the north, they appear in greatest number" in that direction. "For the recent one which we saw during this joyous reign of Nero [Seneca was desperate to insist that the summer comet of 60 A.D. was not a bad omen for Nero] displayed itself to view for six months, revolving in the opposite direction to the former one [the comet of 54 A.D.] in Claudius' time." Seneca now describes rough paths for the two comets, that of 54 A.D. "rising from the North up toward the zenith made for the east, always growing dimmer." On the other hand, the comet of 60 A.D. "began in the same quarter, but making toward the west, turned finally towards the south, where it withdrew from view. No doubt the former found moister elements, more suitable for its fire, and pursued them; the latter in turn chose a richer and more substantial district."[9]

Although comets are distributed across the sky almost at random, in Seneca's own experience, comets coincidentally did favor the sky in the north. He undoubtedly observed the comet of June 54 A.D., blamed for the death of Nero's predecessor Claudius, as it passed through Gemini, which is in the northern sky. Another comet the following year also appeared in the sky north of Cancer, and one in 60 A.D. may have passed near the north celestial pole.

Seneca echoed his favorite Stoic philosophers in his view about the nature of comets; however in an important way, he went beyond the traditional Stoic supposition that comets were temporary events. "I rank it among Nature's permanent creations," he declared.

> In none of the ordinary fires in the sky is the route curved; it
> is distinctive of a star [meaning a planet] that it describes a
> curve in its orbit. Whether other comets had this circular orbit
> I cannot say. The two in our own age [the comets of 54 and

60 A.D.] at any rate had. . . . A comet has its own settled
position. For that reason it is not expelled in haste, but steadily
traverses its course; it is not snuffed out, but takes its
departure.[10]

In writing about the fourth-century B.C. scholar Apollonius of
Myndos, Seneca stumbled on more of the truth, although the cometary conventional wisdom of the time prevented him from rec-
ognizing it. A comet, Apollonius thought, is "a distinctive heavenly
body, just as the sun or the moon is."[11] He even explained how
comets brighten as they approach the Earth, then fade as they
depart. Seneca tried boldly to refute this part of Apollonius' argument. If this is the case, he wondered, then why are some comets
at their brightest when they first appear on the scene? Considering
the era's scant understanding of the comet's orbits, Seneca's reply
is a good one. With a telescope and the ability to compute orbits,
Apollonius could have answered that some comets may approach
from behind the sun, brightening as they arrive, but remaining
entirely unseen until they suddenly appear at their maximum
brightness. Seneca's account of Apollonius is the only surviving
record of this Greek philosopher's precocious insight.

Years later the historian Tacitus looked back on the days of
paranoic Nero and his reaction to the comet of the summer of
60 A.D.

> A phenomenon which, according to the persuasion of the
> vulgar, portended change to kingdoms: hence, as if Nero had
> been already deposed, it became a topic of inquiry, who should
> be chosen to succeed him.[12]

Even though the comet predated his book, Seneca was still desperately trying to stay on Nero's good side, even though the people
were whispering that Rubellius Plautus, a relative of Julius Caesar,
would replace Nero as emperor. Unfortunately, Tacitus notes, the
comet's appearance was punctuated by another sign that hit close
to home: "As Nero sat at meat in a villa called Sublaqueum, upon
the banks of the Simbruine lakes, the viands were struck by lightning and the table overthrown. . . ."[13]

The famous appearance of Halley's comet at the height of the Norman conquest of England in 1066 underscored the perception that the heavens themselves still blazed forth the death of princes. "Nova stella, novus rex!" ("New star, new king!") was the battle cry on the Bayeux tapestry that later depicted the battle. By the fifteenth century, that maxim had still not changed. In a story from the *Illustrated London News*, there is a documented case, in fact, of a comet actually causing the death of a prince. The guilty comet appeared in 1402 and was visible in broad daylight for a record duration of 7 days.

> There is no doubt, however, that comets sometimes really did produce fatal effects. In June, 1402, one appeared in Italy which literally killed the famous John Galeas Visconti. The astrologers of the Prince had predicted that his death would be announced by a comet of extraordinary magnitude, and the celestial phenomenon had no sooner become visible than his Highness, speechless from fright, sank to the ground and died.[11]

Thinking that the comet foretold his death, poor Visconti probably had a heart attack when he saw it. Small wonder. Even with my own modern perspective on the nature of these solar wanderers, I felt my own heart jump and race that night in 1976 when I saw Comet West in all its fiery array arch over the dark Quebec woods.

☾ 3 ☽

Taming the Shrew

On the night in 1864 that Horace Tuttle was observing Tempel's comet from aboard the swaying deck of the Catskill, *a young* English poet was watching the same comet from another shore. Gerard Manley Hopkins later became one of the nineteenth century's best known English poets—his sonnet "The Windhover" is widely read in many schools. The moonless predawn sky was clear on both the English and U.S. coasts; although Jupiter and Saturn had already set, Mars was prominent in the southern sky. High in the east were Auriga and Taurus. Just west of the second magnitude star Beta Tauri shone the head of Tempel's comet, its tail stretching toward nearby Iota Aurigae.

Less than two weeks later, Hopkins wrote these lines:

—I am like a slip of comet,
Scarce worth discovery, in some corner seen
Bridging the slender difference of two stars,
Come out of space, or suddenly engender'd
By heady elements, for no man knows:
But when she sights the sun she grows and sizes
And spins her skirts out, while her central star
Shakes its cocooning mists; and so she comes
To fields of light; millions of travelling rays

23

Pierce her; she hangs upon the flame-cased sun,
And sucks the light as full as Gideon's fleece:
But then her tether calls her; she falls off,
And as she dwindles sheds her smock of gold
Amidst the sistering planets, till she comes
To single Saturn, last and solitary;
And then goes out into the cavernous dark.
So I go out: my little sweet is done:
I have drawn heat from this contagious sun:
To not ungentle death now forth I run.[1]

As both a poet and an observer, Hopkins wrote about comets in human terms. The comet first appears "bridging the slender difference of two stars." While doing my 1979 Master's thesis at Queen's University, I found a letter to the London *Times* in August 1, 1864, that predicted: "On Monday night it will be situated about five degrees to the left of the Pleiades, passing thence between the stars Iota in Auriga and Beta in Taurus . . ."[2]

On first reading, Hopkins was asking some dated questions: Do comets come from space or are they born in our atmosphere? And what about the line that says Saturn is the most distant planet? As it turns out, neither are out of place in this poem, because Hopkins had intended his poem to be part of a play set in Italy during the Renaissance. His poem was supposed to reflect the uncertainty about the nature of comets that prevailed at that earlier time.

It was Aristotle's theory that comets were, as the poem so appropriately notes, "suddenly engender'd by heady elements" high in the atmosphere. For almost 2000 years, Aristotle's *Meteorologica* was the primary reference whenever people discussed comets. Aristotle believed that comets form when the Earth breathes hot, dry air into the upper atmosphere. It is a view that Seneca tried to reckon with—once the exhalations were formed, he thought, they would be permanent. However, Aristotle's view lasted for so long that it became very difficult to challenge, and once adopted by the Roman Catholic Church as dogma, challenging Aristotle's views could be fatal: For his unorthodox beliefs about the existence of other worlds, Giordano Bruno was put to death at the stake in 1600.

The sudden appearance of a supernova in 1572 knocked a hole in one of Aristotle's main ideas; the heavens did not permit change. Just 5 years later, a bright comet appeared, and 3 years after that, another comet provided gist for new studies on the nature of the heavens.

Hopkins's line about the comet shaking "its cocooning mists" probably recalls a different comet, a large one that appeared suddenly over England in the early summer of 1861. As its nucleus rotated in space, its more active side turned toward the sun at set intervals, resulting in periodic eruptions of material—the "cocooning mists" in the poem. These eruptions were seen by many observers, including William Ellis, an observer assigned to a telescope at Greenwich Observatory. Ellis observed this comet in secret, since his boss, Director George Airy, was a stickler for planning and details and objected to any break in the observing routine, even one caused by a huge comet rising unexpectedly over the horizon. In 1986 Halley's comet shredded its cocooning mists so regularly that they were successfully predicted before the spacecraft visited the comet. Hopkins would have been pleased at the importance of his cocooning mists.

THE COMET PROCESSION OF 1618–1619

A procession of bright comets arrived starting in late summer of 1618. The first, which we now call 1618 I, was found by observers in Kaschau, Hungary, on August 25, as well as by Johannes Kepler in Austria. It was a splendid morning object in the constellation of Leo with a long tail pointing to the west. "In the month of August," wrote Jacobus Mascardus, a Jesuit priest, "news was brought to us from many parts of Italy that during that period a comet was seen licking the hind feet of the Great Bear."[3] Kepler took advantage of his new telescope to observe this comet, probably the first telescopic observation of a comet. By September 15 the tail had all but disappeared, and the rest of the comet was fading.

By the middle of November, a second comet highlighted the southwestern sky; its head was in Libra, and its tail stretched for 40 degrees in length (80 full-moon diameters!) A third comet emerged at the same time, creeping across the sky from Libra toward the west. The final act began on February 14, 1619, with the appearance of a fourth comet in the southeastern morning sky with a tail covering more than half the sky. The comets led to a debate on the nature of these objects between Galileo and the Jesuit astronomer Horatio Grassi. Comets have circular orbits around the sun, insisted Grassi, trying to fit comets into the new system proposed by Tycho, where the planets revolve around the sun, but the sun in turn revolves around the Earth. Galileo, who had maintained a publishing silence since his stunning telescopic observations in 1609, so disputed these ideas that he came out of retirement and resumed writing.

In 1623 Galileo published *Il Saggiatore* (*The Assayer*) in the form of a letter. From today's viewpoint, it is quite a disappointment. Considering that only 9 years earlier its author had shaken the world with his observations of Jupiter's moons, Venus's phases, and sunspots, it seems incredible that *The Assayer* doesn't mention that he observed any of these comets through his telescope. During the fall of 1618 however, Galileo was bedridden with arthritis and a hernia and quite unable to use his telescope.

In *The Assayer* Galileo disagreed fiercely with Grassi's views. Comets could not be in circular orbits, he sneered, since it is clear that all comets do not return again and again. Instead Galileo suggested that comets were formed by sunlight reflected from thin vapors. This would seem to put Galileo on the wrong side of history; however Galileo's modern translator, Stillman Drake, argues that in a sense, he was right, for comets do not shine by their own light. It was Tycho's system of regular orbits, not the nature of comets, that Galileo was fighting.

So bitterly did Galileo dispute the views of his Jesuit colleagues that the rift never healed. But the old scholar's volume was a best seller. As a result, Galileo decided to proceed with his *Dialogue of the Two World Systems*, the work that led to his battle with the Inquisition that resulted in his arrest, trial, imprisonment, and a verdict that was not rescinded until 1992, more than 350 years later.

No matter whether their arguments were right or wrong, their allusions were beautiful. Mario Guiducci's *Discourse on the Comets* describes comets behaving "like Penelope unraveling the cloth with one hand as fast as she weaves it with another."[4] Centuries later Hopkins would put a similar allusion into his comet poem, as his brightening comet "sucks the light as full as Gideon's fleece."

Of all the writings of the comet controversy of 1618, I found that the close of Grassi's description of the comets to be the most touching. The long saga of human relations with comets had reached a new level of understanding: "I have believed that the comet," he wrote, "shining on all directly from the same place and appearing the same from all sides, must be considered as worthy of the heavens and very near to the stars." With a flourish Grassi concludes with a quote from Horace: "With my head exalted I shall touch the stars."[5]

By the early seventeenth century, comets were understood to be objects far away from Earth's atmosphere. One writer stated in 1635,

> Neither was it this starre alone, but others also after it, even Comets themselves, whose places were found to be above the moon: for observing more diligently and exactly than in former times, the observers could easily demonstrate this truth also. . . . If Comets be burnt, consumed, and wasted in the starrie heavens, it seemeth that there is no great difference between them and things here below.[6]

EDMOND HALLEY AND THE COMET OF 1682

As I write Chapter 3 at the end of 1992, Halley's comet is almost as far from the sun as Uranus. Its quiet potato-shaped nucleus, some 15 × 8 × 8 kilometers across, is no longer surrounded by the magnificent coma and tail it brandished like a peacock in 1986. Halley's comet will move even further out, lurking in the darkness of the outer solar system well beyond the orbit of Neptune until about 2055 when it crosses the orbit of Uranus on its way to its thirty-ninth observed return.

With its once-in-a-lifetime schedule, Halley's comet brings generations together. The scene of grandparent and grandchild standing together to look at Halley's comet is repeated every 76 years as the comet loops around the sun, checking in a sense on our progress. As comet hunter Leslie Peltier noted, the comet presided over the defeat of Attila the Hun in 451 and terrified the warriors of the Norman conquest of England in 1066. In the year 1456, Peltier's soaring prose goes on,

> The menacing appearance of the comet so alarmed Pope Calixtus that he decreed several days of prayer and established the midday angelus. With a great clanging of bells he then besought the comet to visit its wrath solely on the invading Turks. In 1607 it was watched by both Shakespeare and Kepler and I like to think that it was also seen by Captain John Smith and Pocahontas in the frontier skies of Jamestown. On its following trip around in 1682 the comet was observed by Halley himself, who probed into its periodic past and bequeathed to it an honored name that it can bear with pride throughout the solar system.[7]

In 1835 the comet presided over the trailblazers heading west to expand the young United States, and in 1910 the comet danced by to a comet rag, and comet pills taken to ward off its supposed effects. In 1986 we met it as never before. The International Halley Watch coordinated many thousands of observations as the comet passed, and the Soviet Union, Europe, and Japan sent a flotilla of spacecrafts to meet it. I started a venture called "Project 2061" in which teachers and children were given directions to find the comet and instructions to remember their traveling friend until it returns in 2061.

Finally just 8 years after Periodic Comet Swift–Tuttle arrives, Halley's comet will roar by in 2134 in its closest visit in 1300 years. But Peltier asks what wonders of technology we will have to study the comet then "Or will man himself prove periodic?" "Will the Huns be back again?"[8]

When the breakthrough finally came that allowed us to see comets as full-fledged members of the solar system, it had nothing to do with the appearance or structure of comets but with their orbits. After three major comets appeared in 1680, 1682, and 1683, Edmond Halley thought to calculate their orbits based on accurate observations made by the astronomer John Flamsteed. Halley also determined the paths of 21 other comets that appeared between 1337 and 1698. His results, which he reviewed with his friend Isaac Newton, were astonishing. The comets that appeared in 1531, 1607, and 1682 had such similar orbits that Halley believed they were actually returns of the same comet. At first Halley suspected that other pairs of similar orbits were returns of other comets, but those never panned out. Halley capped his work with a prediction that his comet would return at the end of 1758. Unfortunately he didn't live long enough to see his forecast come true. During 1758 a mélange of mathematicians and astronomers were frantically searching for the comet on paper and in the sky, but it was not until Christmas night 1758 that Johann Georg Palitzsch, a farmer and amateur astronomer, searching with a small telescope near Dresden, first spotted the comet. With his unaided eye that frigid night, he was pretty sure he saw a faint fuzzy spot low in the sky in Pisces. With some agitation he tried to set up his long telescope, but the cold and his nerves cost him precious minutes. Finally his telescope was ready, and he aimed it at the new object in time to draw it position relative to some nearby stars in his field of view.

Halley did have his work cut out for him 4 centuries ago. "He really had the benefit only of the few cometary orbits he computed,"[9] notes Marsden. In addition to the three returns Halley worked on, Marsden adds that Halley suspected that the comets of 1378 and 1456 were earlier appearances of the same comet.

Periodic Comet Halley, 1986 III. (Photograph by Jack Newton, January 11, 1986, from Victoria, B.C., Canada.)

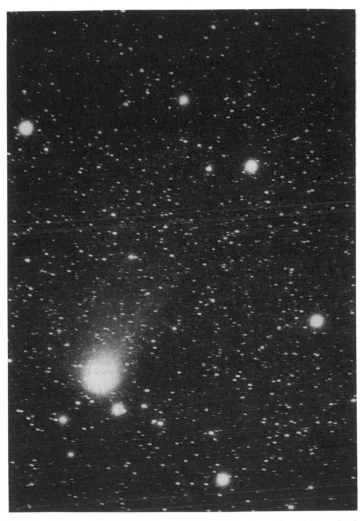

Periodic Comet Halley, 1986 III. (Photograph by Jack Newton, with a 300-mm f/8 lens, April 1986, as the comet moved through the constellation of Scorpius.)

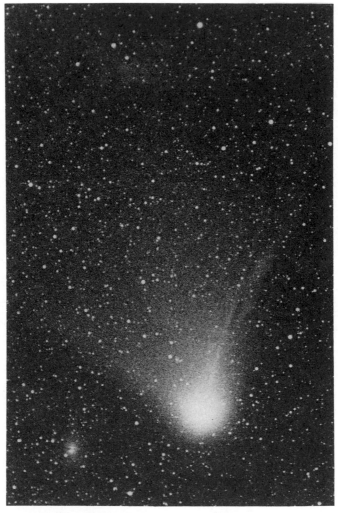

Periodic Comet Halley, 1986 III. (Photograph by Jack Newton, April 14, 1986, from Cuzco, Peru.) Note that the tail has become much wider as the Earth passes through the plane of the comet's orbit.

It was far more difficult to link Halley's comet with comets in the more distant past. Although a bright comet appeared in 1301, Halley thought that the comet he was studying should have returned 4 years later. But it turned out that the comet's orbital period was varied from 74–79 years, depending on perturbations from the planets. It was not until the nineteenth century that celestial mechanicians like J. Russell Hind were able to connect earlier apparitions to Halley's comet, and early this century, Cowell and Crommelin used ancient records to confirm the comet's visit as far back as 240 B.C.

THE ORBITS GET BETTER

Not long after Halley's achievement firmly established that comets can return, Anders Johan Lexell showed in the 1770s that Comet Messier 1770 I (the Roman numeral I means that it was the first comet to round the sun in 1770) was also a periodic comet. It has a period of only 5 years. However Lexell also showed that this wayward comet had come close to Jupiter just before its approach to the Earth and that afterward it came close to Jupiter again. In this second encounter, Jupiter changed the orbit so drastically that the comet would never return to the vicinity of Earth.

As our story gets closer to the present, we come across other ingenious attempts to link one comet appearance with another; some were successful, but others, announced with far more hoopla, were not.

Early in the nineteenth century, Johann Franz Encke became curious about several comet appearances. In 1786 France's Pierre-François Méchain discovered a comet, and Caroline Herschel of England found one in 1795. From his observing sites in France, Jean-Louis Pons found two more in 1805 and 1819. Using accurate observations to calculate their orbits, Encke found that they fit the orbit of a single comet that would next return in 1822. Encke was right, and the comet that now bears his name has by far the shortest orbital period of any comet, a brief 3.3 years.

During the last week of October 1366, a large comet crossed the sky from Ursa Major to Aquarius and was well recorded by Chinese observers. In the mid–nineteenth century, J. Russell Hind suggested that this large comet might be an early appearance of Periodic Comet Tempel–Tuttle, the parent of the Leonid meteor stream. In the early 1960s, John Schubart did the calculations that linked the two comets and found the record of Gottfried Kirsch's single observation (never confirmed by another observer) of Temple–Tuttle in 1699. Schubart predicted that the comet would return in 1965; his prediction was off by only 5 days.

THE COMET OF CHARLES V

Hind was not so lucky with his ideas about a possible return of the comet of 1556, the comet that marked the end of the long reign of Charles V of the Holy Roman Empire. Charles was the Hapsburg emperor who ruled more territory than anyone else before or since. Let others wage war, was his philosophy about expanding his rule. "You, lucky Austria, marry." He retired of his own will around 1556, living quietly on his estate and indulging his interest in clocks, and died 2 years later.

Charles's comet appeared in the southern sky of 1556, moving through Corvus and Virgo. In 1751 Richard Dunthorne suggested that it was the same comet "that created astonishment throughout Europe" in 1264.[10] He went on to prophesy a return in 1848; in 1857 with Charles's comet still unseen, Hind refined that forecast to August of either 1858 or 1860.

In the following 3 years, two very bright comets appeared, Donati's in 1858 and the great comet of 1861. "The new visitor," trumpeted the London *Times*, "which has taken even astronomers by surprise, shone with great brilliancy last night [July 3, 1861], exciting universal admiration. . . . Its size does not at present exceed that of 1858, and it differs from it materially in this respect, that its tail is straight instead of being curved."[11] A competing newspaper described a first view of the comet on June 30: "It then far exceeded in brightness any comet I have observed, those of 1811 and the recent splendid one of 1858, not excepted."[12] All this excitement naturally launched a debate as to whether the 1861 comet might be that of Charles on its long-awaited return. But the original assumption was all wrong: Charles's comet was not the comet of 1264, and neither comet has ever reappeared.

Even in Hind's day, astronomers understood that gravitational pulls of the planets can affect the period of a comet as it travels about the sun. "It is true," he wrote in 1859,

> if a comet experienced no resistance while performing its journey round that luminary, it would make its appearance after equal intervals of time. . . . But the movements of comets are greatly disturbed by the attraction of the various planets belonging to the solar system, particularly by Jupiter and Saturn, which far exceed the rest in magnitude."[13]

Hind even addressed the possible effects of a collision with Charles V's comet: "At worst," he grossly underestimated, "a direct collision would perhaps be comparable only as regards the mechanical effect upon the earth to a meeting with a huge cushion."[14]

Early this century the English astronomer Andrew C. D. Crommelin fit the orbits of comets found by Pons, Coggia, Winnecke, and Forbes into that of a single returning object. Just as the earlier Comets Halley, Lexell, and Encke were named to honor the accomplishments of those who had unravelled their mysteries, this newest comet was renamed Periodic Comet Crommelin.

Some 250 years after Halley showed us how to do it, figuring out where and when a comet will return involves the same difficult mathematics. The result is every bit as exciting as discovering a comet, even though computers compress months of calculations into seconds. "In 1973," writes Marsden, "I had the benefit of a computer for testing out the effect of assumption of slightly different initial revolution periods."[15]

One can argue that Marsden's achievement with Comet Swift–Tuttle is in the same class as those of Encke and Crommelin, even though his computer made his work go faster. To keep up with the tradition, would it not be a good idea to change the name of Comet Swift–Tuttle to Marsden? Maybe not, some people might say; after all is it practical to rename a comet we have called Swift–Tuttle for 130 years? But Periodic Comet Marsden has a nice ring to it. Whether or not the name is changed, I hope that our descendants will look at the comet of 2126 as it surges by and say, "There goes Marsden's comet." It would be a well deserved tribute to him.

☾ 4 ☽

Comet or Planet?

*F*riedrich Wilhelm Herschel *would become one of the greatest figures in the history of astronomy, but in 1760, he was an impoverished* musician who didn't have the funds to return to England from a trip to Genoa, Italy. Desperate to get home, he gave a bizarre impromptu recital—a maestro playing a harp, holding a horn, and having a second horn attached to his shoulder. It may be hard to picture Herschel playing all three instruments in such a pose, but the people of Genoa came in droves, and he made his way back to England.

Born in Hanover, Germany, in 1738, Herschel was the son of a musician, and he became a composer and conductor as well as a skilled performer on horn, harp, and organ. He used the English version of his first name after he moved to England in 1757. At this period of his life, Herschel's highest ambition was to establish his reputation in music. To get from place to place to play, he bought a horse that he frequently rode across the fields in typically damp and stormy British weather. In addition to his extraordinary schedule, he packed his evenings with education: During all this time, he wrote,

> Though it afforded not much leisure for study, I had not forgot
> my former plan, but had given all my leisure hours to the

study of languages. After I had improved myself sufficiently in English, I soon acquired the Italian, which I looked upon as necessary for my business. I proceeded next to Latin, and having also made considerable progress in that language, I made an attempt of the Greek . . . but soon dropped the pursuit of that as leading me too far from my other studies, by taking up too much of my leisure.[1]

These other studies, Herschel goes on, were in music:

The theory of music being connected with mathematics, had induced me very early to read in Germany all that had been written upon the subject of harmony; and when, not long after my arrival in England, the valuable book of Dr. Smith's harmonics came into my hands, I perceived my ignorance and had recourse for other authors for information, by which I was drawn from one branch of mathematics to another.[2]

MUSIC OF THE SPHERES

In May 1773 Herschel made a small purchase that would have major consequences. He records in his diary, "May 10. Bought a book of astronomy and one of astronomical tables."[3] Within a few weeks, his passion for the order and harmony of music had transformed itself into a passion for the sky, and he plunged into his new love with his typical zeal. Buying some lenses, he built a 4-foot-long tube and mounted a lens in it: "With this," he exulted,

I began to look at the planets and the stars. It magnified 40 times. In the next place I attempted a 12 feet one and contrived a stand for it. After this I made a 15 feet and also a 30 feet refractor and observed with them.[4]

Although Herschel enjoyed these refractors, he found them long and unwieldy. Based on Galileo's 1609 design, they involved a single objective lens that bent the light so that it would reach a focus at the eyepiece end of the telescope, down at the other end of the tube. Moving a skinny 30-foot-long tube across the sky was a challenge, especially if the tube failed to stay absolutely straight to allow the light to travel down its length to the eyepiece. Perhaps, he thought, the reflector telescope that Isaac Newton had invented in 1672 by putting a concave mirror at the bottom of a tube and an eyepiece near the top would better suit his needs. So around September 8, Herschel completed a 2-foot-long Gregorian-type reflector, in which a concave secondary mirror sends light through a hole in the main mirror to the eyepiece.

> This was so much more convenient than my long glasses that I soon resolved to try whether I could not make myself such another . . . I was, however, informed that there lived in Bath a person who amused himself with repolishing and making reflecting mirrors.

When Herschel arrived however, he found the optician's interest waning. The craftsman immediately offered Herschel "all his tools and some half-finished mirrors, as he did not intend to do any more work of that kind. . . . About the 21st October I had some mirrors cast for a two-feet reflector." Following the custom of the day, Herschel did not use glass but a form of speculum metal that consisted, he wrote, "of 21 copper, 13 tin, and one of Regulus of Antimony, and I found it very good, sound white metal."[5] Unlike today's glass objectives, speculum mirrors do not need additional reflective coatings, and telescopes over 200 years old still survive, their fragile coats of metal still longing for a skyward look. By the beginning of November, Herschel had become so proficient in completing mirror after mirror that he was getting behind in finishing the telescopes that the mirrors would serve.

So thoroughly did Herschel immerse himself in his zeal for telescopes that he needed a larger house in Bath. His younger sister Caroline Lucretia, born in 1750, moved into it as well, joining him enthusiastically in his work and not minding all the telescopes strewn about in various stages of construction. The backyard of their house was set up as an observing site. About the size of a modern backyard, it had room for several small telescopes.

A MAJOR DISCOVERY

By 1781, only 8 years after he fell in love with the stars, Herschel was deeply involved in a systematic survey of the sky. "On Tuesday the 13th March," he wrote,

> Between ten and eleven in the evening, while I was examining the small stars in the neighborhood of H Geminorum, I perceived one that appeared visibly larger than the rest; being struck with its uncommon magnitude I compared it to H Geminorum and the small star in the quartile between Auriga and Gemini, and finding it so much larger than either of them, suspected it to be a comet.[6]

Although the object was pretty bright, perceiving it not as a point of light but a disk was a real challenge even to a trained eye. Herschel later wrote,

> Seeing is in some respects an art which must be learnt. To make a person see with such a power is nearly the same as if I had been asked to make him play one of Handel's fugues upon the organ. Many a night have I been practising to see, and it would be strange if one did not acquire a certain dexterity by such constant practice.[7]

News of this peculiar comet spread swiftly. Across the English channel, Charles Messier, a French astronomer who would become equally revered, observed the new object at every opportunity. Messier was stumped by both its ultraslow movement from night to night and its shape. "I am constantly astonished at this comet," he wrote to Herschel in the late spring of 1781,

> which has none of the distinctive characters of comets, as it does not resemble any one of those I have observed, whose number is eighteen . . .

> I have since learnt by a letter from London that it is to you, Sir, that we owe this discovery. It does you the more honor, as nothing could be more difficult than to recognize it, and I cannot conceive how you were able to return several times

to this star—or comet—as it was absolutely necessary to observe it several days in succession to perceive that it had motion . . . .

For the rest this discovery does you much honour; allow me to compliment you for it. I should be very curious, Sir, to learn the details of this discovery, and you will oblige me if you will be so good as to inform me of them.[8]

"Life has been one long press conference," Marsden lamented in 1992 about the fuss with his successful prediction of the return of Comet Swift–Tuttle and its possible near encounter with the Earth in 2126. More than two centuries earlier, Herschel was just as annoyed at the mounting publicity about his comet. He was trying to build a mirror for a new 20-foot-long reflector. If a minute could be spared from all the publicity, he would undoubtedly get back to it.

On August 31, 1781, Anders Lexell, the mathematician who had determined the orbit of a comet, blew the whistle on Herschel's claim that his remarkable object was a comet. Its orbit was almost circular, he announced, and it never gets closer to the sun than 16 times the Earth's distance to the sun. The pieces of the puzzle had finally fallen into place. Herschel's object did not look much like a comet because it was not a comet. It was a planet, the first to be discovered in historic times.

With the confidence of a man who once played solo with a harp and two horns, Herschel suggested that his methods were so precise that he could not possibly have missed finding the new object, whether it turned out to be a comet or a planet. Standing toward the top of his instrument, he would sling it to and fro, observing stars as they went through the field of view and noting their positions, colors, and brightnesses. Once the new find was identified as a planet, the politically astute Herschel wanted to name it Georgium Sidus after his patron, King George III, but it is now called Uranus.

At the end of 1781, the Royal Society offered Herschel its Copley medal. The uncannily prescient citation is worth noting:

Your attention to the improvement of telescopes has already
amply repaid the labour which you have bestowed upon them;
but the treasures of the heavens are well known to be inexhaustible. Who can say but your new star, which exceeds
Saturn in its distance from the sun, may exceed him as much
in magnificence of attendance? Who can say what new rings,
new satellites, or what other nameless and numberless phenomena remain behind, waiting to reward future industry?[9]

Almost two centuries later in 1977, Uranus passed in front of a
star. The star blinked out several times before Uranus occulted it,
then the star repeated its performance the same number of times
afterward. Thus a set of rings was found about Uranus. More rings
were found when *Voyager II* sailed past Uranus as part of its od-
yssey through the outer solar system. The planet is known to have
15 satellites, two of which Herschel discovered himself.

After the German-born astronomer was appointed private astronomer to the king in 1782, George III insisted that Herschel
have the best telescope possible. An avid amateur astronomer
himself, George III had established the Kew Observatory near the
present site of the Kew Botanical Gardens. The first meeting at
Windsor castle between George III and Herschel was a great success, and Herschel was delighted with their observing session on
the evening of July 2: "My Instrument gave a general satisfaction,"
he wrote to his sister Caroline, "the King has very good eyes and
enjoys Observations with the Telescopes exceedingly."[10] With the
king's munificence Herschel continued to indulge his love of telescope making. In 1787 he redesigned his 20-foot telescope, taking
out the diagonal and sending the light at an angle directly to the
eyepiece, a design now called the Herschelian telescope. By 1800
he had made some 80 20-foot-long reflectors and double that
number of 10-foot-long telescopes.* By the end of his life, Herschel
had made an estimated 2160 telescopes, few of which survive.

* In Herschel's day the focal length of the telescope, the distance between the
  mirror and the focused eyepiece, was the prime way of referring to a telescope.
  Today we first discuss the diameter of the mirror or the lens.

THE COMETS OF CAROLINE

Herschel's self-discipline and enthusiasm were infectious, especially for his sister Caroline, who became a famous astronomer in her own right. In the early 1780s, she began hunting for comets using a 6-inch diameter reflector her brother had built for her work. By 1783 she had discovered the beautiful spiral galaxy in Sculptor now known as NGC 253. On August 1, 1786, when Herschel was in Germany, she reported finding a new comet, an act that thrilled her brother but got her a somewhat condescending official reply:

> Let us hope the best and that it is approaching the earth to please and instruct us and not to destroy us, for true Astronomers have no fears of that kind, witness Sir Harry Englefield's valuable tables of the apparent places of the comet of 1661 . . . I would not affirm that there may not be some astronomers so enthusiastic that they would not dislike to be whisked away from this low terrestrial spot into the higher regions of the heavens by the tail of a comet.[11]

After Caroline's comet finds became more routine, she was awarded a small income, and observatory replies were more professional and dignified. The Royal Astronomical Society bestowed its gold medal on her in 1828.

Caroline discovered eight comets in all. Her second find, at the end of 1788, turned out to be periodic, returning about every 150 years. When Roger Rigollet discovered a comet in 1939, the celestial mechanician Leland Cunningham determined that it was Herschel's comet returning; it is now known as Periodic Comet Herschel–Rigollet. Another comet turned out to be an appearance of Periodic Comet Encke. Caroline found two comets in 1790 and another in December 1791. By the time she had found her eighth comet in 1797, England's most famous woman astronomer was known throughout Europe for her "eccentric vocation" that included a log of her discoveries lovingly entitled "Bills and Receipts of my Comets." Despite her success with comet hunting, Caroline insisted that her greatest contribution was in assisting her brother.

With two large grants totalling 4000 pounds from King George, Herschel built a mammoth 40-foot-long telescope with a 48-inch diameter mirror. From the first night of its use, when he discovered Mimas and Enceladus, two of Saturn's closest moons, Herschel knew that this was a superb instrument. However its large mirror tarnished quickly, and since the telescope was unwieldy, it spent more time under repair than under the stars. Extremely difficult to use, the telescope's eyepiece could be reached only by standing on a high platform and shouting orders to an assistant.

Caroline had a bad accident on the telescope one night when her ankle was struck. As the story goes, one night Herschel asked her to move the telescope quickly in a particular direction. When nothing happened, Herschel repeated, "Lina, move the telescope!" But a large hook used for pulling the telescope had snagged her ankle and Caroline yelled back "I'm hooked!" As soon as she was almost recovered from this injury, she returned to assist her brother in his work.

In May 1788 Herschel married Mary Pitt. "His wife seems good-natured," Fanny Burney, a visiting novelist, wrote about her. Then noting that she was a widow with a large fortune, she added cattily that "astronomers are as able as other men to discern that gold can glitter as well as stars."[12] The Herschels had a son, John Frederick William, who first distinguished himself as a mathematician but later followed his father's footsteps to the stars. He went to the Cape of Good Hope in 1834 where he discovered and measured many previously unseen clouds of gas and clusters of stars in the southern sky. After he returned from his survey of the southern sky in Africa, John found the 40-foot telescope in poor shape. The scaffolding was weak and dangerous, and with considerable sadness, he decided to dismantle it. Years later lightning hit a tree, which fell on what was left of the huge telescope. All that now remains of Herschel's great 40-foot telescope is the bottom stub from the tube. In a requiem for New Year's 1840, the Herschel family met at the telescope to recite a poem John had written:

In the old Telescope's tube we sit,
And the shades of the past around us flit;
His requiem sing we with shout and din
While the old year goes out, and the new comes in

> *Merrily, merrily, let us all sing,*
> *And make the old Telescope rattle and ring!*

God grant that its end this group may find
In love and in harmony fondly joined!
And that some of us, fifty years hence, once more,
May make the old Telescope's echoes roar.

> *Merrily, merrily, let us all sing,*
> *And make the old Telescope rattle and ring!*[13]

William Herschel's accomplishments were prodigious. He determined the rotation period of Saturn to be a rapid 10 hours. From his careful records of the positions of more than 800 double stars over many years, he concluded in 1803 that some pairs revolve around a common center over a period of years. He multiplied Messier's catalog of nonstellar objects many times, observing and listing more than 2500 deep-sky objects called nebulae. But he loved his telescopes even more than what he could see with them. "It would be hard to be condemned," he wrote,

> because I have tried to improve telescopes and practised continually to see with them. These instruments have played me so many tricks that I have at last found them out in many of their humours and have made them confess to me what they would have concealed, if I had not with such perseverance and patience courted them. I have tortured them with powers, flattered them with attendance to find out the critical moments when they would act, tried them with specula of short or long focus, a large aperture or a narrow one; it would be hard if they had not been kind to me at last.[14]

☾ 5 ☽

The Sport Begins

Comet hunting is by far the slowest of all sports. It is one long game, actually, that began with Messier and is still in full swing. The playing field is worldwide, and players share the competitiveness, the egos, and the envy that electrify other sports. Cutting across class lines, each contender has reasons for finding a new comet, whether it be fame, winning, or just an interest in comets. Japan's Kaoru Ikeya was a worker in a piano factory; Canada's Rolf Meier is an electrical engineer; and Ohio's Leslie Peltier designed juvenile furniture. Howard Brewington, who lives with his wife, Trudy, near a small mountain town in New Mexico just for the dark sky that comet hunting requires, repairs television sets for a living.

Messier was certainly not the first person to find comets; every comet seen was discovered by somebody, although early records are lost. Paolo Toscanelli, the late fifteenth-century cartographer whose map of the Atlantic Ocean encouraged Columbus to set out on his voyages, also made careful drawings of six bright comets that appeared between 1433 and 1472. A man of eclectic interests besides cartography and astronomy, Toscanelli may have observed the sky so often that he saw these comets before others told him about them, but maybe he did not. Centuries later it does not matter. What is important is that his drawings allowed later as-

47

tronomers to compute their orbits, including that of Halley's comet, whose visit in 1456 frightened Pope Calixtus.

THE COMET FERRET

I suspect that Messier got his comet-hunting start thanks to his failure to be the first person to see Halley's comet in 1758. Perhaps he wouldn't admit it, but I like to imagine that he decided to get even with the sky, so to speak, by finding every other new comet that appeared after he was beaten out by Johann Georg Palitzch, a farmer from Dresden. But Messier's relationship with Halley's comet is more complicated still, for when he found Halley he had not even heard of Palitzch, news of whose find somehow did not reach Paris for several months. On January 21, 1759, while working at Nicholas Delisle's observatory at the Hôtel de Cluny in Paris, Messier finally saw the comet. He was thrilled: "It was one of the most important astronomical discoveries," he wrote, "for it showed that comets could return."[1] He summoned Delisle, who observed the comet, and then promptly ordered Messier not to announce it in any way. Messier complied with the request, so the comet was not announced until April 1, 3 weeks after it already rounded the sun. By this time, Messier had already heard of Palitzch's Christmas night sighting and knew that he would have lost the race anyway despite Delisle.

Messier didn't have long to wait to assuage his disappointment. Discovering his first comet in 1760, he made his first eight finds with the playing field virtually to himself. He found comets in 1763, 1764, 1766, 1769, 1770, 1771, and 1773 before his chief rival, Jacques Montaigne, a druggist in Limoges, France, snared his first in 1772, the comet that in 1826 became known as Biela's Periodic Comet or P/Biela. This comet apparently split in two in 1846, returned as two comets in 1852, and only as a meteor storm in 1872. By 1781 Pierre Méchain had also joined the contest. But in 1801 Messier was still in the lead, having added six more notches to his telescope.

The most important commodity needed by Messier and every comet hunter that followed him is patience. Hunting for comets, as we've noted, demands time—not time set by the hunter but by the sky itself. The moon acts as a referee, brightening the sky and limiting the period available for searching. The game is especially competitive just after full phase. For the preceding week, the waxing moon swathes the evening sky in light that makes all but the brightest comets invisible. A comet could brighten slowly during that week under the protective cloak of the moon's light, unnoticed by searchers. But the moon continues its eastward trek across the sky, rising later each night. Within a day or two after the full moon, the evening sky is suddenly thrust into darkness, and comet hunters all over the world rummage through it in a scramble for new comets. Some 10 days later, an almost-new moon opens the morning sky for another inning as sleepy searchers peer through their telescopes to see if anything new has appeared.

Except for the added dimension of photographic finds, the game has changed little in 200 years. A dark country sky is the same sky it was in Messier's time, with one big exception—the French sky gazer would have been amazed to see that the Earth has not one moon but hundreds of them, all artificial. These are the satellites that have appeared in increasing numbers since 1957, all looking like wandering stars moving gracefully across the telescope's field of view. Since Messier observed from the middle of Paris—he noted the passage of every hour by bells from more than 40 churches—he would have known something about light pollution, the bane of big-city sky gazing. Industrial pollutants and lights brighten up the sky, drowning out all the fainter stars and all but the brightest galaxies, clusters, and comets.

Messier's methods and telescopes are similar to what searchers employ now. He used a low power 2-inch diameter refracting telescope, though later he switched to a larger instrument. He moved his telescope steadily back and forth through a region of sky, looking for a fuzzy patch of light that crept so slowly he needed an hour to notice if it had moved at all.

In 1986 while visiting the Paris Observatory, I perused one of Messier's observing logs. As I studied his notes, his descriptions of the telescope he used, his complaints about the weather, and his comments about what he was looking at, 200 years seemed to slip away. Not that much has changed; reflecting the same concerns and joys, his notes could well have been my notes. It is still the same game.

So many comets found their way into Messier's telescope that Louis XV called him a ferret of comets, and President Jean Baptiste de Saron of the Paris parliament, a man versed in comet orbit calculation as well as politics, asked for observations of all Messier's comets so that he could calculate their orbits. Messier happily complied. The two men became great friends. One evening de Saron and his family brought Messier to an oriental garden at the Parc Monceau that had many small pagodas, castles, and passageways. Somehow Messier became separated from de Saron. Seeing a small open door, Messier, curious as always, stepped through. There was nothing inside but a long drop to a storeroom of ice. Messier fell 25 feet, splitting his scalp and breaking an arm, a leg, and several ribs as he crashed onto the ice below. Messier's injury kept him out of commission for almost a year, but by 1782, he was back at the telescope, and in 1785 he discovered another comet.

But the next decade was a difficult one for Messier. The French Revolution saddened and frightened him during the last years of his search. With his social peers literally losing their heads, the gentleman astronomer feared for his own safety. Forced to leave the observatory in Paris, he continued his work in a quieter location. On the evening of September 27, 1793, Messier found a comet in Ophiuchus, and like so many times before, he informed his friend de Saron, who attempted to calculate an orbit using the positions Messier supplied. Although this comet was independently discovered by Caroline Herschel, a comet hunter from England, it was visible for only a few nights before it sank into the evening twilight.

However de Saron was no longer president of the Paris parliament. Accused of being an enemy of reform, he was in prison and awaiting execution by that creature of the Revolution, Madame

Guillotine. It is hard to imagine that de Saron could have cared about comet orbits when he was about to lose his head, but he did manage to calculate an orbit for Messier's comet from his prison cell. If de Saron's orbit was correct, the comet would come closer to the sun, then move away, and reappear in the morning sky.

On December 29 Messier searched the morning sky and found his comet close to the position de Saron had predicted. Messier wrote of de Saron's last success and hid his note in a newspaper that he was able to smuggle to the prisoner. On April 20, just 3 months before the end of Robespierre's Reign of Terror, de Saron was guillotined.

Although Messier survived the revolution and the Reign of Terror that followed it, his pension, which de Saron had arranged for him after his accident, was gone, and the acclaimed astronomer was virtually penniless. Messier did find another comet in 1798. There is a well-known but unverified story from his Russian friend, La Harpe, that Messier found out about a discovery by Montaigne while mourning his wife's death. A friend embraced the grief-stricken man to say, "I am so sorry." Messier glared at his visitor. "Alas," he said, "Montaigne has robbed me of my comet!" Quickly realizing his error, Messier tried to recover. "Poor woman," he muttered. No doubt his friend agreed.[2]

COMET MASQUERADERS

As the first serious comet hunter, Messier learned about the sand traps of the sport in time to warn the rest of us. Fuzzy objects that are not comets lurk all over the sky, waiting to snare naive observers. Peltier called them comet masqueraders. In fact, according to Daniel Green of the CBAT, approximately 98 percent of comet discovery reports from new observers turn out to be spurious. Most of these ecstatically reported sightings turn out to be galaxies, star clusters, or clouds of gas called nebulae. At the end of 1758, when Messier found a fuzzy patch near the star Beta Tauri that never moved, he began to catalog these deceivers.

The first entry in his catalog, now called Messier 1 or M1, is more popularly known as the Crab Nebula because it resembles a ghostly version of the sea animal. Although Messier never realized it, Messier 1 was probably the most interesting thing ever to cast light into his telescope. It is the remnant of the supernova, a near-total destruction of a star, observed on July 4, 1054, to be as bright as Venus. A pre-Columbian petroglyph in northern New Mexico depicting a star near a crescent moon may be a record of this stellar catastrophe. In only 700 years, the explosion has produced a huge expanding shell of gas bright enough that Messier could easily see it. In 1969 observers using a 36-inch diameter telescope at Steward Observatory in Arizona found an object at its center, a pulsar that spins 30 times per second.

Besides the supernova remnant, Messier's catalog includes the best and brightest of the northern hemisphere sky's interesting fuzzies. Some of these Messier discovered; others he merely listed. Observing all of them has become the goal of many amateur astronomers. In 1962 I began my own Messier hunt with a single observation of the Pleiades, M45. (Why Messier included this big, bright cluster, which does not look at all like a comet, is a bit of a mystery.) In spring 1967, using a larger telescope than I had in 1962, I finished my list while observing from my grandfather's cottage at Jarnac Pond, Quebec.

Messier published three versions of his catalog. The first 45 objects appeared in 1774, and by 1781, his list had grown to 103. Besides the roster that Messier created, other objects he recorded but never listed were later added, so that now the Messier catalog includes 110 objects spread over much of the sky.

LE GRAND CHERCHEUR

Messier discovered his last comet on July 12, 1801. However a 40-year-old janitor beat him to it, finding the comet near the Big Dipper a day earlier and receiving full credit for the find. This little comet was the first of 26 comets that now bear the name of Jean-Louis Pons.

Actually Pons had more than 26 comet discoveries, and perhaps as many as 37.[3] Born in 1761, Pons didn't become interested in the sky until 1789, when the observatory at Marseilles, France, hired him as a doorkeeper to keep watch on the grounds. He did, and kept watch on the heavens as well.

Pons was justifiably proud of le grand chercheur—his favorite searching telescope. With a 3-degree field of view (six full-moon diameters), he could cover broad swaths of sky at once. Pons found a second comet in 1802, one in 1804, and another in 1806. While hunting with this telescope just before dawn on February 9, 1808, Pons saw a comet very close to the globular cluster Messier 12. However, Pons typically kept rather poor records of his observations. In a field crowded with stars, the only three objects he drew were the comet, Messier 12, and the nearby globular cluster Messier 10. Since no one else was able to observe this object, no orbit was ever calculated for it, and for some 180 years, the comet remained unconfirmed. Not long ago Pons's 1808 comet was revealed to be an early passage of Periodic Comet Grigg–Skjellerup, a faint comet that returns every 5 years, so this ancient story is now complete.

Despite his growing record of comet finds, Pons was rather slow to gain the respect of his peers, possibly because his rural upbringing made him appear unsophisticated. According to a story told years later by the astronomer Augustus De Morgan, after Pons had gone some time without finding anything, he asked the director of the Seeberg Observatory, Baron von Zach, for a hint on how his comet sweeping could be more productive. Search when there are lots of sunspots on the sun, the German astronomer suggested as a practical joke. Half-expecting that Pons would make a fool of himself and redesign his program to search the night sky when the sun sported large spots, von Zach was very surprised to get a letter from Pons with profuse thanks. Large spots indeed formed on the sun, and soon afterward he dutifully found a new comet.[4] To this day no correlation between comets and sunspots has been found.

In 1811 Pons discovered a comet destined to be one of the best and brightest in history, however he found it 3 weeks after the French observer Honoré Flaugergues. The comet quickly brightened until it could be seen without a telescope, and it remained visible to the naked eye for 10 months. Its appearance was even credited with the coincidentally ultrafine wines that year. In October 1816 the English poet John Keats wrote of the thrill of reading a new work of literature:

> *Then felt I like some watcher of the skies*
> *When a new planet swims into his ken;*
> *Or like stout Cortez when with eagle eyes*
> *He star'd at the Pacific—*[5]

Most critics assume that Keats was recalling Herschel's discovery of the planet Uranus in 1781, an event that occurred 14 years before he was born. I suspect the line harks back to the discovery by Pons and others of the magnificent comet of 1811, which appeared only 3 years before he wrote the sonnet.

In 1813 with growing success as a comet hunter, Pons was promoted from doorkeeper to assistant astronomer, and in 1817, he became director of an Italian observatory near the town of Lucca, not far from Florence, a site from which he discovered seven more comets. In the twilight of his career, Pons became director of Florence's Observatory and Museum for Physics, where he spied another seven comets. He found his last comet in August 1827, and he died 4 years later. Only one person, Carolyn Shoemaker, has beaten Pons's record of 26 named comets.

In 1831 Denmark's Frederick VI added some spice to the comet-hunting game by striking a gold medal for each discoverer of a comet. It was the first of several comet-finding medals given in different countries and times, and it is this medal that gave rise to the tradition of naming comets after their first discoverers. To take up the slack left when this award ended in 1848, the Vienna Academy of Sciences honored each comet finder with a prize; this award lasted another 30 years. The most lucrative of all the comet prizes was given by H. H. Warner to any U.S. discoverer of a comet and helped spur a golden age of hunting during the late nineteenth century.

THE COMET PENDULUM SWINGS WEST

By the middle years of the nineteenth century, the bulk of comet discoveries had moved across the Atlantic Ocean, where Lewis Swift and Horace Tuttle were competing for new comets.

By the 1880s a new generation, led by William R. Brooks and Edward Emerson Barnard, had taken over. With formidable career totals of 22 and 16 named comets, respectively, these hunters found their first comets within a month of each other and were keen competitors.

Born in Scotland, William Brooks moved with his family to New York in 1857, settling upstate in Phelps, where he became a photographer. Brooks made the 9.25-inch reflecting telescope with which he searched. Watching the dazzlingly bright Donati's comet as it made its way past Earth in 1858 had a deep impact on the young man, although it wasn't felt right away.

In the 1870s he started to build his own telescopes. With a 5-inch reflector, he independently discovered Comet 1881 V in October 1881, not long after the British comet hunter William Denning first spotted it.[6] A new periodic comet, 1881 V, faded rapidly after discovery, and it was not seen at its predicted return in 1890. However in October 1978, the Japanese comet hunter Shigehisa Fujikawa rediscovered the comet, and it was renamed Denning–Fujikawa. Again the comet was not seen on its next return in 1987.

Edward Emerson Barnard was born in Nashville, Tennessee, in 1857. He got an early start in optics: When he was less than 10 years old, he took a job as a photographer's assistant after leaving school with but 2 months formal education. Reading Alexander Ewing's *Practical Astronomy* in 1876 ignited his interest in the heavens.[7] With his first telescope, his main love became Jupiter. His intimate knowledge with the giant planet paid off when years later as an astronomer at Lick Observatory, he discovered Jupiter's fifth moon Amalthea, the first Jovian moon spotted since Galileo's discoveries in 1610. Less than a month before Brooks found his first comet, Barnard found his on September 17, 1881.

There is no question that the Warner prize propelled the competition for new comets during this period, for Barnard so much as admitted it: "I had been searching for comets for upward of a year with no success," he writes,

> when a prize of two hundred dollars for the discovery of each new comet was offered by the founder of the Warner Observatory through the agency of Dr. Lewis Swift, its Director. Soon after this it happened that I found a new comet, and was awarded the prize. Then came the question, "What shall I do with the money?" After due deliberation it was decided that we would try to get a home of our own therewith. I had always longed for such a home, where one could plant trees and watch them grow up and call them our own. So we bought a lot with part of the money, which was on rising ground selected in part because it gave me a clear horizon with my telescope.
>
> After some saving and mainly a mortgage on the lot, we built a little frame cottage where my mother, my wife and I went to live. Those were happy days, though the struggle for a livelihood was a hard one, working from early to late, and sitting up the rest of the twenty-four hours hunting for comets. We looked forward with dread to the meeting of the bills which must come due. However, when this happened, a faint comet was discovered, and the money went to meet the payments. The faithful comet, like the goose that laid the golden egg, conveniently timed its appearance to coincide with the advent of those dreaded notes. And thus it finally came about the house was built entirely of comets. This fact goes to prove the great error of those scientific men who figure out that a comet is but a flimsy affair after all, infinitely more rare than the breath of the morning air, for here was a strong compact house, albeit a small one, built entirely of them. True, it took several good-sized comets to do it, but it was done, nevertheless.[8]

Combining the best of a new marriage and new comets, Barnard's playful words capture the enthusiasm with which he followed his mission. When I first read them, I began to look for some small connection to my own program. At the time I had zero comets, so I really had to pull at straws. Moreover his house was under a dark country sky; mine was in a big city. Finally I learned that his house was on Belmont Street in Nashville, and I lived on Upper Belmont Avenue in Montreal. There!

A DECADE FOR COMETS

Barnard had something else going for him. The decade of the 1880s brought one of the most glorious series of bright comets to parade through the inner part of the solar system. The onslaught of comet after major comet must have spurred on Barnard and his competitors to greater glories. Compared especially to the relatively paltry crop we have had in recent years, the procession was truly splendid. It began in 1880 when a large comet dominated the southern sky constellations of Tucana, Grus, and Phoenix; its tail grew to 40 degrees in length to cover a quarter of the visible sky. On May 22 of the following year, the Australian comet hunter John Tebbutt discovered a comet that brightened to naked-eye visibility and dominated the night sky for 2 months.

By the following May, the first great comet of 1882 was a bright naked-eye object, brighter than Jupiter and visible in a twilight sky. Four short months later, the great September comet brightened to magnitude minus 14—much brighter than the full moon—as it reached perihelion in a hairpin dance around the sun. David Gill, director of South Africa's Cape Observatory, described the sight of the comet's rising:

> There was not a cloud in the sky, only a merging into a rich yellow that fringed the blackish blue of the distant mountains, and over the mountains and amongst the yellow an ill-defined mass of golden glory rose with a beauty I cannot describe.

> The sun rose a few minutes afterwards, but to my intense
> surprise the comet seemed in no way dimmed in brightness,
> but becoming instead whiter and sharper in form as it rose
> above the mists of the horizon.[9]

The excitement this comet generated was so intense that when
Barnard went to sleep early in the morning of October 14, he dreamt
about comets—lots of them, comets all over the place. The story
was so real to him that when he awoke some hours later, it took
a few minutes before he realized it was all a dream.

Or was it? The sky was still dark, still clear, and with the
mighty comet just rising in the east, Barnard rushed outside to his
waiting telescope. Turning it to the comet, he studied its marvelous
structure before beginning a scan for new comets. Moving his telescope to the southwest, he didn't have far to go—perhaps 5 or 6
degrees—before he found a group of a half-dozen small comets.
Flabbergasted, Barnard wondered whether he had fallen asleep
on his feet and had resumed his dream. The comets were real—
the observation was confirmed the following night by observers
in Europe. But although the little comets were traveling at the same
rate and direction as the main body, they all disappeared in less
than a day.

Brooks did well with the great comet, too. A week after Barnard's find, on October 21 he found a companion comet several
degrees northeast of the comet. Brooks's object also vanished. Although the main comet broke into several pieces at perihelion—a
comet's most vulnerable time—on September 17, these pieces
stayed within the coma of the main object. The origin of these
objects viewed by Barnard and Brooks is a mystery; they could not
have split off the main comet at perihelion and moved so far from
it in such a short time.

A parade of sun comets that hit the sun a century later may
offer a clue to this mystery. In the 1980s the Solwind and Solar
Maximum Mission satellites discovered what appeared to be comets
that hit the sun. Some of these came in groups, notes Marsden,
one pair only 12 days apart. Speculating that it is possible that the
Barnard and Brooks comets split off from the main comet when it

last rounded the sun, Marsden suggests that they might have rounded the sun unseen in September 1882 and then flared for a few hours, long enough to be seen by these comet sleuths.

Since the next big comet would not appear for 3 years, Brooks, Barnard, and their fellow searchers had a little break. The comet that came along at the end of 1885 reached second magnitude—about the brightness of the North Star—and was followed by a fainter comet that Barnard found a year later. Brooks had a banner year in 1886: In a remarkable 4-week period, he discovered three comets, one on April 27, another May 1, and a third on May 22.

Brooks's triple success was followed by a Barnard threesome—he discovered comets on October 4, 1886, and on February 16 and May 12, 1887. But it was a farmer near Cape Town who walked away with 1887 I, by far the brightest comet in those 2 years. Already visible to the naked eye, as it grew brighter it developed, as one observer noted, a brilliant silver white tail stretching a quarter of the way around the sky. Moreover in 1888 another bright comet came by. Finally as a close to this prolific decade, Barnard found a comet early in 1888 that did not reach perihelion until a year later. Cruising slowly around the sun, this comet was visible for almost a thousand days.

THE HOAX OF THE COMET-SEEKER TELESCOPE

With increasing success and fame, Barnard made the transition from amateur to professional by taking a position at Lick Observatory near San Francisco in 1888. By now he had found so many comets that a competitor, disgusted after losing comet after comet to Barnard, asked him why he couldn't keep them on a leash. Barnard might have felt the same way about reporters when on March 8, 1891, he saw this astonishing headline in the San Francisco *Examiner*'s human interest section:

ALMOST HUMAN INTELLECT

An Astronomical Machine That Discovers Comets All By Itself
The Meteor Gets in Range, Electricity Does the Rest.

As Barnard read on, appalled, he learned about his own fictitious invention of a telescope that would search the sky by itself. It was a hoax, and whoever wrote the piece must have known what he or she was doing. It described how comet seeking is a difficult and time-consuming activity and how wonderfully easy this new machine would make it. On paper at least, the procedure was simple. The device would examine the spectrum of everything as Barnard slept—an unlikely act for him on a clear night. "Stars, nebulae and clusters innumerable crowd into the field [of view of the telescope] with every advance of the clock," the article went on, "but the telescope gives no sign of their presence. . . ." But should any object showing the "three bright hydrocarbon bands" of comet light appear, the device as described by the paper would allow that light to pass through and hit a selenium band, closing a circuit, and setting off an alarm in Barnard's bedroom. The sleepy astronomer would rush upstairs to the telescope, make a simple visual confirmation of the new comet, report it, and return to bed.[10] The clever idea of a selenium band being sensitive to light had been known for some 2 decades, and the public was becoming increasingly aware of its properties.[11]

Barnard became apoplectic. He wrote letter after angry letter, but somehow the *Examiner* had been warned that the reclusive scientist would doubtlessly deny everything, and the paper refused to print them. Although comet hunter Lewis Swift had his doubts that such a device would work, even he wrote to Barnard asking for all the details: "It takes my breath away," he gushed, "and makes my hair stand straight towards the zenith to think of it. Although the article appears somewhat fishy," he went on, "I am inclined to think it is still another of the marvelous inventions of the 19th century."[12]

Almost 2 years passed before Barnard was able to assure the *Examiner* that it—and he—had been had. Finally convinced, the paper apologized on February 5, 1893:

> The *Examiner* seizes the opportunity to express contrition for the annoyance which it caused this eminent scientist by printing some time ago an account of a highly ingenious, but non-

existent, machine for scanning the skies and catching wandering comets on the photographic plate.

At the end of the apology, the paper bequeathed him "all the new moons and comets that may be necessary to his happiness."[13] That same day, the paper ran an article on "How to Find Comets"—an authentic one this time, by Barnard himself.

Barnard never quite got over this hoax. As Heber Curtis, an astronomer and friend of Barnard's, wrote years later, "Even as he told me the story, ten years after the event, he was able to summon only a rather wan and rueful smile."[14] Nor was Barnard ever fully certain who perpetrated the hoax, although the *Examiner* admitted that Charles Hill, who had worked at the Lick Observatory in 1889, had something to do with it. The lack of any great effort by Lick Observatory to support Barnard in his denials led Barnard to believe that one of the senior staff members was behind the hoax. "Well, I never was sure," he told Curtis, "but I have always suspected Keeler."[15] Spectroscopist James Edward Keeler, according to Curtis, "was always ready to laugh at other astronomers, or at himself, if need be."[16]

Why would Keeler, who only 4 years later cofounded the prestigious *Astrophysical Journal*, do such an irresponsible thing and then let Barnard wallow in it for 2 years? One guess comes from John Lankford, who in 1978 wrote in *Sky and Telescope* that Keeler did it as a joke to shore up morale at Lick Observatory. Having worked in observatory environments, I certainly agree that something in the air—the altitude, long nights in a cold dome, or long years with the same few people—eventually creates so much tension that astronomers are at each other's throats. The atmosphere was poisoned at Lick at the end of 1890, with astronomers barely on speaking terms with one another.[17] Barnard himself left in 1895, when he was offered a position at Yerkes Observatory in Williams Bay, Wisconsin, where he stayed until the end of his life.

Curtis himself began his account with this delightful verse from Kipling:

> *The Doorkeepers of Zion,*
>   *They do not always stand*
> *In helmet and whole armour,*
>   *With halberds in their hand;*
> *But, being sure of Zion,*
>   *And all her mysteries,*
> *They rest awhile in Zion,*
> *Sit down and smile in Zion,*
> *Ay, even zest in Zion;*
>   *In Zion, at their ease.*[18]

Curtis didn't add that Kipling's humor grew out of a warning that appears in *Amos* 6:1: "Woe to them that are at ease in Zion." For while the hoaxers were at ease, Barnard put on his armour and unintentionally got the better of them. Eighteen months after the prank, in 1892, Barnard actually did discover a comet in a completely new way. Instead of using his eyes, he used the emulsion of a photographic plate attached to a telescope. On the plate, he found Periodic Comet Barnard 3 (1892 V) near the bright star Altair. Because the exposure was a long one, the moving comet appeared as a fuzzy trail extending from southwest to northeast. A second picture taken of the same area confirmed that the object was really a comet, and not a defect on the plate and that it was moving toward the northeast. It turned out to be the last of Barnard's 17 discoveries, but it started a whole new era of comet searching that continues to this day.

❦ 6 ❧

A Different Drummer

If one advances confidently in the direction of his dreams, and endeavors to live the life he has imagined, then he will meet with a success unexpected in common hours.

If a man does not keep pace with his companions, perhaps it is because he hears a different drummer. Let him step to the music which he hears, however measured and far away.

Henry David Thoreau[1]

*L*ike everyone else, comet hunters are a disparate group of people with diverse jobs and life-styles, but they never veer far from the direction of their dreams, a lonely patch of haze secretly lurking in the sky. The beat to which comet hunters keep pace is set by the moon, whose eastward march defines the dark hours for hunting. Because they hunt for a variety of reasons, some scientists have scorned their work; in 1930 for example, Harvard College Observatory Director Harlow Shapley praised and insulted Messier in a single sentence: "He is remembered for his catalogue; forgotten as the applause-seeking discoverer of comets."[2] And then only 4 years later, Shapley lauded comet hunter Leslie Peltier as "the world's greatest nonprofessional astronomer."[3]

THE PENDULUM SWINGS SOUTH

For most of us, Shapley is wrong about Messier. If comet hunters really seek applause for their play, they can wait years between acts. To find lots of comets takes a lifetime of work and dedication; to find more than one really bright comet takes luck. For all his skill, the Australian comet hunter John Tebbutt was incredibly lucky to find two comets—in 1861 and 1881—whose long tails would dominate the sky.

When Tebbutt discovered the great comet of 1861 from Windsor, New South Wales, on May 13, 1861—the one that made such a sudden grand entrance in the sky over England—it was a faint fuzzy spot, barely visible to the naked eye, and more than 6 weeks away from its best performance. Moreover since there was no reliable rapid communication south to north, the northern hemisphere was quite unaware that a bright comet was on its way. At the end of June, the huge comet's head was in the northern sky near the bright star Capella while its tail stretched more than halfway across the heavens to the constellation of Hercules. Apparently the spectacle became even better than that, for the Earth went right through the outer reaches of the comet's tail on the night of June 30.

Unlike many of today's comet hunters, Tebbutt made a point of observing comets as well as discovering them. In fact after discovering the comet of 1861, he calculated its first preliminary orbit. Since he kept careful journals of all his observations, we are able to read about this remarkable observation:

> In the evening of June 30 I observed a peculiar whitish light throughout the sky, but more particularly along the eastern horizon. This could not have proceeded from the moon, but was probably caused by the diffused light of the comet's tail, which we are very near to just now.[4]

By 1863 Tebbutt had completed his own small observatory by himself, a structure that would last for many years and include a transit instrument for accurately measuring the positions of comets. From his new observatory, he independently discovered Tempel's comet around the same time that Tuttle and Hopkins were observing it from opposite shores in August 1864.

In 1881 Tebbutt found a second great comet. On the evening of May 22, without a telescope, Tebbutt spotted a faint fuzzy object in the constellation of Columba the dove. "Immediately on its discovery I obtained," he wrote, "with the 4.5-in. equatorial, eight good measures of the nucleus from one of the bright stars just mentioned. On the following day I notified the discovery to the Government Observatories of Sydney and Melbourne."[5] By the end of June, the comet had brightened to first magnitude. Considering how few observers were in the southern hemisphere in the nineteenth century, Tebbutt did a big favor to history by making his comet observations as complete as possible. When he retired from active work in 1904, he had completed exactly 50 years of comet observations.

THE PENDULUM SWINGS EAST

Despite the poor weather in England, William F. Denning was another great comet hunter who managed to compete successfully on the comet playing field. His greatest contribution however came in observing meteors. Denning was passionately involved with observing these pieces of space rubble that are the remnants of passing comets. Sitting in an eastward-facing chair on warm nights, standing up and moving to keep warm on cold nights, he recorded more than 9000 meteor trails over a 17-year period, coming from no fewer than 918 different points in the sky, called radiants. Because of the effect of perspective, each meteor shower has its own radiant. Although many of Denning's radiants are no longer recognized, his sheer volume of observational work is astounding. His observations showed, for example, that the Perseid radiant moved from night to night as its aspect with relation to the Earth changed.

On the morning of July 11, 1881, Denning planned to hunt for comets in the pentagon-shaped figure of Auriga, which was just rising in the northeast before dawn. But morning observing can be quite a challenge for tired eyes, and he decided to forego his sweep. On July 14, from Ann Arbor, Michigan, John Schaeberle did hunt through the pentagon and picked up a bright sixth-magnitude comet there. Comet Schaeberle 1881 IV was a tough blow for Denning, for it grew a long tail and brightened to third magnitude—easily visible to the unaided eye—by the end of August. Even under normal conditions, a fairly bright comet in the north circumpolar summer sky would have really been a special treat. But Tebbutt's major discovery, the now-fading great comet of 1881, was only 8 degrees from the pole at the end of July, and for a few weeks, two naked-eye comets were in the same part of the sky at the same time.

Denning had a chance to recover from his disappointment only 3 months later when he did not pass up a chance to sweep the morning sky in Leo on October 4 and found the periodic comet now known as Denning–Fujikawa. (Under today's rules, Brooks would have his name attached to the comet as well, as its third independent discoverer, but at the time, the honor of having your name attached to a comet belonged to only the first one to find it.) Two weeks later Denning suggested that English observers could easily join the

> friendly competition with foreigners. . . . We might act in unison, and arrange a division of labour. Certain regions could be apportioned to different observers; in any case it is very desirable to adopt some method likely to command the interest and labour of observers, and to give a fair measure of success.[6]

The idea of having comet hunters join in a group and divide the sky is good in theory but has rarely succeeded in practice. Different locations have different weather patterns, and the only procedure that has really worked is to have comet hunters sweep the sky from several locations. Moreover comet hunters by nature bridle at the thought of restrictions: They will search through as much sky as possible on a dark, clear night.

At the turn of the century, William Reid, another British amateur astronomer, moved to South Africa, where he discovered Comet Reid 1918 II in June 1918. Within the next 8 years, he found an additional seven comets. Not only did Reid dislike calling attention to himself, but he was also notably generous toward his fellow comet hunters. As a story goes, he once found a comet (probably 1926 III), but before he reported it, he heard that G. E. Ensor, an acquaintance, had independently picked it up as well. Realizing that his competitor had never discovered a comet and feeling that he had enough comets to his credit already, Reid declined to report it himself. Thus the comet Reid is known as Comet Ensor 1926 III.

This comet disappeared for a few weeks as it approached perihelion, and it was too close to the sun to be seen. But only 11 days after the comet rounded the sun, a group of Russians floated into the sky beneath a tethered hot-air balloon. As the balloon climbed past 2000 feet, S. M. Selivanov, a member of the Mirovedenie Society that sponsored the event, spotted the comet through a pair of binoculars.[7]

BACK TO THE STATES

In the United States, three promising comet seekers made their first finds in the first decade of the twentieth century; one was Zaccheus Daniel, who used a 6-inch diameter refractor from the Princeton University Observatory to discover three comets, one of which (Comet Daniel 1907 IV) reached second magnitude and had an easily visible tail. Joel Metcalf of South Hero, Vermont, discovered comets in 1910, 1913, and two in 1919. The third comet seeker was John E. Mellish, a telescope maker who observed from Madison, Wisconsin. He found two comets in 1907 and two more in 1915. But then the story takes a different direction. In 1915 Mellish responded to an ad that Jessie Wood, of Glencoe, Illinois, placed in Chicago newspapers:

> Wanted—a perfect husband, one who wants that happiness
> not of a day, but of a lifetime; who would receive the fullest
> pleasure in staying home at night talking to me and would
> be just as wrapped up in me as in his work.

Out of some 2000 young men who responded to the ad, Jessie chose Mellish, and they were married that year. One wonders if she were expecting someone who would want to stay up all night searching the sky for comets. In 1917 Mellish found a fifth comet, in 1923 he bagged a sixth, and in 1932 he was in Geneva County jail. Apparently he hadn't turned out to be the perfect husband. His wife left him and accused him of chasing after a 15-year-old girl. Although he admitted to the charge, he entered a plea of not guilty. According to a 1932 newspaper article,

> Prosecutor Carbary and Circuit Judge John K. Newhall, under
> whose jurisdiction Mellish is, admitted today they were in a
> quandary over disposition of the case. They said a dozen letters
> from scientists of seven universities had appealed for mercy.

This episode marked the only interruption in a career that was devoted first to comets and later to telescope making. Mellish then moved to California, where he resumed his career and made telescopes almost until his death in 1970.

WALDEN OF THE SKY

Two years after Mellish's last comet discovery in 1923, on a farm near the small town of Delphos, Ohio, Leslie Peltier, born on January 2, 1900, made his first discovery. Peltier's interest in astronomy was sired by sightings of two major comets in 1910, the Great January Comet, and Halley's, but the real spark came on a May evening in 1915: "Something—perhaps a meteor—caused me to look up for a moment. Then, literally out of that clear sky, I suddenly asked myself, 'Why do I not know a single one of those stars?' "[8]

To raise the 18 dollars needed to buy his first telescope, Peltier picked 900 quarts of strawberries on the family farm at 2 cents a quart. Three years later, he started observing stars whose brightnesses change with time and sometimes unpredictably. He was thrilled with the antics of these variable stars. On March 1, 1918 he made the first of what would become a lifetime total of 132,000 variable-star observations.

As Peltier's reputation as a skilled observer spread, he was offered the use of a 6-inch refracting telescope by Henry Norris Russell of the Princeton Observatory. Peltier learned that Zaccheus Daniel had used this telescope to discover three comets, including the impressive naked-eye one in 1907. Knowing that his new telescope was a proven comet finder gave Peltier a connection to a tradition. "It seemed to me," Peltier wrote, "that if ever human attributes would be invested in a thing of metal, wood, and glass, then this ancient instrument now in my keeping must long for one more chance to show what it could do."[9]

It was 3 years before Peltier tasted success in his comet searching. Starting at the horizon, he described the search through his opened observatory dome:

> I slowly worked upward back and forth in horizontal sweeps across that bounded bit of sky. Sweep by sweep I climbed upward through Corona, pausing ever so briefly as I hailed, in passing, the patterned landmark of the R Coronae field, and on I moved into the northern end of Boötes.

> It was just above the peak of that kite-shaped figure of the Herdsman that the steady cross-sweep of my telescope abruptly stopped. A small, round, fuzzy something was in the center of that sea of stars! A closer, calmer look and I was sure just what that something was, for extending downward from it I could dimly see a slender streak that could only be the tail of the comet I had just discovered![10]

The comet was moving so rapidly southward that initial attempts to confirm it were unsuccessful. But A. Wilk, a high school teacher in Krakow, Poland, independently discovered the comet, and thus it was saved. On December 20, 1929 Wilk found his second comet and his third just 3 months later. In 1937 Wilk and Peltier discovered their second comet together, but the comet was announced in Europe as Comet Wilk before Peltier could report it. This was Wilk's final comet discovery. The Nazis incarcerated him along with other teachers and university professors during the war. After heavy international protests, some of the prisoners, including Wilk, were released. But it was too late for the comet hunter, who died shortly after.

FROM FLYING SANDBANKS TO DIRTY SNOWBALLS

By midcentury, astronomy's understanding of the nature of comets was about to take its biggest leap since Halley's breakthrough more than two centuries earlier. As a graduate student at the University of California at Berkeley in 1930, Fred Lawrence Whipple was part of a team that calculated a rough orbit of the newly discovered planet Pluto. By the end of World War II, Whipple, who was now at Harvard, noticed that the orbits of meteors, which are very much like those of comets, were slowing down, and that the meteors should have all fallen to the sun. Something was replenishing the solar system's supply of meteors. Comets were then thought to be huge flying sandbanks. Whipple decided that the sandbank model could not provide a current source for the meteors; instead he proposed that comets were large conglomerates of ices and meteoric particles, now popularly known as dirty snowballs.[11] By September 1951 Fred Whipple had published the results of his work on the orbit of Encke's comet in two of the most important papers in the history of comet science.[12] After four decades of observations, Whipple's comet model was about to be dramatically confirmed when the European *Giotto* spacecraft passed by the nucleus of Halley's comet in March 1986. "Well, Fred," project scientist Rüdeger Reinhard declared, "tomorrow is your moment of truth."

"Yes," the 79-year-old Whipple said. "Things are going to get truthier and truthier."[13] *Giotto* sent back beautiful pictures of a potato-shaped comet nucleus that reaffirmed Whipple's grand reputation as Mr. Comet.

GREAT COMET OF THE SIXTIES

By 1945 comet hunting had become worldwide again. A team of Czechoslovakian observers, including Antonin Mrkos and Ludmilla Pajdusakova, using large 25 × 100 binoculars, found the first of 16 comets at the astonishing rate of 100 searching hours per discovery—about half of what most other observers typically spend.

On August 2, 1957 Mrkos saw the tail of a bright comet rising, and the new surprise visitor was quickly announced as Comet Mrkos. A short time later, Walter Scott Houston, a *Sky and Telescope* columnist, was enjoying his pipe after dinner when Clifford Simpson asked why he had not pointed out a bright comet in the west. Assuming that Simpson was speaking of Comet Arend–Roland, which had been bright some weeks before, Houston, not missing a puff, said that there was no comet. "But there is a comet there!" Simpson protested. Finally Houston gave in, looked up and saw one of the brightest comets of his life. He darted to his telescope, yanked it with one hand, focused it with the other, stashed the lit pipe in his pocket, and observed Comet Mrkos.

"Scotty, you're on fire!" Simpson hollered. Ripping off his burning jacket and throwing it on the grass, Houston was about to return to his telescope when the grass also caught fire. Finally they smothered the flames just in time to lose the comet behind a tree.

By the mid-1950s, Minoru Honda was finding comets from Japan. His record of a dozen comets inspired a generation of Japanese comet hunters, of which the best known were Kaoru Ikeya and Tsutomu Seki.

I first heard about Ikeya when he discovered his first comet early in 1963. Ikeya had felt that his family's name had been dishonored because of his father's business failure and subsequent drinking problem. Leaving school to take a job at a piano factory, Ikeya built an 8-inch telescope for the equivalent of 20 US dollars, and in 1961, he began regular comet searches. Although New Year's Eve 1963 was clear, his family asked him not to search that night and instead to celebrate the holiday. But just before dawn on the following night, Ikeya found a comet in Hydra. Brightening rapidly as it approached the sun, the comet reached third magnitude by March 21. With a comet named after him, Ikeya believed that his family's name had been rehabilitated throughout Japan. And a year later he found a second comet.

Tsutomu Seki, a guitar instructor, was also building a noble record of discoveries by 1965, including a comet that reached naked-eye brightness in 1962. Seki's 1962 find was awaiting confirmation when Richard and Helen Lines, a couple observing near Phoenix, Arizona, also snatched it.

On September 18, 1965, Ikeya was again sweeping in the southern constellation of Hydra when he found an eighth-magnitude comet. Creeping southeastward, the comet was an exciting find for Ikeya, who was now bagging them at the comfortable rate of one per year. But Seki was comet hunting that morning too, and 15 minutes later, he found the same object. Thus confirmed, Comet Ikeya–Seki 1965f was announced to the world by Owen Gingerich, then director of the Central Bureau for Astronomical Telegrams.

This comet's motion was not immediately obvious; in fact the first orbit, issued on September 28 and based on just 2 days of observations, had the comet making a leisurely pass around the sun at slightly less than the distance of the Earth.[14] But with new, accurate positions, in the last week of September Fred Whipple recognized that Comet Ikeya–Seki was extraordinary: "The following parabolic orbit," the International Astronomical Union *Circular* announced, "shows a close resemblance to that of the Great sun-grazing Comet of 1882 and its family. According to B. G.

Marsden, Comet Ikeya–Seki may be as bright as −7 [much brighter than Venus] at perihelion."[15] The comet of 1882, discussed earlier, did a hairpin turn around the sun. At eighth magnitude a month before perihelion, Ikeya- Seki was coming around at the same time of year as the 1882 comet; the Earth was in its most favorable position for a near repeat of the fabled show.

But time was running out. With 3 weeks until perihelion, there was barely enough time to inform everyone that something really big was coming in. To speed things up, on October 1 Gingerich and Marsden, who had just finished his thesis at Yale and was in his third day of work at the Smithsonian Astrophysical Observatory at Harvard, held a press conference to announce that a probable great comet was on its way. Circulars were released frequently with updated orbital elements and visual magnitudes showing that the comet was brightening just as was expected.

Sun-grazing comets are exceptional because they whip around the sun at less than a million miles from its fiery surface. First studied in detail as a single group with a possible common origin by Heinrich Kreutz in 1888, these comets share a similar orbit. Their grandeur depends on the time of year they round the sun. Comet Pereyra, at perihelion in 1963, was bright but far from spectacular. Both the 1882 and the 1965 comets rounded the sun not far from the September equinox, squeaking past the sun at less than 300,000 miles and putting on splendid shows. According to Marsden, these two comets almost certainly last brushed the sun as a single object, perhaps the great comet of 1106.[16]

As the comet approached its October 21 date with the sun, everyone with the slightest sense about the sky was excited. Would the comet immolate itself as it tried to touch the solar surface? Hoping to get a view before perihelion, I set my alarm for predawn every morning, but clouds always blocked the sky. With 3 days to go, Sunday morning, October 17, was clear. I biked a couple of miles from my Montreal home to Summit Park, a site with a good view to the east, which I thought would be the best place. So did a hundred other people: at 5:00 A.M. the park was jammed. But although most of the sky was clear, clouds low in the southeast prevented us from seeing the comet.

Perihelion day was October 21, 1965. From the clear locations in the southwestern United States, the comet was clearly visible to the naked eye at magnitude minus 8, virtually the brightness of a quarter moon. By the twenty-fourth the comet, now visible in a dark sky, had a 20-degree tail.[17] But in eastern Canada, I was still waiting for a clear morning. When I awoke on Friday, October 29, the clear sky outside my window sent a chill through me. I dashed downstairs and hopped on my bike, racing toward Summit Park in time to beat the dawn. Completely out of breath, I reached the Summit lookout and stopped. The view that morning was splendid. Beyond the expanse of the city lights, beyond the distant St. Lawrence River, a mighty searchlight beam rose out of the southeast like an exclamation mark. The crowd from the week before was gone; it was just me, the sky, and my first view of a comet.

Two mornings later and across the world, Bart Bok, director of Australia's Mount Stromlo Observatory, awoke from his sleep. His attention was sparked by what he, like me, thought was a bright searchlight beam dominating the eastern sky. Astonished by the sight, he quickly grasped the opportunity to show the public this majestic apparition. Within the next few hours, the media all over Australia had published Bok's account of the comet, and on the morning of November 1, thousands of Australians arose to see it.[18]

By November 6, several observers reported that the nucleus had split into at least two parts. Later it was predicted that the larger one would possibly return in 8 centuries, the smaller one 3 centuries later.[19]

STARLIGHT NIGHTS

If this wonderful comet was not enough to excite my interest, Peltier's autobiography *Starlight Nights* appeared the same year. The book was a sky gazer's *Walden,* clearly a call for comet hunters.

A decade later, I visited Peltier. In a conversation about comets, variable stars, and politics, he was as vibrant as he had been in his writing. He had found his twelfth comet in 1954, and since a large 12-inch refractor had come his way, he had devoted much of the rest of his observing life to variable stars. "I don't think amateurs have it so easy any more in comet hunting," he said. "Professional photographic searches make it quite difficult for an amateur to come in first." Should we give up then? I asked about today's searchers. "Of course not. You just have to try harder."

During that first visit, I realized how right Shapley had been about Peltier's greatness but how utterly wrong he had been to generalize about Messier's seeking applause for his comet finds. Here was a man so modest that he rarely went to astronomy club meetings. Peltier's friend Walter Scott Houston says that once, to get him to an important variable-star observers meeting, some members virtually had to kidnap him. When presented a major award from the Western Amateur Astronomers in 1967, Peltier had to be strongly encouraged to leave his Delphos, Ohio, home to go to the West Coast. Not much of a traveler, he particularly disliked flying. "Why did you take the train to get all the way out here," someone asked Peltier at that gathering. "I had no choice," he explained. "The stage coach no longer runs."[20]

In fall 1979, I met Peltier for the last time. It was during this visit that I realized how much Peltier's home and telescopes were a part of him. He showed me a corner of the transit room of his 12-inch Clark observatory, where the old mahogany tube sat that at an earlier time had held the lenses of his 6-inch comet seeker. There, carved in deep, proud letters that almost encircled the little tube, were the designations of the three long-gone comets of Zaccheus Daniel and the 12 Peltier comets whose light had passed through that telescope before any other. These hand-cut numbers and letters were the core of a career.

Fifteen times this little telescope had uncovered a new member of our solar system, and the unassuming person standing next to it was responsible for 12 of them. What Peltier did could profitably be done by amateurs today; what he achieved is a worthwhile goal to which any modern observer can aspire. And the mood, the attitudes, and the way of thinking he brought to our avocation have given us a special pride in what we do.

More than any other comet seeker before him, Peltier understood what Thoreau's different drummer really meant to a comet hunter. "Time has not lessened the age-old allure of the comets," he wrote in *Starlight Nights*.

> In some ways their mystery has only deepened with the years. At each return a comet brings with it the questions which were asked when it was here before, and as it rounds the sun and backs away toward the long, slow night of its aphelion, it leaves behind with us those questions, still unanswered.
>
> To hunt a speck of moving haze may seem a strange pursuit, but even though we fail the search is still rewarding, for in no better way can we come face to face, night after night, with such a wealth of riches as old Croesus never dreamed of.[21]

☾ 7 ☽

The Comet Cop

When bright Comet Mrkos suddenly appeared in the western sky in August 1957, a young summer student named Brian Marsden was working in his basement office at the Royal Greenwich Observatory, then located at Herstmonceux Castle in southern England. He was not interested in discovering comets; his passion was calculating their orbits as soon as possible after they had been discovered. And over the next 35 years, Marsden's knowledge of where every comet was at virtually any moment made him one of the most important figures in the comet field.

But during the summer of 1957, Marsden was just an undergraduate student trying to calculate an orbit for a comet on an old mechanical calculator. He had two accurate positions for the comet, but he needed at least one more to calculate the comet's orbit. One evening the telephone rang. At the other end of the line was a voice with the numbers for that badly needed third position. Marsden excitedly sat down to try his hand at the orbit. But it didn't work; no matter what mathematical tricks he used, there was no way that the comet's first two positions would allow it to reach the third one. He could not obtain any kind of an orbit from those positions. "It took me more than an hour to conclude that this observation must have been a hoax," said Marsden, ruefully recalling his wasted evening.

One of the brightest comets of this century, Comet Mrkos's sudden appearance in the evening sky was electrifying for every sky watcher the summer of 1957, and Marsden had an unexpected opportunity to observe it. An evening or two after he had received the bogus comet position telephone call, two young female students warned Marsden of a plot to kidnap him. He was to be handcuffed and driven to parts unknown, the women said, and then he would have to hitchhike back. "I like to think the perpetrators were concerned I was working too hard," Marsden says, a charge many of his colleagues have against him to this day.

So with his newfound allies, Marsden resolved to leave his office discretely that evening, and the three sat on the hillside overlooking the castle. Low in the west, Comet Mrkos dominated the warm summer evening, its long dust tail streaking through the sky. But then they heard some commotion from down near the castle. Unable to find Marsden, the kidnappers' plot was unraveling and one of the kidnappers had become the kidnappee! Hours later the hapless victim returned. Enraged, he went to the other perpetrator—now the distinguished director of a well-known observatory—and threw him into the castle moat.

Two years after the Comet Mrkos episode, Marsden came to the United States, exchanged his mechanical calculator for a klunking IBM 650 computer, and eventually got his doctorate at Yale. On the day after Christmas 1964, he married Nancy Lou Zissell. Their daughter Cynthia remembers, at age 4, when spectacular Comet Bennett lit up the morning sky in 1970—she referred to it at the time as "skywriting."

Marsden arrived at the Smithsonian Astrophysical Observatory some 10 days after two Japanese amateur astronomers, Kaoru Ikeya and Tsutomu Seki, discovered their new comet in September 1965. On Marsden's first day in Cambridge, he was put to work refining the orbit of what was going to be the best comet to graze the sun since 1882. World-renowned astronomer Fred Whipple had just suggested that this one might be a member of the celebrated group of comets described by turn-of-the-century German astronomer Heinrich Kreutz. With 3 weeks until perihelion, there was barely enough time to inform the public. On October 1 Marsden and Owen Gingerich, who at that time directed the Central Bureau for Astronomical Telegrams, held a press conference to announce that the bright comet was on its way.

Since those Ikeya–Seki days, the Kreutz sun grazers have been one of Marsden's particular interests, and he wrote an extensive paper on them in 1967.[1] His article includes an ephemeris for sun grazing comets at specific distances from the sun. Such a table is especially useful for those seeking new sun-grazing comets.

WHO DISCOVERS WHAT

Marsden succeeded Gingerich as director of CBAT in 1968. Marsden now decides who receives credit for finding anything astronomical that moves or explodes; perhaps he is more accurately called a policeman of the sky. Marsden knows where the comets and asteroids are in their orbits, and he makes sure that the 50- or so exploding stars—supernovae and novae—that appear each year are announced promptly.

More than anybody else on Earth, Marsden knows where things are in the sky. One key to his remarkable success comes from his ability as a celestial mechanician; he has been calculating orbits since high school. He also has a phenomenal memory: He doesn't forget details of events or their place in time. One afternoon I showed him my backyard observatory with its decade-old dedication sign: November 15, 1980. "Ah, yes!" Marsden laughed. "That was a Saturday."

Relying more on postcard circulars and electronic mail than on telegrams, Marsden and associate director Daniel Green, who has been at CBAT since 1978, are now issuing circulars at the rate of about five a week. Green brought to his job the active interest in comets that he had had since high school, when he edited the *Comet*. In the last decade, Green's journal, now called the *Inter-*

national Comet Quarterly, has been read widely by comet enthusiasts around the world.

The idea of CBAT circulars is to report events in the sky efficiently, although in 1970 an earthly shooting found its way into *Circular* 2209. The event took place in West Texas at McDonald Observatory's new 107-inch telescope. "Shortly before CST midnight Feb. 5," according to the story,

> a newly-hired employee fired seven point-blank shots into the front surface of the fused-silica primary mirror, using a 9-mm pistol. . . . The harm suffered by the mirror from his bullets, and his several preliminary blows with a hammer, was extraordinarily small.

At the end of August 1975, a bright nova in Cygnus lit up the sky. Although Marsden quickly relayed word to the astronomical community by telegram, dozens of independent discoveries of the stellar explosion kept his telephone ringing at home and at the office all through the long Labor Day weekend. The circular he was finally able to send out after the holiday showed that a panorama of discovery reports had been made round the world as the Earth whirled eastward and observers from country to country looked up at the brightest new star in a generation. The brightest nova was followed by the brightest comet just a few months later. Comet West grew significantly more impressive than expected, its brilliant tail lighting up the morning sky.

In 1978 Marsden took over the directorship of the International Astronomical Union's Minor Planet Center, which moved from Cincinnati to Cambridge together with astronomer Conrad Bardwell as its associate director. On Bardwell's retirement in 1990, his place was taken by Gareth Williams. Since 1987 Marsden has also served as associate director of the Planetary Sciences Division of the Harvard–Smithsonian Center for Astrophysics, one of the nation's top schools.

During all this time, Marsden has also tried to maintain an active research program, including in particular his extensive pioneer work on nongravitational forces—the jets and other cometary eruptions—that affect the motion of comets like Halley's. Understandably Marsden has generally tailored his research papers to his activities as director of the central bureau. Marsden's main interests have been in methods for determining comet orbits based on a few early positions, and in the large spherical shell of comets at the edge of the solar system, called the Oort cloud after the late Dutch astronomer Jan Oort. Marsden has even found time to bring out eight editions of his well-known *Catalogue of Cometary Orbits* and a catalog of minor planet discoveries.[2]

Over the years Marsden has become an inspiration to would-be discoverers and other observers, pushing them to do more when he thought they were getting a bit lazy and cheering them up when they became discouraged. On one depressing day, I wrote him a note saying that perhaps I have found enough comets. "We have plenty of room for many more comets Levy," he replied, "so get out there and keep looking!" In 1983 George Alcock, who had visually discovered several comets *and* novae, complained that his discovery career was likely to end as organized professional searches took over. Marsden's reply typifies how he pushes amateur astronomers to keep looking, and keep succeeding:

> The funny thing is that in this modern mass-produced world so many groups and organizations set themselves up to make astronomical discoveries. Here is this group going to pick up supernovae in other galaxies by the hundred. That automatic telescope in Arizona is going to sweep up all the comets that come reasonably far above the horizon. This infrared-astronomy satellite is going to find scores of earth-approaching asteroids way ahead of Palomar. But I'm still waiting for these discoveries. Their participants have talked endlessly about what they can do—but they have produced absolutely nothing! You—and a handful of other dedicated individuals around the world—go out, without a lot of fanfare, and you make the discoveries. Sometimes years may pass between discoveries (occasionally only five days!), but they do come, because you know what you are doing, although you never know whether chance is going to be a friend or an enemy. So I'm ready now for your next discovery![3]

Comet IRAS–Araki–Alcock 1983d. (Photograph by Jack Newton, May 9, 1983.) This comet was moving so fast that Newton had to move both axes of the telescope during the 6 minutes the camera shutter was open.

Only 3 weeks later, astronomers working with the new infrared astronomical satellite (*IRAS*) thought they had discovered a new near-earth asteroid during the satellite's survey of the sky. Meanwhile Alcock knelt in his upstairs hall, directed his trusty binoculars through the double-glazed windows, and discovered (along with an independent amateur Japanese astronomer) what came to be known as Comet IRAS–Araki–Alcock 1983d, the comet that made the closest known approach to the Earth since 1770.

FALSE ALARMS AND HOAXES

Determining the priority in a discovery is one of Marsden's most sensitive tasks. Since comets started bearing the names of their discoverers in the late eighteenth century, their discovery has been comparable to finding the Holy Grail. I spoke with someone in Brussels who said that he "would do anything—absolutely anything—" to get his name on a comet. I wondered, though, if anything included what one really needed to do—spend hundreds of hours with his or her eye glued to an eyepiece at all hours of the night.

In his quarter-century at the helm of the CBAT, Marsden has received few phone calls in the middle of the night, "and never a useful one," he adds. About 90 percent of reports of new comets turn out to be false—mostly ghost images of bright stars or planets just outside the telescope field, photographic flaws, or two different galaxies thought to be a moving comet. Occasionally there are outright hoaxes: Once when someone from Columbus, Ohio, reported a comet, Marsden replied that he would wait for confirmation before issuing a circular. Some days later, a telegram arrived under the guise of the Tokyo Observatory with the required confirmation. However the telegram's return address was not Tokyo but Columbus, Ohio! Another time an observer tried to claim credit for a comet that had already been announced; he alleged to have observed it the previous night. This time Marsden noted that the would-be discoverer could not have observed the comet, since it had been raining all that night at the site.

Other false alarms have been easier to identify. One didn't even involve Marsden's office, at least at first: A young observer in Western New York announced that he had discovered a comet—but only to the local press and his astronomical society. In the following days, both the newspaper and the society were hoodwinked into publishing follow-up observations. Whether the erstwhile discoverer was deliberately lying or his moving comet was simply a series of observations of different galaxies is still uncertain.

Marsden and Green have amassed a great deal of experience in the field of comets as well as with those who observe them. Since so many reports turn out to be false alarms, the two do not routinely investigate all comet discoveries; instead it is up to a discoverer to confirm the existence of a particular comet. If the new comet is bright enough, another discoverer will probably find it quickly, and the comet will bear the names of both finders. Until a comet is confirmed, up to three discoverers, or two at the same observatory, can have their names attached to it.

Marsden has dealt with a host of other suspect sightings, including one luckless observer who sends his many reports of nonexistent comets by Federal Express, and a would-be-discoverer in Canada who reports the positions of new comets on the basis of his dreams! As we noted earlier, Barnard is the only comet hunter I know of who actually did discover comets after dreaming about them. Marsden generally treats these strange cases with a good deal of patience and even laughs about them when he can. I know of one person who tested his patience to the point that Marsden finally called him an ignoramus. But when that individual showed signs of mending his ways, Marsden immediately worked with him and encouraged his new attitude.

A more serious episode began in July 1980 when an amateur astronomer in Florida sent CBAT a telegram about an object of magnitude minus 25, almost as bright as the sun. Dismissing it as a hoax, Marsden went away for a few days on a rare vacation. Daniel Green then received a phone call from the Florida observer, who was angrily wondering why nothing was being done about the asteroid he had discovered near the sun and could be seen in the glare as it moved off the sun's limb. The amateur was not convinced by Green's logical suggestion that the solar obscurer was probably a weather balloon launched from a nearby air force base. On his return from vacation, Marsden was subjected to a 90-minute Saturday afternoon tirade from the Floridian, who by this time was trying to persuade US government officials of the need for defense against the killer asteroid that he (and apparently no one else) had seen.

The persistent amateur also contacted Tom Van Flandern, then on the staff of the U.S. Naval Observatory, who suggested some 30 other possible explanations for the observation. This time the Florida observer responded with letters to higher-ups in the Naval and Smithsonian managements. Then one day in August 1981, the Florida observer suddenly entered Marsden's office. The subsequent argument became so loud that people down the corridor rushed out of their offices. "Do you want a bouncer?" someone asked. Surrounded by three or four burly astronomers, the unfortunate character rushed out of the building. The sad episode didn't end there, however; for several years afterward, the Florida observer continued to send abusive and even threatening postcards to Marsden, Van Flandern, and Green. Finally the Florida observer committed suicide.

JUST A COMET SUSPECT

All these incidents are part of Marsden's life. My own experience with him includes my reports of 19 new comets, and his request to confirm the discoveries of several others. Confirming other people's finds should be part of the game for every searcher. One December night I was searching with my 16-inch telescope, moving it back and forth through the western sky. Then the telephone rang. It was Doug George, an experienced amateur astronomer from Ottawa, Canada. He had just found a new comet, also in the western sky, and wanted to know if I could confirm its existence for him. When he gave me the comet's position I did a doubletake—if I hadn't answered the phone, I might have discovered it myself within 10 minutes! Another time Marsden asked me to confirm a comet found by Mauro Zanotta in Italy. Although night had begun there, it was still early in the afternoon when I learned of the discovery. That evening I set up my telescope under a partly cloudy sky, turned it to the position Marsden had provided, and there was the new comet. When Marsden learned of my observation, he was about to announce the comet as Comet Zanotta. But then Howard Brewington independently located it from his home in New Mexico, and the comet's name became Zanotta–Brewington.

I remember fondly a day in 1987 that began when I sent Marsden by electronic mail a routine report of a magnitude estimate of Comet Bradfield, which had been prominent in the evening sky that fall. What wasn't routine was that my report ended with a note that I had spotted a comet suspect in the constellation Bootes. Marsden answered immediately, wishing me luck that the new comet was indeed a real one. In the next several hours, we exchanged perhaps half a dozen messages. Could I take a look at a possible comet reported by someone at such-and-such a position? Yes I would, I promised. Then he discussed a man who had bothered both of us as well as almost every other astronomer in Arizona and his theory that planet X may be somewhere, as yet unreported. Supported by a series of biblical passages, this man was convinced that the new planet was now visible. He had shown me a picture of it—it looked like streetlights in a parking lot.

As the afternoon wore on, I got a message from Canadian astronomer Terence Dickinson that he had confirmed my comet discovery from his home near Kingston, Ontario. I sent that along to Marsden, and suddenly the relaxed tone of our electronic mail was over. "Please send the positions from Dickinson as soon as possible, so the announcement can be made." I was typing the all-important Dickinson position as well as my own second night's observation when the phone rang. It was my planet-X friend. "We think we have planet-X," he said, interrupting my concentration. "What is its position?" I asked tersely. "Oh, I won't reveal that information," he replied. The following day all was back to normal. The new comet was announced as Comet Levy 1987y, the suspect Marsden asked me to check turned out to be nothing, and the planet-X guy was mailing his parking lot lights picture to Marsden.

As part of his job's responsibility, Marsden is plugged in to the astronomical community—both the scientific aspect and those who participate in it—more than anyone else. For the many observers around the world who rely on CBAT for announcements and orbits, Marsden has become as much a part of the celestial landscape as the objects they report.

☾ 8 ☽

Comet Tales

Comet hunting has attracted the fancies of many, including William Brooks, who, in the late 19th century, hunted in his yard with a nine-inch refractor and picked up over twenty comets, Charles Messier, better known for his "non-comets," Leslie C. Peltier, who between 1925 and 1954 gathered twelve comets and an assortment of novae, and David H. Levy, who between 1965 and 1970 has found nothing—absolutely nothing.[1]

In fall 1965 I enjoyed watching Comet Ikeya–Seki paint a beautiful picture as it did a hairpin turn around the sun. I decided then that it was time to begin a comet-seeking program of my own. I felt ready for it. Over the past 5 years, I'd trained myself in three areas of observing that are basic to beginning a search for comets. Incongruous as it might appear, observing the moon in detail is one of them. When I first walked into the Royal Astronomical Society of Canada's Montreal Centre in 1960, I was presented with a simple map of the moon on which 300 craters and 26 mountain ranges and other features were plotted. The idea was to identify each of these, an exercise that helped train my eyes to concentrate on details near the limit of vision. Observing the soft markings on Jupiter, Mars, and Saturn helped the process along.

In August 1962 a single observation of the Pleiades, Messier 45, began my second stage of observer training. Observing and describing all 110 objects in Messier's catalog is a superb way of becoming familiar with the sky and all the different types of fuzzy objects that it holds.[2] We know that Messier used a small telescope for most of his objects and a modern telescope would not easily mistake brighter objects for comets. But other objects, like Messier 78 in Orion, can still fool the unwary. Though Messier 78 is a nebula shining by the light of newborn stars more than a thousand light years away, it actually looks a bit like a tiny nearby comet. Although it took me 5 years to finish the list—that happened in May 1967—the second time around went a bit faster. On a single clear night in March 1983, I found, observed, and took notes on all of the Messier objects except Messier 30, which rose after the dawn was too bright.

The sky is a large place, and there are plenty of people moving through it with their telescopes in search of comets. At the end of 1967, Ikeya and Seki shared a second comet, and the following year, Minoru Honda bagged a nice one. One night while hunting outside my parents' home in the middle of a light-polluted city under an almost-full moon, I made an independent discovery of Comet Honda. Considering the poor sky, it still appeared quite bright through the 8-inch reflecting telescope I was using. I realized it had to be a known comet, and it did not take long to find out that it was Honda's comet. I remember my grandmother was visiting at the time, sharing my excitement as I darted in and out of the house between my star charts and my telescope.

SEARCHING FOR A DARK SKY AND A COMET

The next year, Comet Tago–Sato–Kosaka 1969 IX interrupted my college studies at Acadia University in Wolfville, Nova Scotia. This was the first comet to be observed by a spacecraft, the *Orbiting Geophysical Observatory*, which detected a huge envelope of hydrogen gas around the coma. And a few months after this, bright Comet Bennett graced the morning sky in March 1970.

That fall I set up my telescope for hunting at a site a mile north of campus. I must have had a lot of energy then, because I actually walked that mile with telescope, mount, and notebook in hand to set up for an evening's session. But this night I set up the tripod, put the telescope on the tripod, put an eyepiece in the telescope, and looked through it. Near the top edge of the field was a comet! It turned out to be a known one, a comet that Japanese amateur Osamu Abe had snatched earlier. Would that my first new one be that easy!

During the 1970s my comet hunting dropped in intensity thanks to my heavy course load, and by 1979, I still hadn't found anything. I began to think about what I could do to increase the chances of a discovery. More important than a very dark and clear sky, I reasoned, was the need of a site with more frequent clear nights. The Canadian sites from which I had done most of my observing in the 1960s and 1970s seldom offered more than two clear nights in a row at any time of the year except for a week or two in May and again in September.

Certain times of the month that are crucial for comet hunting: right after a full moon and around the new moon. If I wanted a better statistical chance of discovering comets, I needed a site with a greater likelihood of recurrent clear nights during these periods. Therefore in 1979 I decided to move to Tucson, Arizona, where some 300 nights a year are clear enough to stalk comets. I chose the community of Corona de Tucson, some 20 miles east of town, where the sky is pretty dark. I built a small observatory out of a 9 × 10 foot garden shed, designing the structure so that the roof slid off to reveal the open sky. Within a year I had a 16-inch diameter reflecting telescope, and then I resumed comet hunting in a big way.

A comet in spring 1983 attracted my attention because I should have found it myself. It was discovered by *IRAS*, an amateur astronomer G. Araki from Japan, and George Alcock, a nova and comet hunter from Peterborough, England, some 60 miles from London. Although the IRAS satellite detected the comet first, the

Comet Bennett, March 1970. (Photograph by Jack Newton, using a 450-mm telephoto lens; 2-minute exposure using Tri-X film.)

people operating the satellite did not immediately know what they had found. Meanwhile amateur astronomer Alcock was in his pajamas, searching for exploding stars when he saw the large comet through a pair of binoculars and a closed window.

A month later I actually did find a comet. After a brief flurry of excitement, I checked the pages of *Sky and Telescope* magazine and learned that my new comet was actually a well-known old one, Periodic Comet Tempel 2. Then at the end of November, I came very close. This time it was Comet Hartley–IRAS, 1983v. Discovered by the IRAS satellite from space and by Malcolm Hartley, using a large wide-angle Schmidt camera in Australia, this comet was supposed to be a faint fifteenth magnitude, far too faint for my telescope. However I had not heard of the report when I picked it up the comet at the end of a 2-hour evening comet sweep. So I had independently discovered a new comet less than a week after it was first reported. At least I was finding things! I began to think that at last my long wait might be over. Although I was pushing 900 hours of comet hunting, I was nowhere near the record set by California amateur Don Machholz, who spent 1700 hours with his eye at the eyepiece before he found his first comet and another 1700 hours before his second!

My first real discovery took place on November 13, 1984, as I described in the preface to this book, but it was quite a while before my second find. Meantime Halley's comet—the most famous of all—was due back, creating lots of excitement both within the astronomical community and among the general public. Starting in 1985 I joined Steve Larson as part of the Near-Nucleus Studies Network of the International Halley Watch. During the 3 months before perihelion passage in February 1986, we observed the comet every night with either a 20-inch or a 61-inch telescope and an electronic charge-coupled device (CCD) detector system. Our goal was to study the area around the comet's nucleus. We recorded the complex structure of dust jets that erupted frequently, changing the comet's appearance from one night to the next. On January 6, 1986 we saw a dust jet going straight in the direction of the tail, an almost identical repeat of what the astronomer George Ritchey had photographed from Mount Wilson during Halley's previous visit in 1910.

With Halley's comet far in the southern sky in spring 1986, we discontinued the nightly CCD work from Tucson, but in April, I did get to go to Peru to lead a Halley's comet expedition. On the first night, I was scouting our observing area for the best place to watch—just me and Minerva, my 6-inch telescope. It was a remote site on the grounds of an Inca ruin. Surrounded by tall stone structures and a dark sky, the site seemed delightful. Not only was this my first night in a strange country, it was my first night ever in a new hemisphere. I set up the telescope and started looking at Halley's comet, which was just rising.

As I was concentrating on the comet, I didn't hear some faint distant footsteps until they were loud enough so that I could tell somebody was approaching. The steps got louder; there was the clinking of glass. There was conversation in a language I had never heard before, but it was clear that my uninvited visitors were somewhat soused. Not knowing what to do, I looked at the distant comet and then at Minerva. Hmmm, I thought, telescope as a weapons system. If they got threatening, maybe I could hit them over their heads with my telescope.

As the men got closer—in the starlight, they seemed to be awfully big hombres—my fears were confirmed. There were two, they were drunk, and they were staring straight at me. For a minute, the three of us stood there. I looked at them, they looked at me, at my telescope, then at the sky. Then they pointed. "Hal—leee?" I offered them a turn at the eyepiece. We ended up having a good time comet watching together, although I suspected everything looked fuzzy to them that night!

COMET HUNTING BY READING

That same year I interviewed Clyde Tombaugh, discoverer of Pluto, for a biography I would eventually write.[3] I asked Tombaugh what other objects he had found, and as he listed the clusters of galaxies, star clusters, variable stars, and asteroids, he let on that he had also found a comet. "But I've never heard of any Comet Tombaugh," I protested.

"I found it on plates taken many months earlier," Tombaugh explained. Knowing the comet was long gone, he figured that it would be impossible to follow it and therefore there would be no sense reporting it. "Would it be possible to see the image of that comet now?" I asked hopefully. Tombaugh said that the detailed notes he had taken on each plate were still preserved at Lowell Observatory in Flagstaff, Arizona, so all I had to do was locate the correct plates. Then finding the comet on them would be easy. "Great!" I said. "When did you take the plates?" "Sometime between 1929 and 1945," he replied impishly.

February 9, 1986—the perihelion day of Halley's comet—found me in the subterranean plate vault at Lowell. The room was furnished in a spartan way with an old wooden chair and table. All the old plate envelopes on which Clyde had recorded his meticulous notes had been replaced with modern archival ones, but the old ones were still filed away. I took out several boxes of them and set to work. On each big brown envelope, Tombaugh had listed the numbers of variable stars, asteroids, comets, and other unusual objects. On envelope after envelope, I saw a procession of "no comets —no comets" recorded in his scrawling hand.

After about an hour, Arthur A. Hoag, director of Lowell Observatory, came by to visit. He looked at me and the large boxes of envelopes spread around. "Now that's a new one!" he smiled. "Comet hunting by reading!"

When I had progressed to the middle of February 1930, I picked out the envelope for January 23, which listed the usual notes, then at the bottom: "4. No comets. 5. Planet X (Pluto) at last found!!!"[4] Interrupting my own search, I carefully removed, examined, and replaced the historic first discovery plate of Pluto. Then I went back to work. It was already late in the afternoon by the time I reached the end of January 1931; still "no comets—no comets— no comets," then "Comet?"

Was that it? A quick check of the plate showed the telltale trailed image of a comet sitting on the plate like a faint smudge with a tail on it. But this one had never been reported, never before announced. The soft image, recorded black on white on the plate, was a comet that passed by without revealing its secret till it was gone, leaving only a few photons of light frozen on the photographic emulsion. Even now only two people knew it existed, Clyde and I, and I was the only one who knew where it was!

Now with the help of my friend Brian Skiff, an observer on the Lowell staff, we set out to measure the comet. Then Skiff found that Lowell Observatory had actually reported the object back in 1931 as an asteroid, not a comet, and it had been given the asteroid designation 1931 AN. When we reported the object—correctly as a comet and with accurate positions—to Marsden at CBAT, he said that he would not be able to announce the comet unless an accurate orbit could be determined. And for that I needed more observations. That summer I went to the gargantuan plate collection at Harvard College Observatory, but Comet Tombaugh was too faint to appear on any of the plates in its collection. Over the next 2 years, whenever I had the chance and money to travel, I visited plate collections as far away as Heidelberg in Germany, Mount Wilson in California, and other collections around the world. Heidelberg had a plate so close that I was sure the comet would be there; sadly it was just off the edge. Mount Wilson also had a plate that was close. Of course had the comet appeared on either of these plates, someone might have discovered it at the time.

The moral of this tale? Comet hunting by reading would have worked if I had found more observations of this comet. Although Marsden is pretty sure that Comet Tombaugh was never seen before and it is possibly periodic, without more observations he can't be positive. A year later Skiff found that Tombaugh had discovered a second comet, so now we had two unannounced comets. Will either comet eventually be announced as Comet Tombaugh?

BIGGER AND BETTER COMETS

The next year I snared two new comets, but both were close to the horizon at discovery and found under difficult conditions. The first appeared only 5 days into 1987. I had not found a comet in a while, but I was also on a tight deadline for my book, a guide for observing variable stars. So on New Year's day 1987, I made two resolutions: one to find a comet and the other to finish the book. On the morning of January 5, after working hard all night, I finally typed the last sentence of my book and started to print it. The sky had been very cloudy all night in advance of a storm. Each time I checked, it got cloudier and cloudier, so when I started printing the manuscript, I was not expecting to see that a clear spot was beginning to open up in the eastern sky. As fast as I could, I turned my house from a writing office into an observatory. I turned off white lights and turned on red ones so that my eyes would adapt to the darkness outside, and I walked into the back yard. There I had a garden shed that I had made into an observatory some 5 years earlier. These metal sheds are set up so that the roof supports the walls, but for my purpose, the roof had to slide off on rollers. It was quite a challenge making wooden supports to turn my garden shed into a place for comet hunting.

Out in the garden shed observatory that morning, I grabbed a handle and gave a shove. Slowly the big roof started moving, and a minute later the observatory was open to the sky and I began a slow eastern sweep with Miranda, my 16-inch diameter reflecting telescope. But the search was interrupted by both the threatening clouds and my need to check the printing of my book from time to time. After my second printer check, I asked myself what would stop this hunt, the clouds or the dawn. It was neither. I returned to the telescope, moved one field to the east, and there was a comet.

I had barely 45 seconds to observe and record this object before clouds and dawn rushed in. The position I had estimated was therefore very poor, and besides there was a faint object marked on the atlas that I keep for handy reference, so I assumed that it must be just a galaxy of some sort. By now the sky was quite bright, and as I looked outside into oncoming day, I was glad I had remembered to close the sliding roof observatory, because now it was raining heavily. I remember how exhausted I was, having been up all night writing and then observing. As I looked toward the now-closed observatory and the rain, I asked myself if I really had discovered a comet in the last hour.

By the following morning, the sky had still not cleared, but I did check the best sky map of all, the Palomar Observatory Sky Survey and found that the faint object on the other atlas was not the object I had seen. By the morning of January 7, the sky had cleared at last, and I quickly found the object some distance from its earlier position. Marsden then announced it as Comet Levy, 1987a. Within the first week of the new year, I had finished my book and found a comet—I had achieved both of my New Year's resolutions.

In spring 1990 the world was waiting for a bright comet. Found by Rodney Austin from New Zealand at the end of 1989, Comet Austin $1989c_1$ promised to become pretty bright as it swung around from the south. At that time, I was observing with Steve Larson from the Lunar and Planetary Laboratory in Tucson, and we had planned to spend a week at the large 61-inch telescope in the Catalina Mountains north of town observing the comet in different filters and obtaining spectroscopic images of its light. But by the fifth night of our run, it was clear that Comet Austin, though a pleasant object, was not nearly so bright or so active as we had hoped. David, Steve said early in the morning of May 19, "Comet Austin is a one-person job. Tomorrow night you should stay home and find us a bright comet!"

With morning sky washed out by a last-quarter moon, I decided to accommodate Steve by hunting earlier than usual. I opened the roof and began hunting around 2:30 A.M.; I had intended to continue until moonrise, but patchy clouds were interfering even with that plan. Then the sky improved as the moon rose an hour later, so I decided to keep on searching for a while. Swinging the telescope north to keep as far from the moon as possible, I hunted through the constellation of Andromeda, past the bright star Alpheratz, and swept on into Pegasus.

Not far from that bright star, my telescope stopped, and my brain snapped out of its lazy state as a soft fuzzy patch of light entered the field of view. Since I knew this part of the sky very well, I quickly thought that this patch must be a comet, but it did not move over the next hour. A check of the Palomar Sky Survey showed nothing in that position. Twenty-four hours later, the comet had crept along barely an eighth of a degree, by far the slowest motion I had ever seen for a comet at discovery. Announced as Comet Levy 1990c, this new visitor was far from the Earth and heading toward us. Plodding toward Alpheratz, a star in the Great Square of Pegasus, the comet seemed to be preparing for its onslaught of the Earth's sky.

By early July Comet Levy was picking up speed and brightness as it approached both sun and Earth. In late July while visiting my family in Montreal, I went south of town to show the comet to a reporter for the Montreal *Gazette*. The sky had been cloudy for a few days, so I was not sure what the comet would look like. But when we arrived at the site, I looked up and saw the comet visible to the naked eye, and through Minerva my 6-inch diameter portable telescope, it was a marvelous sight. By the middle of August, the comet cut a striking path right near the summer Milky Way. That was the year I was the main speaker at the annual Stellafane Telescope convention in Vermont. The talk was in a large natural amphitheater, and my audience consisted of 1500 people and one comet rising in the east.

Seven months later the comet was still a striking sight. In February 1991 it crossed the plane of the Earth's orbit and for 2 or 3 weeks sported a beautiful antitail. Composed of sunlit particles around the comet, the antitail points toward the sun instead of away from it and becomes visible when the Earth crosses the plane of the comet's orbit. In May 1991 I observed my comet on the first anniversary of its discovery. Its show was over; it had faded a great deal and was hardly visible at all.

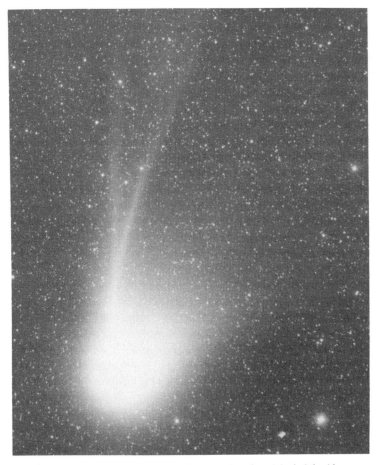

Comet Levy 1990c. (Photograph by David Levy using the 18-inch Schmidt camera at Palomar, August 24, 1990; 8-minute exposure.)

A NEW PERIODIC COMET

A week later, with dawn less than an hour away on the morning of June 10, I awoke to search the morning sky. But as usual for that time of year, it was still cloudy. Not wanting to give up

Comet Levy (1990c). (Photograph by David Levy, January 1991, using the Palomar 18-inch Schmidt camera.) Since the Earth was passing near the plane of the comet's orbit, dust near the comet is visible as an "antitail" that points downward in this photograph.

just yet, I opened the sliding roof on my garden shed and went back inside to watch a "M∗A∗S∗H" rerun. After the episode had finished, I stepped outside. The sky was looking a bit more promising, but it was still far too cloudy. I checked the sky a final time, for by now the first signs of dawn were appearing. There were still a lot of clouds, but growing patches of clear sky made me decide to begin comet hunting low in the eastern sky. I decided to search in the constellation of Aries, which was just coming up over the trees.

The telescope's field of view was about 1 degree across, or two moon diameters, and full of faint stars. I found nothing fuzzy or unusual in that field, so after a few seconds, I moved the telescope eastward and checked the adjacent field of view. After a minute of slow sweeping in this way, I moved the telescope again. Now a bright fuzzy patch of light entered the field of view, and for a second, a now-familiar "red alert" went off in my brain. But this fuzzy patch didn't fool me for long: By its elongated shape and its position, I knew that this was a distant galaxy called Messier 74. This galaxy is a highwayman, guilty of stopping comet hunters dead in their tracks. More than 200 years ago, it duped Messier, who sketched its position and then checked back later to see if it had moved, as all comets do. When the object remained frozen in the sky, he added it to his catalog as he went on in search of slowly moving cometary prey.

I've encountered Messier 74 so many times that I know it as an old friend. But the sky was brightening, so there was no dawdling over M74 now. I nudged the telescope down a field and another and another, slowly moving toward the horizon. When it got low enough to see distant treetops, I turned the telescope southward and then started sweeping back upward along an adjacent track. Another minute passed by, and then the mental alert went off again: There was another fuzzy spot.

For an instant I thought it was Messier 74 again, since the galaxy was close by. But wait a minute: This object was quite a bit brighter. With mounting tension I put in a higher power eyepiece and looked more closely. While M74 had relatively sharp edges all around, this thing had a bright center, then faded off so slowly that I could hardly tell where it ended and the sky began. Sharp edges are characteristic of a galaxy filled with stars; the gradual fading is a comet's typical signature. This, I decided, was a comet.

It was my seventh discovery from my back yard. I marked the comet's position not far from M74 on the star atlas. Then putting the telescope on two stars whose brightness I knew and changing the telescope's focus so that they appeared fuzzy, I estimated the comet's magnitude as a bright eighth magnitude. Although that is about five times fainter than the faintest naked-eye star, through my 16-inch telescope the comet was quite distinct. A closer look, and I noted a short tail pointing away from the sun.

Finally with the sky now so bright that the comet was virtually invisible, I plotted its position again. It had moved a tiny minute of an arc—only one-thirtieth the diameter of the full moon—in the 20 minutes since I had first seen it. It was time to report. Armed with all this information about an object whose existence might still be a secret to the world, I went inside to compose a message to Marsden. An hour or two later, a one-page announcement circular appeared at observatories and universities around the world.

But what was the orbit? Where was the comet coming from? Was it heading in, like 1990c had been, or had it already rounded the sun? Was it visiting the inner part of the solar system for the first and only time, or was it a new periodic comet that would return on a regular schedule? To answer these questions, astronomers take lots of photographs of the comet, either on film or electronically, and then measure precisely where the comet is each night as it crawls across the sky. With that information, Marsden could calculate the comet's obit. Within a few days, another CBAT circular appeared with a preliminary orbit for the comet, but it was a full month before enough accurate positions from telescopes all over the world told a better story. Curving around the sun in just a bit over 50 years, Comet 1991q is now called Periodic Comet Levy, a newly welcomed permanent member of the sun's inner circle. What's more, the orbit is similar to that of a bright comet that appeared almost 500 years ago when Columbus was discovering America. Determining whether the new comet is actually a return of the comet of 1499 will have to wait until the comet rounds the sun and appears again in 2042. Until then we simply will not know the orbit well enough.

A NEW LOOK AT COMETS

For any comet hunter, each find has its own fond memory. Like my comets of 1990 and 1991, some finds come easily, with the suspense-filled moments from discovery to certainty taking less than an hour. With the comet I found in 1988, the uncertainty lasted a lot longer, but it was worth the wait, for it was the comet find that year that led me to Eugene and Carolyn Shoemaker and a whole new way of looking at comets.

Early in 1988, my friend Steve Edberg encouraged me to accompany him on an expedition to see the total eclipse of the sun on March 17. He wanted me to join a special boat charter to a site where the eclipse would be total. The cruise sounded like fun, but since it would happen right in the middle of the best time for sweeping comets, I said I would pass. "Why can't total eclipses of the sun," I asked, "take place when the moon is in waxing gibbous phase? You know, a few days after first quarter? Then it wouldn't interfere with dark sky observing."

"You're probably not going to find a comet this one time!" Steve protested. But there was also a meeting on asteroids going on in Tucson that I didn't want to miss. No comet hunter should be indifferent in these comet cousins. And besides Eugene and Carolyn Shoemaker, who together had discovered 17 comets, would be at the Tucson conference, and I very much wanted to meet them.

It was a very successful meeting, and the Shoemakers and I had a chance to become familiar with each other's methods for patrolling the sky. Even though their methods were photographic and their main targets not comets but asteroids, we found that our work had quite a bit in common. I left that meeting invigorated.

New moon and the eclipse approached less than 2 weeks later, and on the morning of March 19, about a day-and-a-half after the eclipse, I was searching through the constellation of Pegasus when I saw something that looked like a galaxy. I was about to throw it back into the sky like an unwanted fish—it was symmetrical on both sides, like a long spiral galaxy—but it seemed a tiny bit suspicious, so I sketched its position and went on. The next morning was also clear, so I resumed searching even though my asthma was making me a bit wheezy. But when I checked the position of the previous night's galaxy, it wasn't there! Had I marked the position incorrectly? But half a degree to the north, there was a very different-looking galaxy. While yesterday's galaxy was evenly diffused over its whole surface, this one had a bright, almost starlike central core.

Quite confused by what I was seeing, I first wondered how I could have been so far off with the first object. I was skeptical about the whole thing, and not trusting my instincts, I decided to give it another day. The third morning was also clear, and when the object rose, I was ready for it. I pointed the telescope toward the first night's position; no galaxy there. Then I moved to the second night's position. The central core was still there, but the rest of the galaxy had disappeared.

Now I had the answer. This must be a comet, unusually elongated, that passed right in front of a star on the second morning. To confirm my hunch, all I had to do was move the telescope one-half degree to the north. I was about to push the telescope when the thought hit me: This was an important moment; my next motion of the telescope should, if I were right, yield a brand new comet. I took a deep breath, grabbed on to the telescope, and moved it one-half degree to the north. There in the middle of a circlet of stars lay my new catch. "Aha," I said, "I have you now."

By now I should have known what to do. I should have been a picture of serenity as I sketched the comet's position, opened an atlas of the sky, and plotted it, then estimated its brightness. But it didn't happen quite that way. Comet hunting is normally one of the most relaxing of pasttimes, but when a discovery occurs the atmosphere changes like still air cut by lightning. Hardly serene, my mind was a mass of quivering impulses as I paced around the telescope without the slightest idea of what to do next.

Other comet finders tell me that they also get carried away by the excitement of the moment. But this morning I couldn't afford that luxury. There were a dozen or so active comet hunters throughout the world who at that very moment were in search of the Holy Grail that I had just found. Come on, David, get with it, I told myself; now is not the time for a holiday.

Quickly logging into Marsden's CBAT computer service, I reported the three nights of positions and the comet's faint eleventh magnitude. Feeling triumphant but exhausted, I went to sleep. A few hours later I awoke, logged into the service once more and saw that Comet Levy 1988e had already been announced. But the story of this faint little visitor was far from over.

On March 22, 1988 Eugene and Carolyn Shoemaker were getting ready for a night of searching for asteroids and comets with the 18-inch Schmidt. It looked like the sky would stay clear, so with exposures lasting 8 minutes each, they would take as many as 40 exposures that night, each one on a 6-inch diameter piece of black-and-white film.

Like all photographic hunting expeditions, the Shoemaker search game is played quite differently from that of the visual searchers. Instead of hunting the sky with eyepiece and telescope, the husband-and-wife team captures comets and asteroids on the emulsion of photographic film. With the first film of the night safely loaded into the telescope, they move the telescope to a new location, then center the telescope on a star. After a countdown, two metal shutters squeak open at the top end of the telescope.

When the Shoemakers heard of Comet Levy 1988e, they decided to try to photograph it to help determine its orbit, even though the comet would not be high in the sky before morning twilight began. On that night, they finished their regular program late, so they quickly moved the telescope toward the east and took a short exposure of the comet field. To their surprise, despite the brightening dawn sky they got a good image and submitted the first accurate positions of my comet.

At their next observing run, the Shoemakers, now accompanied by their colleague Henry Holt, again put my short-tailed comet on their observing schedule. This list is set up graphically, with a sheet of paper on which dozens of nickel-sized circles outline the observing fields around the sky. But since the comet was so far north of where they usually observe, the extra circle would have to be placed way off the top of the "nickel diagram." Instead, Shoemaker simply inserted an extra circle at the top left-hand side of the page.

On the morning of May 13, the Shoemakers finally turned their telescope to the position indicated by the extra circle. But this was 5 days into an exhausting week of observing. They turned the telescope to the position indicated by the circle, and took a set of exposures. Carolyn did not get to scan those films until the start of the seventh and final night of the observing run. Gene and Henry were about to leave to set up the telescope upstairs.

Carolyn quickly found what she was looking for. "Gene," she called, "would you like to see David's comet?" Gene came downstairs and looked through the stereomicroscope. "Why is the comet so far off the center of the field?" he asked, and then added that it was brighter than they expected. Gene then went back upstairs to continue setting up for the night's work while Carolyn wondered why the comet was not at the center of the field as she had planned. After a few minutes, she called upstairs again: "Gene, I cannot identify any stars on this film. I don't know what field this is!" Shoemaker was already guiding on a star at the telescope. "Henry," he said and quickly handed over the guide paddle, "Take over." After he rushed downstairs, it took him a few minutes to identify the mistake: They had taken the field represented by the position of the circle on the nickel diagram, not the position where Comet Levy was—a difference of 17 degrees. Satisfied that he had solved the riddle, Gene was about to go upstairs again when Carolyn asked the question, "But if this comet isn't David's, then whose is it?"

A quick check showed that it would be theirs, since there was no known comet at all in that position. Before the night was over, they had reported their quite accidental discovery of Comet Shoemaker–Holt, 1988g. I heard about this discovery after I had returned from a star-observing party in Texas. The comet seemed bright enough that I might be able to detect it in the morning sky using my own 16-inch telescope. Sure enough, I was able to see a faint fuzzy patch. As the sky brightened at the approach of day, I closed up the telescope and went back to sleep.

A few hours later the telephone rang. It was my friend Charles Morris, an experienced comet observer who lives in California. "David," he wanted to know, "did you see Comet Shoemaker–Holt last night?" "Yes. Can't this wait? I am still asleep." "Have you seen the orbit?" he interrupted breathlessly. "Conrad Bardwell noticed this yesterday. Comet Shoemaker–Holt's orbit is almost exactly the same as Comet Levy's except that it comes to perihelion 3 months later!"

Then associate director of the Minor Planet Center, Conrad Bardwell, was working with Marsden at that time to calculate orbits for asteroids and comets.[5] As soon as enough positions were available for the new Shoemaker–Holt comet and a rough orbit calculated, Bardwell noticed how similar its orbit was to that of Comet Levy. Inclined some 63 degrees to the plane of the ecliptic, the two orbits were almost identical in every respect except that Shoemaker–Holt had arrived at perihelion on February 13, 1988, about 3 months after Comet Levy's closest approach to the sun on the nineteenth of the previous November. The orbits were too similar to be a coincidence. More likely this was the first instance, aside from the various sun-grazing comets, of a pair of related long-period comets being discovered independently.

When more positions were available for both comets, the calculated orbits became almost identical. At the end of 1988, Marsden suggested a scenario: Some 12,000 years ago, a single comet broke in two as it rounded the sun. The two parts did not separate right away but stayed together as a double comet until millennia later and far from the sun, they began to drift apart.[6] It is lucky that I went comet hunting instead of eclipse chasing that eventful night of March 19, 1988. The first comet was faint and close to the dawn sky. I observed it for three nights before reporting it, and there was no independent discovery by another observer—in fact there is no record of any independent find. The other comet was far from the Shoemakers' usual search area, and they would have missed it had they not been trying to record the first comet.

It is often from accidents like these (through serendipity) that interesting scientific discoveries are made. Moreover the confluence of visual and photographic comet searching has enhanced our abilities to make a find. Comet Levy 1988e and Comet Shoemaker–Holt 1988g are a remarkable pair of comets, but for me, the co-incidence was even more important because it led me to the Shoe-makers, a whole new way of finding comets, and a whole new way of looking at comets. Instead of just being beautiful objects in the sky, I now saw comets as forces that could plow into the Earth and even change the course of life here.

❨ 9 ❩

An Asteroid Hits the Earth

Imagine living in Flagstaff, Arizona, the day that Meteor Crater was made. A blinding flash of light in the eastern sky startles you; you look toward it. There is a billowing cloud of debris rising into the stratosphere and mushrooming out. But you don't hear anything. Like a scene in a silent movie, the events 45 miles away seem somewhat detached, as in a dream. Three minutes and a few seconds later, the illusion is shattered with a glass-breaking thunderclap. Then a low rumble goes on and on, and the ground trembles.

But all this happened some 50,000 years ago, possibly long before the first human beings explored the new world, longer still before they came across the flat-topped formation we now call Coon Butte and its huge hole in the ground—200 meters deep, about 1.2 kilometers across, and made in 5 seconds by an asteroid only 50 meters wide that smashed against the Earth.

Nowadays the crater's climate has all the harshness of its mile-high desert location, hot by day and cold by night. But on the day the asteroid hit, the Earth was in the midst of an ice age, and Northern Arizona's climate was wetter and cooler than now. The object careened into a thick pine forest, before an audience of mammoths, ground sloths, bison, large lions, and sabertoothed tigers. For thousands of years, this huge scar just sat there, part of the landscape, and slowly eroded, until 1886 when shepherds watching their flock on the plain surrounding the crater discovered some pieces of iron. In a pretty ingenious bit of reasoning, the shepherds figured that a single explosion had somehow expelled the iron as it formed the crater.

Grove Carl Gilbert, one of the top geologists in the country at the time, was the first to study the crater scientifically. But his hunch that the crater was the result of an iron-rich asteroid impact didn't pan out in the tests he conducted. He hoped that a huge mass of iron beneath the crater floor would cause an anomaly in his compass reading. It didn't, so he assumed that if the crater were the result of an impact, then the object must be too far below the surface to cause a magnetic blip. Gilbert described the failure of his test in his retiring presidential address at the Geological Society of Washington from a philosophic point of view.[1] The paper discussed how a hypothesis is born, figured through, and then either accepted or discarded. Meteor Crater served the purpose of an example. "The mental process by which hypotheses are suggested," he wrote, "is obscure. Ordinarily they flash into consciousness without premonition." Gilbert proposed that hypotheses come out of analogy: To explain an unusual event or a peculiar feature, the scientist considers what aspects are already known, then builds the hypothesis on that.

Gilbert's paper addressed the two likeliest ways that a crater is formed: by the explosive eruption of a volcano or by the impact of an object from space. For craters here on Earth as well as on the moon and other planets and moons, scientists are forever debating which giant pockmark was caused by the one and which by the other. In fact Gilbert gave the first clear exposition on lunar craters being formed from impacts with other objects in space. "What would result," Gilbert then asked, "if another small star should now be added to the earth, and one of the consequences which had occurred to me was the formation of a crater?" Gilbert thought that the main body would be composed of iron and if it lay beneath the crater, it would cause "a local deflection of the magnetic needle."[2] He noticed that the crater 45 miles east of

Flagstaff was not circular but squarish. Perhaps the star "struck the earth and bounded off, finally coming to rest at some point further east?" But he found that the crater's shape was inconsistent with an asteroid hitting and then ricocheting.

Gilbert concluded that the crater was formed by a steam explosion, like what happened to Mt. Vesuvius in A.D. 79 or to Krakatoa in 1883. After all the crater is less than 10 miles from a known volcanic crater. But—and Gilbert noticed this too—most volcanic craters are on top of their mountains; this one bore only a casual relationship to the butte it indented. And what about the nearby meteorites? Could the meteorite fall have "touched the volcanic button," setting off a volcanic explosion?

THERE'S PLATINUM UNDER THAT THAR HILL

In 1903 Daniel Moreau Barringer, a successful mining engineer and lawyer, heard about the crater and the platinum-laden meteorites surrounding it. He believed that the main body of the meteorite, still hidden under the crater, must be loaded with the stuff. His agents went out, staked the claims, and then sight unseen, he bought the land. He put half a million dollars into exploring for what he thought would be a big mass of meteoric iron under the crater. Much of the rest of his life was spent in a search for this main mass of iron and in a fruitless attempt to mine it. The government later established a post office in the area and named it Metcoi, not for the crater but for the meteorites surrounding it.

Barringer's dream was never fulfilled. He died in 1927, one year before Eugene Shoemaker, the man who would finally figure out Meteor Crater, was born.

METEOR CRATER ON THE ROAD TO THE MOON

When Muriel Shoemaker gave her 7-year-old son a set of marbles in 1935, she thought she was simply passing on some unusual family keepsakes. But these marbles, some of which were real agate, fascinated him. A year later during a trip with his father to South Dakota's Black Hills, Shoemaker was so impressed with the rose quartz and other minerals in the area that he began to collect them. His dad knew just enough about them to whet Shoemaker's appetite for more. That year their family separated briefly when his mother took a teaching position at the School of Practice at Buffalo State Teachers College in western New York, while his father worked at the Civilian Conservation Corps in Wyoming.

Fresh out of fourth grade, Gene enrolled in an unusual program in science education for children. It included field trips in geology and evening courses in several sciences—quite an opportunity for a child. Combined with the fossil-rich geological formations on Eighteen-Mile Creek, south of Buffalo, the program's 5-year duration left Gene convinced that he wanted to be a geologist. With his family planning to reunite in Los Angeles where his father had found a job as a grip on a Hollywood sound stage, he graduated from ninth grade and moved West in 1942.

Gene brought his growing love of minerals to Fairfax High School in Los Angeles, where his activities on the gymnastics team gave him his later goatlike agility on field trips. Although he played violin in his high school orchestra, he was pretty single-minded about the direction his career would take even then. He decided to spend his first Los Angeles summer working as an apprentice lapidary. He enjoyed cutting and polishing stones so much that his parents worried that he might never go to college. But their belief in the value of a higher education—preferably at Caltech— was not lost on him.

Gene Shoemaker started at Caltech in fall 1944. To train navy engineers, the school had adopted an intense wartime routine in which the year was divided into three semesters instead of the usual two plus summer vacation. "I squirted out of Caltech in 2⅔ years," is how Shoemaker describes his undergraduate career and graduation at the young age of 19. He stayed on at Caltech to earn his master's degree in 1948, this time after having completed a thesis about the petrology of a small area of Precambrian metamorphic rocks in northern New Mexico.

That year Gene Shoemaker joined the US Geological Survey to complete an important project: searching for deposits of uranium in western Colorado. At the dawn of the nuclear age, the United States had very limited knowledge of where uranium deposits were. Headed by geologist Richard Fisher, this project was vital both for the production of nuclear weapons and for the fledgling nuclear power industry. Those were the days when we were told that nuclear power would be too cheap to measure—but first we needed a supply of uranium.

STARTING A DREAM

Out in the western Colorado boondocks that year, Shoemaker was sure that human beings would land on the moon in his lifetime. "It all came to me in a flash one morning while driving to breakfast," he recalls. Only 20 years old, he was living in a mill camp in West Vancoram, Colorado, preparing for a diamond-drilling project. He had already made up his mind that the Earth would be his laboratory, but on that morning, the Earth was suddenly no longer enough.

"I had my meals 5 miles away in Naturita, down at the headquarters of the Vanadium Corporation of America," he reminisces.

> I was driving along the road along this beautiful river. Aha! That is what I will aim to do: to be one of the first people on the Moon. Why will we go to the moon? To explore it, of course! And who is the best person to do that? A geologist, of course! I took the first fork that went to the moon that morning.

If that daybreak drive saw the start of Shoemaker's road to the moon, joining the US Geological Survey that summer was his first turn. "I didn't tell anybody about it at the time—it was a secret goal and it might have been considered silly," he said. Since craters are the most dominant feature on the moon—even the smallest telescope will show at least 300 of them—early on that road, his thoughts turned to craters. How did they form? Were they volcanic? Were they the result of comet or asteroid crashes? "I deliberately studied those aspects of geology that I thought might be turns on the road to the moon," he says. "I studied violently explosive volcanoes—a turn on the road to the moon." After 2 years in the field, he was accepted at Princeton University for his Ph.D.

THE LANGUAGE OF THE EARTH

At this time in his career, Shoemaker's goal was to go into the study of igneous and metamorphic petrology—the study of rocks formed by volcanism or changed by heat and pressure—and he looked forward to working under Arthur Buddington, one of the nation's top petrologists. Since his early weeks at Princeton were slow, Shoemaker decided to use them to dispose of his language requirements: French and German. Designed to give Ph.D. candidates the ability to read journal articles in the world's major scientific languages, the requirement was handled not by language departments but the geology department itself. French was taught by the department's invertebrate paleontologist, Benjamin Howell. Shoemaker got a copy of Eduard Seuss's *Le Face de Terre*, a famous turn-of-the-century summary of the geology of the Earth printed in French, German, and English. About a week later, he returned to ask Howell a routine question. Howell rose from his desk and fetched a book written in French. "Translate this!" Howell said. With some surprise Shoemaker began translating the paper orally. Howell provided a few missing words, and in less than a half-hour, Shoemaker passed his French requirement. "Not bad!" Shoemaker thought. "Now I'll try German." Shoemaker then went to the German version of the book, *Das Antlitz der Erde*, but finishing German took longer.

Game plan is one of Shoemaker's favorite expressions, and for good reason. Since early in his life, he has always had a clear idea of where he wanted to go. For his doctorate, the Shoemaker game plan was to finish up completely in 2 years. Moreover in the 2 years after leaving Caltech, he had completed most of the field work for what he expected to be his dissertation, the geology of the beautiful Fisher Valley–Sinbad Valley salt structure that spans the Colorado–Utah border. So in the summer of 1951, Shoemaker returned to Grand Junction, Colorado, for two reasons: to prepare some geologic quadrangle maps of his thesis area for publication and more importantly, he hoped to marry Carolyn Spellmann, a young woman he had met a few years earlier.

Gene first met Carolyn when he was best man at her brother Richard's wedding. Gene and Richard had roomed together at the Caltech. Although Carolyn had a boyfriend, Richard wanted to introduce her to Gene. "If you will give us some time," he bribed his sister, "I'll give you this wonderful tablecloth." Carolyn agreed. "I was easily bribed," she admitted.

Born in 1929 in Gallup, New Mexico, Carolyn grew up in Chico, California, at the northern end of the Sacramento Valley. Her father was a poultry farmer and her mother a schoolteacher. Carolyn got her A.B. and M.A. degrees from Chico State College, now the University of California at Chico.

FROM URANIUM TO IMPACT CRATERS

Gene Shoemaker fully expected to return to Princeton in the fall of 1951, write his dissertation, and finish his Ph.D. on schedule. But before that summer was over, the geological survey's directors turned Shoemaker's plan on its head by calling on him to return to studying uranium deposits and the regional pattern of their chemistry. The prospect excited him. Thinking that there may be clues in this pattern that would lead to important discoveries of ore, he set out on an adventure. This one small change in his game plan is what led him to have an impact on craters and space.

Gene Shoemaker's road to space began in a field of ancient volcanoes in northern Arizona's Navajo reservation, called the Hopi

Buttes. In the course of his regional investigation, Shoemaker had discovered uranium deposits in the eroded volcanic vents of those ancient volcanoes, and now he had the chance to study them. "I already had that in mind as a stepping stone to the moon," Shoemaker remembers of his time spent there mapping the eerie-looking structure of the ancient volcanic vents. "I wanted to understand how violent volcanoes work. They actually make craters that in form are quite similar to some lunar craters." At the time he suspected that some lunar craters might have been created by the same process.

In fall 1952, returning with Carolyn and a colleague from a field trip to the Grand Canyon, Shoemaker paid his first call at the crater on Coon Butte near Winslow, Arizona. The three exulted in the prospect of seeing Meteor Crater as they rumbled along Route 66 in an old government-issue jeep station wagon. When they arrived, they found that it cost money to get in. "We had just enough money to get some fried rice for dinner," Carolyn remembered. "We were down to nickels and dimes." With a peek over the rim at sunset, they got a sneak preview of their future occupation.

THE FINAL SEARCH FOR THE CRATER'S ORIGIN

Meteor Crater was obviously the result of some sudden convulsion, but by 1954, Shoemaker still wasn't sure what had caused that convulsion. Could it be a salt dome that had collapsed or even a volcanic explosion? Or could it be the result of a hit from an asteroid from space? In 1954, a paper by geologist Dorsey Hager turned Gene's mind back to Meteor Crater and started his final sprint to figuring out its cause. The paper described how petroleum drillers had discovered structures called evaporites a few tens of miles east of the crater. Since the crater was nearby, Hager suggested that perhaps it was the result of a collapsed salt dome, but Shoemaker was skeptical. The crater, he thought, is in a pretty busy geological area; in addition to the evaporites, it is also near a region filled with ancient volcanoes. It was just as possible that the crater could be a Maar-type volcano similar to volcanoes he was studying in the Hopi Buttes.

Shoemaker and Hager started writing to each other, and Hager sent a sample of pumiceous silica glass by mail. Years earlier when digging shafts beneath the crater floor in his search for the huge mass of iron, Barringer had found this glassy material. To test whether this glass were volcanic, as Hager suggested, or melted sandstone as Barringer had thought, Shoemaker sent the sample for spectrographic analysis.

The result: Both the salt dome and volcano ideas were blown out of the water. The glass had the same composition as the Coconino sandstone he had sampled in the Grand Canyon, and the same formation was exposed in the crater. No doubt, Shoemaker thought, the glass had been formed when the nearly pure quartz sandstone fused. For quartz to fuse in this manner, the temperature had to be about 1500 degrees celsius, some 300 degrees higher than the hottest lava flow. Not a collapsed salt dome, not even a volcanic explosion—Shoemaker now knew that only a high speed impact from an asteroid from space could have created enough heat for this glass to form. After almost half a century, Barringer at last was proved right: Meteor Crater was indeed an impact crater.

Shoemaker had to wait to test his idea of an impact origin for the crater until he'd completed his doctoral course and examination at Princeton. He had expected to finish his dissertation while continuing his uranium work on the Colorado–Utah border. By 1956 the roster of known uranium deposits was building quickly, and material for the growing nuclear power industry was known to be more abundant than expected, but now plutonium was the problem. This was the height of the cold war, the "balance of terror," as Churchill called it, between the United States and the Soviet Union. With the arms race in full swing by 1956, the amount of plutonium needed for the increasing numbers of weapons exceeded the supply. Enter Project MICE—for megaton ice-contained explosion. Simply stated, this involved wrapping a blanket of uranium around a nuclear device. The resulting explosion would breed a lot of plutonium. The explosion could occur buried in ice or in salt; however there was no body of ice, at least none under US control, large enough to handle an explosion equivalent to a million tons of dynamite that would produce the needed plutonium. So the answer came down to searching for large, relatively pure bodies of salt.

Shoemaker was asked to participate in MICE to answer a specific question: Would this underground explosion produce an eruption at the surface, somewhat analogous to the eruptions of ancient volcanoes in the Hopi Buttes? Shoemaker concluded that salt melted in the nuclear blast would not erupt at the surface at a later time.

But Shoemaker did find something else to worry about. Visiting the Nevada nuclear test site at Yucca Flats, he studied two 100-meter-wide craters, fancifully named Jangle U and Teapot S. Small subsurface 1.2-kiloton nuclear explosions had formed them—nothing too large but large enough to give an idea of what much larger forces could create. "I discovered that the shock-melted materials that had been close to the nuclear device were dispersed along the floors of both craters," Shoemaker remembers. The plutonium produced in the large explosion might not be neatly stowed in a puddle on the floor of the explosion cavity; instead it might be hidden in the larger volume of broken rock.

To extrapolate the effects that he observed in the small nuclear craters to those expected from a much larger explosion, Shoemaker decided to visit Meteor Crater. By this time he was almost certain that the crater was the result of an impact. "I was astonished to discover that the structure of Meteor Crater was pretty much a scaled up version of that of Teapot S," he remembers. But Meteor Crater taught him something else. Barringer's attempt to find a large iron meteorite under the crater was defeated because the meteorite, melted by the shock of impact, was largely dispersed in a thick lens of breccia, or broken rock, beneath the crater floor. Similarly the plutonium formed in a contained megaton nuclear explosion might be widely dispersed—both difficult to use and extremely dangerous.

Project MICE was abandoned later when other ways of increasing plutonium production were found. For Shoemaker the effort wasn't wasted. The project gave him a detailed understanding of the structure of an impact crater and the mechanisms by which it is formed.

A VISIT TO THE CRATER

In 1991 some 200 scientists from all over the world assembled at Meteor Crater to see the final resting place of an asteroid that had come to stay. Some had traveled from the soon-to-be-former Soviet Union to explore this place. "Miss a trip down Meteor Crater with Gene Shoemaker?" someone said. "You gotta be kidding!" As we clambered down the three-quarter mile wide bowl, slithering along its slope, the immensity of what happened so long ago became clear. What was causing us so much sweat, cuts, and bruises was carved out by a rock from space.

Gene Shoemaker *is* Meteor Crater, for although others suggested that it is the remains of an impact, Shoemaker proved it. He discovered layers of sediment that had been turned upside down, the new mineral coesite that was formed by the shock of the blast, and a host of other geological clues. All this created a picture in his mind of a thunderous impact, a mushroom cloud, and a parcel of land 2.5 kilometers wide, including the crater and the surrounding rim, that permanently reshaped itself in 5 seconds.

The vision of the ancient impact Shoemaker described to us strengthened as we started down the crater. It looked huge. How could an asteroid no larger than 50 meters in diameter have done such a thing in 5 seconds? Among the scientists at the crater rim was Fred (dirty snowball) Whipple, who had suggested more than 40 years earlier that comets were conglomerates of ices and dust orbiting in the solar system. At 85 years of age, he was still one of the most active conference participants that week. But as he looked down the precipitous trail, he decided not to attempt the hike. "I've done it before," he announced. "This time I'll walk the perimeter." Whipple's plan was hardly a visit to a shopping mall—it meant several hours of hiking across steeply rolling rocky terrain—but he did it.

Shoemaker did not intend to start us down the crater right away, instead we crept across the steep talus slope several hundred feet below the rim, hugging the wall and avoiding loose stones displaced by other hikers. We visited several interesting outcrops of rock layers that the impact had turned upside down. Shoemaker showed us other evidence he had chronicled over the years that pointed to the direction, speed, and type of the asteroid's fall.

Suddenly—very suddenly—Marsden whooshed past me as everyone struggled down the talus. With a relieved grin, he slalomed to a stop inches from Shoemaker, who looked at him somewhat startled. "Gene! Just trying to keep up!" he quipped. One person descended on crutches, another in a suit, tie, and vest.

As I made my way to the center of the crater floor, I finally caught my breath. There was water there—warm water, but it tasted so good! I looked up at the surreal late afternoon scene. Surrounding me were the towering walls of the crater, all carved out in 5 seconds.

We started back up. Shoemaker's group seemed to be heading straight up the crater wall. I had had enough, so I took an easier way on an old mule trail. As people passed me, their conversations now contained less science and more politics. Back in that early summer of 1991, the world was in such upheaval. The middle of this crater was somehow an appropriate place for a visiting Russian astronomer to bemoan the changes taking place in his country: "Four whole generations have grown up on Leningrad," he said, wiping perspiration. "Is it really necessary to toss out such a tradition and return to St. Petersburg?"

Finally making it to the top, I looked back at the huge crater now lit by a setting sun. Exhausted, we sat down to a rimside dinner, united in our appreciation of the importance of learning about these tiny marauders of the solar system. Despite the beauty and grandeur they created in sculpting the Earth, we appreciated that they could bring about untold damage.[4]

☾ 10 ☽

A Turn on the Road to the Moon

Now strongly suspected to be the result of a hit from an asteroid from space, Meteor Crater sparked Shoemaker's curiosity. What could hit the Earth from out there? What has hit the Earth? The answers would be hard to find on Earth, since most of the ancient craters have eroded or are buried, but on the nearby moon, a crater lasts almost forever. To answer his questions, Shoemaker needed to study the moon.

In 1956 Shoemaker spoke with Thomas Nolan, then director of the U.S. Geological Survey, about the possibility of launching a photographic study of the moon to produce the first geologic map ever made of something other than the Earth. It may have sounded wild at the time, and Nolan was the first person to hear the details of his moon dream, but to Shoemaker's surprise, Nolan didn't laugh. "It is to his credit," Shoemaker remembers, "that Nolan took the project quite seriously." He steered the young geologist to the right people, who explained that while a topographic map of the moon had been thought of, a map emphasizing its geological features had not. A year later the moon-mapping project was still at the idea stage, kept pretty much in the background as other work, particularly the MICE project, demanded Shoemaker's attention.

The early days of 1957 were not the time to sell the government or the military establishment on space exploration. Large missiles were being built and tested at places like White Sands in New Mexico by people with big ideas, like Werner von Braun, once a rocket scientist from Nazi Germany, now working for the United States. But when these same people suggested that the rockets being tested—particularly the Redstone and the Atlas—could some day hurl satellites into orbit around the Earth, and maybe on to the moon, they were ordered to forget the idea. Missiles were for defense, they were told, not for scientific exploration. Mr. Wizard, the popular science teacher, held no fascination for the U.S. government.

All that changed on October 4, 1957. Returning from a MICE meeting to a survey camp in the Hopi Buttes, Shoemaker heard big news on the portable radio. The Soviets had launched an artificial satellite called *Sputnik.* "Oh hell!" he winced, "I'm not ready for that yet!" But if Shoemaker wasn't ready, neither was anyone else in the nation. At the highest levels of government, U.S. policy turned 180 degrees overnight. The United States couldn't let its archenemy take control of space by default. Now there had to be a satellite program. Although the Naval Research Lab had its Vanguard satellite program, its first attempt collapsed in a cloud of exploding metal on the launch pad. Von Braun was put to work to get something—anything—into orbit within 90 days. Barely making the deadline, in 1958 a *Jupiter-C* rocket launched *Explorer I* into orbit. People cheered across the country, and the Pentagon brass breathed a sigh of relief. There would be more science in the schools. Where before Shoemaker worried that people would scoff at his ideas, now he was being listened to.

After MICE was shut down, the Shoemakers moved to Menlo Park on the San Francisco peninsula. With a group of people interested in exploring the moon and planets, Shoemaker participated in a colloquium at the start of 1959. He then began making a precursory lunar map to demonstrate that one could explain the stratigraphy of rocks exposed on the lunar surface.

BACK TO METEOR CRATER

With the National Aeronautics and Space Administration (NASA) established under the guidance of Senator Lyndon Johnson in 1958, Shoemaker believed his road to the moon was about to be paved. But despite his attempts to get the U.S. Geological Survey involved in a moon program, Shoemaker kept running into indifference. Then in the spring of 1960, something that seemed innocuous—an article in the *Journal of Geophysical Research* by geologist Joseph Boyd—set Shoemaker on yet another turn on the road. The article established temperature and pressure conditions under which a high pressure form of silica may crystallize. The impact of a comet or an asteroid, Shoemaker thought, would create an environment for such a mineral to form in the real world. Could this be the signature, the giveaway for other impact craters? With colleague Beth Madsen, Shoemaker intended to look for this mineral in the extensive collection of shocked rocks he had gathered from Meteor Crater. But before he had a chance to do that, another colleague, Edward Chao in Washington, detected the mineral in a specimen from Meteor Crater on display at the National Museum.

Soon Shoemaker and Madsen found samples of the mineral and mapped out the occurrence of this high-pressure mineral at Meteor Crater. This newly identified mineral was named coesite, after Loring Coes, the physical chemist who had discovered its crystalline phase in the laboratory. Thus, by 1960 there was a reliable basis for demonstrating that other craterlike structures on Earth were the wounds of ancient impacts. The timing was perfect. The fledgling NASA finally decided to fund Shoemaker's proposal for a detailed quadrangle-by-quadrangle geologic map of the crater-pocked moon.

The summer of 1960 saw another turn on the road to the moon. The Shoemakers planned a trip to the International Geological Congress, which was being held that year in Copenhagen. On the way they planned to vacation in southern Germany and visit the Ries basin, a 27-kilometer-wide structure that Shoemaker suspected of being an impact crater. "My father died that spring," Shoemaker noted,

> and so we encouraged mother to join us. We bought a VW microbus, took delivery of it in Hamburg, headed south along the Rhine to look at some volcanic craters, then turned east toward the basin. We drove through rain and reached the site near the end of the day.
>
> The rain had stopped. By the light of the setting sun we looked at the shock-formed rocks that had been supposed to be volcanic. I took one look at these rocks with a hand lens. No question these were impact rocks!
>
> With night falling, the three found a wooded campsite. The next morning they went to the post office, airmailed two samples to Edward Chao in Washington, and then visited the St. George's Cathedral in Nördlingen. "The whole cathedral was built of suevite—it was made of stuff that had suffered the shock of the impact," Shoemaker marvelled. "And at that moment, I was the only geologist in the world who knew it![1]

Back in Washington Chao's X-ray diffractometer quickly confirmed Shoemaker's suspicion that an impact some 15 million years ago had left its coesite signature. Whatever hit back then must have been pretty big, something perhaps 2 kilometers across. The discovery sparked a flurry of activity, both among German geologists, who had a field day with their newly anointed impact crater, and among other geologists, who were interested in finding other impact sites around the world. In Canada, an aerial search for impact craters had already led to the discovery of some promising sites, including a 3-kilometer-wide crater a short distance from Kingston, Ontario, that formed when something slammed into the Earth 500 million years ago, one of the oldest events on record.

Years later Shoemaker revisited Nördlingen, this time to receive, along with Chao and a German geologist, the first Ries cultural prize. "It was so good to see that geology is part of their culture," Shoemaker noted.

A GEOLOGIC MAP OF THE MOON

Now that the lunar mapping project was started, Shoemaker proceeded in much the same way he did out on the Colorado plateau. He wasn't on the moon—not yet—but he had pictures. Some 40 years earlier, on exceptionally steady nights when the 100-inch Hooker telescope at Mt. Wilson Observatory had been new, Francis G. Pease had taken such high-quality photographs of the moon that they picked up craters as small as 1 kilometer in diameter. Shoemaker had enlargements made of the region around the crater Copernicus, a huge feature that might have resulted from a comet impact about a billion years ago. From these photographs his team made the first geologic map of a lunar feature. Besides Copernicus the map showed a whole set of geological features in a region about the size of Arizona. Later Shoemaker expanded the mapping into adjacent areas. Once completed, the project included 50 quadrangles covering much of the entire side of the moon visible from Earth.

In 1960 Shoemaker joined the television team for Project Ranger, the widely publicized program to send a small spacecraft to the moon. The next year the U.S. Geological Survey set up a formal Branch of Astrogeology with Shoemaker as branch chief. Although Shoemaker didn't want to administer the branch, that seemed to be the best way to advance the program. Despite President Kennedy's decision in May 1961 to send an American to the moon by 1970, the concept of geologic mapping as a technique for deciphering the history of a planetary body was unfamiliar to most of the managers at NASA, and it was still difficult to get funding for lunar research. Still the program expanded slowly. With two of the highest resolution telescopes then available, the 36-inch diameter refractor at Lick Observatory in northern California and the 24-inch refractor in Flagstaff, Arizona, Shoemaker's team worked to decipher the stratigraphy and geologic history of regions that were destined to be explored by unmanned spacecraft and later by *Apollo*.

The team showed that a covering of material (called an ejecta blanket) thrown off when something hits the moon lies on top of much older blankets and other geologic structures. These blankets gave the team a way of ascertaining the relative age of the craters. The blankets also showed that when a comet or asteroid hits the moon, pieces of the lunar surface are hurled up and land again, forming secondary craters that could also help establish the sequence of events and the stratigraphic relation of ejecta blankets. It was a good start, but Shoemaker felt he needed more: a special telescope dedicated to lunar mapping. Once he received funding for this 31-inch diameter telescope, Shoemaker decided to move his family and the headquarters of the U.S. Geological Survey's astrogeology branch to Flagstaff, Arizona.

By then the Shoemakers had two daughters and a son. Flagstaff wasn't just close to Meteor Crater, it was also a good place to raise a family. But it would no longer be a turn on Shoemaker's road to the moon. The medical requirements for astronauts were unyielding—if you had sniffled once or twice in your life, you could forget it. In 1963 Shoemaker was diagnosed with Addison's disease. Although it was under good medical control, Shoemaker knew that he could not be an *Apollo* astronaut. If he planned to go to the moon at all, he would have to do it on Earth.

In 1964 Harry Hess, an old friend and professor from Princeton, chaired the committee that would review the scientific qualifications of scientists who wished to join the *Apollo* astronaut corps. "What I thought about in 1948 seemed to be coming to pass," Shoemaker says.

> Harry Hess chose to head up the committee himself; he asked several people, including me, to work with him. But when the time came for the committee to do its work, he was on sabbatical in England so he said, "Here, Shoemaker, you chair the committee!" Instead of being there at the head of the line with my application to go to the moon, I ended up chairing the committee that reviewed the other applicants.[2]

Out of a thousand applications for scientist astronauts, only 15 qualified. Of those, only six passed NASA's incredibly tough physical exam. And only one—Harrison Schmidt—actually made it to the moon.

Exploring Craters
From Ranger to Apollo

Now there was a bright new moon, and as usual in that phase its horns were tilted towards the east. Suddenly the upper horn split in two. From the midpoint of the division a flaming torch sprang up, spewing out, over a considerable distance, fire, hot coals, and sparks. Meanwhile the body of the moon which was below writhed, as it were, in anxiety, and to put it in the words of those who reported it to me and saw it with their own eyes, the moon throbbed like a wounded snake. Afterwards it resumed its proper state. The phenomenon was repeated a dozen times or more, the flame assuming various twisting shapes at random and then returning to normal. Then after these transformations the moon from horn to horn, that is along its whole length, took on a blackish appearance.[1]

Forgotten for almost 800 years, this narrative by a group of British monks captured the fancy of a geologist named Jack B. Hartung in 1976. He suspected that this report could be an accurate observation of a comet or an asteroid hitting the moon.[2] The chronicle describes an extraordinary event—the upper part of the crescent splitting in two as debris from the crash blasts a dark cloud hundreds of miles across the moon and finally a pall of dust giving the moon a short-lived atmosphere and preventing its light from reaching us— blackening it in a sense.

But if this were a major impact, where is the crater? On the moon, where there is virtually no erosion, there is little to indicate relative youth. Its surface is pockmarked with craters that do not disappear. New craters even form on top of old craters. However there is a key: As debris flies across the moon after an impact, it lands again in long streaks of small craters and boulders that are easily seen from Earth as systems of rays. Tycho, the largest crater to be dug out of the moon in relatively recent times—it is thought to be only a hundred million years old—is the best example. This crater is named after the famous sixteenth-century Danish astronomer who was also familiar with impacts in a sense—he lost part of his nose in a fight. Although the moon's craters become virtually permanent features, the youngest craters are surrounded by long, soft rays of rocky material that radiate from their centers. These systems of rays do not last more than a few hundred million years. Thus if a crater has its ray system, it is probably relatively young.

Tycho's ray system stretches out over half the moon's surface. The moon's second most substantial system of rays originates in a crater on the far side, never visible from Earth. This crater is named Giordano Bruno in memory of the scholar—a contemporary of Galileo—who was put to death in 1600 for suggesting that Earth was but one of many worlds and these worlds could harbor intelligent life. Crater Giordano Bruno is just beyond the side of the moon that is visible from Earth, but it has been photographed by spacecraft. The crater is about 20 kilometers in diameter, the size of a small city. Although it is only one-fifth the size of Tycho, its ray system is almost as large. Had the object that caused it, probably about 2 kilometers across, fallen on Earth instead, the result would have been catastrophic, perhaps even capable of wiping out civilization.

Even with the evidence of Giordano Bruno's youthful ray system, however, we can't say conclusively that the crater was formed in 1178. The chronicle is dated the end of June, placing it near the maximum of the Taurid meteor shower, which consists of a large number of remnants of a comet that must have disintegrated long ago. Comet Encke is the largest member of the Taurid swarm.

Illustration of rays on the moon (see Chapter 11). The author took these photographs during a partial eclipse of the moon. In the brighter photograph, the large crater Tycho is near the top, and its ray system, stretching away from it and extending across the moon's surface, can be seen in both pictures. During eclipses the long rays of material coming from craters like Tycho stand out more clearly.

Kenneth Brecher of Boston University suggests that a smaller relation of Encke's comet could have struck the moon as it passed through the Taurid swarm in 1178.[3] Other scientists suggest that the same effects could have been produced by a meteor in our own atmosphere chancing across the position of the moon. But some unusual phenomenon in the Earth's own atmosphere may also have produced a similar effect. In any event, by far the weakest link in this chain of evidence is the ancient observation itself, since no one else recorded the event. Bradley Schaefer, who studies the visibility of thin lunar crescents, insists that the moon was too low on the night mentioned in the chronicle, which is June 25 by our calendar.[4] However it would not matter much if the date were off by one and the event really took place on June 26. Was a bright comet visible that year that could have hit the moon? (There was, but its appearance 6 months early rules it out as the possible culprit.) Or was the object an asteroid, which would not have been observed? According to physicist Graeme Waddington, who suggested the June 26 date after studying the *Chronicles*,

> Gervase is highly regarded and the details in his Chronicle are considered to be remarkably accurate. It is precisely because of this high esteem that Gervase's record of the "Canterbury event" must be taken seriously. . . .[5]

Unless someday we can collect material from Giordano Bruno, we may never know whether it really is as young as some evidence might suggest.

TO THE MOON WITH RANGER

Eight hundred years after the British monks looked toward the moon in shock and wonder, other eyes looked in wonder at the moon. By 1960 it was time to explore the lunar surface with spacecraft. Although the crater Giordano Bruno mystery was not a factor in the late 1950s when lunar exploration began—the crater's existence wasn't even known until the Soviet unmanned spacecraft *Luna III* passed by the moon in October 1959—the mystery of how so many craters were formed on the moon was a prime motive for going. The Earth and the moon were likely formed at the same distance from the sun, but the cratering record on our active planet has been largely erased by erosion and other geological and climatological processes; not so on the moon. If we could understand what happened there, we would understand what happened here. It is that logic that drove Shoemaker to the moon—if not in person, then through the eyes of machine probes and other men.

Shoemaker was asked to join the *Ranger* television team around 1960, along with Gerard Kuiper and Harold Urey, then two of the leading authorities on the moon. Shoemaker was being let in on the ground floor of Project *Ranger*, an exciting new endeavor, and he accepted eagerly. Conceived by a group of engineers at the Jet Propulsion Laboratory (JPL), *Ranger's* aim was ambitious almost beyond belief for its time. "The Jet Propulsion Lab was a really vigorous place," Shoemaker notes. "They were going to build a spacecraft fast and send it to the moon." The hexagon-shaped spacecraft bristled with an array of instruments for conducting several experiments. There was a television camera, and a gamma ray spectrometer to measure detectable radioactive elements on the moon. Tucked inside was a balsa instrument container atop a retrorocket. The idea is that the balsa package would detach from the main spacecraft as it approached the moon. The retrorocket would fire as long as it could, slowing down the balsa container and landing it on the surface. Then a small seismometer would right itself while a small antenna pierced the encasement and started sending data to Earth.

After the first two test *Rangers* were successful in trial runs, all was ready for the real mission. But then the problems started. *Ranger 3* missed the moon by almost 40,000 kilometers a few days after its launch on January 26, 1962. A few months later, *Ranger 4's Atlas-Agena* rocket worked flawlessly, sending the craft on a direct course to the moon. But a failure on the spacecraft prevented any of the experiments or cameras from operating, and the craft, its balsa container still aboard, shattered on the moon. *Ranger 5,* launched in the early fall of 1962, came the closest to success of the original *Rangers,* but despite the fact that all its experiments seemed to work, it missed the moon by a few hundred kilometers.

By this time, the hope and excitement at the JPL had turned to gloom. "Either the spacecraft was great," Shoemaker lamented, "or the *Atlas* booster was great. Trouble is in five tries, we couldn't get a good rocket and a good spacecraft at the same time."[6]

After *Ranger 5's* dismal failure, NASA put the whole program on hold while the project was redesigned. There was another consideration. In May 1961 President Kennedy had committed the United States to landing a man on the Moon by the end of 1969, so engineering firms all over the nation were gearing up for mighty Project *Apollo.* After the failure of *Ranger 5,* scientists still had no idea what the lunar surface was really like. Would it be firm enough to support a manned spacecraft? Where was the best and safest site to land a manned spacecraft? Thinking that the problem with *Ranger* was that the craft design was too complicated, NASA tried simplifying the idea on the notion that a few good close-up pictures would be better than a spacecraft full of expensive but useless instruments. The balsa container vanished as well as the boom with the gamma-ray detector. Instead a simple conical tower appeared on top of the hexagonal frame to support a set of six television cameras. Of all the scientific teams associated with the Ranger project, only the Kuiper–Urey–Shoemaker team directly benefitted from the new design. A good picture was all that mattered now.

Although this sounds unscientific, the real cause of the early *Ranger* flops was simply bad luck. After all a similar version of the same spacecraft flew successfully to Venus as *Mariner 2* in 1962. In any event, four newly designed spacecraft were built. Finally at the end of January 1964, all was ready for the launch of *Ranger 6.* Shoemaker recalls the cutting tension at the JPL:

> The *Atlas* performed like a jewel. The *Agena* performed like a jewel. The spacecraft was fine. It was sending a clear signal as it made its final approach to the moon. Everyone in the lab

was huddling around the speakers, listening to the reports from the Goldstone tracking station. When the spacecraft was about a thousand kilometers from the lunar surface, the final critical signal was sent to turn on the cameras.[7]

Nothing. "No video." The signal was sent a second time. "Still no video." For the next few minutes the room was silent except for the announcer's repeated, "Still no video." Then the spacecraft crashed into the moon, its faint signal silenced. The control room at JPL was as silent as a crypt.

The cause of *Ranger 6's* frustrating failure turned-up soon afterward—a simple short circuit had killed the television cameras during the strain of launch. When it was time for *Ranger 7* that summer, once again the launch went flawlessly, and as *Ranger 7* approached the moon on target a few days later, the control room at JPL was filled with people. As the spacecraft neared its thousand-kilometer distance from which it would begin photography of the moon, everyone in that room knew that JPL's future rested on what would happen in the next few seconds.

The signal was sent to turn on the cameras. "We have video!" It was an indelible moment. "Suddenly everyone was jumping up and down," Shoemaker raved. "We didn't even know what the pictures were yet, but that didn't matter. There were pictures!"

Before the craft smashed into Mare Cognitum, its cameras caught the first view of what the ray of a crater looked like up close. It recorded a beautiful tapestry left over from the impact of the comet or asteroid that produced the Crater Tycho a hundred million years ago. The crash point was near one of the bright rays that extend from the crater—rays filled with hundreds of secondary craters that were produced when material hurled upward from Tycho's main impact point landed far away. Some of these craters were as large as 100 meters or as small as 2 meters across.

The JPL desperately needed the success of *Ranger 7*. For *Ranger 8*, the scientific team tried to persuade engineers to aim the spacecraft closer to the moon's terminator, the moving zone of lunar sunrise or sunset where lower sun angles would result in far better pictures. However the engineers feared that these areas would not provide sufficient light for the craft's cameras. It was not until *Ranger 9's* assault on the crater Alphonsus in March 1965 that the program reached its zenith. *Ranger 9* was aimed at one of the moon's most interesting areas. In 1958 the Soviet astronomer Nikolai Kozyrev had seen whitish glows in this crater, and his observations through a spectroscope showed evidence that gases were being emitted. *Ranger 9* was sent to answer a specific question: Was there volcanic activity in Alphonsus? *Ranger 9* arrived just after Alphonsus' sunrise, snapping almost 6000 pictures before crashing into the crater. The pictures revealed some halo craters that might be volcanic in origin. Apparently there was plenty of past volcanic activity there, but no current action.[8] Like the earlier *Rangers, Ranger 9* taught scientists about the fine structure of the lunar surface.

ON THE MOON WITH SURVEYOR

Soon it was time to make the transition to a craft that would do everything the earlier *Rangers* tried to do and more. Instead of having a wooden box bounce around on the moon, *Surveyor's* entire Christmas-tree-like frame would land so delicately that it would barely disturb the soil it lighted on. It would then photograph the surface for more than a week before setting down to rest for the long and frigid lunar night during which temperatures would plummet to more than 200 degrees below zero. Shoemaker was invited by JPL to participate as an investigator.

The early designs for *Surveyor* loaded the craft with cameras and other instruments, but as failure after failure dogged the *Ranger* program, NASA and JPL decided to scale down *Surveyor*. "They threw off all the instruments," Shoemaker laments, "leaving only a single camera atop the tree as an engineering test."

Wondering when he would ever get his first close-up view of the lunar surface, Shoemaker spent much of his time experimenting and planning how the camera would do its work once it finally landed. But the first view happened sooner than he expected. In early February 1966, the Soviet craft *Luna 9* gently landed on the moon much as the original *Rangers* had tried to do. But Western nations could spy on this craft, thanks to Sir Bernard Lovell, England's famous radio astronomer, and the giant dish of the world's largest radio telescope at Jodrell Bank. As they examined *Luna 9's* signal, someone noticed that it resembled transmissions that wire services used for newspaper pictures. Wondering if it were really as simple as that, the observers rushed to borrow a facsimile machine and played the signal through it. It worked! They secured a good, though somewhat distorted, picture that showed a surface strewn with rocky rubble.

With memories of the *Ranger* experience still fresh in their minds, Shoemaker's team did not expect anything from the first *Surveyor*. "Of all the people on the *Surveyor* project," Shoemaker says with not too much exaggeration, "only three of the engineers were confident that the craft would actually make it to the Moon. They had really worked that spacecraft over." So when *Surveyor 1* finally made it off the launch pad atop an *Atlas–Centaur* rocket on May 30, 1966, a few months after the Soviet venture, Shoemaker saw it as only the first step in a long process where a single malfunction would doom the journey. At least, most people thought, *Surveyor 1* would be a good learning experience. There was a long way to go, and getting past the first stage of the *Atlas* was the easiest step. Next came the *Centaur's* firing—the upper stage designed to hurl the craft into Earth orbit and then to refire, sending it off to the 25,000 miles per hour velocity needed to escape the bonds of Earth and head off to the moon. Although the *Centaur* had succeeded in tests, this was its first operational flight.

The *Centaur* did its job. Now cautiously optimistic, Shoemaker and his team watched the flight phase from the Earth's orbit to the vicinity of the moon go well, and they assembled at the control room at JPL with the craft still operating nominally. Traveling at 6000 miles per hour only 60 miles away from the moon, *Surveyor's* main rocket fired for about 40 seconds, slowing it down to 250 miles per hour as a radar altimeter connected to an on-board flight programmer monitored the quickly approaching moon. Everything was still fine as the retrorocket dropped away and three smaller rockets took over, slowing the craft to a virtual stop 13 feet above the surface. The rockets then shut off to leave the surface below as pristine as possible. *Surveyor 1* fell quietly to a landing, the strong shock absorbers in its landing legs absorbing much of the shock.

Back in the control room on Earth, the engineers were stunned. "It really landed! We were still communicating with it!" Shoemaker reveled. "It was the most surprised bunch of people you ever saw!"

The next hour passed interminably as Shoemaker and his team waited for the spacecraft's systems to be checked out. But then the camera was on and taking pictures. "I slept about 2 hours over the next 5 days," Shoemaker remembers of the hectic week spent looking at the stream of data from the camera. In that newly finished Spaceflight Operations Facility at JPL, Shoemaker had attained his dream. At *Surveyor's* camp there was a blanket of material that had been thrown off by ancient impacts. The surface was riddled by impact craters from a few centimeters to 30 meters in size.

The second *Surveyor* did not make it to the moon intact, but in April 1967, the third one landed right in the middle of a crater several tens of meters wide. Although the landing was a fine place from which to study what a crater floor was like, the camera couldn't see beyond the crater walls. The fourth *Surveyor* failed, and were it not for a special aspect of its design, the fifth one, launched in September 1967, would have flopped as well. After it turned off its rockets 13 feet above the surface, *Surveyor 5* settled on the wall of a small crater not much larger than it was. Then it started to slide into the crater, its feet gouging out trenches for about a meter before the craft finally came to a stop perched at an angle of almost 20 degrees. Fortunately the spacecraft was designed not to tip over if it set down at an angle that steep. Of course nobody knew of *Surveyor's* dangerous adventure until it was over and the camera was turned on and looking about, taking in the crazy angle and the three footpad trenches.

Launched at the end of 1967, the sixth *Surveyor* took the first stereographic pictures of its site. After its main photographing mission was done, the rockets were turned on and the craft hopped a few meters to a new location. By shooting the same areas a second time, Shoemaker's team put two pictures together to see a three-dimensional representation of what the surface looked like. The stereographic pictures provided a sense of depth that would be very useful when working out distances and heights of the surrounding terrain.

The team had hoped *Surveyor 6* could be targeted to a highland area, since the lunar plains, or maria, had been pretty carefully studied by that time. But the idea of sending *Surveyor 6* to the region of Fra Mauro was rejected; instead *Surveyor 6* went to the Moon's belly button—Shoemaker's term for the Sinus Medii, the small lava plain right at the middle of the side of the moon pointed toward Earth.

With just one *Surveyor* to go, Shoemaker and the other scientists had a plan. "Let's see something different," they suggested. "Let's go to Tycho!" By this time another series of missions called *Lunar Orbiter* had shown the Tycho area to be very rough, so the idea was risky. But the payoff would be handsome. Some 90 kilometers wide, with walls 20 kilometers high, Tycho is most probably, Shoemaker suggests, the site of a comet nucleus impact that happened perhaps a hundred million years ago. At that time dinosaurs were in the middle of their dominance here on Earth. Had these creatures had the presence of mind to watch the sky, they might have seen a comet getting brighter and then suddenly vanishing in a flash of light as it crashed into the moon's southern hemisphere. The crash raised a moonwide cloud of dust as huge chunks of material tore out of the surface and flew as far as halfway around the moon before crashing again to form secondary craters—something quite like what the British monks thought they saw in 1178. We can still see how this impact affected the moon, using a small telescope to view both the crater and its system of rays. The rays are seen at their best when the moon is near full phase.

To Shoemaker's surprise, NASA welcomed the proposal despite the fact that Tycho was far from any of the proposed *Apollo* landing sites. *Surveyor 7* landed quietly on a gentle 5-degree slope on Tycho's northern rim. The first picture told how precarious the landing was: *Surveyor 7* was in the middle of a field of boulders, many of which could have punctured the craft or tipped it over. There was a great variety of rock types, including rocks crushed and deformed by high pressure. "Tycho offered a much younger surface than anything else we had seen," Shoemaker noted.

Surveyor's call on Tycho happened a decade before the discovery of a worldwide layer of iridium led nobel laureate Luis Alvarez, his son Walter, and their colleagues to suggest that a comet or asteroid impact had destroyed most of the life on Earth 65 million years ago. And a quarter-century after *Surveyor's* work was finished, the remains of a larger crater than Tycho were found at Chicxulub on the Yucatan Peninsula of eastern Mexico. Chicxulub and Tycho would appear to have little in common. While Chicxulub is buried, Tycho and its moonwide system of rays dominate the view through even a small telescope. But comet impacts possibly caused both features. Chicxulub is at least twice Tycho's diameter but possibly only two-thirds as old.

APOLLO: THE LAST STEP

Shoemaker was the principal investigator for the field geology experiments for the first three *Apollo* moon landings. With a great deal of enthusiasm, his team set up a mock lunar-landing site, complete with small artificially made craters and a full-size model of the lunar module to give practicing astronauts a chance to practice geological field techniques. "Some of those test pilots were very good observers," Shoemaker remembers, adding that their flight training and alertness gave them the potential to be ideal field geologists—if they could get sufficient training.

Since hanging either tools or devices on an astronaut, such as a geologist's hammer, was out of the question, Shoemaker came up with an ingenious device he called Jacob's staff that the astronaut could carry like a cane. It would have a TV camera, an antenna, and a transponder, so that the lunar module could track it. All the astronaut would have to do was pull a trigger. Then the staff would take a picture while its leveling devices recorded the orientation. But NASA never funded the staff, and Shoemaker worried that the astronauts were not given enough time to practice the methods of field geology. Would *Apollo* be a more complex version of the Mercury "man in a can" program where the astronaut went along for the ride while ground controllers and simple computers gave all the instructions? As a field geologist, Shoemaker hoped for more than that from the *Apollo* moon walks.

On Christmas Eve 1968, a few months after the last *Surveyor* had seen Tycho, three astronauts were orbiting the moon and sending an unforgettable Christmas greeting to all of us on "the good Earth." It was a poetic and moving way of building excitement for the landing that was to follow a few months later. On July 16, 1969 *Apollo 11* surged to life and roared off its launching pad. This was the culmination of a generation's dream. As Armstrong, Aldrin, and Collins left the Earth's orbit and headed moonward, the flight was proceeding as though manned landings on the moon took place every day. But at the very last minute, the astronauts saw trouble on the moon. "We had carefully mapped every crater in the landing strip on Mare Tranquilitatis," Shoemaker recalled. It was an ellipse about 10 kilometers and 2 kilometers wide. But although *Lunar Orbiters* 4 and 5 had recorded some gravity anomalies in the moon—the mascons, or mass concentrations associated with the moon's huge lava-filled basins—the *Apollo* planners had ignored them. As a result, instead of heading for the center of the ellipse, *Apollo 11* was about to land near the far end—right down in one of the largest craters in the whole ellipse.

"Every *Surveyor* that made it to the moon—blind—landed safely," Shoemaker notes. "But the first time we had a man in the spacecraft we really needed him." The crater's blanket of ejecta was full of huge boulders that would have caused the *Eagle* to tip over and crash. As Neil Armstrong urgently steered the craft away from the crater, Buzz Aldrin noted his progress, both downward and across:

> Houston: 60 seconds [of fuel left]
> *Apollo:* Altitude 1600
> 1400
> 400 feet, 8 forward
> 300 feet, 47 forward
> 13 forward
> 11 forward
> down one-half; picking up some dust . . .
> 4 forward, drifting to the right a little
> Houston, urgently: 30 seconds!
> *Apollo:* 4 forward, 40 forward[9]

With less than half a minute of fuel left, Armstrong set *Eagle* between two of the crater's rays. "OK, engines are off." One-sixth of the world's population heard Armstrong's next words: "Tranquility base here. The *Eagle* has landed."

Although Armstrong had by far the shortest of the moon walks, his 90-minute traverse was, to Shoemaker's mind, one of the most successful in the entire *Apollo* program. "He saw more stuff, and he made more pertinent observations, in the precious little time he had on the surface, than many of the astronauts who followed him."

For Shoemaker, *Apollo 11's* return to Earth was the beginning of one of his biggest disappointments. "NASA wanted to plot out every minute of every field traverse," he huffed. "That plan mitigates against discovery." Thinking as a field geologist, Shoemaker believed that the *Apollo* program, successful as it was, was a big lost opportunity.

> Discovery begins when you see something you don't expect. Then you stop and say, "wait a minute, what is this? Maybe I'd better look over here." Then you start out on a completely unplanned traverse to understand what you have seen. *Apollo* never provided that opportunity.[10]

Harrison Schmidt, the lone geologist chosen for the astronaut program from the committee Shoemaker chaired 5 years earlier, managed to make some fascinating discoveries despite the confining schedule. The orange soil found in Shorty crater turned out to be an interesting glass formed in a fountain of ancient volcanic activity. But although Schmidt collected some, mission planners didn't allow the time to take the kind of care that was needed to see how the glass was distributed. *"Apollo* provided outstanding science," Shoemaker concludes,

> But the scientific discovery came from the analysis of the samples brought back, not from the observations of the astronauts. And that was the issue. Why send human beings into space, if not to be prepared for the unexpected?[11]

Shoemaker's condemnation of the *Apollo* program may be a little harsh; after all, this was hardly a normal geologic traverse being monitored from 240,000 miles away. Although the astronauts did not spend so much time at Shorty crater as a field geologist would have liked, Schmidt handled the situation expertly. As soon as his partner reported something highly unusual—the orange soil—Schmidt immediately warned him to delay collecting so that he could study the material in its original, undisturbed setting before he collected any samples. "Don't move it till I see it!" he said repeatedly. Only after Schmidt had a chance to inspect the soil did the astronauts start collecting samples, and the cameras recorded the scene in detail. Meantime a hot discussion took place on the ground as to whether it would be possible to extend the visit to Shorty crater. It was decided that extending the visit so far from the Lunar Excursion Module (LEM) would be too risky.

"My dream for *Apollo*," Shoemaker remembers,

> was to try to create the opportunity to show what a well-trained human being could do, what kind of science he could do on the spot. This is not a kind of science that most practicing scientists understand because they don't do it. But in the six Moon landings, we never demonstrated that important discoveries could be made from field observation.
>
> *Apollo* was not a highlight in my career by any means. The main issue for me was not flags and footprints, but to show why you needed a human being there.[12]

The proof of *Apollo's* failure in Shoemaker's mind comes from what happened afterward. "We stopped. Had *Apollo* really succeeded, we'd still be there exploring." We came, and we saw, but instead of conquering, we went home and did not return.

One important thing that the *Apollo* astronauts did, however, brings us back to the story of crater Giordano Bruno. On *Apollo 11*, Armstrong and Aldrin installed a small reflector off which Earth-based telescopes could bounce laser beams, thereby yielding very accurate measurements of any delicate wobbling motions of the moon, movements we call librations. With the *Apollo 14* and *15* missions as well as the Soviet *Luna 21* expanding the reflector network to cross the moon, astronomers Odile Calame and Derral Mulholland used McDonald Observatory's 107-inch reflector to fire laser beams at these reflectors more than 2000 times. In 1978 they independently calculated the possible effects of an impact exactly 800 years earlier and came up with the same conclusion Hartung did. The event, they wrote, "would have been not only visible but sufficiently apocalyptic to have justified the description given in the Canterbury chronicle."[13] Even more encouraging—though still not definitive—were their laser ranging results, which showed that the moon is indeed swaying by a few meters in a 3-year cycle. Like a huge bell vibrating after it has been clanged, the moon is acting as if it had been struck by a large object within the last millennium.

The *Apollo* astronauts also left a series of seismometers designed to detect moonquakes and impacts on the moon. In late June 1975 near the anniversary of the supposed Canterbury observation, the seismometers recorded the impact of 29-kilogram-sized objects.[14] Could these be part of the swarm that included the Canterbury object if it were real?

Of all the threads that weave this tapestry together, the laser-ranging results from Calame and Mulholland are by far the most impressive, clearly suggesting that the moon has been banged about in the recent past, possibly during the last millennium. It is my hope that some future astronaut may land near crater Giordano

Bruno and conduct field traverses that Shoemaker would be proud of—and sample materials not just at the surface but below it as well. For like all geological mysteries, the answer to the mystery of crater Giordano Bruno is written in rocks that await our return to the moon.

☾ 12 ☽

A Pretty Good Moon for You, Shoemaker!

If 1969 were a time for exploring craters on the moon, it was also a time to start looking for other things in space—not just craters but the comets and asteroids that cause the craters. It turned out that Caltech's Palomar Observatory had a small 18-inch diameter Schmidt telescope that was not being used very much. Palomar is most famous for its mighty 200-inch reflecting telescope, but three other telescopes atop that mountain northeast of San Diego also do important work. As Palomar's first telescope, the 18-inch has a noble history. Astronomer Fritz Zwicky used it to photograph fields of distant galaxies, and in these galaxies he discovered many exploding stars called supernovae. The 18-inch telescope is a photographic telescope capable of taking pictures of large areas of the sky at once—each film covers 8.75 degrees of sky, the equivalent of more than 17 full moons lined up. On a single film, a searcher could record a large nugget of sky. Here was an ideal telescope for searching for comets and asteroids.

The first thing that comes to mind when we think of asteroids is the large belt of them between Mars and Jupiter. We now know of thousands of those main-belt objects. But for an asteroid to hit the Earth or the moon, it has to wander way outside the main belt. It is these errant asteroids that Shoemaker wanted most to study.

A small subset of the Mars-crossing asteroids, objects we call Amors, go so far inside Mars's path that they approach the orbit of the Earth and briefly make close passes to our planet. Still other asteroids, called Apollos, actually venture across the Earth's orbit. In 1969 astronomers knew of about a dozen of these Apollo-type asteroids, each a kilometer or more in diameter.

THE EARTH AS A DARTBOARD

One of the most dramatic Apollos sprinted within 800,000 kilometers of Earth, about twice the distance of the moon, on the night before Halloween 1937. It has not been seen since, but that asteroid, named Hermes, will be back some day in the distant future, either to pass close by the Earth again or even to hit us. Meteor Crater is the result of what happened when an asteroid about 50 meters across—much smaller than Hermes—hit home.

If the Apollo asteroids pose a danger to the Earth, then the two most urgent questions are how many Apollos are there and more important, how close will they get to us? Becoming interested in that question in fall 1969, Shoemaker hired a Caltech scientist named Eleanor Helin "to track down every scrap of information" on the dozen or so Apollo asteroids that had been discovered up to that time. This included getting copies of the original discovery plates from places as far apart as Germany, Belgium, France, and South Africa to learn as much as possible about where the objects were in the sky when they were first spotted and how large they are.

For Shoemaker the problem of how to calculate the current rate of collision of objects with the Earth was already answered in the lunar craters. The crater record there however did not answer questions about the nature of the objects that hit—were they asteroids or comets? The 18-inch telescope, available as a part of Caltech, presented a golden opportunity.

With leftover funds from his role in the Apollo project, Shoemaker and Helin drew up a proposal in 1972 to take the 18-inch telescope on a test run to see what would be involved in searching for asteroids in the vicinity of the Earth. "Glo deserves a lot of credit," Shoemaker said, using Helin's nickname, "for pushing to start this program at the beginning." At the time Shoemaker thought that about 2000 asteroids the size of Hermes (2 kilometers or larger) could be around—all potential bullets aimed at Earth, each packing the wallop of a multimegaton bomb. He figured that if they were to photograph 250 fields a year, they would perhaps find some two new Apollos and two Amors each year. Their plan was to take a 20-minute exposure followed by a 10-minute follow-up shot, giving any new asteroid time to leave its signature as a trail of light across the star-filled photographs. "There was a lot of sweat and tears for each observing run," Helin recalls those difficult early days. And getting the telescope working was only part of the problem. "Roadblocks appeared on a regular basis," she explains. "I'm sure Palomar didn't think I would last a year." Her program is still going strong after 25 years.

Helin averaged seven films per night during her monthly observing runs at the 18-inch telescope. In summer 1973 only 6 months after the project started, she found her first object—one that was designated 1973 NA and now numbered 5496. Encouraged by the rapid find, they pressed on, with Helin doing most of the work. But that new Apollo was just a teaser; it was two-and-a-half long years before the next discovery. For a time after that, the finds remained scarce, although Helin discovered Aten, an asteroid orbiting the sun mostly inside the orbit of the Earth.

FINDING THE DARTS

By the program's fifth anniversary in 1978, Shoemaker knew that his estimate of 2000 near-Earth asteroids was about right but only if he included asteroids down to 1 kilometer instead of 2 kilometers in diameter; and the former were more difficult to find. The discovery rate was so discouraging that Shoemaker thought of applying for time on Palomar's larger Schmidt camera, the mighty 48-inch. Some 20 years earlier it had completed the Palomar Observatory Sky Survey, when it photographed the entire heavens in the northern hemisphere in more than 900 sections.

The first few years of the Shoemaker–Helin Planet-Crossing Asteroid Survey disappointed Shoemaker but they also set him to work on ways of obtaining a better return from Palomar's 18-inch telescope. A report in the planetary science journal *Icarus* reviewed the progress the team had made and its find of 12 new planet-crossing asteroids.[1] How would one get more out of the 18-inch telescope? The solution soon came to Shoemaker's geologist mind: Why not use the same stereographic principle used in some of the stereographic pictures *Surveyor* and the *Apollo* orbiters took of the moon? These pictures gave the features a perception of depth. If he took short exposures and then examined the films in pairs, Shoemaker thought, the moving asteroids would appear not as trails but as single images standing above the starry background. Helin found a California firm called McBain Instruments that built a stereomicroscope capable of holding two 6-inch diameter films at one time. They produced a fine machine for about $10,000— and it was worth every penny. In May and June 1980, Shoemaker and Helin conducted the first tentative observing runs using the stereomicroscope at the 18-inch telescope. The early results were encouraging. By comparing the brightnesses of new discoveries with those of known objects, Shoemaker calculated that they were finding asteroids as faint as the eighteenth magnitude—asteroids perhaps as small as a kilometer in diameter.

Shoemaker and Helin also had a brief flirtation with the 48-inch telescope at that time. Although the first images were badly guided—the stars looked like little seahorses—this telescope later proved capable of finding asteroids even fainter than those studied with the 18-inch telescope. But Shoemaker thought that the smaller telescope was more versatile, since its design allowed faster coverage of the sky each month. "We were coming back from every dark run with lots of new asteroids," he noted.

Feeling more comfortable with the new procedures, Shoemaker added a new twist to the program in fall 1981. In addition to the survey photographs, he and Helin also took films of specific regions in hopes of recovering periodic comets on their way back to the inner solar system. Using both Schmidt telescopes—the 18 inch and the 48 inch—in January 1982, they began a heavy observing schedule.

Because the eruption of the Mexican volcano El Chichon spewed tons of fine particles of sulfuric acid into the upper atmosphere, the sky over Palomar suffered during much of 1982. Helin did discover an Apollo asteroid in February—1982 DB, now named (4660) Nereus. "A benevolent sea-god associated with ancient origins (mythology, if not science)," the citation read, this deity "had the power of prophecy."[2] But if Nereus was prophesying anything that February, it was a change in the program. In fall 1982, Shoemaker and Helin went separate ways, mounting competing programs.

Now working with his wife Carolyn, Shoemaker made several changes. "We stopped taking long exposures, got rid of the filters, dropped down to 4-minute exposures, and really started to cover a lot of sky." The IIa-D film they were using was fast, but a little grainy, resulting in many artifacts and possible new asteroids and comets that did not really exist. By 1983 they switched to Kodak's 4415 technical pan, a slower film requiring longer exposures of 6, 8, or even 10 minutes, but its finer grain was capable of recording fainter objects with fewer film artifacts.

Since then time on the 18-inch telescope has been partitioned equally between the Shoemaker team and the Helin group.

BACK INTO SPACE

Something else brought Shoemaker back into space in the mid-1970s. Lawrence Soderblom, one of his former students and now deputy chief of the *Voyager*-imaging team, paid him a visit. "Gene," he invited, "you paid your dues on the moon. Why not come and join us on the *Voyager*-imaging team?" It was a first-rate opportunity. *Voyager* was the one great hope for studying all the outer planets but Pluto, as well as their moons, in one grand mission. As a multiyear project, *Voyager* was the most ambitious planetary mission ever flown. Two spacecraft would pay calls on Jupiter and Saturn. *Voyager 1* then would visit Saturn's great moon, Titan, before heading out of the solar system, leaving *Voyager 2* to travel outward to Uranus and finally Neptune. At the time of Soderblom's invitation, the spacecrafts were already in the asteroid belt, their cameras calibrated and ready to go. "All the hard work was already done," Shoemaker admitted. "It was an offer I couldn't refuse."

As *Voyager 1* closed in on Jupiter in spring 1979, the imaging team wondered what its coterie of four big moons would be like. Called the Galilean satellites after the man who discovered them in 1610, Io, Europa, Ganymede, and Callisto orbit Jupiter like a solar system in miniature. Earlier observations had already shown that Ganymede, the largest moon, had an icy surface. The big question was, would there still be craters left on it to study, or would the viscous flow of the ice have erased them? Shoemaker hoped that at least one of the Galilean satellites would have a crater record. The bet was that of all the moons, rocky Io would still have its craters.

Not so; Io was a real shocker: That moon had no impact craters—not a single one. In fact as they watched, its surface was being created by eruptions of several huge volcanoes. There were black lakes, calderas, and at least one volcano actually spewing sulfur as the spacecraft tore by. Europa's surface in contrast was glassy smooth with ice. Then came Ganymede, a moon strewn with impact craters and complicated terrain. "Shoemaker!" called John McCauley, one of the team members and a U.S. Geological Survey colleague, "this looks like a pretty good moon for you!" He was right. Ganymede was surprisingly similar to our own moon, with lots of craters, and some of the newer ones had ray systems. Shoemaker took one look at the first Ganymede picture and agreed. This moon had preserved some of its oldest craters. And yet unlike our own moon, all of the younger craters may have been formed by comet impacts. It is possible that asteroids were (and are) very rare this far out in the solar system.

Larger than Mercury and Pluto, Ganymede is the solar system's largest moon. It consists of ancient dark areas crossed by lighter expanses distinguished by long grooves representing its more recent history. Ganymede is a careful recorder through all but its oldest craters of comets that once inhabited the outer solar system. So, it turns out, is the Jovian moon Callisto.

"On Ganymede," Shoemaker explains, "we have an independent source of information of the size distribution of comet nuclei." While both asteroids and comets can make craters on our moon and on other bodies of the inner solar system like Mercury, Shoemaker theorizes that comets dominate the population of small objects in the outer solar system. The only asteroid craters are caused by rogue asteroids that have been put into Jupiter-crossing orbits by repeated encounters with the inner planets. Once an asteroid becomes Jupiter crossing, its fate is almost certainly to be ejected from the solar system.

Craters on Ganymede and Callisto, Shoemaker believes, "tell us something about comets that is hard to find out any other way." The oldest craters may represent an early episode of heavy bombardment by planetesimal objects.[3] One such older feature on Callisto is called Valhalla. Almost 2000 kilometers in diameter, this basin was formed before the surface hardened, its rim resembling a series of frozen waves.

In 1981 the *Voyagers* found a very different story on the moons of Saturn. The inner moons had craters that were generally smaller than those in the Jovian system but with one grand exception: Mimas had one crater, called Herschel, so large that the impact that formed it must have come perilously close to shattering the entire moon. Shoemaker believes only the latest phase of Mimas's history is preserved by Herschel and the smaller craters. Previous large impacts may have repeatedly broken Mimas apart, with gravity reassembling the pieces each time in a different order.

By the time *Voyager* 2 left Neptune and its moons in August 1989, it had unlocked a door to our solar system's past that had not been opened before. To learn about comets, we have to observe comets, but comets in the outer solar system are difficult to follow.

Thanks to the appearance of craters on these moons, we now have a record of what the comet population is like out there.

Voyager's encounter with Neptune took place a few days before one of the Shoemakers' monthly observing runs at Palomar. Since her husband would be tied up at the JPL, Carolyn asked me to observe with her at the 18-inch telescope. It would be my first observing run at Palomar. As I prepared to leave for California, I wanted to see *Voyager's* views of Neptune and its big moon Triton. Tucson's public broadcasting station was carrying *Voyager's* images live, and it seemed like my TV set was connected directly to the spacecraft then speeding by Triton. What a night to remember, I thought. But it was also a clear night. In between views of Triton's crater-scarred surface, I went outside to the backyard to do my thing—that is hunting for new comets. At 9:00 P.M., I opened my backyard observatory and aimed Miranda, my 16-inch telescope, on a patch of sky in the west. For a half-hour, I'd scan, then I would go inside to catch a few minutes of *Voyager* as it sped by Triton. Back out to the observatory, back in again.

It would have been simpler to just spend the evening in front of the tube watching the most riveting broadcast since Armstrong's 1969 walk on the Moon, but I was glad I didn't. Just past 11:00 P.M., I nabbed my fifth comet, Okazaki–Levy–Rudenko, 1989r.

☾ *13* ☽

Eagle-Eyed Carolyn
30 Comets and Counting

*F*ive *hundred miles west of the site from which I found Comet Okazaki–Levy–Rudenko, the sun was about to set over Palomar* Mountain in Southern California. At Palomar this is like those few moments in a theater when the audience awaits the curtain rising. Slowly, majestically, the dome shutters at this magnificent observatory move apart, revealing the darkening sky whose brightest stars are already tuning up for the overture. The smallest of the four domes houses Palomar's 18-inch Schmidt, a telescopic camera whose films can record large sweeps of sky—almost 9 degrees across—on a single photograph. Although I have seen hundreds of these observatory nights, I'm still struck by the wonder of the moment the domes open.

Only 2 days after my comet discovery, I experienced this wonder first-hand, for I had gone to Palomar on my first observing run. In December 1988 the Shoemakers and I tried observing together with a recalcitrant Schmidt camera in the Catalina Mountains north of Tucson, but now I was at their Palomar site. I walked into the small observatory building to be greeted by Carolyn's warm smile. "A new comet, David!" she said. "Congratulations!" Since the sky was getting darker, we didn't talk too much about the comet, except that she did say we would photograph it tonight.

But it was time to get to work. Carolyn taught me to load film into the filmholder and then walk up the 12 steps to the dome and load the filmholder into the telescope. "It's a little tricky," she explained. "First you open the telescope doors, then you do this, then you do that, and then a miracle occurs—and the filmholder is ready!" Loading the film into the telescope is something you have to do by practice and feel, not sight. But although I practiced with an empty filmholder before dark—no miracle yet—I was awfully slow when the observing started. The next day I loaded filmholders again and again, and suddenly the miracle occurred—I was doing it right and fast. By the second night, I felt a part of things.

Within a few months, I was getting pretty used to the routine, and Gene, Carolyn, the telescope, and I were becoming a real team. I was getting better at guiding the telescope. I was also learning that photographic and visual observing are equally exciting but in different ways. And the time I notice that the most is when I am actually guiding on a star in the eyepiece.

To prepare for that, Gene loads a film into a special filmholder in the downstairs darkroom and walks upstairs with it; he hands it to me. I install the filmholder in the telescope, lock it in place, set the focus, remove the filmholder's cover, and close the telescope's doors. Gene calls out two numbers, the right ascension (the celestial equivalent of longitude) of the new position and its declination (latitude). I move the telescope and center it on a star. When I am ready he counts down, "five, four, three, two, one, open!" I open the shutter, and the film starts to gather light.

For the next 6, 8, or 10 minutes—the exposure varies according to the brightness of the object we are after—I really appreciate the difference between visual comet hunting and its photographic counterpart. If I were using my own telescope, I would be watching field after field of stars move through the eyepiece, and I might pick up an eleventh-magnitude or brighter comet. But now I concentrate on a single solitary star. In this curious exercise called guiding, I must keep the star exactly centered on the crosshairs of the eyepiece. It is a challenge, for even though the telescope is electrically driven to follow the star, it often lurches forward or

Eugene and Carolyn Shoemaker and the author at the 18-inch Schmidt telescope at Palomar. (Photograph by Terence Dickinson.)

backward a bit. If I can't keep the star centered perfectly on the crosshairs of the guiding eyepiece, the resulting film will show jerks and wiggles instead of starry points of light. This is a battle between me and the telescope, with the distant star as referee. For 8 minutes I freeze the sky on film and only imagine the wonders that may later be found there.

Gene is back with a new film he has loaded in the downstairs darkroom. Ending my reverie, I close the shutter, move the telescope to a horizontal position, cover the film, remove the filmholder, grab Gene's new filmholder, load it, focus the telescope, point the telescope, and find another star to guide on—all in less than 2 minutes. Gene's countdown starts a new exposure, and I acquaint myself with a new star all over again. After each set of eight films has been taken, they are developed.

A perfectionist by nature, Gene loses patience quickly when things do not run smoothly and quickly, so I try to learn fast. The 12.0 steps I climb to the telescope each few minutes don't seem like much, but after 8 or 9 hours of climbing, the decimal point disappears, and I start getting really tired. But despite the pressure of trying to take as many as 70 good photographs on a long winter night, I love the experience. There is a lot of pressure but also a lot of good humor; Gene and Carolyn are a lot of fun to work with.

COMETS BY CAMERA

"One ounce of aluminum and photographic emulsion," Helen Wright wrote about Palomar's biggest telescope, "constitutes the essential optical surfaces of the 200-inch telescope. To permit the surfaces to function properly, however, some 35,000 lbs. of glass and about 1,000,000 lbs. of steel are required."[1]

It is a miracle of optics that the whole purpose of all those tons of metal is to keep a microscopically thin coat of aluminum in the right shape and at the right distance from an equally microscopically thin, light-sensitive emulsion. Although it is a much smaller telescope, the 18-inch Schmidt camera works the same way. Named after its Estonian inventor, Bernhard Voldemar Schmidt, this type of telescope uses both a mirror and a specially matched glass lens to provide photographic views of large areas of the sky—in our case, the field of view is 8.75 degrees (or about 16 full moon diameters) across. It is the resulting film that Carolyn examines in the hope of finding a comet or asteroid.

As we discussed earlier, Edward Emerson Barnard began the photographic tradition by finding Periodic Comet Barnard 3 (1892 V) as a trailed smudge on a photographic plate. In 1981 a space satellite called *Solwind 1* found a comet that crashed into the sun. The several *Solwind* satellites, the Solar Maximum Mission, and the *IRAS* satellite all detected comets, and with the catch of Comet Spacewatch 1990x on a CCD array, that legacy has expanded into the modern field of electronic detectors. The visual finds are made mostly by amateur astronomers, and the photographic detections are made mostly (but not always) by professional astronomers. They do not often compete. Most of the visual finds are in areas relatively close to the sun. The visual searchers also avoid the richest parts of the Milky Way. Photographic discoveries tend to be in areas far from the sun, of comets usually too faint for small telescopes to detect. A single comet rarely bears the names of professional and amateur observers. In 1968 Mark Whitaker, a 16-year-old amateur astronomer from Texas, began comet hunting as a summer project with his 4-inch diameter reflector and found a ninth-magnitude comet after only three evenings! Only two nights later, Norman Thomas used Lowell Observatory's 13-inch telescope with which Pluto had been found in 1930 to discover the same comet, and the comet was named Whitaker–Thomas.

COMET HUNTING AT A DESK

Using a special stereomicroscope, Carolyn Shoemaker scans each pair of films. Just as in any stereophotographic pair, any object that is in a different position from one photograph to another stands out clearly, not unlike those stereo movies people saw during the 1950s. Two hundred years ago Caroline Herschel turned a career of assisting her brother into a comet-finding vocation of her own. Now the Shoemaker effort, which began with her husband's ideas, became a team effort whose findings are in large part due to the eagle eyes of Carolyn Spellmann Shoemaker.

FROM CAROLINE TO CAROLYN

After Gene and Carolyn were married in 1951, for much of the next two decades, Carolyn was a homemaker. "Going through the period of my life when I was raising the family," she recalls, "was just great." Near the end of this stretch however, she became restless. "I would feel like that there had to be something else that was really stimulating for me out there. What I really wanted was something that would absorb all my time and energy like Gene's work does his."

With Gene often away with field geology or work on lunar missions, Carolyn found their Pasadena home getting a little lonely. In the middle 1970s, Carolyn ventured out, but not immediately, to work with her husband. For 2 years she learned a lot about plants, not planets, by working in a flower shop. Although this transitional career was fun, she never intended it to be permanent. In the late 1970s under the guidance of Bobby Bus, an undergraduate student at Caltech, Carolyn began to look at photographic plates that had been taken with a large Schmidt telescope in Australia. Using a blink comparator, she compared images taken on one plate with those on another.

A blink comparator is a device designed to compare plates taken of the same areas of sky. Conceived by Max Wolf in Heidelberg early this century to help in his survey of asteroids, it involves looking through an eyepiece while a small motor alternates the light source from one plate to another. If a moving object is on the plates, the observer can detect it as it appears to move back and forth. There is an apocryphal story that Wolf had also conceived the idea of using the stereomicroscope so that both films could be studied simultaneously, but he abandoned that idea because he had good vision in only one eye. In any event, the blink comparator was the instrument of choice for photographic searches for many years, becoming famous when Clyde Tombaugh used it to discover Pluto in February 1930.

At first Carolyn was uncertain about using the instrument. "I was tremendously nervous the first time I used even a simple calculator," Carolyn remembers. "I thought I would make a mistake and the whole thing would blow up!" But by 1980 she was gaining confidence, and she joined the Palomar planet-crossing asteroid survey, a project directed by her husband and Caltech astronomer Eleanor Helin.

In 1979, Gene developed a plan using a stereomicroscope. Instead of blinking on and off, a moving object now appeared to rise above the background of stars. The process is the same as looking at a pair of identical photographs of a landscape; when viewed in stereo, the nearby trees force themselves dramatically in front of the distant mountains. Developing a proficiency with this new instrument was quite a learning experience. At first both Shoemakers anxiously looked at their pairs of films, discovering every possible speck of dust and emulsion defect. But with some experience, Carolyn quickly learned to differentiate between what was real and what was not. With experience, she says, "your eye and your mind will tell you when you have something." Occasionally that something might be in an area she looked at a few seconds ago. Moving slowly through the field, she would suddenly become alert and move back to check.

"Carolyn went gangbusters on the stereomicroscope," Gene raves. "It was a natural thing for Carolyn, who has a high ability to pick small things out, to recognize small anomalies." In 1982 Carolyn and her husband started working together at the 18-inch telescope. For Carolyn this was an even more basic change. "I am a morning person," she notes, "so I was uncertain whether I could stay up all night and work with the telescope." By early 1983 the Shoemakers were getting used to the 18-inch telescope, and Carolyn was enjoying the stereomicroscope thoroughly. One afternoon while scanning two films they had taken a few nights earlier, Carolyn came across two small hyphens in the sea of surrounding stars. Looking first at one film and then another, she realized that something was moving across those films, and fast. "We were both elated to find something like that." Later named Nefertiti, this was an Amor-type asteroid whose orbit crosses that of Mars. It was the first of a long series of near-Earth objects that Carolyn would discover through the stereomicroscope. Later in 1983 Carolyn found a second Amor, designated 1983 RB and seen again 10 years later.

Carolyn's first view of a comet was a disappointment. Found by Ted Bowell in 1980, it was far away and faint when she first saw it on her films 2 years later. As a result of its encounter with Jupiter, Bowell's comet was off on a new orbit that would take it out of the solar system forever. "It showed up pretty well on one of our films," Carolyn noted, "but not on the other. I thought that if they are that diffuse and faint, I'm never going to discover a comet." By 1983 Carolyn had observed several comets, including a few Comets IRAS, detected not by a human directly but by the Infrared Astronomical Satellite. Learning that not all comets were as difficult to see as Comet Bowell, Carolyn started anticipating the excitement she would feel if she ever found one of her own.

The time for wondering came to an end on a September afternoon in 1983.

> Gene was out of town, and I was trying to get through what seemed like a monumental number of films before we went observing again. And all of a sudden, there it was, and I knew it was a comet. I had a feeling that it might be a new comet, but I wasn't sure. We didn't have a catalogue of comet positions at the time, or anything else to tell us if a comet was known or not. So, I hastily wrote down the approximate positions, plotted them on my star map, telephoned Brian Marsden, and said, "I have a comet."[2]

Comet Shoemaker 1983p was the first of a procession of comets. By 1987 Carolyn had found eight, surpassing Caroline Herschel as the woman who found the most comets. "Passing Herschel's record was a special goal for me—not because there was anything personal at all there, but because it was a landmark and special in a way to find more than any other woman had found so far," she told me. With her fifteenth comet find just 2 years later, Carolyn surpassed William Bradfield's 14 comets, her second goal. From Adelaide, Australia, Bradfield had more comets than any other living person. But other than comparing totals, the methods of visual versus photographic hunting are quite different. "I have just the greatest admiration for the kind of comet hunting that Bradfield does," Carolyn insists.

> Visual comet hunting takes an awful lot of patience that I'm not sure I would have. It involves a lot of cold hours and a lot of discomfort, and a lot of looking before you find anything. What I do involves a different sort of persistence. But the stereomicroscope is a better tool than many amateur comet hunters have.[3]

SURGING TO THE TOP

With the discovery of Periodic Comet Shoemaker–Levy 4 in February 1991, Carolyn surpassed Brooks's long line of 21 comets, and a year and five comets later, she broke Pons's all-time record of 26 named comets. In 1991 our team found a record number of seven new comets. "I am enormously proud of her," Gene brags. "As long as we have been together, I have known that eagle-eyed Carolyn is a great observer."[4]

With so many discoveries, it might be difficult to remember the stories of each. But some, like Comet Shoemaker, 1984o, stand out. Carolyn had been scanning films all morning and then went for lunch with her husband.

> After lunch, I went back and put a pair of films on the stereomicroscope. I looked through the eyepiece, just to see if the films were lined up, and there was this glorious comet sitting there. My heart leaped; it was faint, but to me this comet looked absolutely spectacular.[5]

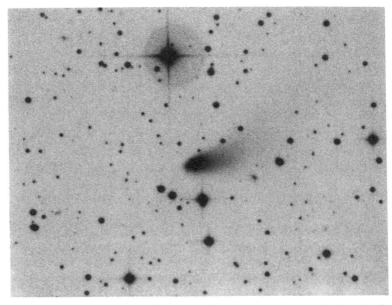

Discovery picture of Comet Mueller (1993p). This comet was discovered by Jean Mueller on a photographic plate taken for the second Palomar Observatory Sky Survey by Mueller and J. D. Mendenhall, using the 48-inch Oschin Schmidt telescope. One of the world's most successful comet discoverers, Mueller has nine comets to her credit.

A month after the Shoemakers found their comet that had split from Comet Levy, Henry Holt, his son Hank, and Tim Rodriguez took a series of films at Palomar, including the field of an asteroid that the Shoemakers hoped to observe. Back in Flagstaff and anxious to know if the films had indeed recorded the asteroid, Carolyn asked Henry if she could examine his films. In no great hurry to scan a film that was dense with stars in the richest part of the Milky Way, Henry agreed. "The films were almost wall-to-wall stars," Carolyn explained. "I was plowing along and hoping to find that asteroid."

When films are so crowded with stars, scanning is difficult, but in less than an hour, Carolyn found the asteroid. She plotted its position and then kept on looking. "Not far away was a comet," she grinned. She called her husband, who confirmed by checking a catalog that this was a new comet. After they telephoned Marsden, Gene smiled broadly at his wife. "Carolyn," he said, "it's June 24. Happy birthday!"

After examining some 8000 pairs of films in the last 13 years, it now takes Carolyn only 20 minutes to scan each pair of films, and she averages about 100 hours of searching per comet. Although this is half the average time reported by most visual searchers, it does not include the time spent exposing the films at the telescope, developing them, or preparing them for scanning. It also doesn't include the 500-mile drive the Shoemakers take just to get to their telescope each month.

After 30 comets Carolyn still experiences that nerve-jangling thrill with each discovery. "I do try to contain it for a while," she says, "at least until we find out if the comet is already known. But when I see a comet, my heart gives a big leap of joy." The day will never come when comet finding is routine; each new comet brings with it the freshness and thrill of that first discovery.

ℭ *14* 𝔇

Are We the Progeny of Comets?

Imagine a large dark cloud sitting passively in space for an incredibly long time. Known as a giant molecular cloud, it is more than 300 light years across—one of the largest objects in the galaxy. It is also one of the coldest, consisting of molecular hydrogen hovering near absolute zero. Somewhere nearby a massive star filled with heavier atoms like carbon suddenly runs out of material for nuclear fusion. In a fraction of a second, the huge sun collapses on itself, and then blows apart in the awesome explosion of a supernova, spreading carbon into nearby space and into our giant molecular cloud. With the injection of carbon and the possible help of some ultraviolet irradiation, the cloud slowly begins to evolve into a different place. Over millions of years, particles heat up and re-combine spontaneously into organic substances.

WHEN STARS EXPLODE

It is said that in 1572, Tycho Brahe asked his neighbor to pinch him as he looked at a completely new star in Cassiopeia. Bright as the planet Venus, this star had simply appeared out of

167

nowhere. Viewed from outside the galaxy, Tycho's star would have been as bright as the rest of the Milky Way galaxy. In this age before the telescope, almost 2 full years passed before the star faded from view. In 1604 Tycho's student, Johannes Kepler, saw a second bright new supernova that also remained bright for a long time. After that our galaxy and its closest neighbors, the Magellanic Clouds, remained quiet for almost four centuries. In the long years since then, through the development of the telescope and the spectroscope, which can analyze the light from a star, there was no nearby supernova to study.

At least there was none until February 1987. The best place to be at that moment would have been the office of the CBAT, where Marsden had quietly settled down to work. Just before 9:00 A.M., the telex machine in the corner sprang to life with a message suggesting that a supernova had appeared in the Large Magellanic Cloud, which at a distance of 169,000 light years, was one of the galaxies nearest to ours. Actually the message was somewhat vague, and as he was thinking about making further enquiries, a telephone call from Chile brought complete assurance that astronomers Ian Shelton and Oscar Duhalde had independently found the first bright supernova in 380 years. Seconds later CBAT administrative assistant Donna Thompson took a call from Rob McNaught in Australia with further observations of the fifth-magnitude star. It later turned out that variable-star observer Albert Jones in New Zealand had been an independent discoverer. "It is very important in this business to give proper credit where it is due," says Marsden, "for otherwise the historical record can so easily be distorted."

By 11:00 A.M. CBAT was a madhouse. Telephones were ringing and astronomers from all over Cambridge's Harvard–Smithsonian Center for Astrophysics come by to see what was going on. Then the first spectroscopic observations came as night fell in South Africa. As new observations came in, Marsden had to keep revising his important announcement circular, but when it finally went out quite late in the afternoon, all the significant details were there.

Comet Bradfield, 1974 III. (Photograph by Jack Newton, using a 12.5-inch f/4.3 reflecting telescope, 10-minute exposure with 103AF film.)

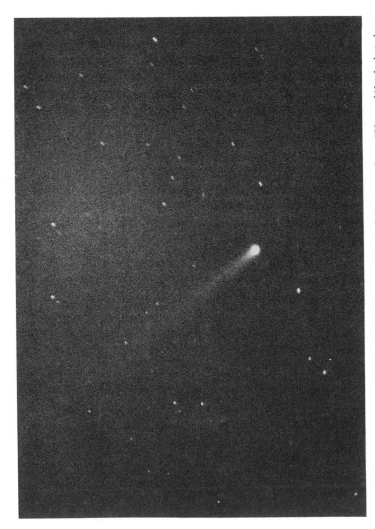

A different view of Comet Bradfield, 1974 III. (Photograph by Jack Newton, using a 450-mm f/8 telephoto lens, 5-minute exposure with Tri-X film.)

We learn so much by watching from the sidelines as a nearby supernova blazes out, for it is in the very moment that a star evolves to its limit of nuclear fusion and collapses that all of the heavier elements necessary for life, like oxygen and carbon, are released into space. But although they are the most dramatic source, supernovae are not the only source of these life-starting elements. Large, cool, carbon-rich stars also have contributed these materials more gradually.

THE BIRTH OF THE SOLAR SYSTEM

Let us return to that giant molecular cloud, still made mostly of hydrogen but now enriched with heavier elements from the supernovae and possibly carbon stars. Gradually a fragment of this cloud became unstable and started to collapse, the force of its own gravity causing it to coalesce into a thicker cloud, with its tiny grains covered by a thin layer of organic molecules like frosting on a cake. What caused the cloud to start collapsing? Possibly the shock wave from the supernova itself set it off, or for some other reason, the cloud began to lose its magnetic field and start compressing. It also started to rotate slowly, and gradually the grains settled in the nebula's central plane. The particles clumped together—the scientific word we use is accretion—very slowly as individual particles that settled to the central plane found one another. At the center of the accretion disk was a body that would grow and grow until one day it began nuclear fusion and became the sun. All this took place about 4.5 billion years ago.

Although the accretion disk's organic grains were almost pure carbon, they might have contained some carbon monoxide (CO), water (H_2O), and formaldehyde (H_2CO), which are pivotal materials in the chemistry in which simple organic materials combine to form biological molecules. For example formaldehyde reacted to form carbohydrate sugars. These "prebiotic" reactions could have taken place in the original large molecular cloud, later in the nebula that condensed to form the solar system, or later still in comets.

What happened after that is the subject of considerable debate, and the scenario I present is just one possibility. Perhaps the disk became unstable as more and more grains coalesced into solid clumps of material some 1–10 kilometers in diameter. As the clumps ran into each other, they grew into larger bodies called planetesimals, and into smaller bodies some call protocomets or cometesimals. Some scientists don't believe that scenario. Instead they theorize that planetesimals grew larger until many collisions from smaller objects started to fragment the primordial bodies.

As the accretion disk continued to rotate, its center grew hotter and hotter. As temperatures soared, the delicate organic matter was at risk. Unable to survive the intense heat, it began to disintegrate. Meanwhile the outer part of the accretion disk, which did not get so hot, retained some of its organic materials.

The time scale for the formation of the planets is critical. The entire process between the collapse of the molecular cloud, the building of the planets, and the ignition of the sun probably did not last more than 100 million years. The big gas giants Jupiter and Saturn had to have accreted before the sun turned on its fusion furnace, for soon after that, the remaining gas in the primordial nebula would have been blown away. Uranus and Neptune were probably the last to grow.

Once formed, the infant solar system had a group of warm inner planets without a large amount of organic material; some cold outer planets; the asteroids; and the comets, where organic grains still existed. If life were ever to evolve on Earth, there had to be a way of transporting the still intact organic material at the outer edge of the solar system to the Earth.

THE COMET UNDERGROUND

Were it not for comets, the inner solar system (including the Earth) would still be a place without organic compounds while the outer solar system would continue to house them. The scattering of the comets made the difference. Over a long period of time, they might have provided the underground railroad that brought the organic materials here. Comets provided the Earth with its supply of carbon and its supply of water. Whether they also provided the seeds for life in the form of amino acids is far less certain. In 1982, J. Mayo Greenberg of the University of Leiden predicted that a large fraction of a typical comet would be composed of frozen water—others say as much as three-quarters of a comet is water—and that another large fraction would consist of organic molecules.[1]

While it worked in Greenberg's laboratory, it took an actual visit to determine if these materials were present in a comet. In March 1986 this happened. A flotilla of spacecraft visited Comet Halley, and together with observations from Earth-based telescopes, they confirmed the existence of hydrogen cyanide, water, and formaldehyde. The spacecraft discovered something even more special, that Halley is surrounded by very fine organic particles, now called CHON grains, because they contain carbon, hydrogen, oxygen, and nitrogen. These grains may be the seeds of life, since they contain elements from which amino acids and other compounds essential to life are made. As Gerrit Verschuur explained, CHON is "the simple alphabet of life."[2] (These particles were possibly observed from Earth as jets rich in cyanogen material spiraling out of the comet's nucleus.)

From what we learned from the Halley spacecraft, roughly 11 percent of the comet's mass is carbon. The Earth's crust, by contrast, does not have more than a tenth of 1 percent carbon. But for comets and human beings, the relative amounts of carbon and other materials are close. The University of Toledo's Armand Delsemme points out the closeness from a study of Comet Halley: carbon 9.5 percent in human beings, 11 percent in Halley; hydrogen 63 percent and 55 percent; oxygen 26 and 28 percent; and nitrogen 1 percent and 2 percent. Taken together both comets and human beings are made up largely of the same stuff.[3]

THE COMET EXPRESS

A current line of thinking is that comets were formed in the region moving outward from Uranus. One type of evidence is found in the heavy hydrogen, or deuterium, that they contain. For example the ratio of deuterium to ordinary hydrogen in Halley's comet is significantly higher than what is likely to have occurred in the interstellar medium, the primordial sun, or even the giant planets Jupiter and Saturn. However the amount of deuterium is about the same as that found on Uranus and Neptune as well as Earth. This is evidence that comets did form in the outer solar system beyond Saturn, and it also supports the idea that comets provided much of the Earth's water.

Why would Jupiter not capture the comets instead? Jupiter's gravity was already so strong that it would have flung most of them right out of the solar system. As Uranus and Neptune grew more massive, their gravitational pulls started to scatter the comets much as they both hurled the *Voyager 2* spacecraft out of the solar system in 1986 and 1989. Over hundreds of millions of years, a dispersal of the comets in the region between Uranus and Neptune resulted in an expanding swarm as comets left the hive. Some four-fifths of these comets were ejected from the solar system. Others were ejected directly by Neptune and Uranus into a spherical shell of comets located about a light year away. Named after the Dutch astronomer Jan Oort, this Oort cloud remains as the main storehouse of comets in the solar system. The other half of the original swarm found their way toward Jupiter and Saturn, and some of these went into Earth-crossing orbits. Still other comets were never redistributed at all; these might remain in the outer solar system as a group now called the Kuiper belt, named after the late University of Arizona scientist Gerard Kuiper. It is possible that a few objects recently discovered by David Jewitt and Jane Luu may be Kuiper belt objects. During this period of the dispersal of the Uranus–Neptune swarm, the Earth was bombarded by thousands of these comets, each carrying its supply of organic grains from the outer solar system.

There is one problem with the scenario of the comet express carrying with it the ingredients for life. Comets are also terrible swift swords, capable of destroying the same delicate materials for the origin of life that they help to create. As the comet hits the atmosphere and seconds later the ground, its temperature rises suddenly and rapidly to several thousand degrees, incinerating its supply of organic materials within half a second after impact. It is important to note that the surviving cometary material ends up widely scattered in the atmosphere, where it later settles on Earth.

In March 1989, Cornell University's Paul Thomas suggested a way around the problem of incinerating comets. Perhaps some of a comet's organic materials could survive, he suggested, if the comet were moving slowly enough and if it landed at the bottom of an ocean. During the early period of heavy bombardment some 4.5 billion years ago, Thomas claims, the Earth's atmosphere was 10–20 times denser than it is now—dense enough to slow down a small comet considerably before it hit the atmosphere. The process, known as aerobraking, could slow a 100-meter diameter comet from 25–10 kilometers per second. If the comet then landed in an ocean, it would take less than half a second more to reach the bottom. It is possible that despite the violence of such an impact, the center of the disintegrating comet may not climb above a few hundred degrees Celsius, thus allowing some of the organic molecules to survive. Further if the comet hit the thick atmosphere at a sharp angle, it would be going even slower when it reached the Earth's surface.[4]

A variation of that idea has the comet hitting the Earth at such a slow speed that some of its organic materials incredibly survive an impact on land. This is a very unlikely scenario, but of all the comets that hit Earth, such a "soft landing" would have had to happen only once for this process to spread some organic compounds here. The impact might then form a large crater with a central mound, and it would rapidly fill with melted material from the comet—material consisting of water as well as other organic compounds. Hydrogen cyanide would react to form formamide or formic acid, or nucleic acid bases. As the process continued, the level of this curious lake would fall and rise from seasonal and climatic changes, allowing for periods of drying and rehydration, and resulting in more complicated organic reactions both in the lake and on the wet soil of the central mound.[5] However although this might have happened, a soft landing is not really needed. In a typical crash, the comet disintegrates in the atmosphere, releasing its organic materials to fall gently to Earth, with some of them intact.

We cannot get an idea of the early rates of impacts and cratering directly on Earth, since all the evidence of impacts from this heavy bombardment period has been erased by a planetary lifetime of motion of the crust and rock erosion. However we can get an idea of the rate of early cratering from the moon, whose highland areas preserve the footprints of visiting comets. In astronomical terms, the moon and Earth are so close that they would have been subject to similar bombardments. The Earth could have accreted enough cometary matter—10^{23} grams—to account for all the carbon buried in the Earth's crust and also in all the oceans. The fact that comets are a rather inefficient delivery system, a case of the messenger killing the message, doesn't defeat that argument, since if even only 1 percent of the cometary amino acids or other organic compounds had survived, 10^{20} grams of comet-delivery carbon would still have endured.

Of course there is a big difference between having the ingredients for life and having life itself. Just what brought life to these materials is still a mystery. We are pretty certain that life probably originated after a lot of false starts and accidents. A limerick heard at Oxford sums it up:

> There once was a brainy baboon
> Who always breathed down a bassoon,
> "For"—he said—"It appears
> That in billions of years
> I shall certainly strike on a tune."[6]

Was it a physical electric spark, like lightning, that produced the amino acids that are the ingredients of the primordial soup, or did they come precooked, perhaps by ultraviolet and x radiation from the stars on the CHON grains when they were in space? We have no solid answer for that yet, although there is more evidence now that lightning was not required.

Since Watson and Crick's startling discovery of the structure of the DNA molecule in the 1950s, biologists puzzled over what was considered to be alive first: DNA, RNA, or the proteins. In 1986, T. R. Cech found that RNA itself might be the enzyme catalyst for life, a discovery that earned him the Nobel prize in chemistry 3 years later. The RNA, which stores information like a gene, could have enzyme activity as well. As a living molecule, RNA is probably older than both DNA and proteins.[7]

THE COMET MILK RUN

Comets and asteroids that hit the Earth deposited their dusty grains directly, but many other comets left a huge band of granulated organic matter in a cloud around the sun. We still see a version of that cloud when the evening or morning sky is lit by a peculiar tepee-shaped glow called the zodiacal light. This light covers a large part of the sky, and it is centered along the plane of the ecliptic. This beautiful effect results from the sun's light reflecting off interplanetary dust.

Although current particles of the zodiacal cloud have been orbiting for periods of at least a thousand years, the cloud has had an influx of particles since the beginning of the solar system. In the 1950s, Harvard's Fred Whipple suggested that much of that material might come from comets, in particular, perhaps, from Periodic Comet Encke or a much larger ancestral comet of which P/Encke is but a remnant. However on its way to the outer solar system, the *Pioneer* spacecraft detected a good deal of dust as far out as the asteroid belt, but the dust dropped sharply past the asteroid belt. This indicates that at least a portion of the dust in the zodiacal cloud is asteroidal, not cometary, in origin.

In recent decades we have seen that tiny cometary particles from the zodiacal light cloud, some of which are from ancient comets, actually arrive on Earth. In 1970 the first balloon experiment to collect dust particles in the stratosphere retrieved artificially produced and volcanic dust as well as some microscopic samples of feathery cometary dust. According to Donald Brownlee, who described the balloon findings, these Brownlee particles are extraterrestrial in origin. Specially equipped planes flying some 20 kilometers into the stratosphere routinely collect such particles today. Brownlee particles eventually drop to the Earth's surface at the rate of a single particle on each square meter of the Earth's surface every day.[8]

In the early years of the solar system, zodiacal dust was far more massive than it is now. Over a long period of time, uncountable billions of such grains entered the Earth's atmosphere. They were not large enough to be consumed as the meteors we see in the sky at night. Instead they were so tiny that they came to a stop in the upper atmosphere and then floated down. Drifting gently down in far greater numbers than at present, they added a weighty amount of additional organic materials to the primordial mixture. In fact more of the organic materials of life may have come through this indirect comet milk run, where comets leave their organic residue as individual grains that fall gently to Earth, than by direct impacts.

GETTING THE STUFFING KNOCKED OUT

In addition to providing the substance of life, comets may also be responsible for setting life's house in order. Their carbon, which later oxidized to CO_2 in the atmosphere, began the greenhouse effect that prevented the oceans from freezing. During a period of several hundred million years after the formation of the Earth, a great deal of cometary material was delivered here, either as direct comet hits or as tiny grains left from these comets in the inner solar system. Some 4.5 billion years ago, the onslaught dropped off gradually, then some 3.9 billion years ago, a second blitz swung into action. Just what caused this "late heavy bombardment" is a mystery. Perhaps a single 500-kilometer diameter object, or maybe a large number of objects from the zone between Uranus and Neptune, broke up after a tidal encounter with one of the inner planets. In any event the damage to Mercury, Venus, Earth, the moon, and Mars was immense. From samples collected via the early *Apollo* missions, we can tell that huge impact basins like Mare Imbrium were carved out of the moon by impacts from this period of late heavy bombardment. As Carolyn Shoemaker describes the two assaults: "There was an earlier period when planets were formed, and a later period when the planets got the stuffing knocked out of them."

A WORD ABOUT COMETARY PANSPERMIA

We can take the comets and life idea a bit too far. If comets carried biological building blocks to Earth, could these building blocks actually contain biologically active materials? Could life have originated directly inside comets? Some years ago the British astronomer Sir Fred Hoyle and others suggested that the chances for the formation of even the simplest of enzymes are so low that they could not have formed spontaneously here on Earth. Therefore they proposed, the enzymes must have formed elsewhere in the universe and then been transported here directly by comets. However this part of his argument is self-defeating. Chances of life evolving here are no more likely than for any other spot in the universe, and a very high proportion of the transported enzymes would have been destroyed during the impact with Earth. In short Occam's Razor, the philosophical principle that the simplest explanation should be the correct one, applies, and since having comets transport real enzymes would unnecessarily complicate things, that probably isn't how life on Earth began.

Going further out on a limb, Hoyle expanded his idea to suggest that certain viruses, particularly those that cause common colds and flu epidemics, come from comets. Moreover he suggested that large comets might have caused mass extinctions not from the actual impacts but from viruses that comets spread after impact.

Although current evidence cannot completely exclude the possibility of comets having brought life directly to Earth, the probability of that actually happening is very small. The rhinoviruses that cause colds, for example, are specifically designed to enter the human nose and mouth and then thrive once they get inside. Therefore they would have to have evolved along with their human hosts.

The tapestry of life's beginning is very complicated and leads in any number of directions. We are only now beginning to piece it together. Evidence we have suggests that comets may have played a fundamental role in this picture. As Shoemaker says, "We are the progeny of comets." We now suppose that when the Earth finally formed into a planet, the organic grains were mostly still at the other end of the solar system and over hundreds of millions of years, a large number of long-gone comets carried them past the orbits of the outer planets to the orbit of the Earth. When we gaze at a comet, we may be looking at our own past.

❦ 15 ❧

Could a Comet Have Slain the Dinosaurs?

*I*magine *a peaceful, steamy night with mighty* Triceratops *drinking water from a pond, watching for their enemy* Tyrannosaurus rex. Brighter than the brightest stars, a comet dominates the night. For several weeks now, the comet has brightened as it approached the sun, its long tail making it look like a sword in the sky. By the next afternoon, it is all over. With large thunderclaps and a huge crash, the comet slams into the Earth in what is now the Caribbean basin, just off the coast of the present-day Yucatán. Unlike a small meteoroid, which glows brightly as it encounters the atmosphere and is vaporized, the comet is so large that it plows through as if the air weren't even there. High walls of water race out from the point of impact, and millions of tons of dust surge upward in a gigantic cloud. The excavated material rushes out with such force that it quickly circles the Earth. All over the world, the sky is blindingly bright with meteors as the debris reenters; the light and heat make the atmosphere like a furnace. Intense as it is, the meteor storm lasts for half an hour as the surface is bombarded with debris, and surface temperatures are as high as an oven set to broiling. Dry vegetation ignites everywhere (soot in exposed rocks from that time provides evidence of worldwide ground fires). The larger, more slowly moving debris lands a little later in secondary hits close to the main crater, in the gulf of Mexico, causing giant tsunamis to head tens of miles inland on the shores of Mexico and Florida. Soon the whole planet is shrouded in a cloud of dust and soot. The sky is absolutely black, and for over a month, there is no sunlight whatsoever on Earth. The huge amount of nitric oxide results in rain dense with sulfuric acid.

This is an apocalypse, but not the only one: 9 million years earlier, another object struck Earth near the present site of Manson, Iowa.* But the main event was much, much worse. The large dinosaurs disappeared probably within a few days or weeks. Within a year or two, many plant and animal species were gone. Responding to the long-term environmental change brought about by the disaster, some simple but vital plants like algae and nanoplankton disappeared too.

EARLY IDEAS

The scenario just presented is buttressed by the physical evidence in ancient rocks. Had I offered it a generation ago, it would have been ridiculed as fiction, smacks of *catastrophism,* mainstream geologists would have said. I took Geology 100 during those peaceful days of *uniformitarianism,* a geologic school that says the Earth evolved slowly and deliberately, without the need for sudden shocks to its ecosystem, and the dinosaurs died out not over a few months but over millions of years. Between 73–65 million years ago, some geologists still insist, a number of dinosaur species began to decline, due perhaps to gradual changes in the distribution of plants, the climate, or ocean currents. This evidence may concur with new data about an impact. Perhaps the crash was a final

---

* In fact the date of the Manson crater was a subject of hot debate during the writing of this book. As research progressed, various drafts of this chapter suggested the date to be several hundred thousand years later, then earlier, before its current age of 74 million years was determined.

blow to an already declining dinosaur population. Also the idea of asteroid and comet impacts does not mean that the vast majority of Earth's lifeline did not take place in a uniformitarian way.

In any attempt to understand what happened at the end of the Cretaceous period, the sheer magnitude of the carnage is the most important thing to consider. Of the vast numbers of large land-roaming animals that had flourished for more than 150 million years—compared to humanity's 100 thousand year span—not a single one was left. Land and sea-dwelling creatures were affected. Plankton at the ocean surfaces that had been forming the chalky rock at places like the White Cliffs of Dover also vanished.* Some of the smaller reptiles managed to ride out the cataclysm as did some plants. To our great fortune, some small mammals survived also.

The idea of a catastrophe is one of the oldest theories of the dinosaurs' extinction. First offered by Baron Georges Cuvier not long after the first mosasaur remains were discovered around 1770, the idea was that something dramatic interfered with Earth's climate, causing large animals to die out suddenly. The violence of the French Revolution itself, during which scientists were not immune to the guillotine, may have helped put the idea of rapid extinction into Cuvier's mind.

A DINOSAUR DECLINE?

In any case, during much of the twentieth century the idea of a slow extinction reached prominence. There was an argument that dinosaur skeletons were becoming increasingly rare as the Cretaceous/Tertiary boundary approached, but it has been refuted

---

* The Cretaceous period gets its name from these chalky formations that dead bodies of the plankton formed. The chalky rock remained undersea for a long time before finally being lifted above sea level.

by better geologic sampling. At the time that argument supported the theory of an orderly process well.* Paleontologist Robert Bakker, among others, suggests that not enough species died to make the impact theory plausible. Why for example would turtles survive and dinosaurs not? Possibly, other geologists speculate, because they were cold blooded, but the warm-blooded dinosaurs could not adapt to the sudden drop in temperature.

Having survived for so long, dinosaurs are the most successful of the complex animals, and were it not for whatever killed them, they should still be here today. (The recent discovery of *Mononychus*, a predator the size of a turkey but with a keeled breastbone similar to that found in birds, may represent a link between one brand of dinosaur, the *Archaeopteryx*, and modern birds. However evidence for that link is not solid yet.)

One of the earliest theories is that dinosaurs simply evolved themselves out of existence. Some evidence that their skulls became overossified—the development of a strange bone in the back of Triceratops is an example—suggests that extinction may have come about through a kind of species senility. But that idea does not explain why so many species perished at once.

Did chemical warfare kill off the dinosaurs? At the start of the Cretaceous period some 120 million years ago, ferns and conifers provided the major nourishment. The emergence of flowering plants added a new variable however. They produced a strong alkaloid toxic to animals that tried to eat them. By eating too many of these flowering plants, one theory goes, the dinosaurs were poisoned and they perished.

How flowering plants got started is a mystery in itself. Possibly, one theory suggests, the herbivores had grazed on their plants so heavily that these plants disappeared, making a niche for the evolution of new flowering varieties. So the dinosaurs ate off the older

---

* Geologists refer to this geologic boundary as K/T instead of C/T, because C refers to the Cambrian period.

plants and avoided the flowering ones, but with flowering plants showing up everywhere, the dinosaurs adapted to them.

Supporting the idea of a villainous plant is the contorted position that many dinosaur fossils show. With their long necks warped over their backs, the skeletons imply that the animals suffered greatly as they died. Since muscular contraction is a symptom of strychnine poisoning, these contortions do support the plant theory. But there is a big problem with that idea. Why are the remains contorted throughout their history instead of just at the end of the Cretaceous period? Even *Compsognathus*, who thrived during the Jurassic period before the rise of flowering plants, shows these contortions. Actually there is a much simpler answer. The contortions developed after death as the long and delicate ligaments in the neck dried out, slowly pulling it backward.

All available evidence indicates that the emergence of flowering plants did not pose a danger to the dinosaurs. The chemical they released, like sour milk, caused the animals to avoid eating the plants long before the amounts they consumed became deadly. Another point: The dinosaurs reached the height of their development, with their greatest diversity and extent, some 30 million years after these plants appeared. In fact both the dinosaurs and flowering plants coexisted during the entire 50 million years of the Cretaceous period, and mighty *Triceratops* was in full spread at the very end of the Cretaceous.

A SUDDEN EXTINCTION

By 1960, geologists were examining the idea that a drop in temperature, possibly a sudden one, led to the extinction. At this time there was still some question whether the disappearance was sudden or progressive. Catastrophists argued that sampling errors led to the false conclusion that dinosaurs were already in decline.

Toward the end of the 1970s, a new catastrophic theory about the extinction began to make the rounds of geologists. Perhaps the cause was the explosion of a nearby supernova. Chapter 14 discussed the beneficial effects of the explosion of a star, but what if the star was only a hundred light years from Earth and for several months, the supernova shone like a second sun in the sky, bombarding the Earth's atmosphere with enough radiation to knock out most species of life? While typical radiation levels from space average 0.03 roentgen (a unit of radiation exposure) per year, such an explosion would expose the world to some 3000 roentgens inside a few weeks.

This theory sounds plausible except that it is virtually impossible to know if a nearby star did explode precisely that long ago.[1] Victor Hughes of Queen's University discovered two pulsars 456 and 196 light years away that may have affected Earth in a small degree 62,000 years ago and 440,000 years ago.[2] However the remains of an supernova from 65 million years ago would be extremely hard to locate, let alone date. A case of a theory popping up before the evidence was there, this idea caught the attention of the geologic community. But like Einstein's General Theory of Relativity, this is often how science is done: A theory arises, and then scientists look for evidence to support it.

All along our planet was ready to tell us exactly what happened, for the story, like an unread book, was hidden in pages of rock. There was an explosion, but the cause was not a distant star. Two lines of evidence were in these pages, one easily available to some clever geologists who could examine the rocks that marked the boundary between the Cretaceous and Tertiary periods of Earth's history, and the other deeply buried more than a thousand meters beneath the land and water of southern Mexico.

A group led by Walter Alvarez and his father Luis, both from the University of California at Berkeley, found that first line of evidence. In the mountain village of Gubbio, Italy, there is a rocky outcropping of chalk similar in age and appearance to England's White Cliffs of Dover. Atop the chalk is a tiny layer of clay no more than 6 millimeters thick. That thin layer, found in outcroppings around the world, contains more than 30 times more iridium than the surrounding layers. Rare on Earth, the element iridium is more common in comets, asteroids, and meteorites. After a large comet or asteroid hits Earth, the theory goes, a huge amount of dust rises into the atmosphere, then slowly settles down again all over the world. A quarter-inch layer of an extraterrestrial dust rich in iridium—everywhere.[3]

Could the iridium have come from the effects of a nearby supernova, as was earlier thought? The Alvarez paper ruled that out, for among other reasons, a supernova would have deposited some Plutonium-244 with a half-life of some 80 million years, which they did not detect. Also considering the amount of iridium a supernova would emit, we know that the star would have had to be about one-tenth of a light year from us—much closer than the nearest star is today, though not necessarily back then.[4]

To leave a layer of so much iridium all over the planet, a colliding object from space would presumably have had a diameter of about 10 kilometers. Only one known object with that diameter could conceivably hit the Earth sometime in the next several thousand years, and that is Periodic Comet Swift–Tuttle.

THE SMOKING GUN

If a comet or an asteroid that large did hit Earth 65 million years ago, where is the crater? On our plant and water-covered planet, finding it is a daunting task. On the moon, a 100-million-year-old, hundred-kilometer diameter crater stands out like a sore thumb; in fact the rays of Tycho's ejected material virtually go around the moon. The Earth has a very different story. With an atmosphere that erodes geological features constantly and quickly and water that allows new sediment to cover up older features, a 65-million-year-old crater would likely be buried. Given the 75-percent chance that the object hit an ocean, because at least that much of the Earth's surface is covered with water, how could the crater ever be found?

It is part of the beauty of the scientific process that whenever a new idea is presented in a paper, someone else points out its flaws. In the early years after the startling Alvarez paper, Charles

Officer and Charles Drake offered the alternative view that iridium could have come from below, not from above, that is, from the Earth's mantle rather than from an asteroid or comet. These geologists suggest that iridium was deposited by a period of heavy volcanic activity lasting as long as a 100 thousand years. An eruption of the Kilauea volcano in Hawaii, they cite as an example, produced up to 20,000 times the concentrations of iridium found in normal Hawaii basalt.[5] The geologists also suggest that the volcanism could have resulted in cooling and intense acid rain. Recent evidence from India indicates that heavy basaltic flows may have been generated in the 4 million years prior to the end of the dinosaurs.

Arguing against this is evidence that some of the boundary samples are less contaminated with other materials than are others. The purer ones suggest the rapid deposition that an extraterrestrial body would cause, while the more contaminated samples—one even yielded iridium-rich material some 40 centimeters below the K/T boundary—suggest either a slower rate of deposit or deposits from more than one impact.

Noting the lack of an obvious large crater of the right age on the planet, the Officer paper suggested that it would be "encouraging to find some direct evidence of the event itself."[6] So while the impact versus volcanism debate raged on during the 1980s, the search for the crater, and for more evidence from the iridium deposits, began in earnest. By the end of the 1980s, some hundred sites with significant iridium anomalies had been found worldwide. Some of these sites offered a different kind of testimony: They contained small quartz grains that were badly deformed—the result of a shock far too great to have been caused by even a steam explosion from a volcano. This shocked quartz suggested something else: Since ocean basins are composed of basalt, which has a low percentage of quartz, the impact area was on or near a continent and should be still detectable.

By the turn of the decade, Alan Hildebrand and David Kring of the University of Arizona were looking closely at yet another aspect of the K/T-boundary layer. Embedded in the layer at some

Comet Kobayaski–Berger–Milon 1975 IX. (Photograph by Jack Newton, August 4, 1975, using a 12.5-inch f/4.3 reflecting telescope; 15-minute exposure and Tri-X film.)

Comet Kobayaski–Berger–Milon 1975 IX. (Photograph by Jack Newton, August 12, 1975, using a 12.5-inch f/4.3 reflecting telescope; 13-minute exposure and Tri-X film.) Notice subtle differences in the appearance of the tail from the earlier photograph. Particles in the tail are actually moving away from the comet so quickly that changes can appear in as little as 5 minutes.

sites were large amounts of rock fragments that could have been lifted from another place and dropped in their new location by a giant tsunami. Although these giant ocean waves are best known as following earthquakes, an impact of an object from space would have generated tsunamis several hundred meters high, moving hundreds of kilometers inland. Hildebrand noted that these deposits, which were several centimeters thick, cluster around the Caribbean sea and the Gulf of Mexico, an area known as the Caribbean basin.

In 1990, Hildebrand and Kring explored a K/T-boundary exposure in Haiti near a mountain village called Beloc. In its greenish brown clay, they found iridium as well as the same type of shocked quartz grains they had seen in other places. They also found small bits of glass known as tektites—rocks that had melted due to an impact and then cooled rapidly during a brief flight through the atmosphere. Here the boundary layer looked like it was full of material tossed out of the impact spot—so much material in fact that Hildebrand and Kring concluded that the crater could not be very far off.

The missing link was finally supplied by Carlos Byars, a reporter from the Houston *Chronicle* who happened to be at the 1990 Lunar and Planetary Science conference, a meeting held each spring in Houston. Byars had heard of a circular configuration with out-of-the-ordinary magnetic readings 60 kilometers wide, surrounded by a second much larger ring buried under 1100 meters of limestone directly below the city of Mérida and the town of Puerto Chicxulub on the north coast of Mexico's Yucatán Peninsula. Discovered in the late 1970s by Glen Penfield, a geologist from Houston conducting an aeromagnetic survey, the arc was mostly on the water side of Puerto Chicxulub. When he tried to compare the arc with specialized maps made more than a decade earlier, he found gravitational anomalies that showed the land portion of the ring, and he found that the anomalies resembled those of such known impact features as Quebec's Lac Manicouagan.

The story's next stage was a comedy of errors. Although Penfield quickly suspected that the 180-kilometer-wide feature was the buried remains of an impact crater, the Mexican national oil company, Pemex, which had originally ordered the survey, kept the data to itself until the project had been completed. Then Penfield presented his results at a petroleum geology meeting at which few impact specialists were present. Finally Pemex had some material that had been drilled from more than a kilometer below the surface. Before the samples could be confirmed as material that had been metamorphosed by an impact, some were lost in a fire in 1979. When Penfield first examined the specimens, he found that they appeared to be volcanic in origin, but he was puzzled that there was no other indication of volcanic activity anywhere near that region. The melted rocks under Chicxulub were later found to contain higher amounts of iridium than other boundary samples.[7] Chicxulub is an impact crater.

In retrospect, it is strange that the crater's positive identification took so long. Penfield's discovery was written up as a news note in *Sky and Telescope* magazine as early as March 1982, but for the next 8 years, no one paid any attention to it, even though the note included Penfield's suspicion that it might be related to the K/T extinction.[8]

By spring 1991, things were rapidly coming together. Two surviving samples were found to have a large amount of shocked quartz, and images from satellites showed some evidence at the Earth's surface. A large number of cenotes, the local term for large sinkholes that abound there, form a semicircle that matches the ring far below. Perhaps, geologists think, these cenotes resulted as the rim of the ancient crater slumped, producing local collapses in the overlying limestone.[9]

WAS IT A COMET OR AN ASTEROID?

Fifteen years ago the idea of an object hitting the Earth and killing the dinosaurs was so outlandish that few considered it seriously; now the theory is generally accepted. What's left is deciding which of the two types of object could cause that much damage—

an asteroid or a comet. Small meteors appear in the sky every night. Even meteors as bright as the brightest star could be any-where from sandgrain to golfball sized. A comet nucleus however could be bigger than 10 kilometers across—large enough with a high-speed hit to make a 200-kilometer diameter crater and cause real damage. Asteroids can be that large, too, and during the early 1980s, the prime dinosaur-killing suspect was an asteroid. One reason for thinking this was the amount of iridium in deposits around the world. Since a comet contains a proportion of ices as well as its solid material—basically it has to have room for more types of substances—it would have to be larger than an asteroid to carry the same amount of iridium. Several lines of reasoning now suggest that a comet, and not an asteroid, caused the extinction of more than 70 percent of the species of life on Earth.

Sizes of Asteroids and Comets

Of all the known asteroids presently in orbits that cross the Earth, only one—1627 Ivar—is large enough to make a crater approaching the size of Chicxulub. But even with its 9-kilometer-wide bulk, should Ivar ever hit, the crater it would carve out would be quite a bit smaller than Chicxulub. So if the largest Earth-crossing asteroid we know is too small and the next largest is quite a bit smaller, we have to conclude that statistically the present group of Earth-crossing asteroids is a poor choice for suspects. Chances are that 65 million years ago, while individual asteroids in Earth-crossing orbits were different, their size distribution was about the same as it is now.

Could there be a large asteroid out there with our name on it that has not yet been discovered? Given our present discovery experience with these objects, this is not likely. Asteroid search programs have come across Ivar many times, and if there were another object that large or larger, someone would have found it by now. What if some huge asteroid breaking up somewhere should send a pulse of large, Earth crossing asteroids toward Earth? It is not likely that such a minor version of the late heavy bombardment previously discussed would have occurred as recently as 65 million years ago.

Comets on the other hand do not drop off so radically as asteroids the larger they get. Both Comets Halley and Swift–Tuttle are large enough to cause the kind of damage that was seen at the K/T boundary, and comets in that size range appear rather often.

Frequency of Comet Appearances

How often do comets in this size range get close to the Earth? Two comets have closed in on us in only the last 200 years— Periodic Comet Lexell, which in June 1770 zipped by at a distance of 1.4 million miles, and IRAS–Araki–Alcock in 1983—virtually just the other day. Comets are always taking potshots at us, and if every 200 years or so, a comet misses us by less than 3 million miles, statistically we may get dangerously close to a large comet, or even hit by one, once in 100 million years.

Noble Metals at the K/T Boundary

Rare elements that do not easily form compounds—metals like iridium, osmium, platinum, and nickel—exist in certain outcroppings at the K/T boundary in proportions that are similar to what we would expect in comets. But since a carbonaceous asteroid (a primitive carbon-rich asteroid) may have a similar "primitive abundance pattern," all this shows is that the impactor was either a comet or a carbonaceous-type asteroid.

A Shower of Comets?

In the western United States, some outcroppings have been found that show more than one iridium layer. Early in the 1980s, some geologists tried to explain this observation as a long series of volcanic eruptions instead of as an object from space. But the existence of several sharply defined layers of iridium seems easily to suggest a series of several distinct events rather than a continuous series of eruptions.

Pockmarking the Earth, many large craters are the signatures of impacts through a stretch of geologic time. Of the craters that have been dated, some are grouped in relatively close time spans of about a million years. A comet shower does not mean that comets fall on us like rain. Over geologic time an increase of 30–100 times the number of hits over a period of a million years would be considered a comet shower.

OTHER MAJOR IMPACTS

In the last 250 million years, there have been four well-documented mass extinctions associated with impacts. Near the end of the Devonian period, some 345 million years ago, a mass extinction, known mostly for the loss of reef-building corals, may be associated with impacts in places as far apart as Belgium and China.

The next major event marked the end of the Triassic period 190 million years ago. Quebec's Manicouagan Crater appears to have been formed at that time and may have been related to that episode. This extinction was actually good for the dinosaurs, for with the drop in population of other animals, the giant reptiles evolved rapidly to fill niches. Tiny mammals also evolved at about this time. After the final extinction of the dinosaurs, this line of life evolved, in a sense, to take their place.

In the mid-Cretaceous period about 92 million years ago, another extinction took place in stages that took about a million years. However the ratio of platinum to iridium in exposed boundary layers is unlike that found in asteroids and comets. It is possible that this extinction was caused by some geochemical episode, such as a long period of intense volcanic activity.

About 25 million years after the great K/T extinction, in the late Eocene period some 40 million years ago, many species of life were extinguished in several steps lasting some 2 million years. The 100-kilometer diameter Popigai crater, east of the Urals in northern Siberia, may be related to part of this extinction. Although the resulting wipe-out took longer, it was almost as gargantuan as the one at the end of the Cretaceous period.

The most recent documented extinction from an extraterrestrial cause took place in the middle Miocene period some 15 million years ago. Limited to a single sample taken from deep waters near Antarctica and another in Australia, the evidence of this is not very strong.

IMPACTS AND EVOLUTION

Could a comet have killed the dinosaurs? Yes. There is a worldwide layer of matter that probably came from space, and a very large crater that appears to date from the same time. Were the dinosaurs already on their way out? Some geologists say yes, and others say no. However whether or not dinosaurs were on the rise, at their peak, or in decline, an ambush from space quite likely ended them.

One last question: How serious are these impacts for the long story of the evolution of life? Darwin's idea of natural selection as a mechanism for evolution portrays an orderly march to more and more complex life forms. But the fossil record adds that the progress of evolution is sometimes reset. While some life forms do evolve to greater degrees of complexity, mass extinctions are often followed by a burst of speciation. Although dinosaurs had been slowly evolving for some millions of years, the extinction event at the end of the Triassic cleared the decks for the dinosaurs to evolve in many directions and probably allowed them to thrive. Had the K/T extinction not taken place, the mammals could not have evolved to fill the niches that were left open in the ecosystem. Whatever the reason for extinctions, they appear to be good for the development of new species—exactly what would follow us however is unpredictable. And if comet and asteroid impacts can be found to have driven most of the major extinctions, then they play an important role in organic evolution.

It is a good thing then that our neighborhood of the solar system is so bombarded. Were there no comets hitting us from time to time, evolution might have stalled out long ago. On the other hand, we are lucky that it is not too active, as it was in the time of the late heavy bombardment discussed in Chapter 14. With K/T-type impacts happening every million years, new species would not have the quiet time they need to proliferate. We can thank Jupiter for that. Throughout much of the solar system's history, this gas giant has been affecting the orbits of many comets, in most cases tossing them right out of the solar system. If Jupiter's enormous gravity were not there, we might have as many as a hundred times the number of impacts, one every million years.

It is also good we don't see too many comets the size of Chiron, a 200-kilometer diameter object that orbits in the outer solar system beyond Saturn. Were something that size to hit just once, it would do so much damage that all life on Earth might be extinguished. Without stopping the process altogether, comets the size of Halley and Swift–Tuttle shake up evolution from time to time, and the dice are thrown again.

☾ *16* ☽

Getting Hit Again

Friday, October 9, 1992 was the kind of clear, warm evening that draws people outside. In the town of Ashland, Ohio, David Hartsel, a well-known amateur astronomer, was enjoying the Ashland High football game with his children, Heather and Sean.

It was late in the first quarter, and a play had just brought Ashland to the 10-yard line against Wooster. The two teams huddled to work out their next strategies. Suddenly a yellow green fireball emerged out of the twilight high in the southwest. Bright as a first-quarter moon, it raced across more than a sixth of the sky within the next 10 seconds, leaving a bright trail and breaking up into small pieces.

On the field players and referees on both teams pointed to the heavens, and everyone in the west stands saw the meteor fade as it approached the northeast horizon. "Wow!" someone cried out. "What the hell was that? Was it a rocket?" "That was a meteor!" Hartsel exulted. "But it's the brightest one I've ever seen." Play resumed, and almost everyone was home in time to learn on the evening news that people all over the midwestern United States had seen the fireball.

Hundreds of miles to the east, a Peekskill, New York, high school senior named Michelle Knapp thought she heard a car crash right outside her window. When she went to investigate, she found her car's trunk crushed and a warm rock the size of a football next to the gas tank. She reported what she thought was vandalism to the police. But later that evening, geologist William Menke, whom the police had contacted, identified the rock as a stony chondrite meteorite with a high iron content. By the following day, a horde of prospective buyers, including Sotheby's auctioneers from London, were bidding for the meteorite.[1] The event ended happily. Knapp received the grand sum of $69,000 for her rock *and* her car, both of which were displayed several months later at Tucson's international gem and mineral show. And back in Ohio, Ashland beat Wooster 20-zip.

It's funny how nature seems to play deliberate tricks on us. When national networks announced the 1992 Peekskill fireball, they reported that it was a member of the Draconid meteor stream, a logical conclusion, since the Earth was passing through the Draconid swarm that very evening. There had been a swarm of meteors from the same Draconid meteor stream many years earlier, on October 9, 1946. They lit the sky in spite of a bright moon that night. These Draconid meteors were remnants of Periodic Comet Giacobini–Zinner, which, at its return in 1985, became the first comet ever visited by a spacecraft. But although there were Draconid meteors that night in 1992, the great Peekskill fireball was not one of them. It came from the southwest instead of the northeast, where Draconid meteors were centered. Also the fact that the fireball produced a meteorite showed it as the remnant of a tiny asteroid, perhaps less than 1 meter across before it broke up. Although only one piece was found, other debris might have fallen over a 50-mile swath. This means, it is thought, that the meteorite was too dense to have been the residue from a comet.

Knapp was lucky that only her car was hit. On November 30, 1954, Mrs. E. H. Hodges was in her Sylacauga, Alabama home when a meteorite weighing in at 2 kilograms shattered her roof and proceeded to ricochet off her radio set and then bruise her thigh.[2]

Actually the Earth has been bombarded from space repeatedly in the past, and like Damocles, we will be hit again. Damocles was punished for irritating his master Dionysus by having to sit at a banquet with a sword on top of his head. The sword was fastened to the ceiling by a thread. Recently the British astronomer John Davies suggested that if an asteroid were found to be on a collision course with Earth, it should be named Damocles.[3]

Meteorites as large as the ones that bashed Knapp's car or Hodges's thigh are not uncommon visitors. On the afternoon of August 10, 1972, many people in the western United States and Canada saw a bright fireball enter the atmosphere some 60 kilometers above the Earth's surface. Between 4–14 meters in diameter, this object apparently survived its encounter with Earth. Grazing through the upper atmosphere, it went back into space and continued in a new and different orbit around the Sun. It may make another approach to Earth in 1997.[4]

FIND THEM BEFORE THEY FIND US

On January 18, 1991, astronomer David Rabinowitz discovered a tiny object still in space. It was far above the Earth's atmosphere but closer than the Moon. He was using the Spacewatch telescope at Arizona's Kitt Peak in a survey of Earth-approaching asteroids. Named 1991 BA, the object he saw was zipping along at the rate of 24 degrees per day and accelerating fast. By the end of the night, it had speeded up to 60 degrees per day—that's a third of the way across the sky. Estimated to be 10 meters in size, this small asteroid came so close to the Earth that someone wondered if it were artificial. With the Gulf War only 3 days old, perhaps it was some sort of Iraqi missile. But Marsden's orbit calculation showed that it was a small asteroid in orbit about the Sun. "Had it hit," one newspaper reported wildly, "it would have caused extensive devastation." Hardly—however it was some 10 times larger than the Peekskill asteroid and had 1000 times its energy.

Earth may encounter objects that size every year or perhaps several times in a year. Usually they fall unseen over distant oceans or in daylight. While these minor falls are difficult to take seriously, they could have catastrophic side effects. The Peekskill fall was seen by thousands of people, some of whom asked if it were a rocket. What would be the effect of such a sighting on the leaders of a nation at war? Would they mistake it for an incoming missile and then retaliate with a nuclear weapon? What if 1991 BA itself had hit the Earth? Just a day or two into the Gulf War, it could conceivably have changed the course of geopolitical events. An observant amateur astronomer who had seen lots of meteors as well as a slow-moving reentry of an artificial satellite would know by the object's high speed and its color (often yellow–green) that it came from space. Sometimes it might be hard to tell the difference, but military institutions around the world should be able to test the possibility that an explosion in the sky could be from natural phenomena.

HOW GREAT IS THE DANGER FROM IMPACTS?

Besides the consequence of a misidentified fireball, what exactly must we fear from the fall of a comet or an asteroid? That is not an easy question to answer. We have to consider several variables, some of which are well known, others about which we can only speculate. In a seminal paper in 1983, Shoemaker estimated the frequency of impacts of asteroids and comets of various sizes throughout history from the point of view of what size "bang" they would cause.[5] Although he began with the few actual discoveries of Earth-approaching asteroids and comets known at that time, Shoemaker used the size and frequency distribution of craters on the moon to complete his estimate of danger. A crash that is equivalent to an explosion of from 6–20 kilotons of TNT, he judged, would happen as often as once per year. The carbonaceous meteorite that fell near Revelstoke, British Columbia, in the mid-1960s is an example of such a crash. If we can expect this type of encounter once a year, such an object would actually pass through the atmosphere somewhere over North America every 25 years or so.[6]

A 20-meter diameter asteroid probably hits somewhere in the world every 25 years, producing a 200- to 600-kiloton explosion, equivalent to a small nuclear detonation, every 25 years. A 1–3 megaton impact might occur every century and a 10-megaton jolt, resulting from a 100-meter diameter object and duplicating the potential of our strongest nuclear weapons, takes place every millennium. The latest of these impacts occurred quite recently on June 30, 1908, when a small asteroid exploded over the Tunguska River in Siberia. It passed almost directly above the small town of Kirensk but was seen in broad daylight as far as 1000 kilometers away. The fall ignited trees up to 15 kilometers away from the center of the fall and toppled trees for 40 kilometers from ground zero.

All these effects were relatively local, except for two major ones. There were dramatic sunsets all over the world, and the airburst deposited a very large amount of nitric oxide in the upper atmosphere, a substance capable of damaging Earth's ozone layer. Since scientists then did not have today's monitoring devices, we cannot be certain of the extent of the ozone depletion. However observations at California's Mount Wilson Observatory for a completely different project—variations in the sun's luminosity—serendipitously recorded a 30 percent drop in the amount of ozone in the stratosphere between 1909 and 1911.[7]

The Siberian object did its damage without even bothering to hit the ground. As it entered the atmosphere, it encountered such high pressures that at 8.5 kilometers up, it disintegrated in a tremendous explosion. Coincidentally Siberia was hit again less than half a century later, this time by a much smaller 70-ton iron meteorite that left dozens of small craters, the largest about 27 meters across.

The Earth would encounter larger objects at less frequent intervals. A dense, iron-rich asteroid 50 meters wide produced a 30-megaton explosion in 5 seconds when it excavated Meteor Crater in northern Arizona. Something ten times that size, half a kilometer in diameter, would arrive every 30,000 years, producing a 2000-megaton blast.

By some calculations an object 1 kilometer wide would hit every 125,000 years, and a 2-kilometer diameter projectile might disrupt civilization about once per million years on average. Depending on location and time of year, *i.e.*, early spring in the northern hemisphere, where most of the world's crop production takes place, such a strike could set our civilization back, killing millions. An ocean impact, or even a land hit just before winter, so that the following year's food production would not be badly affected, would not be so disastrous. It would also be better if the object didn't break up much before it hit, for if it did, the energy would be spread over a wider area.

In any case a 2-kilometer object would not extinguish our species. How large an object would it take to render *homo sapiens* extinct? Although scientists differ on the threshold size, there is no doubt that a comet or asteroid from 5–10 kilometers across, producing a bang equivalent to tens of millions of megatons, would do so much damage to the Earth that those left alive would begrudge those who had died. Such species killers have arrived in the past about every 30–100 million years.[8]

DEPENDS ON THE SIZE

How many dangerous objects could lie in our planet's path is only part of the equation. What actually happens when one of these things hits the Earth? In January 1993, planetary scientists David Morrison and Clark Chapman classified the different effects as follows.[9]

High-Altitude Disintegration

If the projectile falls apart at least 40 kilometers above the Earth's surface, like the Peekskill meteorite, there is virtually no damage at the surface. The object would be up to 10 meters across, depending on whether it is a small asteroid or a comet.

Blast Damage and Other Local Effects

If the object explodes in the lower atmosphere (as the Tunguska asteroid did in 1908) or if pieces survive to crater the surface, the destruction could be severe over hundreds or thousands of square kilometers. A comet greater than 200 meters in diameter, or a stony asteroid a quarter that size, would penetrate the upper atmosphere and survive long enough to cause some local destruction, including forest fires.

The 1908 Tunguska object managed to do a lot of damage even though it exploded far above the ground and did not leave a crater. Whether an object lands and forms a crater or explodes in the air depends on its density, speed of entry, and angle of entry. If it comes in at a sharp angle, it will travel through much more atmosphere, giving it a greater chance to break up in flight. Some aspects of the physics of comet and asteroid impacts are similar to those of nuclear bombs, except for one important thing: A cosmic impact produces no radioactivity. Since we've witnessed the effects of a nuclear bomb on Trinity Site, Hiroshima, and Nagasaki and we have the results of years of nuclear testing, we can extrapolate what a far larger explosion could do.

Global Effects (Environmental Degradation)

How large does a comet or asteroid have to be before the consequence of its hitting us became global? If a projectile a 100 meters or so wide plummets down, the damage to plants and animals could be great—perhaps life over the area of a large city would be extinguished. A kilometer-wide object would do about as much damage as exploding all the world's nuclear weapons at once. If the object struck a continent, so much dust would enter the stratosphere that it would disrupt life around the world. Either a comet or an asteroid a kilometer long may be about the threshold size to cause a worldwide cataclysm. The exact threshold size depends on the composition of the object, its velocity, and many other variables. I've seen a number of newspaper articles state that "scientists have calculated that an object larger than 0.62 miles in diameter would cause worldwide damage." But scientists haven't calculated the threshold to that degree of precision. The newspaper writers should say about a kilometer or about three-fifths of a mile.

When a kilometer-sized comet or asteroid hits the Earth, the catastrophe could begin with the deaths of thousands—or millions—of people in the immediate area of the impact. They could be killed directly by falling debris, the shock wave, or resulting fires—millions would die from incineration from the tremendous heat that the impact would generate. Over a longer term, the result could be climatic changes over a period of a few months to a few years. The explosion of 10,000 megatons could put enough dust into the stratosphere to cause a significant drop in land temperatures—an impact winter, like the nuclear winter we've been warned of. However as any weather forecaster knows, the atmosphere is affected by so many variables that we have trouble accurately forecasting the weather let alone a sudden climate change. After an impact average temperatures in some places may fall by as much as 10 degrees Celsius. The impact of a kilometer-sized object may also affect the ozone layer significantly.

Mass Extinction (Environmental Catastrophe)

Morrison and Chapman end their scale with the crash of an object between 5–10 kilometers in diameter, from which there would be environmental damage great enough to cause extinction or near-extinction of our own species. The impact winter would be long and severe, with absolutely no daylight at all for months, conditions similar to what happened at the end of the dinosaur era. We'd be gone, and so would most of the other large animals.

HOW OFTEN DO COMETS HIT?

Earth doesn't keep its craters very long. As of 1993 there are only 140 known craters formed by comets or asteroids hitting us at high speed.[10] But Jupiter's large moon Ganymede, where virtually all the impact craters may have come from comets, displays a better record. From it, Shoemaker has calculated that the frequency of hits on any planet in our solar system is approximately inversely proportional to the square of the impacting object's diameter. We should expect to be hit by large comets a lot less often than small ones. Using the Ganymede data as well as observed comets, Shoemaker and his colleague Ruth Wolfe suggest that the Earth should encounter long period comets whose nuclei are a kilometer in diameter or larger only once every million years.

On the same basis, the Earth should meet a 10-kilometer diameter comet, one big enough to produce a K/T-boundary event, every 100 million years. As I mentioned earlier, Shoemaker notes that this prediction is consistent with a K/T-sized comet approaching to within 5 million kilometers of the Earth every 200 years.[11] In the past two centuries, the Earth has been grazed by large comets coming in from distant space. Comets passed closer than 6 million kilometers from Earth several times, including P/Tempel–Tuttle in 1366; 1491 II, 1743 I, and P/Lexell in 1770; P/Biela in 1805; P/Pons–Winnecke in 1927; and IRAS Araki Alcock in 1983. Just one month after the 1983 comet, another comet, Sugano–Saigusa–Fujikawa, came almost as close. In the future P/Finlay in 2060 and P/Giacobini–Zinner in 2112 will come within a few million kilometers of Earth, as well as some comets, perhaps, that are still undiscovered.[12]

Comets rounding the sun on near-parabolic orbits that do not bring them back here very often are the most dangerous of the impacting objects, since they can come with almost no warning. Along with these far-ranging invaders, we have to worry about a population of periodic comets, which include Halley, Swift–Tuttle, Levy, and Brorsen–Metcalf, as well as Jupiter-family comets and comets so nearly dead that they are hard to distinguish from asteroids. The chances that Earth may encounter any one of these is about the same as for the nonperiodic comets. In addition there are probably about 2000 asteroids 1 kilometer or larger that are capable of hitting the Earth.

PUTTING THE RISK IN ITS PLACE

If you feel threatened by these predictions, remember that life is full of risks. Even if we stayed in bed all day, the chances of hitting our heads on the night table are very slim, but if we wake up and drive to the grocery store, our chances of dying in a car crash on the way are about 1 in 4 million. At a conference in St. Petersburg in 1991, Clark Chapman offered the statistics that follow. I have added lightning strikes, which are not always fatal, and state lottery wins, which, one hopes, are never lethal. Chapman's figures do not take into account the obvious caveats: Someone who drinks while driving faces a far higher risk of dying in a car wreck than does a safe driver, and frequent flyers have a higher chance of dying in airplane crashes than people who have never flown.

Ways of Dying	Probability
Motor vehicle accident	1 in 100
Homicide	1 in 300
Fire	1 in 800
Firearms accident	1 in 2500
Accidental electrocution	1 in 5000
Comet or asteroid hit	1 in 20,000
Airplane crash	1 in 20,000
Flood	1 in 30,000
Tornado	1 in 60,000
Bites or stings	1 in 100,000
Fireworks accident	1 in 1,000,000
Botulism	1 in 3,000,000

Ways of Dying	Probability
Lightning strike	1 in 4,000,000
Water with EPA limit of TCE	1 in 10,000,000
State lottery win	1 in 15,000,000[13]

The number of deaths in a single accident is another factor we look at when determining how much attention to give the danger. While an airplane accident is very rare, so many people die in each one that public alarm has been high enough to motivate a lot of research on making aircraft safe. There is a far greater risk of dying in an auto accident where the number of people affected per crash is much lower.

A comet impact is potentially the most extreme case of risk versus consequence. Since none of us knows of anyone who has actually died from a comet or asteroid impact, most people are not inclined to take the risk seriously. The possible repercussions of a hit by an object a kilometer or two in diameter are enormous. It would be equivalent to the energy of a full-scale nuclear war and greater than any other natural disaster. Millions of people may die at once, and the Earth as we know it could be quickly transformed into an alien and inhospitable environment. From this statistical point of view, comet and asteroid impacts rank as catastrophes that grip our imaginations.

ℭ 17 ℌ

Deflecting the Terrible Sword

Almost 50 years ago, the famous astronomer Bart Bok revealed that the Milky Way was filled with dense concentrations of gas that could be the birthplaces of new stars. Although these Bok globules, as they are now known, are faint and esoteric objects, they captured the public imagination, thanks to a 1957 science fiction story by astronomer Fred Hoyle, called *The Black Cloud*. As the story opens, astronomers using Palomar's 18-inch Schmidt telescope (the same one used in real life to discover all the Shoemaker comets) spot a big black cloud approaching the Earth. "Such globules are not uncommon in the Milky Way," the astronomer says, "but usually they're tiny things. My God, look at this! It's huge, it must be the best part of two and a half degrees across!"[1] As the drama unfolds, the globule appears to get bigger as it closes in on the Earth. Finally one morning the assistant appears in a great panic: "It's not there, sir, it's not there!" "What isn't there?" "The day, sir! There's no Sun!"

People going outside that awful morning see an eerie sight: It is "pitch black, unrelieved even by starlight, which was unable to penetrate the thick cloud cover. An unreasoning primitive fear seemed to be abroad. The light of the world had gone."[2]

But this is no ordinary globule: In Hoyle's science fiction, this globule has intelligence and the ability to communicate with scientists on Earth, and it is very surprised to find that life forms inhabit an actual planet instead of living freely in space. The globule hangs around for several months before it finally decides to leave, and daylight returns.

We should be so lucky that a comet would be that understanding, were it to decide to envelop the Earth. If we could only reason with it, perhaps it would go away! But Nature doesn't allow that. Instead some people think that we need to come up with more ingenious solutions that would prod the comet or asteroid off its deadly course.

WHAT WE COULD DO

Suppose we found a comet or asteroid ready to hit us in the next quarter-century, a time span close enough to be threatening to a great number of people right now. Here are some sensible things that we could do.

Educate Leaders about Fireballs

The Earth is bound to be hit by something soon. The Peekskill meteorite was harmless except for wrecking a young woman's car and disturbing a football game. However it could just as well have fallen over a country in the midst of turmoil, and it could have easily been misidentified as a missile or even a nuclear airburst.

Fireballs as bright as the one that left the Peekskill meteorite come through the atmosphere somewhere on Earth every week or so. If some nervous government were to respond to a fireball with a retaliatory strike at another country, then the incoming asteroid or comet could trigger a war. As more and more countries acquire nuclear weapons, the chances that one will be launched by mistake increase. A real attempt to educate national leaders and military establishments about sights in the sky could prevent a war started by accident.

Move People Away from the Impact Point

If we should find a large interloper on a collision course with Earth, we would observe it often enough to know its orbit with great accuracy. We might then calculate where it would hit on Earth. Even if we learned that it would land in an ocean, which would be the most likely scenario, we would have to plan the evacuation of shoreline residents to prepare for tsunamis or tidal waves. Evacuation decisions would have to be made and carried out quite quickly, for in all likelihood, we would not know the path that well until a few days or even hours before impact.

Store a Full Year's Supply of Food

Impact winter as a result of a long period of darkness could result in the loss of a full growing season. Food would vanish. If—and that is a big if—we had lead time of a year or more, we could plan to store immense quantities of food. But this would present tremendous political problems. Who would distribute this food on a worldwide basis? How would it reach everyone in every nation? Who would be responsible for making sure it were neither hoarded nor destroyed? Dangerous as it would be, maybe a comet could provide a great incentive and opportunity for the world's nations to pull together to avert a global crisis.

Deflect the Object to Crash in Midocean

If pushing an encroacher to a new orbit so that it would miss the Earth entirely were not possible, perhaps we could use a nuclear blast to nudge it away from hitting a metropolis like Los Angeles and have it land instead in open water. So long as the invader were not too large, an ocean impact would be best. We would then interrupt air and sea traffic and evacuate people on the coastline from the danger of tsunamis. However if a large Swift–Tuttle-sized comet were coming, where it hits would make no difference. It would plow through miles of ocean in seconds. But such an event comes about once every 100 million years. A strike by a 1-kilometer object is far more likely, coming every 100,000 years.

Trying to deflect an object so that it hits one part of the Earth instead of another is an idea with one big problem. We might not know the object's path well enough until it is too late to deflect it. Think of the global crisis that would result if an object aimed at Toronto, Canada, were moved incorrectly and hits Iran instead.

Deflect the Object away from Earth Altogether

Of all the possibilities for dealing with an incoming comet or asteroid, deflecting it away from us is by far the most publicized and desirable option *if* we find the object years, preferably de-cades, in advance. We could deflect the object with a nuclear bomb exploded near the intruder. A series of such explosions could slowly prod the object into a new path that would avoid the Earth. We would do this slowly, a bit at a time, instead of catapulting the object away all at once. Smaller blasts would be less likely to rip apart the incoming object, thereby making it much more dangerous.

Deflecting the object would likely be the end of a long series of actions that would begin right after someone found something that after several months or more of observations, appeared to be heading directly toward the Earth. Such a proposal is based on the assumption that the possible collision is far enough in the future—several years or even decades—to allow sufficient time to mount a deflecting program. Unless we mount a serious campaign to dis-cover virtually all the kilometer-diameter objects whose orbits cross the path of the Earth, chances are that we will not have the luxury of decades to prepare.

If we find a threatening comet or asteroid, first we would observe it with the best telescopes we had to understand its orbit as well as we could. We could use optical telescopes and with large radio telescopes, we could bounce radar waves off the object to get an even better idea of its orbit and its shape. It would be important to know the shape, partly to make sure that we were dealing with one intruder and not two. At the end of 1992, radar astronomer Steve Ostro took such clear images of the asteroid 4179 Toutatis, then near the Earth, that it appeared to be two asteroids loosely held together by gravity. An asteroid or comet like that would be very difficult to deflect in a controlled way as it entered the atmosphere, breaking into 2 parts and causing even more damage.

By this time—still some years before impact—we should have the impact site plotted to within a 100-kilometer radius—say, somewhere around the Los Angeles basin. But we could do better than that. A small spacecraft would meet the object, take pictures of it, determine its structure and composition, and—most important—leave a beacon to send back signals to Earth. With that signal we could track the intruder with very high precision. We would know its impact target to within a kilometer—now centered, say, in southwest Santa Monica.

Armed with all this information, we are now ready for the dangerous and controversial part. Engineers would send a spacecraft loaded with a 100-kiloton nuclear bomb. The explosive would not blow up on the intruder's surface but about a kilometer away from it, close enough to change its orbit slightly but not so close that it would blow the object apart. To plant a bomb on the surface would be a terrible mistake. If it were an extinct comet, a surface explosion could blow the thing into several pieces, and then each piece would become an active comet! With a bundle of small comets all changing positions as their newly released gases formed jets, we would have lost all control of where they were going.

Instead a bomb placed nearby would gently nudge the mighty object. Moreover the bomb would be set to explode when the intruder was at perihelion, where an explosion would result in the greatest orbit change. After the explosion we would calculate the new orbit to see how effective the first try was. We'd try a second shot a few years later when the trespasser returned to its next perihelion, and after two or three more tries, the object should be in an orbit that would take it safely past Earth. As we can see however, changing the orbit of an object a kilometer across is not a small task.

WHOA! IS DEFLECTION A BAD IDEA?

At this point we need to stop and ask if this whole idea is far too dangerous to proceed with. Even if we knew precisely what effect a nuclear explosion would have on a comet or an asteroid, launching nuclear weapons into space is dangerous business, and exploding them would be a violation of current UN treaties. The idea of a series of nuclear-tipped missiles heading off into orbit is scary. Like the old *Star Trek* episode in which a malfunctioning nuclear warhead plunging back to Earth is disarmed in the last seconds, a program to launch a series of nuclear bombs into space would be just as frightening to many people as the intruding asteroid itself. Moreover we have no current idea of how a nuclear weapon would behave in space near a comet or an asteroid. Would it simply shatter the object, sending a hail of shrapnel down on us that could be even more deadly than if the original object came down intact? The only reason that the idea of deflecting an intruder in this manner is being thought of at all is that there might not be any alternatives.

BEING MORE AGGRESSIVE

To answer some of these objections, some planners are suggesting that we set about learning exactly how a bomb would deflect a comet or an asteroid. We could try nudging a periodic comet each time it passes perihelion just to see how its orbit changes. But even this idea is controversial; in fact some scientists call it stupid. Messing around with orbits of kilometer-wide bodies, they say, could even send one from a harmless orbit into an orbit that could be dangerous to us in years to come.

What about deflecting a comet toward us on purpose? Once we get the technology right, goes one suggestion, we should go to an extinct comet, drill into it to circulate hot water and evaporate just enough of the comet's gases to steer it into a safe orbit about the Earth. In addition to honing the technology of moving comets and asteroids around in space, this opportunity would give us access to the comet's supply of fresh water. But the risks of such an enterprise would be immense. If our aim were wrong, we would bring this supposedly helpful comet crashing right down on Earth. Also should we not worry about preserving the comet's environment too? Perhaps we need a Comet Environmental Protection Agency.

In any case the idea of gradually moving a space intruder would work for an object found way in advance of its hitting us, and one that wasn't much bigger than a kilometer across. If Periodic Comet Swift–Tuttle were about to hit the Earth, we would really be in trouble. Ten times larger, a thousand times more massive, and moving faster than any object we could ideally move, it would be almost impossible to divert. Astronomer Donald Yeomans compared such an attempt to pushing around a tank with a popgun. For this comet we are talking about launching bombs with hundreds of megatons of destructive power on rockets far larger than any now available.

WHAT WE ARE ALREADY DOING

Will a comet or an asteroid hit the Earth in the next 50 years? For asteroids with their 1–3 year orbital periods, there is a way of finding out. But with comets on thousand year plus orbits, the assessment is far more difficult. While potentially dangerous asteroids orbit the sun for short periods, allowing us to find them years before an impact, a comet can swoop in on us from the depths of space with no more than a few weeks advance notice— hardly more than the dinosaurs had if they could have seen it coming. If the comet comes from directly behind the sun, we may get virtually no notice at all.

Begging governments to fund comet research because one might squash us is misleading. Let's face it. According to the table in Chapter 16, the chances of anybody we know being hit by a comet are very slim. If someone is going to fund our efforts to find these things, we should offer a different point of view. Those who search for comets and near-Earth asteroids are like the mapmakers of generations past. Wanting to find new routes and new destinations, they made ever-more accurate maps of the Earth. Today our world has expanded into space, and it is interesting and proper to find out what orbits the sun in our neck of the woods. It doesn't cost much to do that. While working toward that goal, we could conceivably find a bullet with our name on it, but that should be a bonus, not an end in itself.

By searching for comets and asteroids that approach the Earth, we will, like the cartographers of past ages, learn a lot about our environs. That is a good thing, and at a few million dollars per year, it doesn't cost too much. The money would go to upgrading the three currently operating projects.

Spacewatch Survey

Find them before they find us! was the call for a program to search for Earth approachers from the summit of Kitt Peak, southwest of Tucson, Arizona. It is the brainchild of Tom Gehrels, a planetary scientist who has devoted his career to studying asteroids and who has discovered five comets as part of various survey projects.

A colorful and lively scientist, Gehrels has what is probably the most elaborate story about confirming a comet suspect. While searching a photographic plate in Tucson, he discovered a fuzzy trailed image that could be a comet. Since the suspect was faint, he thought that the best telescope to confirm the comet would be Palomar's stalwart 48-inch Schmidt, some 400 miles away. He surprised the director of Palomar with a request to travel that very night to Palomar to take a single photographic plate. The director approved Gehrels's request but only for an hour at the start of that very evening. Racing to the Tucson airport, Gehrels caught a mid-afternoon flight to San Diego and rented a car to speed to the observatory. Driving up Palomar Mountain, Gehrels was thinking more about his comet than about his driving. "The road had zigs and zags," he told me, "and I zagged when I should have zigged." The car went off the pavement, leaving its former driver to hitch-hike the rest of the way to the 48-inch Schmidt. He got his picture, but there was no comet on the photographic plate.[3]

In 1982, Jim Scotti joined the Spacewatch effort, and since then he has added enormously to its success. Using the 0.9-meter diameter telescope and a primitive electronic CCD system, Scotti helped prove the system's mettle with 38 recoveries of faint comets since 1982. In one banner year, Scotti picked up a third of the entire year's supply of comets. He also pioneered the development of a means of determining accurate positions of the objects found with the CCD system. Although the project still uses its original telescope, it has a new and much larger CCD system. Under the current system, their discoveries have skyrocketed. Although many of the objects are less than half a kilometer wide, Spacewatch found the first comet discovered with a CCD and discovers as many Earth approachers as everyone else in the world combined.

Although Spacewatch gets more observing time each month than any of the other projects—18 nights centered on the new moon and divided among Gehrels, Scotti, and Robert Jedicke—their system's narrow field means that they cover less sky; however they can see much fainter objects. Spacewatch has found a number of objects with nearly circular orbits about the sun that are so small that they can be seen only when near the Earth.

Planet-Crossing Asteroid Survey

Using the 18-inch Schmidt telescope at Palomar, Eleanor Helin has achieved some spectacular results. Accompanied by a small group of assistants, sometimes including her husband, Ron, during a clear 6-night period Helin will take enough 6-minute exposures to cover a lot of sky. The program has yielded 15 new comets and some 80 near-Earth asteroids, including several asteroids that passed within several million kilometers of Earth—close enough that astronomers with radio telescopes could bounce radar signals off them.

During the Camp David meetings in 1978, Helin discovered an Earth-approaching asteroid that she subsequently named to honor the peace accord between Israel and Egypt. Using the Egyptian sun god Ra, standing for enlightenment and life, and the Hebrew salutation shalom, which means peace, Helin named the asteroid Ra-Shalom in hope that the peace process would continue and an object orbiting in space would forever honor it.

Palomar Asteroid and Comet Survey

Already discussed in previous chapters, the Shoemaker program has yielded 30 comets as well as many asteroids. An interesting byproduct of this search has been discoveries of a large number of Trojan asteroids.

Early in this century, Max Wolf found the first of a group of asteroids so distant that they apparently "shared" Jupiter's orbit, circling the sun some 60 degrees ahead or behind the giant planet along the curve of Jupiter's orbit. Known as Trojan asteroids, they oscillate about the Lagrangian points ahead or behind Jupiter. They are named for characters in the Trojan War. Those on one side of Jupiter are named for the Greek heroes, while those on the other side are named for Trojan heroes. In June 1990, astronomer Henry Holt and I found something completely new—a Martian Trojan, an asteroid some 2 kilometers wide in a Trojan orbit with respect to Mars. Now called 5261 Eureka, the name recognizes the excitement Archimedes felt after making an important discovery. When asked to tell the difference between a crown made of real gold and a fake, Archimedes solved the problem while taking a bath and thinking up his principle that objects of different densities displace different amounts of water. So thrilled was he, the story goes, that he leaped out of his bath and ran out of the house, presumably still unclad, yelling "Eureka! Eureka!" ("I found it!") We hope that other Martian Trojans will have names that express similar joy in making a discovery.

The lucky find of a Martian Trojan excited the community of planetary scientists. There may have been Trojans around Mercury or Venus at one time, but there do not appear to be any now. "The fact that you two found a Mars Trojan is just really remarkable to us," Carolyn Shoemaker remarked. "It is a real unicorn in the astronomical zoo."

ENHANCING THESE PROGRAMS

Each of the three programs has had its own golden moments under the stars. The logical best step would be to build on the expertise that people in these programs have attained over years of observing. Cataloging every object out there that could potentially hit us would be the cheapest insurance against being hit by an incoming projectile. In 1973 we knew of about 12 Earth-crossing asteroids and several Earth-approaching comets; now we see fewer than 200 Earth-approaching asteroids. Since there are an estimated 2000 near-Earth asteroids a kilometer or more across, we have a lot of finding to do. Augmenting the three programs just described would continue that process, and over the next several decades, we would have a far clearer picture of the environment in space in the vicinity of where the Earth crosses in its journey about the sun.

A group of scientists has launched a proposal to speed things up. Project Spaceguard, as it is called, would mount an array of several large telescopes at sites around the world. By searching much of the sky each week, Spaceguard could discover and calculate the orbits of about 95 percent of all 2000 near-Earth asteroids a kilometer across or larger. (The estimated population of earth-crossing asteroids is ten objects that are 5 kilometers or more across, 2000 at 1 kilometer, and at least 300,000 at a 0.1 kilometer.) But the price tag for this program is at least 250 million dollars. Do we really need to know our environment in nearby space that well so soon? Indeed we have the technology to do it. Moreover for a relatively minor investment, we could significantly reduce our chances of having an asteroid or comet come hurtling toward us.

Does the danger justify the expense? We do not always pay attention to risks on a rational basis; airline safety is an example. Even though the annual loss of life in airplane crashes is far less than in auto accidents, each air crash is so visible that we invest heavily in airline safety. Some risks are so high that we do not question the need to prepare for them in some way. We develop ever more complex weapons to defend ourselves in case of war, for instance, in the hope that they will act as a deterrent to war.

SOME PHILOSOPHICAL QUESTIONS

The comet or asteroid impact risk needs to take its place among all these others. Even if we decide that the costs of a search program are reasonable, other considerations persist. Early in 1993, David Morrison, who has chaired a committee to study the problem, posed several important questions[4]:

Is It Appropriate to Interfere with the Natural Process?

After all, if dinosaurs had deflected their comet 65 million years ago, they might still be here and we might still be tiny burrowing animals. Believing that the comet was fulfilling a biblical prediction of Armageddon, some would object to any attempt to meddle with our predestined future. In any event, getting international agreement on what to do could be exceedingly difficult. "What if you made a mistake?" some suspicious nation might demand; "You could deflect the thing on us!"

Should We Protect against Large and Small Impacts?

While the first question is an ethical one, this is a practical one. The Olympian perspective, Morrison notes, is that we could. At one extreme, we could try to protect everyone and everything from a meteorite that hits the trunk of a car, and at the other, we could change the path of a large comet coming to deliver a bang that would destroy our species. Somewhere in between are the 1-kilometer comets and asteroids that would have an effect on the global environment, and the smaller ones that could have severe but local consequences.

Should We Defer Action until A Threatening Object Has Actually Been Found?

Some scientists maintain that we should spend almost no money at all on plotting a defense against an intruder, instead we should concentrate only on searching for them. Then if one were found, we would hope to have enough time to develop a means of deflecting it. This plan might work in the case of an errant asteroid whose discovery would hopefully come many years before it hit us. But it begs the question of the greatest danger of all, which is from a long-period comet arriving with little warning. When Comet IRAS–Araki–Alcock was discovered in 1983, only 1 week passed before it came within a few million miles of Earth. It is hard to imagine any defense we have now that could deflect a speeding comet that close to impact. As we've seen, had the dinosaur comet been a long-period one, their Spaceguard program wouldn't have worked either unless it detected the comet far enough out.

We have to look at the statistics before making a rational decision. One estimate of the bottom line: Each century there is about a 1 in 1000 chance that there will be an impact on Earth of an asteroid 1 km or larger; over 10,000 years the chance increases to 1 in 10. "But if there is a guy out there," Shoemaker says, "we should know about it. It is one of the most predictable catastrophes you can imagine." Unless we search we cannot know whether we are destined to be hit in the next century. With a modest search program, we could at least find out if an asteroid or comet in a short-period orbit were headed our way.

One final question: Should we take the risk seriously?

THE GIGGLE FACTOR

The main problem with the impact hazard is that it seems so terribly remote that people laugh it off. Although there are Chinese records of deaths from probable meteorites, it is a risk from some poorly defined thing out there in space. In their concern over this problem however, some scientists have made alarming statements the press has harped on. Would an object only 500 meters in diameter cause a global catastrophe? Most scientists say no, but there is disagreement. Astronomers using telescopes may insist for example that the greatest danger comes from intruders larger than a kilometer, which happens to be the size of the smallest objects they typically find. On the other hand, people studying ways of deflecting these objects may say that far smaller objects, which are the easiest ones to reroute, pose the greatest hazard.

By the early 1990s, excitement was building for a search-and-destroy program, aimed at first locating all asteroids larger than a kilometer, and then designing great big nuclear weapons to go out and nudge them into more benign orbits. At New Mexico's Los Alamos National Laboratory, astronomers met with nuclear bomb experts, notably Edward Teller, designer of the hydrogen bomb. The result was a severe clash of views and a flurry of bad publicity. One group proposed an armada of ten ground-based missiles, each with a 100-megaton warhead, ready and waiting for the attack of the comet about to hit us with 2 weeks' notice.

The press responded with a battering ram of derision. "Never mind the peace dividend," the *Wall Street Journal* warned, "the killer asteroids are coming!" Quoting one of the meeting participants who shouted "Nukes forever!" the paper depicted the confab's dispute between those who would spend a small amount of money to catalog all asteroids and those who would hunt them down with all means possible. "Killer Asteroid Dooms Earth!" shrieked a San José paper, adding that "if you believe that, Edward Teller and friends have several billion dollars worth of space weaponry to sell you."[5]

With the fuss surrounding predictions that Comet Swift–Tuttle may hit the Earth in 2126, some scientists questioned whether too much was being made of the possible impact. "After all," says comet scientist Paul Weissman, "even if the comet were 15 days late coming to perihelion in 2126, it would miss the Earth, according to one orbit calculation, by about than the distance to the Moon."[6]

"Despite all the hopes pinned on it," a *Nature* editorial intoned, "Swift–Tuttle is resolutely refusing to be the agent of wild destruction. Too bad!"[7] Even the staid *New York Times* mentioned the skeptics' view that the problem "is a result of scheming by astronomers and bomb makers by practicing the kind of threat inflation the Pentagon excelled at in the cold war."[8]

There is no such scheming. Defending Earth against an errant comet is a whole new field of study bringing together scientists who observe the sky, scientists who calculate orbits, and engineers who design weapons and delivery systems. The controversy will rage for some time, long after the snickers have subsided, and we get back to looking at the real promise here. For the first time in the history of all the civilizations ever to live on Earth, we *can* do something about a comet or an asteroid headed for Earth like a dart about to hit a bull's eye.

Over thousands of years, we have come full circle with comets. Feared at first and later studied and enjoyed, they are now feared again as harbingers of doom. But unlike the soothsayers of yesteryear, today, with a considerable amount of planning and a lot of care, we may be able to travel to a comet and change its path so that it sails harmlessly by.

❆ *18* ❂

Maxwell's Silver Hammer
A String of Pearls Strikes Jupiter

L ittle did I know when I started this book about comets and impacts in summer 1992 that a string of comets would smash into Jupiter around publication time. In July 1994 on the twenty-fifth anniversary of the *Apollo* moon landing, pieces of Periodic Comet Shoemaker–Levy 9 will plow into Jupiter, explode in its atmosphere, and release a million megatons of energy.

FIRST SURPRISE: WHAT A COMET!

Its icy interior long since cloaked by an inert crust, in July 1992 a comet wandered so close to Jupiter that the planet's tidal forces tore it apart. As the ancient body traveled away from Jupiter, its pieces moved slowly apart, and a string of new comets was born, their freshly exposed materials brightening rapidly.

Unaware of the event that had taken place so far away, the Shoemakers and I were discouraged about losing another observing run due to bad weather. It was March 1993, and the year had not been a good one for us. Our 7-night observing run in January, we had only one clear night, and the February run had only one clear

The discovery photos of Periodic Comet Shoemaker–Levy 9. (Photographed by David Levy the evening of March 23, 1993 [March 24 Universal Time], using the Palomar 18-inch Schmidt camera.) Taken more than an hour apart, these pictures are designed to be viewed as a stereo pair. A viewer using a stereo eyepiece sees the comet "floating" above the background stars.

hour out of 7 nights. With poor weather predicted for our March run too, we began to feel despondent. The clouds did give us a chance to work on our other projects. Shoemaker had much work to do for the forthcoming *Clementine* mission that was planned for a 1994 trip to the moon and the asteroid Geographos. Although the little craft would not exactly go excavating for a mine, as the song goes, the observations it made would pave the way for later work that would make *Clementine's* dad proud. And I used the cloudy hours to work on this book.

From the two previous cloudy observing runs at the 18-inch Schmidt telescope at Palomar, we had gathered a collection of blank films, all hypersensitized for 6 hours to increase their sensitivity and be ready to gather starlight in the telescope. Philippe Bendjoya, an astronomer from France who had just completed his thesis on families of asteroids that result when a large asteroid breaks up after colliding with another asteroid, joined us for this week. Finally the night of March 22, the first night of our run, was clear—a breathtakingly beautiful night. The stars were steady, and a marine layer of low clouds beneath our mountaintop hid the skyglow from nearby Los Angeles and San Diego. This was the kind of night astronomers' dreams are made of.

At least it was a dream until I finished exposing the fourth film. By this time Gene had developed the first two films and found to his horror that sometime during the long cloudy interregnum, *someone* had opened the box and exposed the films to light. For a few minutes we thought we had blown the night, for the next films were 6 hours away from being ready for use. Gene quickly developed films from the center and bottom of the box and found that while these were light-struck round the edges, they were still usable. Relieved, we loaded a new film into the telescope and got back to observing.

That turned out to be the only clear night of the entire week. With cirrus clouds coming in at the start of the second night, we hurriedly began our vigil and managed to expose 20 films before the clouds thickened and we had to stop. We stood morosely outside the dome, looking at a sky covered with cirrus clouds. The

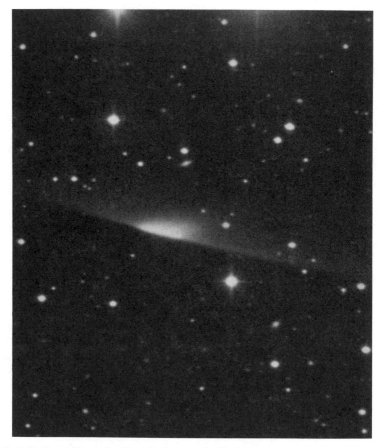

Periodic Comet Shoemaker–Levy 9, photographed by James V. Scotti on March 30, 1993 using the University of Arizona's 0.91-meter Spacewatch telescope. The photograph shows about eleven cometary pieces spread out in a bar. A tail extends toward the top from each nucleus. The wings on either side of the bar form a large dust train.

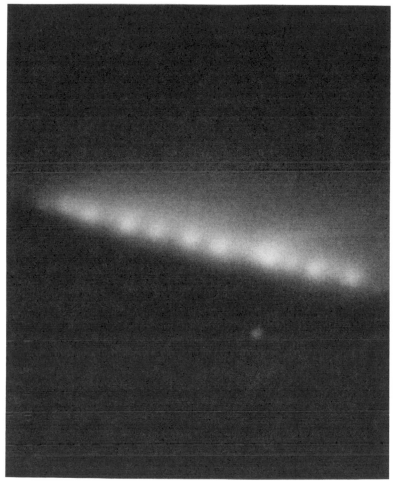

A close up of Periodic Comet Shoemaker–Levy 9, taken by Wieslaw Wisniewski on March 28, 1993 with the University of Arizona's 2.3-meter telescope on Kitt Peak.

clouds were not very thick, I noticed, and I suggested that we continue observing right through them. But with film prices edging $4 per shot, we had to watch the bottom line. Then I had an idea. "Don't we have a dozen light-struck films left? Why don't we just keep going and use them!" Gene looked at the sky again, then at me. "Let's get to it!" he said.

With the telescope horizontal, I loaded the filmholder and focused the telescope—a setting that depends on the air temperature—and Gene read the coordinates as I thrust the telescope toward a seventh-magnitude star right on the ecliptic. "Yuk!" I sneered as a bright glow almost swamped the star. "Dollars to doughnuts, Jupiter's in this field. Okay. Gene, star is centered!"

With a turn of a handle, the telescope's shutter swung open, and for the next 8 minutes, the film gathered light. We took a second film, then a third before the clouds got so thick we had to stop again. For the next hour and a half, we watched and waited. When a small break came, I retook the Jupiter field, and finally we finished the set. Except for a few more fields the following night, we were clouded out for the rest of the week.

By the afternoon of March 25, Carolyn had completed scanning the films from the first night. "I used to be a person who found comets," she chuckled. Shaking her head, she then placed the two films encompassing Jupiter in the stereomicroscope. Suddenly Carolyn sat up tensely. "I don't know what this is," she said. "It looks like . . . like a squashed comet."

This we had to see. Gene stared through the eyepieces, then gave me the most perplexed look I've ever seen on his face. Then it was my turn. Hovering above the stars was the strangest fuzzy thing I have ever seen. It looked like a comet, all right, but instead of the nice round coma that comets should have, this one was a bar of cometary light. What's more, in the hour and 49 minutes between films the whole thing had moved only slightly. Puzzled, I yielded the eyepieces to Philippe Bendjoya.

We puzzled over this for some time. It couldn't be a ghost image of Jupiter, which appeared as a huge black blotch on the film. The ghost image was on the other side of the film where it belonged, and so were some other familiar optical reflections. This was completely different. "The image is most unusual," we reported to Marsden, director of CBAT, "in that it appears as a dense, linear bar very close to 1 arcminute long, oriented roughly east-west. No central condensation [a starry point sometimes marking the comet's center] is observable in either of the two images. A fainter, wispy 'tail' extends north of the bar and to the west." Finally each side of the bar ended with a long, thin line.

Although our sky was cloudy and threatening, I hoped that the incoming storm hadn't moved far enough eastward to cloud Arizona's Kitt Peak, where my friend Jim Scotti was observing that very night. Using the University of Arizona's 36-inch Spacewatch telescope, Scotti was in the middle of his search for asteroids near the Earth. Fortunately the Kitt Peak sky, though "cirrusy," was not clouded out yet. But Scotti worried that the object's motion so closely matched Jupiter's that it could somehow be a reflection of Jupiter in the telescope. While we waited for his attempt at confirmation, Jean Mueller of Palomar helped us measure the comet's precise position.

SECOND SURPRISE: A STRING OF PEARLS

As soon as we returned to the 18-inch dome, I called Scotti. "Have you got a comet!" he exulted. "There are at least five separate condensations!" Later that night he sent this electronic mail message to Marsden:

> It is indeed a unique object, different from any cometary form I have yet witnessed. In general, it has the appearance of a string of nuclear fragments spread out along the orbit with tails extending from the entire nuclear train, as well as what looks like a sheet of debris spread out in the orbit plane in both directions. The southern boundary is very sharp while the northern boundary spreads out away from the debris trails.[1]

The following afternoon Marsden announced Comet Shoe-maker–Levy 1993e. Because the new comet was mimicking Jupiter's motion, we and other astronomers guessed that the comet had been torn asunder in a recent close encounter with Jupiter. One observer however countered (incorrectly, it turns out) that he suspected the original object might have been rotating too quickly and just fallen apart without assistance from Jupiter's gravity.

In the days immediately following this dramatic discovery, Scotti's observations were reduced and fine tuned by David Rabinowitz at Spacewatch, while a host of observers around the world provided early accurate positions that allowed Marsden to compute an orbit. Then Jane Luu and David Jewitt, observing with the 88-inch telescope on Mauna Kea, Hawaii, provided a breathtaking picture that showed 17 nuclear condensations arrayed, they wrote, "like pearls on a string." The University of Arizona's Wieslaw Wisniewski used a 90-inch telescope to take an equally beautiful picture of this unique comet.

THIRD SURPRISE: TWENTY NEW SATELLITES OF JUPITER

As word spread about the weird nature of this comet, more people started looking at it. Using my 16-inch diameter backyard telescope, I could see it as a slender bar of faint light. On April 3 came surprise number three. Marsden wrote that he suspected that this comet was in orbit about Jupiter, but unlike the satellites moving safely in almost circular orbits about Jupiter, the comet's orbit would take it very close to Jupiter at what we call the perijove, and a year later, as far away from Jupiter as Mercury is from the Sun at apojove, the farthest distance from Jupiter. Other comets have been presumed to orbit Jupiter briefly, but until now no one had ever seen a comet orbit Jupiter this way. Meanwhile Luu and Jewitt had counted 20 comets in the train. So temporarily at least, instead of its normal retinue of 16 known moons, Jupiter had 36!

Marsden later renamed it Periodic Comet Shoemaker–Levy 9, the ninth periodic comet found by our team.

WHAT CAUSED THE BREAKUP?

In the months after discovery, there was some doubt that the comet came close enough to Jupiter to be torn apart by tidal forces. Comets do not necessarily need to be near giant planets or the sun to break up. Comets Levy 1988e and Shoemaker–Holt 1988g, discussed earlier, broke up 10 thousand years ago when they were not much closer to the sun than the Earth is. As Scotti whimsically notes, you can sneeze on a comet, and it will break up. At one point he suggested that a sudden explosion of the comet's volatile material might have helped the destruction along. As it turned out, these ideas faded away once we knew that the comet passed close enough to Jupiter so that tidal forces tore it apart in July 1992.

All this speculation changed by May 22, 1993, however. Using more than 200 precise positions, Marsden was able to compute an accurate orbit that tells of the comet's extraordinary adventure. In July 1992 it passed within 50,000 kilometers of Jupiter's cloud tops, which is well within Jupiter's Roche limit. During the nineteenth century, French mathematician Edouard Roche determined the distance from a planet at which a liquid sphere—or any object without cohesion to hold it together—would be torn apart by tidal forces. An object that passed within Saturn's Roche limit sometime in the last few billion years was completely torn apart and formed the planet's majestic ring system. But until Periodic Comet Shoemaker–Levy 9, we have never seen this effect actually happen. "Never before," says astronomer Clark Chapman, "has there been such a clear case of disruption of a body by tidal splitting."[2] On that day Marsden announced that in July 1994, the comet would collide with Jupiter.

HAS THIS HAPPENED BEFORE?

While Periodic Comet Shoemaker–Levy 9 is a dramatic example of a comet that probably has been torn apart by tidal disruption, it is not the only one. Some famous sun-grazing comets, like the ones in 1882 and 1965, may be traced back to an earlier large comet, possibly the comet of 1106, that broke apart into smaller fragments as it did its hairpin turn round the sun.

In July 1889, William Brooks discovered a comet brightening slowly as it approached the sun. As soon as the comet's discovery was announced, other observers began watching it. On August 1, Edward Emerson Barnard was stunned to see two small companions. He thought that each mate looked like a flawless replica in miniature of the main comet. The next morning Barnard found four or five new objects. Although these single-day wonders vanished by the morning of August 3, two others appeared on the fourth, one lasting a few hours, the other a week. One of the original small comets lasted for several months. Although the main comet has returned 12 times since, the companions were never seen again.

Using logarithmic tables and orbit formulae, orbit computers were able to trace Periodic Comet Brooks 2 back to 1886, when it passed within a distance equal to Jupiter's own diameter from the giant planet. It is the only other comet known to have been torn apart by Jupiter's strong tidal force, and we can compare it to Periodic Comet Shoemaker–Levy 9. But there are major differences: The main body of P/Brooks 2 survived; the other fragments, which were far smaller, apparently did not for very long. Periodic Comet Shoemaker–Levy 9 was catastrophically disrupted after coming too close to Jupiter, forming a substantial number of pieces that must have been bright for half a year or more. Moreover P/Brooks 2 was seen as it approached perihelion near two astronomical units (basically the average distance between the Earth and the sun), while our new comet is putting on its show way out at the orbit of Jupiter.

Some 3.9 billion years ago, the moon and all the solar system's inner planets were hit by a platoon of objects that may have been the result of a catastrophic breakup of a large object. Astronomer George Wetherill has suggested that a body about 500 kilometers across could have passed within the Roche zone of a planet, perhaps Earth or Venus, and broke apart to form a pesky swarm of debris that orbited in the inner solar system, wreaking havoc on all the inner planets, including the Earth and moon. With this new comet, we may be witnessing a small example of that process.

WHY DO THE PIECES APPEAR TO BE STRUNG OUT IN A LINE?

As P/Shoemaker–Levy 9 broke up, Scotti suggests, the large pieces moved out in slightly different orbits. The orientation, he notes, is a direct result of the slightly different orbits that the pieces have. Fragments farther from Jupiter than the comet's center of mass move in orbits with very slightly longer periods than those closer to Jupiter than the center of mass. The slight difference causes the fragments to appear to be strung out in a line.[3]

According to Zdenek Sekanina of the JPL, since the breakup occurred in July 1992, by the time of discovery in March 1993, the pieces were moving away from each other at the rather leisurely rate of 3 meters per second, about a runner's pace.

CAT-AND-MOUSE WITH JUPITER

This remarkable comet probably got into its scorpion's embrace with Jupiter very gradually. It may have begun its journey out in the Oort cloud of comets far beyond the planets or perhaps closer to the sun as part of the Kuiper belt of comets closer to Neptune and Pluto. Over a very long period of time, the comet left its ancestral home and began to travel toward the sun. For many hundreds of thousands of years, the comet roamed in a wide, almost

238 of Chapter 18

parabolic orbit about the sun. During one of these orbits, it happened to wander close enough to Jupiter so that the giant planet's gravity changed the comet's orbit, and it became a periodic comet. Several approaches to Jupiter later, perhaps as recently as 1971, the comet's orbit now so closely matched Jupiter's that it became locked in the planet's space, looping around the gas giant in a highly elliptical orbit. The comet had become a satellite of Jupiter.

Actually the Periodic Comet Shoemaker–Levy 9 comet club may not, even in 1993, be the only broken-up comet orbiting Jupiter as a group of satellites. Jupiter's moons VIII Pasiphae, IX Sinope, XI Carme, and XII Ananke could be orbiting indefinitely as fragments of a large comet that broke up near Jupiter long ago. (They could also merely be trapped asteroids.) But unlike the unfortunate fragments of Periodic Comet Shoemaker–Levy 9, these four bodies are in stable orbits that could last indefinitely.

As the train of comets approaches Jupiter in 1994, comet pieces will rapidly increase their distance from each other. The train will rapidly become longer, and large fragments will hit Jupiter, although some of the outer dust particles may miss.

FOURTH SURPRISE: COLLISION WITH JUPITER

In these pages we have wondered what damage a major comet would inflict were it to hit Earth. A few days before the May 22 circulars appeared, Marsden sent me a note saying that the orbit he had worked out predicted a collision. I thought at first he was joking. A comet about a kilometer in size hitting the Earth is a once-in-100-thousand-year event. With big Jupiter the frequency is much greater, perhaps once in several decades or once a century. When the circulars actually appeared, I could hardly believe my eyes. Over the next few weeks, a lot of people thought about the consequences. Dismissed at first as "throwing a pebble into the ocean," by CBAT Associate Director Dan Green, the ante was raised as astronomers calculated the energy that the crash would release.

"More like dropping an olive into a martini!" quipped JPL astronomer Steve Edberg. Both are extremes. As the kilometer-wide
comets fall toward Jupiter at about 60 kilometers per second, some
astronomers speculate, each one will disintegrate in a sudden explosion, releasing as much energy as a million megatons of dynamite. Hiroshima's 20,000-ton blast and the 60-megaton strength
of the largest nuclear bomb ever exploded would be firecrackers
compared to this awesome cataclysm.

Shortly after the May 22 announcement that a crash was inevitable, A. Carusi of Rome University, suggested that surviving
nuclei would continue as satellites of Jupiter or be thrown closer
to the sun as independently orbiting short-period comets.[4] But later
modeling suggested a different story however—that the whole
train, comet after comet, will fall into Jupiter.

The comet's collision with Jupiter is predicted for July 1994,
a few months after this book first appears. The material here reflects
the state of our knowledge about the comet and its orbit about 9
months before the collision. But despite the fact that our understanding of this comet and its orbit is changing rapidly, this chapter
won't be dated; instead it will offer a historical perspective of the
comet during the critical period several months after its discovery
but before its impact with Jupiter.

As astronomers anticipated the coming explosions, the story
began to shift from the effects on the comet to the comet's effect
on Jupiter's atmosphere. Already very turbulent with Earth-sized
storms and the much larger Great Red Spot, the Jovian atmosphere
is divided into belts and zones containing many ever-changing
patterns. What will the sudden addition of material and energy
from 20 exploding comets do to this churning mass? Astronomers
and physicists in the midst of figuring out what a large comet
would do to Earth, will now have a natural laboratory and find
out. For Periodic Comet Shoemaker–Levy 9 may be compared to
some of the great impacts in Earth's past. For the first time in our
history, we have the chance to watch what happens when a comet
strikes a planet.

ℭ *Epilogue* ⅅ

Cole of Spyglass Mountain

*M*y *love of comets began with a 3-minute speech I gave in sixth* grade. *I think I said that comets have heads and tails, that they* fly about the sun, and maybe even that some people could discover comets. Looking far into the future, I would have said that Halley's comet, the most famous comet of all, wasn't due back for more than a quarter-century.

Within a few months, a fortuitous fall off a bicycle and a get-well present of a book about the solar system got me firmly single-tracked toward the sky. I remember wondering why my little telescope made everything look like a doughnut; then I realized that if I moved the eyepiece, the telescope would focus. Soon the stars were points of light, and Saturn became a ball with a ring around it. Glorious! I had seen the rings in pictures, but to see them for myself was thrilling. I was so excited that I called my parents, who came out to look. It took only a few minutes to see this planet with the rings, but I've never forgotten that night.

For Dad, watching me discover Saturn's ring brought him back to his childhood. One evening over dinner, he told me about a novel he had read when he was a youngster. Called *Cole of Spyglass Mountain*, it was Arthur Preston Hankins' story about a boy whose love of the sky led him to observe Mars through his small home-made telescope.[1] The novel ended with Cole finding evidence of life on Mars one night and becoming an instant celebrity. "If you ever find that book," Dad said, "I'd like to read it again."

Five years later I began my long search for comets. As the years went by and Dad grew older, he would often ask if I had found *Cole of Spyglass Mountain*. Then with the onset of Alzheimer's disease, his memory began to fail. As his time grew short, we spent more of it together, and I watched helplessly as he forgot names, forgot people, and once even forgot that I was his son. But somehow he never forgot that euphoric story about a boy and a mountaintop that had captured his imagination so many years earlier.

When I finally found my first comet in 1984, I felt as though I had rewritten *Cole of Spyglass Mountain* in a private way just for my father. But Dad was too ill to appreciate it, and he died only a few months later. I will always regret that I could not share the most significant moment in my life with the most important person in it.

A few years later, my friend Peter Jedicke found a copy of *Cole of Spyglass Mountain* in a library, and I was able to see its words in print for the first time. Dad had remembered them very well, I found. Though spyglass mountain is fiction, it evokes the magic of discovering new things in the sky. Whether it's a new comet on its way to a meeting with the sun or the remains of a long-departed one as a crater on the moon, the enchantment reverberates through time as each generation first looks toward the sky and wonders about it. Spyglass mountain didn't turn Dad into an astronomer, but it helped him understand what discovery is like, and I like to think that it helped him understand my love of comets. Since then 19 of them have come my way, and somewhere in the excitement of each one, I remember Dad, his long-gone book, and our first look at the sky together.

❦ Afterword ❧

How to Discover a Comet

If you are serious about comet hunting, you should first learn to recognize the different types of fuzzy deep-sky objects like galaxies, clusters, and nebulae, both to avoid mistaking them for comets and because they are interesting in themselves. You will find these in the Messier catalog. Representing every type of deep-sky object, this catalog offers excellent training for a would-be comet hunter. Finding these objects at different times of the year and under varying observing conditions will build the discipline that is needed in comet hunting—a skill that does not come overnight but builds on a special love of the sky.

This is more of an invitation to study the Messiers than a warning to stay away from hunting. The Messiers are a *cordon bleu* of the finest deep-sky objects you can behold—the exquisite wisps of M42, Orion Nebula; the nearest spiral galaxy, M31; the spectacular globular M13 in Hercules; the Ring Nebula M57; even the mysterious misshapen galaxy M82—this is the grandeur of the Messiers. If you don't find a good proportion of them before you begin a serious comet search, then you are denying yourself the appropriate introduction to what your nocturnal hunts could offer.

If your study of Messiers gives you an indication of what comets are not, observing comets that are already present and accounted for will give you an idea of what they are. Using positions and descriptions from such sources as the *Circulars* from the International Astronomical Union's (IAU's) CBAT—the IAU's clearinghouse for new astronomical discoveries—or from such magazines as *Sky and Telescope* or *Astronomy*, keep an eye on the comets you can see with your instrument. You will probably find that most comets, even the ones listed in magazines, are quite faint and difficult to observe from light-laden city skies.

Patterns of Search

Although comet hunting can be done with almost any telescope, I recommend one that offers a wide-field view of the sky. Comet hunting works best if you follow a definite plan. Moving the telescope slowly, search a small area of the sky thoroughly, for example, rather than a large one haphazardly. You can also expect better results if you search for 1 hour for 10 nights through areas more likely to have comets rather than searching 10 hours on 1 night through sections of the sky far from the sun and unlikely to produce a comet. Since comets shine brightest when they are near the sun, you have a much better chance of finding a new one in the western sky after dusk or in the eastern sky before dawn. Most important, if you really want to find a comet, don't give up on your quest. During the long years before I spotted my first new comet, I took heart from the advice of Robert Burnham, who discovered several comets during the 1950s and 1960s; he told me that "if you hunt for comets long enough, sooner or later you will find one."[1]

Equipment Required

I have used three telescopes for visual comet hunting, an 8-inch, a 6-inch, and a 16-inch reflector. Your telescope needs to be capable of at least a three-quarter degree diameter field of view. Exactly how large the telescope should be depends on a number of factors: how much money you wish to spend; whether you plan to mount the telescope at a dark site or to carry it around from place to place. The size of your telescope also determines the brightness range of comets you are likely to find. For comets of the eighth magnitude or brighter, a 6-inch telescope will suffice, but such a telescope cannot catch anything much fainter, since the diffuse quality of some comets makes them more difficult to see than clusters and many nebulae of the same brightness.

Methods of Hunting

There are as many variations in comet-hunting procedures as there are successful comet hunters. My telescopes are all mounted on simple altazimuth mounts with motions across and up and down. Canada's Rolf Meier hunts with an equatorially mounted telescope, checking suspicious objects quickly from their right ascension and declination. He never overlaps fields, and he searches at the rate of about a degree a second. In Australia, William Bradfield makes horizontal sweeps with an altazimuth-mounted telescope over a wide arc of sky and always in the same direction. On one point most hunters agree: Patience, skill and luck are necessary ingredients for a successful comet search.

Depending on the peculiarities of your own telescope and its mount, you might try different ways of hunting. You can hunt up and down strips of sky in a zigzag pattern, although this procedure may leave gaps in your search pattern as the setting sky goes past your telescope. You can sweep horizontally along a strip that is at some altitude above the horizon, or you can hunt along specific strips of declination or right ascension. The procedure you follow is not nearly so important as making certain that your search area is thoroughly covered. With my 40-centimeter diameter reflector, I hunt in an up-and-down pattern partly because my telescope moves more easily that way than in azimuth as it crosses the sky.

When to Hunt for Comets

Comet hunting requires some judgment in choosing the best times for sweeping. On successive nights after a full moon, you will see more and more hours of dark sky. Since the areas closest to the sun have the best chance of containing an undiscovered comet, begin searching in the western sky in the nights following a full moon. Until moonrise you have a chance of looking through a sky that has been blocked by moonlight long enough to have masked from other observers the approach of a comet that is getting brighter as it nears the sun or Earth. Although any dark, moonless sky is good, the best time to hunt in the evening sky is just after a waning moon in an hour of darkness after evening twilight ends. Such an event that takes place some 2 days after a full moon. It is important to start your hunt when the western sky is dark enough to show at least fourth-magnitude stars to the naked eye. There may still be light in the West, but your sky is getting darker and so is your adaptation to the dark. Stop hunting when the moon rises in the eastern sky.

Fruitful morning searches begin as the waning lunar crescent is thin enough not to interfere with the dark sky. The adage, "it is darkest just before dawn," makes sense, since pollution from the previous day has had a chance to dissipate, some of the lights from human activity have been extinguished, and the environment is much quieter than on the previous evening. For me the most enjoyable time for comet sweeping is undoubtedly in the morning sky in the last 2 hours before dawn. I begin a few days before and continue for about 5 days after a new moon.

Sun's Vicinity

Would you like to find a comet in broad daylight as it whips round the sun? The procedure is simple and requires only a sharp pair of eyes and a clear sky free of haze or cirrus clouds. Simply place an object, such as street lamp, between you and the sun and scan the surrounding area. A number of comets have been discovered this way. In 1910 a group of South African diamond miners found a bright comet that had kept itself under wraps by approaching the sun from the opposite direction from us. When

Comet Austin. (Photograph by Jack Newton, August 23, 1982, using a 16-inch f/5 reflecting telescope; 14-minute exposure using Tri-X film.)

the comet rounded the sun, it was discovered quickly by anyone who happened to look toward it. Such finds, it should be pointed out, are extremely rare and also obviously competitive, for a comet bright enough to be seen in daylight will undoubtedly be discovered independently by other observers. But by searching in the sun's vicinity, you may find such a comet first.

It is also important to ensure that your object is a comet, and not a cirrus cloud that is close to the sun. A Montreal amateur astronomer reported a streak of cirrus as a comet early in 1967. Watch the size, shape, brightness, color, and apparent motion of anything you suspect to be a comet.

Horizon at Twilight

Searching for bright comets that are visible in the darkening sky with either the unaided eye or binoculars can be rewarding. With the unaided eye, scan the horizon about a half-hour after the sun has gone down. With binoculars, sweep the western horizon in the evening, or the eastern in the morning, from the horizon to an altitude of about 15 degrees. Sweep slowly with deliberate hand movements every 2 seconds from field to field. Although comets can appear at any time and any location, an evening search is best done just after the full moon has left the area, so the 2–5 nights just after full moon are the ones most likely to bring success. The nights around a new moon are the most promising for hunts in the dawn sky.

Plot any suspects on a sketch of the star field as you see it in your telescope's eyepiece. Note the time. Make sure that the object is not a background deep-sky object plotted on a star atlas or listed in a catalog, or the predicted return of a known comet.

Areas to Skirt

If you use a small telescope, avoid the star-rich areas of the Milky Way, and definitely overlook areas of Coma Berenices, Leo, and Virgo. Otherwise you'll be eyeball-deep in galaxies to check, some of which mimic faint comets. Also the Milky Way contains so many stars that small concentrations of them may look like comets through a small telescope.

Checking Out Suspects

The larger your telescope, the more comet suspects you find, and the more time you will need to spend checking out suspicious objects. Of the two ways of doing this, the most common is simply to locate the object you see in some atlas, like Wil Tirion's *Sky Atlas 2000.0* or his *Uranometria 2000.0*.[2]

If your atlas or catalog shows no fuzzy object where there is clearly one in the field of your telescope, sketch your find's position and continue sweeping, going back in half an hour to check if the object has moved.

Discovering a Comet

If you hunt long enough, sooner or later you will find something that doesn't appear in an atlas. The first thing to remember is to stay calm, for the next minutes will be busy and critical ones. Follow these steps:

1. Sketch the object and its surrounding stars three times: As you see them through you telescope's finder, its low-power eyepiece, and its high-power eyepiece.

2. See if the object has a tail. Although most faint comets do not show obvious tails, there are very few objects in the sky that are not comets but do have tails.

3. Verify that it is not a ghost image of a nearby bright star. Try moving your telescope a bit. If you have a ghost image, it should change its position relative to nearby stars as you move the telescope.

4. Determine that the object is neither a faint star nor group of faint stars. Use high power to rule out this possibility.

5. Check the position in a star atlas or catalog.

6. Note if the object has moved when you look a half-hour later. If there has been no motion by the dawn or the suspicious object's setting has occurred, I strongly advise against sending a telegram. All comets do show motion eventually. You should wait to confirm motion even if you must wait another 24 hours.

7. Locate known comets in the sky. Check even the positions of comets that should be too faint for your telescope, although if you should be the first to notice an unexpected increase in a known comet's brightness, you definitely should report it. Positions of brighter comets are published in the major astronomy magazines, while IAU *Circulars*, the *Minor Planet Circulars*, and the International Comet Quarterly's *Comet Handbook* are good sources for known comets. If you subscribe to the computer service of CBAT, you can ask their program to identify known comets or asteroids in the area around your suspect.

8. If possible have your sighting confirmed by an experienced comet observer of good reputation. Tell that person the object's position, suspected nature, and direction of motion.

9. Once you detect motion, rule out previously known objects in the area and have your observation confirmed locally, it is time to notify CBAT in Cambridge, Massachusetts. Its addresses are:

Telex: TWX 710-320-6842 ASTROGRAM CAM (Use this number for telegrams. If you address your wire to the Smithsonian Astrophysical Observatory, it could be delayed.)

Email: MARSDEN@CFA or GREEN@CFA (.SPAN, .BITNET or .HARVARD.EDU) or EASYLINK 62794505

Marsden and Daniel Green need the following information:

Suspected nature of the object.

Right ascension and declination; although CBAT uses epoch 2000 coordinates, remember to state which epoch you are using.

Direction and rate of motion, preferably this is supplied with a second position taken a half-hour or more after the first. This motion is *very* important, since it may be some time before a clear sky somewhere permits another observer to confirm your finding. By the same token, fuzzy objects on single photographs should be ignored unless you are willing to take a second photograph or search visually to confirm the object's identity and motion.

The comet's magnitude.

Whether the discovery was a visual or a photographic one; if you observed the object both ways, clearly distinguish how you made each observation.

Your description of the object's appearance, including remarks about its size, angular diameter, and shape and length of the tail if you see one.

The date and time of your observation converted to Universal Time or at least with time zone included.

The instrument you used; include the telescope's aperture, type, and magnification. If you are reporting a photographic or CCD find, add the film emulsion (or for electronic observations, the CCD type), exposure time, limiting stellar magnitude of the photo, and the size of the field in degrees or minutes of arc.

Your name as discoverer, your address, and your telephone number.

Remember: Do not send a telegram unless you are certain that the object is a new comet. The philosophy of sending your announcement telegram, as some people have done, just to make sure you are the first, is hardly scientific and may embarrass you. Imagine the chagrin of the observer I know when he reported having "discovered" the Andromeda galaxy. According to Marsden approximately 98 percent of comet discovery reports from unknown observers turn out to be false alarms.[3] Just because an object is fuzzy does not mean that it is a comet, and even if it is a comet, it may be a known one. Galaxies, nebulae, and ghost images of bright stars are often reported as new comets. Again don't bother reporting fuzzy spots on single photographs without some other observer's confirmation.

If your discovery is confirmed, then the comet will be named for you unless others have also found it. Traditionally a comet is allowed a maximum of three names, which represent the first three people to have seen and reported it until the comet's existence is confirmed (see below). Technically you are in competition with other amateurs, professionals using photographic plates and CCD imaging systems, and even orbiting satellites.

HOW COMETS ARE NAMED

A comet is known by as many as three different designations— after its discoverer or discoverers, in the order of its discovery in a certain year and its passage around the Sun.

Discoverer

A comet is named after its discoverer—up to three independent observers or two working together. Prolific comet hunters like Bradfield should have their comets referred to by name and designation to avoid confusion, such as Comet Bradfield 1992b and Comet Bradfield 1992i. The discoverer need not be human: Periodic

Comet Hartley–IRAS 1983v, was first discovered by astronomer Malcolm Hartley and independently by IRAS. A comet orbiting the sun in fewer than 200 years is called a periodic comet. We write Periodic Comet Levy or simply P/Levy. A handful of comets are named not for their discoverers but for those who computed their orbits. The most famous of these is P/Halley, which has been well observed since at least 240 B.C.

Astronomers who discover more than one periodic comet have an Arabic numeral included in the comet's name to indicate which comet is being referred to. Periodic Comet Shoemaker–Levy 7, for example, is the seventh discovered by the team of Carolyn and Eugene Shoemaker and me. Incidentally all of the Shoemaker–Levy comets were discovered by Carolyn on films taken by the team of Eugene and Carolyn Shoemaker and David Levy. Thus it is possible to get your name on a comet if you are part of the discovery team even though you did not actually find the comet.

On rare occasions a comet is discovered by so many observers that no one receives priority as discoverer. Such a comet is usually very bright, and it is generally known by some other name. Examples include the Great Comet of 1843, and the Eclipse Comet of 1948.

Year of Discovery

Immediately on its acceptance as a new or recovered periodic comet by the CBAT, a comet is assigned a designation that includes the year followed by a lower case letter of the alphabet indicating the order of its acceptance by CBAT that year, Comet Levy 1990c, for example. In those years when the number of comets exceeds 26, the alphabet is started again with the subscript one added for each designation, like $1989c_1$. Periodic comets that have a known period of orbital revolution less than 200 years are known by the name or names of their discoverers, preceded by a P/. Some periodic comets that are observed throughout their whole orbits do not receive a year-and-letter designation, including P/Encke,

P/Gunn, P/Arend–Rigaux, and P/Schwassmann–Wachmann 1. Such comets are sometimes called annual comets.

If a discoverer (like Bradfield) or a discovery team (like Shoemaker–Levy) finds more than one periodic comet, a number follows the comet. Periodic Comet Shoemaker–Levy does not exist, for instance. Following the rules, the comet became Periodic Comet Shoemaker–Levy 1 when the second periodic comet was found. Now there is a Periodic Comet Shoemaker–Levy 9. There is however only one Periodic Comet Levy.

Occasionally a periodic comet that had been considered lost (since it wasn't seen for several predicted apparitions) is accidentally rediscovered and then identified as the missing comet. It may then be assigned the rediscoverer's name in addition to the first discoverer's name, as happened recently with 1991a, P/Metcalf–Brewington. Previously known as Periodic Comet Metcalf, it had not been seen since its discovery by J. H. Metcalf in 1906. Howard Brewington, an amateur astronomer hunting from New Mexico, rediscovered it in 1991.

Passage Around the Sun

Some time after the end of each year, all comets reaching perihelion in that year receive a Roman numeral designation giving the order in which they reached perihelion. Thus, P/Halley in 1910 was the second comet to reach perihelion in 1910, and is known as 1910 II. P/Halley is also known as 1759 I and 1835 III, as well as 1982i. Now following its 1986 perihelion, it is also referred to as 1986 III.

ELEMENTS OF AN ORBIT

Every planet, comet, asteroid, and tiny meteoroid in the solar system has a path we call an orbit. We know the orbits of the nine major planets very well, since we have observed them over many years. As each new comet is found, the first thing we want to know is its orbit, which is really a definition of the comet's place in space over a period of time.

An equinox is that point in the Earth's orbit when the Earth's equatorial plane meets the orbital plane, a plane we call the ecliptic. (The ecliptic is the apparent path of the center of the sun around the sky.) The Earth crosses that point twice each year, once in March and once in September. On about March 21 of each year, the Earth crosses the equinox as the sun moves north. In the northern hemisphere, we call this point of the Earth's orbit the vernal equinox. We use the vernal equinox as an important reference point.

We picture the orbits of comets in relation to the orbit of Earth. With at least three (and preferably a lot more) precise positions of the comet, we can determine the six orbital elements we need to describe a comet's journey through the solar system. Admittedly this is a somewhat oversimplified explanation of a complex process. Here are the six basic orbital elements:

The comet's perihelion date T: The date and time the comet is closest to the sun.

How close the comet will be to the Sun at perihelion: This factor, q, is expressed in terms of a yardstick called an astronomical unit—approximately the average distance between Earth and sun.

The eccentricity e: If the orbit were a perfect circle, e would be 0; if the orbit were a parabola, e would be 1. The earliest orbits for most comets are figured as if $e = 1$. If the comet turns out to be periodic, traveling in an ellipse, it will quickly deviate from the predicted path in the days and weeks after discovery.

How far the comet is inclined to the ecliptic: This angle of inclination is called i. Most periodic comets have inclinations less than 20 degrees. Long-period comets can have any inclination. Inclinations of 90–180 degrees refer to comets moving backward with respect to those with inclinations from 90–0 degrees.

The longitude of the ascending node (Ω): This is the angular distance between the vernal equinox and the point, which we call the ascending node, where the comet crosses the plane of the Earth's orbit as the comet moves northward.

The argument of perihelion (ω): This is the separation, measured again as an angle, between the ascending node and the point where the comet is closest to the sun. Finally all these elements are accurate only at one time, which we call the epoch. Orbits can be computed for other epochs of interest to observers.

For example, here is a set of orbital elements for Comet Shoemaker–Levy 1993h, as described in *IAU Circular* 5808.[4] My comments are in brackets.

COMET SHOEMAKER–LEVY (1993h)

[The circular begins with a description of the observations, followed by accurate positions of the comet.]

The following precise positions have been measured by B. A. Skiff and C. S. Shoemaker from exposures by C. S. Shoemaker, E. M. Shoemaker and D. H. Levy with the 0.46-m Schmidt telescope at Palomar (the first R.A. [right ascension; the position in the sky roughly equivalent to longitude on Earth] and the second Decl. [declination; the position in the sky roughly equivalent to latitude on Earth] are uncertain, and the third image was involved with a star): [It was hard to measure the comet, since a star was almost obscuring it.]

1993 UT R.A. (2000) Decl. [Because the Earth precesses, the positions need to be given relative to what the coordinate system is at a certain time or equinox; this one is the year 2000.]

Circular No. 5808

Central Bureau for Astronomical Telegrams
INTERNATIONAL ASTRONOMICAL UNION

Postal Address: Central Bureau for Astronomical Telegrams
Smithsonian Astrophysical Observatory, Cambridge, MA 02138, U.S.A.
Telephone 617-495-7244/7440/7444 (for emergency use only)
TWX 710-320-6842 ASTROGRAM CAM   EASYLINK 62794505
MARSDEN@CFA or GREEN@CFA (.SPAN, .BITNET or .HARVARD.EDU)

COMET SHOEMAKER-LEVY (1993h)

The following precise positions have been measured by B. A. Skiff and
C. S. Shoemaker from exposures by C. S. Shoemaker, E. M. Shoemaker and
D. H. Levy with the 0.46-m Schmidt telescope at Palomar (the first α and
the second δ are uncertain, and the third image was involved with a star):

1993	UT	α_{2000}	δ_{2000}
May	23.20885	$13^h 24^m 50^s.49$	$-33°58'19''.7$
	23.24809	13 24 48.61	-33 58 22.2
	24.20572	13 24 01.91	-33 59 22.2
	24.23836	13 24 00.19	-33 59 23.0
	26.20329	13 22 26.46	-34 01 18.4
	26.25729	13 22 23.84	-34 01 21.2

Preliminary parabolic orbital elements by B. G. Marsden, Harvard-
Smithsonian Center for Astrophysics:

$$T = 1993 \text{ May } 14.144 \text{ TT} \qquad \begin{array}{l} \omega = 199°.384 \\ \Omega = 31.929 \\ i = 72.368 \end{array} \Big\} 2000.0$$

$$q = 5.41446 \text{ AU}$$

1993 TT		α_{2000}	δ_{2000}	Δ	r	ϵ	β	m_1
May	13	$13^h 33^m.84$	$-33°44'.4$	4.503	5.414	151.8	5.1	16.6
	23	13 25.01	-33 58.1	4.568	5.415	143.4	6.4	16.6
June	2	13 17.45	-34 06.8	4.660	5.416	134.2	7.7	16.7
	12	13 11.38	-34 13.5	4.773	5.419	124.9	8.8	16.7
	22	13 06.90	-34 20.7	4.904	5.422	115.7	9.7	16.8
July	2	13 04.04	-34 30.7	5.047	5.426	106.6	10.3	16.9
	12	13 02.71	-34 45.2	5.198	5.432	97.9	10.7	16.9
	22	13 02.83	-35 05.4	5.352	5.438	89.5	10.8	17.0
Aug.	1	13 04.25	-35 32.1	5.504	5.446	81.4	10.6	17.1

NOVA AQUILAE 1993

Visual magnitude estimates: May 21.04 UT, 8.0 (T. Vanmunster, Lan-
den, Belgium); 21.97, 7.8 (H. Dahle, Oslo, Norway); 23.96, 7.5 (S. Baroni,
Milan, Italy); 25.97, 7.9 (B. H. Granslo, Fjellhamar, Norway); 26.95, 8.0
(Dahle); 28.96, 8.3 (J. D. Shanklin, Cambridge, England).

1993 May 31   *Daniel W. E. Green*

May	23.20885	13 24 50.49	−33 58 19.7
	23.24809	13 24 48.61	−33 58 22.2
	24.20572	13 24 01.91	−33 59 22.2
	24.23836	13 24 00.19	−33 59 23.0
	26.20329	13 22 26.46	−34 01 18.4
	26.25729	13 22 23.84	−34 01 21.2

Preliminary parabolic orbital elements by B. G. Marsden, Harvard–Smithsonian Center for Astrophysics:

T = 1993 May 14.144 TT Argument of Perihelion. = 199.384
[Longitude of Ascending] Node = 31.929 2000.0

q = 5.41446 AU   Incl. = 72.368

[Finally from the elements that follow, the comet's future path is predicted.]

1993 TT	R. A. (2000) Decl. Positions	
May 13	13 33.84	−33 44.4
23	13 25.01	−33 58.1
June 2	13 17.45	−34 06.8
12	13 11.38	−34 13.5
22	13 06.90	−34 20.7
July 2	13 04.04	−34 30.7
12	13 02.71	−34 45.2[4]

COORDINATES IN THE SKY

Celestial coordinates are a projection onto the sky of the coordinate system of Earth. The celestial equator is a projection of Earth's equator, and the celestial poles are projections of Earth's rotational poles.

Declination in the sky is measured like earthly latitude, in degrees, minutes, and seconds north and south of the equator. Right ascension is equivalent to longitude, it is measured in units of time—hours, minutes, and seconds, rather than degrees. The zero hour of right ascension is the position of the Sun at the first moment of spring in the northern hemisphere—the *vernal* equinox—and it is along the line of intersection of the Earth's equatorial plane and its orbital plane or ecliptic. Hours in right ascension are measured eastward from the vernal equinox.

Since the Earth's poles wobble because of tidal effects of the moon and sun, the direction of the vernal equinox shifts in the sky. The entire coordinate system shifts with that wobble. The wobble is called precession. Hence we must find a precise moment in time to define our celestial coordinates; that moment is called the epoch.

THE MAGNITUDE SCALE

How do we describe the brightness of stars, planets, and comets? Anyone going outside on a clear night will notice that not all the stars are the same brightness. Our system of magnitudes dates back to the second century B.C. Greek astronomer Hipparchus, who divided the stars into six brightness groups, with the 20 brightest stars called first magnitude and the faintest stars sixth magnitude. By 1856 Norman Pogson of Radcliffe Observatory had quantified this relationship, making a first-magnitude star 100 times brighter than the faintest star visible without a telescope, a second-magnitude star 2.5 times fainter than a first magnitude star, and a third-magnitude star, 2.5 times fainter again.

Vega, the brightest star in the summer triangle, is a zero-magnitude star. Pogson defined Polaris, the North Star, as being second magnitude. Most of the stars in the Big Dipper are also about second magnitude. Most of the stars in nearby Cassiopeia are a magnitude fainter.

Why are the stars of different brightnesses? There are two reasons. Like lights on a street, stars are fainter the further away they are, and some stars are intrinsically more luminous than other stars. The result is a hodgepodge of stars of different brightnesses.

Because comets are not points of light but fuzzy objects that cover an extended area of sky, their magnitudes are not so easy to determine. In trying to estimate the brightness of a comet, observers usually compare the comet to out-of-focus stars of known magnitude. Observers deliberately unfocus their telescopes so that stars as bright as the comet appear the same size as the comet. The procedure takes practice, but when we say that a comet is magnitude 7.1, that is how we arrive at that estimate.

ℭ ⅅ

References

CHAPTER 1

1. G. W. Hough, "Observations of Comet II. 1862, made with the Olcott Meridian Circle, at the Dudley Observatory," *Astronomische Nachrichten* **59**, no. 1394 (1863), col. 29.
2. *Ibid.* See also S. K. Vsekhsvyatskii, *Physical Characteristics of Comets* (Jerusalem: Israel Program for Scientific Translations, 1964), 215; *Illustrated London News,* Aug. 16, 1862, 179.
3. H. P. Tuttle, "Schreiben des Herrn Tuttle an den Herausgeber," *Astronomische Nachrichten* **59**, no. 1404 (1863), cols. 187–90.
4. Many of the interesting details about Horace Tuttle's life come from an unpublished study circa 1980 "H. P. Tuttle: Cometseeker," by Richard E. Schmidt, US Naval Observatory.
5. The basis for this story comes from an unpublished memoir (Ref. 4).
6. W. T. Lynn, "Comet III. 1862," the *Observatory* **25** (1902), 304–305. The author notes that the *Astronomische Nachrichten,* the journal of record at the time, called it Comet II. 1862 but that it was the third comet to reach perihelion that year and is correctly III. 1862 (or in today's parlance, 1862 III).
7. B. G. Marsden, "The Next Return of the Comet of the Perseid Meteors," *Astronomical Journal,* **78**, 656 (1973).
8. B. G. Marsden, *Astronomical Journal* **78**, 654–662 (1973); see also *IAU Circulars* 5330 (August 28, 1991) and 5586 (August 14, 1992).
9. *IAU Circular* 5330 (August 28, 1991).
10. B. G. Marsden, personal communication, Oct. 18, 1992.

11. B. G. Marsden, "Comet Swift–Tuttle: Does It Threaten Earth?" *Sky and Telescope* **85,** 1 (1993), 11.
12. *IAU Circular* 5620, Sept. 27, 1992.
13. B. G. Marsden, personal communication, Oct. 18, 1992.
14. B. G. Marsden, *Astronomical Journal* **78,** 658 (1973).
15. B. G. Marsden, personal communication, Oct. 12, 1992. See also *Time Magazine*, Nov. 9, 1992, 27.
16. B. G. Marsden, personal communication, Oct. 31, 1992.
17. B. Marsden, interview, 7 January 1993.

CHAPTER 2

1. *Julius Caesar*, II, ii, 29–30.
2. Chronicles I, 21:16.
3. A. A. Barrett, "Observations of Comets in Greek and Roman Sources before A.D. 410," *Journal of the Royal Astronomical Society of Canada* **72** (1978), 81–106.
4. Seneca, *Quaestiones Naturales*, VII, "De Cometis" XVII, 2.
5. Seneca, *Quaestiones Naturales* VII, "De Cometis" I, 1.
6. Seneca, I, 4–5.
7. Seneca, *De Cometis* XVI, 2.
8. R. F. Rogers, "Newly Discovered Byzantine Records of Comets," *Journal of the Royal Astronomical Society of Canada* **56,** 5 (1952), 177.
9. Seneca, *De Cometis* XXI, 2–3.
10. *Ibid.*, XXIII, 1–3.
11. *Ibid.*, XVII, 1.
12. The *Works of Tacitus*, Oxford translation (London: G. Bell and Sons, 1910), 367–68.
13. *The Works of Tacitus.*[11]
14. *Illustrated London News*, July 1861, 65.

CHAPTER 3

1. *The Poetical Works of Gerard Manley Hopkins*, ed. N. H. MacKenzie (Oxford: Clarendon Press, 1990), 40.
2. J. R. Hind, Letter, *Times*, Aug. 1, 1864, 5, col. e.
3. S. Drake, *The Controversy on the Comets of 1618* (Philadelphia: University of Pennsylvania Press, 1960), 7.
4. S. Drake, 25.
5. S. Drake, 19. The thought from Horace is from *Carmina* I, i, 36.

6. J. Swan, *Speculum Mundi: or a Glasse Representing the Face of the World* (Cambridge, England: by the Printers to the University, 1635), 80–81.
7. L. C. Peltier, *Starlight Nights: The Adventures of a Star Gazer* (Cambridge, MA: Sky Publishing Corp., 1980), 17.
8. *Ibid.*
9. B. G. Marsden, personal communication, Oct. 1, 1992.
10. J. R. Hind, The Comet of 1556; Being Popular Replies to Everyday Questions, Referring to Its Anticipated Reappearance, with Some Observations on the Apprehension of Danger from Comets (London: John W. Parker and Son, 1857), 1.
11. *The London Times*, July 4, 1861, p. 12.
12. The *London Review*, July 13, 1861, 46, col. 2.
13. Hind, 14.
14. *Ibid.*, 45.
15. B. G. Marsden, personal communication, Oct. 1, 1992.

CHAPTER 4

1. C. A. Lubbock, *The Herschel Chronicle* (Cambridge, England: Cambridge University Press, 1933), 15.
2. *Ibid.*, 15.
3. *Ibid.*, 60.
4. *Ibid.*, 66.
5. *Ibid.*, 66.
6. W. Herschel announced his discovery at the end of March 1781 to the Bath Literary and Philosophical Society. This "Account of a Comet" appears in *The Scientific Papers of Sir William Herschel*, J. L. E. Dreyer, ed. (London: The Royal Society and the Royal Astronomical Society, 1912), 1· 30–38.
7 W. G. Hoyt, *Planets X and Pluto* (Tucson: University of Arizona Press, 1980), p. 12.
8. Charles Messier to William Herschel, in Lubbock, 86.
9. Lubbock, p. 95.
10. W. Herschel to C. Herschel, July 3, 1782. See also "America's Last King and His Observatory" in J. Ashbrook, *The Astronomical Scrapbook* (Cambridge, MA.: Sky Publishing Corp., 1984), 17.
11. Lubbock, 246.
12. N. A. Mackenzie, "He Broke through the Barriers of the Skies," *Sky and Telescope* 8, no. 5 (1949), 119. The title is a translation of the words on Herschel's tombstone, Coelorum perrupit claustra. *See also; Lubbock, p. 177.*
13. P. M. Millman, "The Herschel Dynasty" *Journal of the Royal Astronomical Society of Canada* 74 (1980), 211.
14. Hoyt, 15.

CHAPTER 5

1. K. G. Jones, *Messier's Nebulae and Star Clusters*, 2d ed. (London: Cambridge University Press, 1991), 347.
2. Although this story appears in several sources, a particularly good one is K. G. Jones, 365. Some of the details of Messier's relationship with de Saron come from this source as well.
3. If we count some independent discoveries of comets where he was not the first finder, several others for which he was far too late to have his name attached, two discoveries years apart of the periodic comet now named after Encke, and comets that were never confirmed by other observers, his total is about 37.
4. R. K. Marshall, "Astronomical Anecdotes," *Sky and Telescope* 3 (Apr. 1944), 19.
5. John Keats, "On First Looking into Chapman's Homer".
6. J. Ashbrook, "Harvester of the Skies," *Sky and Telescope* 25 (1963), 198–199.
7. A. Ewing, *Practical Astronomy* (Burlington, NJ: David Allinson, 1812).
8. Different parts of this quotation appear in two excellent Mary Proctor books on comets: *The Romance of Comets* (New York: Harper and Brothers, 1926), 27; M. Proctor and A. C. D. Crommelin, *Comets: Their Nature, Origin, and Place in the Science of Astronomy* (London: Technical Press, 1937), 154–55.
9. See J. Bortle, "Comet Digest," *Sky and Telescope* 64 (1982), 294.
10. At Tennessee's Arthur J. Dyer Observatory, Robert Hardie noted in "The Story of the Early Life of E. E. Barnard" that the university named one of its dormitories after the great comet finder, who was known not to need much sleep.
11. H. B. Curtis, "The Comet-Seeker Hoax," *Popular Astronomy* 46 (1938), 70.
12. *Ibid.*, 70.
13. *Ibid.*
14. *Ibid.*, 75.
15. *Ibid.*, 75.
16. *Ibid.*
17. J. Lankford, "E. E. Barnard and the Comet-Seeker Hoax of 1891," *Sky and Telescope* 57 (1979), 420–22.
18. Curtis, 71.

CHAPTER 6

1. H. D. Thoreau, *Walden*, 1854; W. Harding, ed. *The Variorum Walden* (New York: Twayne, 1962), 259, 261.
2. Jones, 371.
3. *Ibid.*, Peltier, 237.
4. Proctor and Crommelin, 112.

5. *Ibid.,* 117–18.
6. *Observatory* **4,** 331 (1881).
7. This story comes from G. Kronk, *Comets: A Descriptive Catalog* (Hillside, NJ: Enslow, 1984), 120.
8. Peltier, 36.
9. *Ibid.,* 127.
10. *Ibid.,* 134.
11. F. L. Whipple, *The Mystery of Comets* (Washington, DC: Smithsonian Institution Press, 1985), 145–147.
12. Whipple announced his theory in two papers. "A Comet Model. I. The Acceleration of Comet Encke," *Astrophysical Journal* **111** (1950), 375–94, explains how the orbit of periodic Comet Encke, which is shrinking with each return, is interpreted if the structure of its nucleus consists of meteoric material embedded in ices that sublimate to gases. As the freed material rushes out of the comet with some force, it can accelerate the comet. The second paper, "Physical Relations for Comets and Meteors" *Astrophysical Journal* **113** (1951), 464–74, expands on this model.
13. R. Gore, "Much More Than Met the Eye: Halley's Comet '86," *National Geographic* **170** (1986), 778.
14. *IAU Circular* 1924, Sept. 28, 1965.
15. *Circular* 1925, Oct. 1, 1965. See also B. G. Marsden, personal communication, Jan. 2, 1993.
16. B. G. Marsden, "The Sun-Grazing Comet Group," *Astronomical Journal* **72** (1967) 1179.
17. *Circular* 1932, Oct. 26, 1965, and personal communication, August 1993.
18. P. L. Brown, *Comets, Meteorites, and Men* (London: Robert Hale and Co., 1973), 91.
19. *Circulars* 1937, Nov. 9, 1965, and 1949, Feb. 8, 1966. The suggested periods were 830 and 1110 years.
20. W. Houston, personal communication.
21. Peltier, 231.

CHAPTER 7

1. B. G. Marsden, "The Sun-Grazing Comet Group," Astronomical Journal **72** (1967), 1170–83.
2. See B. G. Marsden, "Catalogue of Discoveries and Identifications of Minor Planets" (rev. Identifizierungsnachweis der Kleine Planeten) 2d ed. (Minor Planet Center, International Astronomical Union, 1986).
3. Marsden to Alcock, April 13, 1983.

CHAPTER 8

1. D. Levy, "The Art of Comet Hunting," *Royal Astronomical Society of Canada*, **65** (1970), L8.
2. C. Messier, "A Catalogue of Nebulae and Star Clusters Discovered among the Fixed Stars above the Horizon of Paris. Observed at the Observatory of the Navy with different instruments by M. Messier." *Historire de l'Academie Royale des Sciences* (1771). Numbers 1–45 appeared here; Numbers 46–68 appeared in *Connaissance des Temps*, (1781); Numbers 69–103 surfaced in *Connaissance des Temps*, (1784); 104–109, added to by Méchain, in *Berliner Astronomisches Jahrbuch*, (1786). Messier 110, a companion to M31, the Andromeda Galaxy, was added a few years ago, based on solid evidence that Messier had drawn it.
3. D. H. Levy, *Clyde Tombaugh: Discoverer of Planet Pluto* (Tucson: University of Arizona Press, 1991).
4. C. Tombaugh, plate envelope notes for No. 171, courtesy Lowell Observatory.
5. One of the unsung heroes of asteroidal astronomy, Conrad Bardwell has worked at the Minor Planet Center since 1958. He has contributed to the computerization of the Minor Planet Center and was among the first to use a computer to find minor planets. B. G. Marsden, personal communication, Jan. 22, 1993.
6. B. G. Marsden, "Original and Future Cometary Orbits IV," *Astronomical Journal* **99** (1990), 1971–73. As the original comet moved away from the Sun, the nongravitational force of the gases leaving the comet decreased, but it was still sufficient to allow Comets 1988e and 1988g to separate.

CHAPTER 9

1. G. K. Gilbert, "The Origin of Hypotheses: Illustrated by the Discussion of a Topographic Problem," presidential address, the Geological Society of Washington, March 1896. See also *Science*, N. S. 3 (1896), 1.
2. *Ibid.*, 11.
3. E. M. Shoemaker, interview, Oct. 23, 1992.
4. A version of this story first appeared in *Sky and Telescope* **83** (1992), 219–21.

CHAPTER 10

1. E. M. Shoemaker, interview, Jan. 27, 1993.
2. E. M. Shoemaker, interview, Jan. 27, 1993.

CHAPTER 11

1. Stubbs, ed., *Gervasii Cantuariensis Opera Historica: Chronica Gervasii, Rerum Britannicarum Medii Aevi Scriptores*, (London, 1879), 73a.
2. J. B. Hartung, "Was the Formation of a 20-km Diameter Crater on the Moon Observed on June 18, 1178?" *Meteoritics* 11 3, (1976), 187–94. Calame and Mulholland, cited below, state that the correct Gregorian date is June 25, 1178.
3. K. Brecher, "The Canterbury Swarm: Ancient and Modern Observations of a New Feature of the Solar System," *Bulletin of the American Astronomical Society* 16 (1984), 476.
4. B. E. Schaefer, "The 'Lunar Event' of A.D. 1178: A Canterbury Tale?" *Journal of the British Astronomical Association* 100 (1990), 211.
5. W. G. Waddington, "More on the 'Canterbury Event' of 1178," *Journal of the British Astronomical Association* 101 (1991), 79.
6. E. M. Shoemaker, interview, Feb. 11, 1993.
7. E. M. Shoemaker.[6]
8. R. L. Heacock, G. P. Kuiper, E. M. Shoemaker, H. C. Urey, and E. A. Whitaker, "Technical Report No. 32-800: Ranger VIII and IX" (Pasadena: Jet Propulsion Laboratory, 1966), 2.
9. Apollo 11 and NASA; July 20, 1969.
10. E. M. Shoemaker, interview, Feb. 17, 1993.
11. E. M. Shoemaker.[10]
12. E. M. Shoemaker.[10]
13. O. Calame and J. D. Mulholland, "Lunar Crater Giordano Bruno: A. D. 1178 Impact Observations Consistent with Laser Ranging Results," *Science* 199 (1978), 875.
14. F. K. Duennebier, Y. Nakamura, G. V. Latham, and H. J. Dorman, "Meteoroid Storms Detected on the Moon," *Science* 192 (1976), 1000–02.

CHAPTER 12

1. E. F. Helin and E. M. Shoemaker, "The Palomar Planet-Crossing Asteroid Survey, 1973–1978," *Icarus* 40 (1979), 321–28.
2. L. D. Schmadel, *Dictionary of Minor Planet Names* (Berlin: Springer-Verlag, 1992), 593; *cf.* MPC 19338.
3. D. Morrison and M. Shapley Matthews, *Satellites of Jupiter* (Tucson: University of Arizona Press, 1981), 435, 438–451.

CHAPTER 13

1. H. Wright, *Palomar: The World's Largest Telescope* (New York: MacMillan, 1952), 135.

2. C. S. Shoemaker, interview, Nov. 30, 1992.
3. C. S. Shoemaker.[2]
4. *Sky and Telescope* **81** (1991), 659.

CHAPTER 14

1. J. M. Greenberg, "What are Comets Made of? A Model Based on Interstellar Dust," in *Comets*, ed. L. Wilkening (Tucson: University of Arizona Press, 1982), 131, 157.
2. G. A. Soffen, "Life in the New Solar System?" in *The New Solar System*, 3d ed., eds. K. Beatty and A. Chaikin (Cambridge, MA: Sky Publishing Corp., 1990), 276.
3. J. N. Marcus and M. A. Olsen, "Biological Implications of Organic Compounds in Comets," in *Comets in the Post-Halley Era*, 449.
4. "Comets and Meteorites: Harbingers of Life on Earth," *Sky and Telescope* **78** (1989), 242.
5. Benton C. Clark, "Primeval Procreative Comet Pond," *Origins of Life and Evolution of the Biosphere* **18,** (1988), 209–38.
6. V. A. Firsoff, *Life among the Stars* (London: Allan Wingate, 1974), 31.
7. T. R. Cech, "RNA as an enzyme," *Scientific American* **255** (1986), 64–75.
8. M. Bailey, S. Clube, and W. Napier, *The Origin of Comets* (Oxford: Pergamon, 1990), 454–55.

CHAPTER 15

1. D. A. Russell, "The Disappearance of the Dinosaurs," *Canadian Geographical Journal* **83,** 6 (1971), 204–15.
2. D. A. Russell, "The Environments of Canadian Dinosaurs," *Canadian Geographical Journal* **87** (1973), 4–11.
3. L. Alvarez, W. Alvarez, F. Asaro, and H. Michel, "Extraterrestrial Cause for the Cretaceous–Tertiary Extinction," *Science* **208** (1980) 1095–1107.
4. Alvarez *et al.*, 1102–1104.
5. C. B. Officer and C. L. Drake, "Terminal Cretaceous Environment Events," *Science* **227,** 1161–67.
6. Officer and Drake, 1165.
7. V. L. Sharpton, G. P. Dairymple, L. E. Marin, G. Ryder, B. C. Schuraytz, and J. Urrutia-Fucugauchi, "New links between the Chicxulub Impact Structure and the Cretaceous–Tertiary Boundary," *Nature* **359,** 6398 (1992), 819–21.
8. "Possible Yucatan Impact Basin," *Sky and Telescope* **63** (1982), 249–50.

9. The story about the Yucatan Crater includes details from J. Kelly Beatty's "Killer Crater in the Yucatan?" *Sky and Telescope* **82** (1991), 38–40.

CHAPTER 16

1. D. di Cicco, "New York's Cosmic Car Conker," *Sky and Telescope* **85**, 2 (1993), 26.
2. J. K. Davies, *Cosmic Impact* (London: Fourth Estate, 1986), 185.
3. *Ibid.* 169.
4. Z. Ceplecha, "Earth-Grazing Daylight Fireball of Aug. 10, 1972," Hazards Due to Comets and Asteroids Conference, Tucson, AZ, Jan. 5, 1993.
5. E. M. Shoemaker, "Asteroid and Comet Bombardment of the Earth," *Annual Review of Earth and Planetary Sciences* **11** (1983), 476.
6. Shoemaker, 480.
7. "The Tunguska Meteorite and Atmospheric Ozone," *Sky and Telescope* **63** (1982), 14.
8. C. R. Chapman, "Hazard to Civilization of Asteroid and Cometary Impacts," Asteroid Hazard Conference, USSR Academy of Sciences, St. Petersburg, Oct. 10, 1991.
9. D. Morrison and C. R. Chapman, "The Nature of the Impact Hazard," Hazards due to Comets and Asteroids Conference, Tucson, AZ, Jan. 5, 1993.
10. R. A. F. Grieve and E. M. Shoemaker, "The Record of Past Impacts on Earth," Hazards Due to Comets and Asteroids Conference, Tucson, AZ, Jan. 5, 1993.
11. E. M. Shoemaker and C. S. Shoemaker, "Collision Rate of Comets with Earth," Hazards Due to Comets and Asteroids Conference, Tucson, AZ, Jan. 5, 1993.
12. B. G. Marsden, personal communication, May 11, 1993.
13. C. Chapman, "Hazard to Civilization of Asteroid and Cometary Impacts," Asteroid Hazard Conference USSR Academy of Sciences, St. Petersburg, Oct. 10, 1991.

CHAPTER 17

1. F. Hoyle, *The Black Cloud* (New York: Signet, 1959), 16. Two-and-a-half degrees are roughly equivalent to five full-moon diameters.
2. F. Hoyle.[1]
3. T. Gehrels, *On the Glassy Sea: An Astronomer's Journey* (New York: American Institute of Physics, 1988), 108, and personal communication.
4. D. Morrison, lecture at Hazards Due to Comets and Asteroids Conference, Tucson, AZ, Jan. 5, 1993.

5. San Jose *Mercury News*, Mar. 22, 1992.
6. P. R. Weissman, "Scientific Objectivity and the Impact Hazard: Responsible Reporting vs. Crying Wolf," Hazards Due to Comets and Asteroids Conference, Tucson, AZ, Jan. 5, 1993.
7. D. Lindley, "Earth Saved from Disaster!" *Nature* **360** (1992), 623.
8. The *New York Times*, Nov. 3, 1992, B5.

CHAPTER 18

1. J. Scotti to B. G. Marsden, March 26, 1993.
2. C. Chapman, "Comet on Target for Jupiter," *Nature* **363** (1993), 492.
3. J. Scotti, personal communication, Aug. 29, 1993.
4. *IAU Circular* 5801, May 22, 1993.

EPILOGUE

1. A. P. Hankins, *Cole of Spyglass Mountain* (New York: Dodd, Mead, and Co., 1923).

AFTERWORD

1. R. Burnham to D. Levy, June 7, 1967.
2. W. Tirion, *Sky Atlas 2000.0* (Cambridge, MA: Sky Publishing Corp. and Cambridge, England: Cambridge University Press, 1981). W. Tirion, B. Rappaport, and G. Lovi, *Uranometria 2000.0*, vols. I and II (Richmond, VA: Willmann-Bell, 1987–1988).
3. B. G. Marsden, personal communication, July 17, 1993.
4. *IAU Circular* 5808, May 31, 1993.

Index

DATE DUE

MAR 1 9 2002	

BRODART, CO.   Cat. No. 23-221-003

#2970320&4